Chemical, Medical, and Pharmaceutical Books Printed before 1800

Chemical, Medical and Pharmaceutical Books Printed before 1800

In the Collections of the
University of Wisconsin Libraries

Edited by JOHN NEU

Compiled by Samuel Ives,
Reese Jenkins, and John Neu

The University of Wisconsin Press ∗ Madison and Milwaukee, 1965

Published by
THE UNIVERSITY OF WISCONSIN PRESS
Madison and Milwaukee
P.O. Box 1379, Madison, Wisconsin 53701

Printed in the United States of America by
Cushing-Malloy, Inc., Ann Arbor, Michigan

Library of Congress Catalog Card Number 65-24186

Foreword

As is true of most libraries with specialties, at Wisconsin the books on chemistry, medicine, and pharmacy owe much to the efforts of private collectors. On the medical side, we have profited from the collecting efforts of William Snow Miller, an authority on the anatomy of the lung who taught at Wisconsin from 1892 to 1924, and Dr. Byron Robinson of Chicago, a graduate of the University who died in 1910. Also important to the growth of the medical collections was Mr. Maurice Richardson, whose generous benefactions included funds for the purchase in 1958 of the collection of books on anatomy brought together by Edgar Goldschmid, well-known author of *Entwicklung und Bibliographie der pathologisch—anatomischen Abbildung*.

In pharmacy, the gift to the University in 1927 of the main part of the personal library of the first head of the School of Pharmacy, Frederick Belding Power, helped set the basis and tradition for a pharmaceutical collection having historical depth. Power's successor, Edward Kremers, was an outstanding collector of manuscripts, letters, clippings, and the like, materials not represented in this catalog; nevertheless, because of his leadership and direction the Library purchased and otherwise received a considerable body of pharmaceutical literature.

In chemical literature, Wisconsin is widely known as owner of the library put together by Denis I. Duveen. This library, minus the Lavoisier items listed in the Duveen catalog, consisted of about 3,000 items. Many items in that collection were not listed in the catalog of the Duveen Collection, nor were all of the items in the catalog included in the purchase. For this reason, and because the Library has avidly purchased additional chemical literature, the present bibliography will serve as a valuable companion to the catalog of Mr. Duveen's library. Illustrative of the purchases made since the Duveen Collection was acquired are the Boyle and Priestley libraries brought together by Hugh Sinclair of England.

Among the twentieth-century professors who gave direction to our purchases, I would like to mention George Urdang (deceased) and Glenn Sonnedecker of Pharmacy; Aaron J. Ihde of Chemistry; and Erwin Ackerknecht of Medicine.

Madison, Wisconsin   Louis Kaplan
June, 1965   Director of Libraries

Introduction

Planning for this catalog began in 1951 after the acquisition of the Denis I. Duveen Collection in chemistry and alchemy. Many things have caused the long delay in its completion, the most unfortunate being the sudden death in 1958 of Samuel Ives, Curator of Rare Books, who had made a good start on the compilation of the catalog. Work on the project then had to be abandoned until 1961, when funds were obtained to employ Reese Jenkins, a graduate student in the history of science. Working under the direction of Felix Pollak, present Curator of Rare Books, he considerably advanced the project, until new activities took him away from the staff. The compilation and editing were completed by John Neu, History-of-Science Librarian.

Since this catalog was compiled over a number of years by three people working successively, a number of inconsistencies in style resulted. It is hoped that the final editing has eliminated most of these. The following rules of cataloging have been followed:

Entry: The main entry for each work is under personal or corporate author in the form used in the card catalog of the University of Wisconsin Library. In most cases this will correspond to that used by the Library of Congress. Contrary to Library of Congress practice, the umlaut has been ignored in the alphabetizing of German names. If a work is anonymous and the author cannot be determined, entry is made under the first filing word of the title. In cases of multiple authorship, the entry is under the first author named, with cross-references from all others. Dissertations have been entered under the praeses, when one is indicated, with a cross-reference from the respondent.

Title: For the most part titles have been shortened, with all omissions except the author's name indicated by the use of ellipses. Editors and translators are given, as well as all statements of edition. Other works mentioned on the title page as being included in the text are transcribed, but they are not cataloged as separate items. Cross-references, however, have been made from them to the work in which they are included. Spelling, punctuation, and abbreviations, as well as any non-Roman characters, have been transcribed as on the title page.

Imprint: The place of publication is given as it appears on the title page. When more than one place is mentioned, normally only the first is indicated. The names of printers and publishers are given in the nominative case except when they are used with prepositions that indicate printer-publisher relationships; then they are transcribed as they appear on the title page or in the colophon. The number of names has sometimes been shortened and this is indicated by an ellipsis. The date is always given in Arabic numerals.

Collation: The collation includes the number of preliminary leaves, the number of pages or columns, and the number of terminal leaves. Blank leaves have not been counted in the foliation. In certain cases of complicated pagination, the abbreviation "var. pag." is used. Imperfections, such as missing leaves or plates, are generally indicated in a note. When the work has been issued in separate parts or volumes, only the number of parts or volumes is given. A note is added indicating the use of illustrations; but except for maps, portraits, and charts, various types of illustration are not differentiated. Books over forty centimeters in height are indicated as "folio"; otherwise, no sizes are given. A note is added to indicate when a separately published work has been bound after another separately published work; however, the card for the first book in the volume does not indicate all the works bound with it.

Arrangement under entry: The titles under an author's name are arranged alphabetically. However, all editions of the same work in the original language follow one another chronologically regardless of a change in title. When editions of the same work follow one another, the title is not repeated unless it differs from that preceding it; only the imprint and collation is then given. Translations of a work follow the original language editions and are arranged alphabetically by language, i.e., English, French, German, Greek, etc. Dissertations for which the author acted as praeses follow the listing of his own works.

The editor wishes to acknowledge the patient answering of many questions by Felix Pollak, Curator of Rare Books; Aaron J. Ihde, Professor of the History of Chemistry; and Glenn Sonnedecker, Professor of the History of Pharmacy. Much help and encouragement was also given by Louis Kaplan, Director of Libraries; Helen Crawford, Medical Librarian; Robert Stauffer, Professor of the History of Science; Robert O. Lindsay, Social Studies Librarian; co-compiler Reese Jenkins; and the excellent staff of the University of Wisconsin Press.

John Neu

Chemical, Medical, and Pharmaceutical Books Printed before 1800

A

1.   A., J.D. Thom., *ed*.   Collectańea chimica curiosa, quæ veram continent rerum naturalium anatomiam ... Francofurti: vidua H. à Sande, 1693.
    4 *l*., 927 p., 12 *l*.

2.   ABATI, Giovanni Battista.   ... De præcipua aëris atmosphærici tam in perficiendis, quam in dissolvendis organicis coporibus potestate. Dissertatio habita in magno Pisani Athenæi avditorio id. Dec. an MDCCLXIII. Pisis: I.P. Giovannelli, 1764.
    xxiv p.

    ABBATIA, Antonius de.   Bericht von Verwandelung der Metallen. *In* Zwey chymische Bücher ... 1759.

    ——. Ein Send-Brieff von Berwandelung der Metallen. *In* Joannes Ticinensis, Chymische Bücher ... 1691.

3.   ABRAHAM E PORTA LEONIS.   De avro dialogi tres ... Venetiis: I.B. à Porta, 1584.
    4 *l*., 178 p., 14 *l*.

4.   ABRAHAM ELEAZAR.   Uraltes chymisches Werck ... wie auch beygefügten Schlüssel derer in selbigen vorkommenden fremden Wörter ... In II. Theilen ... befördert worden durch Julium Gervasium. Erfurt: A. Crusius, 1735.
    15 *l*., 122 p., 7 *l*.; 1 *l*., 87 p., 14 *l*. illus.
    Seven leaves of index in contemporary German script added at end.

5.   ACCADEMIA DEL CIMENTO, Florence. Saggi di naturali esperienze fatte nell' Accademia del Cimento ... Napoli: B.M. Raillard, 1714.
    6 *l*., cclxix p., 7 *l*.   illus.

6.   ——. Essayes of natural experiments made in the Academie del Cimento ... Written in Italian by the secretary ... Englished by Richard Waller ... London: for

B. Alsop, 1684.
    13 *l*., 160 p., 5 *l*.   illus.

    ——. *See also* Musschenbroek, Petrus van, Tentamina ... 1731, etc.

7.   ACHILLINI, Allesandro.   Opera omnia in vnvm collecta ... Cvm annotationibvs excellentissimi doctoris Pamphili Montii ... Omnia post primas editiones nunc primum emendatiora in lucem prodeunt. Venetiis: H. Scotus, 1551.
    4 *l*., 148, 36 numb. *l*.   illus.

8.   ACKERMANN, Johann Christian Gottlieb.   Institutiones historiae medicinae. Norimbergae: Bauero-Manniano, 1792.
    7 *l*., 404 p., 6 *l*.

    ACOSTA, Cristovao. *See* Costa, Christovam da.

    ACREL, Johan Gustaf.   De morsura serpentum. *See* Linné, C. von, *praeses*. Entry 2428.

8a.   ACXTELMEIER, Stanislaus Reinhard. Calendarium perpetuum universale: das ist, Immerwährender allgemeiner Calender, der Natur und Zucht, Kunst und Wissenschafft, Tugend und Gesundheit, Vernunsst und Weisheit, Wirtschafft und Vergnüglichkeit ... Nürnburg und Schwobach: zu finden bey J.L. Buggel, drucks M. Hagen, 1707.
    10 *l*., 488 p.   illus.

9.   ——. Des Natur-lichts weit eröffneter Pallast ... Schwobach: gedruckt bey M. Hagen, zu finden bey D. Walder, 1706.
    4 *l*., 270 p.   illus.

10.   ADAM, Melchiore.   Vitae Germanorum medicorum: qvi seculo superiori, et quod excurrit, claruerunt ... Haidelbergae: impensis heredum J. Rosæ, excudit J.G. Geyder, 1620.
    16 *l*., 451 p., 12 *l*.

With his Vitae Germanorum jureconsultorum
... 1620.

11.   ADAMS, George.   An essay on vision,
briefly explaining the fabric of the eye, and
the nature of vision: intended for the service
of those whose eyes are weak or impaired ...
The second edition. London: R. Hindmarsh
for the author, 1792.
     xi, 172 p.   illus.

12.   ADEPTUS fatalis, das ist: Geld,
spricht die Welt! Freyburg: 1721.
     15 *l.*
     With Spectrvm spagiricvm ... 1721.

     AEGINETA, Paulis.   *See* Paulus
Aegineta.

     AFZELIUS, Pehr von.   Chemiae pro-
gressus. *See* Bergman, T.O., *praeses*.

13.   AGGRAVI, Giovanni Francesco.   Pro-
tolvme chimico che con chiarezza dimostra
di fabricare diuersi magisterij spargirici,
spiriti ... Seconda editione. Parma: G. Rosati,
1680.
     8 *l.*, 347 p.

     AGNELLO, Giovanni Battista.   *See*
Apocalypsis spiritus secreti.

14.   AGRICOLA, Georg.   De ortu & causis
subterraneorum lib. v. De natura eorum quæ
effluunt ex terra lib. IIII. De natura fosilium
lib. X. De ueteribus & nouis metallis lib. II.
Bermannus, siue de re metallica dialogus lib.
I ... Basileae: Froben, 1558.
     4 *l.*, 470 p., 20 *l.*

15.   ———. ——— recensiti ... à Joanne Sig-
frido ... Accesserunt de metallicis rebus &
nominibus observationes variæ ... Georgii
Fabricii ... Wittebergæ: sumptibus Z. Schü-
reri, typis A. Rudingeri, 1612.
     12 *l.*, 1014 p., 55 *l.*

16.   ———. De re metallica libri XII ...
Eivsdem de animantibvs svbterraneis ...
Basileae: Froben, 1556.
     6 *l.*, 502 p., 37 *l.*   illus.

17.   ———. ———. Quibus accesserunt hâc
editione ... De animantibus subterraneis lib.
I. De ortu & causis subterraneorum lib. V. De
natura eorum quæ effluunt ex terra lib. IV. De
natura fossilium lib. X. De veteribus & novis
metallis lib. II. Bermannus sive de re metallica dialogus lib. I ... Basileæ: E. König, 1657.
     7 *l.*, 708 p., 45 *l.*   illus.

18.   AGRICOLA, Johann.   Erster [ander]
Theil ... commentariorum, notarum, observationum & animadversionum in Johannis Poppii
chymische Medicin ... Leipzig: in verlegung
T. Schürers, gedruckt bey G. Ritzschen, 1638-
1639.
     2 v.   port.

19.   ———. Deutlich-und wolgegründeter
Anmerckungen über die chymische Artzneyen
Johannis Poppii ... mit neuen höchsinöhtig-
und nützlichen Anmerckungen Herrn Joh. Hel-
frici Jungkens vermehrt ... Nürnberg: in Verlegung J. Ziegers, gedruckt bey J.M. Spörlin,
1686.
     4 pts. in 1 v.   port.

20.   AGRICOLA, Johann *Ammonius.*
Medicinæ herbariæ libri dvo ... Basileæ:
B. Westhermerus, 1539.
     336 p., 32 *l.*

21.   AGRIPPA, Livio.   Discorso ragionale
trattato sopra remedii de ueneni materiali,
compositi, simplici, corporali, e pestilentiali
... [n.p.: ca. 1590?]
     4 *l.*

22.   ———. Secreti medicinali nouamente
dati in luce ... Con vn discorso di fisionomia.
Fiorenza: C. Giolita de' Ferrarri [n.d.].
     4 *l.*   illus.

23.   AGRIPPA VON NETTESHEIM, Heinrich
Cornelius.   De incertitudine & vanitate
scientiarii & artium ... Parisiis: I. Petrus,
1531.
     4 *l.*, clix numb *l.*
     Lacking the last leaf, which contains the
printer's device.

24.   ———. ——— denuo ab autore recognita,
& marginalibus annotationibus aucta ...
[Cologne?: 1536?]
     200 *l.*

25.   ———. Of the vanitie and vncertaintie
of artes and sciences. Englished by Ja. San.
... London: H. Wykes, 1569.
     8 *l.*, 187 numb. *l.*, 2 *l.*

26.   ———. ———. London: H. Bynneman, 1575.
     7 *l.*, 187 numb. *l.*, 1 *l.*

27.   ———. ———. London: J.C. for S. Speed,
1676.
     9 *l.*, 368 p.   port.

28.   ———. Declamation svr l'incertitvde,
vanité, et abvs des sciences, traduite en Fran-

cois ... [Paris]: I. Dvrand, 1582.
8 *l*., 551 p.

29. ———. ———. Traduit en Francois par
Lovys de Mayerne Tvrqvet. Geneve: P.
Chouët, 1630.
12 *l*., 526 p.

30. ———. De occvlta philosophia libri
tres. [Coloniae: 1533.]
6 *l*., ccclxii p. illus.

31. ———. Three books of occult philosophy ... Translated ... into the English tongue,
by J.F. London: R.W. for G. Moule, 1651.
11 *l*., 583 p., 6 *l*. port.
Elias Ashmole's copy with his marginal
notes.

32. ———. Opera omnia ... qvibvs post
omnivm editiones de nouo accessit ars
notoria ... Lvgdvni: Beringos fratres, 1600.
2 v.

33. AHMAD IBN 'ABD ALLAH, *al-T̄ulaitͩulī*.
Tratado de las aguas medicinales de Salam-
Bir, que comunmente llaman de Sacedon,
escrito en lengua Arabe, por Agmer-ben-ab-
Dala ... Traducido al idioma Castellano ...
por ... Mariano Pizzi y Frangeschi ... Madrid:
A. Perez de Soto, 1761.
xxxxii, 239 p.

34. AIGNAN, Francois. L'ancienne
medecine a la mode, ou Le sentiment uniforme
d'Hippocrate & de Galien sur les acides &
les alkalis ... Paris: L. d'Houry, 1693.
5 *l*., 219 p.

35. ———. Le prestre medecin ou Discours
physique sur l'établissement de la medecine.
Avec un traité du caffé & du thé de France ...
Paris: L. d'Houry, 1696.
18 *l*., 263 p.

36. AIKIN, John. Biographical memoirs
of medicine in Great Britain from the revival
of literature to the time of Harvey. London:
for J. Johnson, 1780.
xi, 338 p., 6 *l*.

37. AILLY, Pierre d', *cardinal*. Tractatvs
... super libros metheororum: de impressionibus
aeris ... [Viennæ Pannoniæ: per H. Vietorem,
expensis L. Alantse, 1514.]
xxv numb. *l*.

38. ALAIMO, Marco Antonio. Consigli
politico-medici ... Palermo: N. Bua, 1652.
1 *l*., 12, 460 p., 16 *l*.

ALANDER, Olof Reinh. Inebriantia.
See Linné, C. von, *praeses*. Entry 2432.

ALANUS *de Insulis*. Dicta Alani.
In Bernard, *of Trevisano*, Von der Hermetischenn Philosophia ... 1586.

39. ALBERTI, Michael, *praeses*. Dissertatio inauguralis chymico-medica, de
borace ... Halæ Magdeburgicæ: J.C. Hendel
[1745].
34 p., 2 *l*.

40. ———. Dissertatio inauguralis
medica, de epilepsia ... Halae Magdeburgicae:
C. Henckel [1718].
44 p., 2 *l*.

41. ———. Dissertatio inauguralis
medica, de morbis animi ex anomaliis
haemorrhagicis ... Halae Magdeburgicae:
C. Henckel [1719].
46 p., 1 *l*.

42. ———. Dissertatio inauguralis
medica, de risus commodo et incommodo
in oeconomia vitali, ob das Lachen zur
Gesundheit nützlich oder schädlich sey ...
Halæ Magdeburgicæ: J.C. Hendel [1746].
26 p., 1 *l*.

43. ———. Dissertatio inauguralis
medico-forensis, de melancholia vera et
simulata ... Halae Magdeburgicae: E.
Schneider [1743].
4 *l*., 26 p., 4 *l*.

ALBERTUS MAGNUS, *bp. of Ratisbon*.
Compendium. *In* Alchymistisch Sieben-
Gestirn ... 1697.

———. De mineralibus & rebus
metallicis. *In* Lull, R., De secretis naturae
... 1541, etc.

44. ———. Secreta mulierum et virorum
... nuperrime correcta et emendata. [Cologne?:
ca. 1505?]
44 *l*.

45. ———. De secretis mvliervm libellus
... Eiusdem De virtutibus herbarum, lapidum,
& animalium quorundam libellus. Item De
mirabilibus mundi ... Adiecimus ... Michaëlis
Scoti ... De secretis natura opusculum ...
Lvgdvni: A. de Harsy, 1598.
381 p., 4 *l*.
Lacking pages 5-38.

46. ———. ———. Francofvrti: excudebat

I. Bringervs, impensa P. Mvscvli, 1615.
  411 p.

47.   ——.   ——. Argentorati: haeredes L.
Zetzneri, 1637.
  340 p., 5 *l*.

48.   ——.   ——. Amstelodami: H. et T.
Boom, 1702.
  329 p., 3 *l*.

49.   ——. The secrets of Albertus Magnus: of the vertues of herbs, stones, and
certain beasts. Whereunto is newly added,
a short discourse of the seven planets ...
Also a book ... of the marvellous things of
the world ... London: M.H. and J.M. [ca.
1690?].
  64 *l*.

50.   ——. Secrets merveilleux de la
magie naturelle et cabalistique ... traduits
exactement sur l'original latin ... Nouvelle
edition corrigée & augmentée. Lion: héritiers
de Beringos fratres, 1745.
  6 *l*., 252 p. illus.

51.   ——.   ——. Lyon: héritiers de
Beringos fratres, 1758.
  4 *l*., 307 p. illus.

52.   ——. Les admirables secrets ...
contenant plusieurs traités sur la conception
des femmes, des vertus des herbes, des
pierres précieuses, & des animaux. Augmenté
d'un abregé curieux de la phisionomie ...
Divisés en quatre livres. Lyon: héritiers de
Beringos fratres, 1758.
  8 *l*., 312 p., 5 *l*. illus.

53.   ——. Das buch der versamlung,
oder Das büch der heimligkeiten Magni
Alberti, von artzney vnd tugenden der kräter
vnnd edel gestein, vnd von etlichen wolbe-
kanten thieren. [Strassburg: M. Flach, 1519.]
  40 *l*.

54.   ALBERTUS OF ORLAMUNDE. Cōpen-
diosum insigne ac putile opus philosophie
naturalis seliciter incipit ... Brixiæ: B. de
Farfengo, 1490.
  54 *l*. illus.

    ALBINEUS, Nathan. *See* Aubigné de
la Fosse, Nathan.

55.   ALBINIUS, Petrus Constantinus.
Magia astrologica, hoc est ... Clauis sympathiæ septem metallorum & septem selectorum lapidum ad planetas ... Parisiis: C.

Sevestre ..., 1611.
  14 *l*., 56 numb. *l*.

    ——.   ——. *In* Leonardi, C., Specu-
lum lapidum ... 1717.

56.   ALBINUS, Bernhard Siegfried.
Academicarum annotationum. Leidae: J. & H.
Verbeek, 1754-1768.
  8 v. in 2. illus.

57.   ——. De sceleto humano liber.
Leidae: J. & H. Verbeek, 1762.
  489 p., 3 *l*.

58.   ——. The explanation of Albinus's
anatomical figures of the human skeleton
and muscles ... Translated from the Latin.
To which is added the explanation of the
supplement to Albinus, containing a compleat anatomical description of the blood-
vessels and nerves ... London: for J. and P.
Knapton, 1754.
  xxiv, 332, 106 p., 1 *l*.

59.   ——. Historia musculorum hominis.
Leidae: T. Haak & H. Mulhovius, 1734.
  696 p. illus.

60.   ——.   ——. Editio altera, notis
avcta. Francofvrti: T. Goebhardt, 1784.
  1 *l*., 604 p., 7 *l*. illus.

61.   ——. Physiologia, of natuurkundige
van het menschelyke lichaam ... Amsterdam:
K. van Tongerlo, 1758.
  xii p., 3 *l*., vi, 636 p., 33 *l*.

62.   ——. Icones ossium foetus humani.
Accedit osteogeniae brevis historia. Leidae
Batavorum: J. et H. Verbeek, 1737.
  2 *l*., 162 p., 1 *l*. illus.

63.   ——. Tabula vasis chyliferi cum
vena azyga arteriis intercostalibus aliisque
vicinis partibus. Lugduni Batavorum: J. et H.
Verbeek, 1757.
  1 plate, 1 *l*. folio.
  With his Tabulae ossium humanorum ...
1753.

64.   ——. Tabvlae anatomicae mvscvlorvm
hominis. Londini: J. & P. Knapton, 1747.
  51 plates. folio.

65.   ——. Tabvlae ossivm hvmanorvm.
Leidae: J. et H. Verbeek, 1753.
  70 plates. folio.

66.   ——. Tabulae sceleti et musculorum

corporis humani. Lugduni Batavorum: J. &
H. Verbeek, 1747.
　36 *l*., 40 plates.　folio.

67.　——.　Tables of the skeleton and
muscles of the human body. Translated from
the Latin. London: W. Woodfall for J. & P.
Knapton, 1749.
　2 pts.　folio.

68.　——.　Tabulae VII uteri mulieris
gravidae cum jam parturiret mortuae. Lugduni
Batavorum: J. et H. Verbeek, 1748.
　8 plates.　folio.
　With his Tabulae sceleti ... 1747.

　　　　——.　*See also* Eustachi, Bartolomeo.

69.　ALCHYMIA vera, das ist: Der waren
vnd ... edlen Kunst Alchymia wahre beschreibung ... Jetzo aber zum andermal auffgeleget
... durch I.P.S.H.M.S. [n.p.: 1610?]
　184 *l*.　illus.
　With Paracelsus, Zween underschiedene
Tractat ... 1608.

70.　ALCHYMISTISCH Sieben-Gestirn.
Das ist: Sieben schöne und ausserlesene
Tractätlein vom Stein der Weisen ... aus
dem Latein ins Hoch-deutsche treulich übergesetzet ... Hamburg: G. Liebezeit, 1697.
　4 *l*., 231 p.

71.　ALCHYMISTISCHES Bruchstück aus
der Verlassenschaft eines verstorbenen Mit-
gliedes des Ordens der Rosen- und Golden-
Creutzer. Leipzig: J.G. Beygang, 1788.
　93 p.

72.　ALDROVANDI, Ulisse.　Mvsaevm
metallicvm in libros IIII distribvtvm Bar-
tholomæus Ambrosinvs ... composuit ...
Marcvs Antonivs Bernia proprijs impensis
in lucem edidit ... [Bononia: I.B. Ferronius,
1648.]
　3 *l*., 979 p., 6 *l*.　illus.

73.　ALENCE, Joachim d'.　Traittez des
barom, thermométres, et notiométres, ou
hygrométres. Par Mr. D. Amsterdam: H. Wetstein, 1688.
　6 *l*., 139 p., 2 *l*.　illus.

　　　ALESSIO, *Piemontese*.　*See* Ruscelli,
Girolamo.

　　　ALETHOPHILUM, *pseud*.　*See* Metternich, Wolf, *freiherr von*.

　　　ALEXANDER, *of Aphrodisias*.　Prob-

lematum.　*In* Aristotles, Problematum ... 1534.

　　　——.　Super questionibus nonnullis
physicis. *In* Aristotles, Problemata ... 1569.

74.　ALEXANDER, William.　Experimental
essays on the following subjects: I. On the
external application of antiseptics in putrid
diseases. II. On the does and effects of
medicines. III. On diuretics and sudorifics
... The second edition corrected. London: for
E. and C. Dilly, 1770.
　1 *l*., viii, 238 p.

75.　ALEXANDRE, Nicolas.　Dictionnaire
botanique et pharmaceutique, contenant les
principales propriétés des minéraux, des
végétaux, et des animaux d'usage, avec les
préparations de pharmacie ... Paris: P.F.
Didot, 1768.
　viii, 627 p., 26 *l*.

76.　ALIPILI.　Centrum naturæ concentratum. Oder: Ein Tractat von dem wieder-
gebohrnen Saltz ... versetzt und herausgegeben von Johann Otto Helbig ... [Heidel-
berg]: 1682.
　80 p.　illus.

　　　——.　——.　*In* Quadratum alchymisticum ... 1705.

77.　——.　Centrum naturæ concentratum:
or The salt of nature regenerated. For the
most part improperly called the philosopher's
stone. Written in Arabick by Alipili ... published in Low Dutch, 1694, and now done
into English, 1696. By a lover of the hermetick
science ... London: for J. Harris, 1696.
　90 p.

78.　ALLEN, Benjamin.　The natural history of the chalybeat and purging waters of
England ... London: S. Smith & B. Walford,
1699.
　20 *l*., 185 p.

79.　ALLETZ, Pons Augustin.　L'Albert
moderne, ou Nouveaux secrets éprouvés, et
licites, recueillis d'après les découvertes
les plus récentes ... Paris: la veuve Duchesne,
1768.
　xxiv, 430 p., 1 *l*.
　Lacking pages 347-350.

80.　——.　——. Seconde edition ... Paris:
la veuve Duchesne, 1771.
　viii, 429 p., 9 *l*.

81.　——.　——. Cinquieme édition ...

Neuchatel: S. Fauche, 1780.
  2 v. in 1.

82.   ALLEYNE, James.   A new English
dispensatory, in four parts ... London: for
T. Astley and S. Austen, 1733.
  2 *l*., xiv p., 1 *l*., 646 p., 29 *l*., 20 p.

83.   ALLIETTE.   Fragment sur les hautes
sciences, suivi d'une note sur les trois
sortes de médecines données aux hommes ...
Amsterdam: Petit, 1785.
  64 p. illus.

84.   ——.   Les sept nuances de l'oeuvre
philosophique-hérmétique, suivies d'un traité
sur la perfection des métaux, mis sous
l'avant-titre L.D.D.P.   ... [Paris: 1785.]
  1 *l*., 48, 60 p. illus.

85.   ALMELOVEEN, Theodoor Jansson van.
Inventa nov-antiqua ... Subjicitur ejusdem
Rerum inventarum onomasticon. Ad virum
clarissimum Iacobum Vallan. Amstelædami:
J. Waesberghe, 1684.
  16 *l*., 249 p., 3 *l*.; 3 *l*., 85 p.

ALPHONSO. *King of Portugal*. A
treatise concerning the philosophers stone.
In Five treatises ... 1652.

86.   ALPINI, Prosper.   De medicina
methodica libri tredecim ... Editio secunda.
Lugduni Batavorum: Boutestein, 1719.
  12 *l*., 765 p., 19 *l*.

87.   ——.   De praesagienda vita et morte
aegrotantium libri septem ... cum praefatione
Hermanni Boerhaave ... accuravit, Hieron.
Dav. Gaubius. Francofurti: Fleischer, 1754.
  10 *l*., 559 p., 19 *l*. port.

88.   ——.   Medicina Aegyptiorum. Accedunt huic editioni ejusdem auctoris libri de
balsamo & rhapontico. Ut et Jacobi Bontii
medicina indorum. Editio nova. Lugduni
Batavorum: Boutestein, 1719.
  4 pts. in 1 v. illus.

89.   ALSINET, José.   Nuevas utilidades
de la quina demonstradas. Madrid: A. Munoz
del Valle ..., 1763.
  5 *l*., 46 p.

90.   ALSTED, Johann Heinrich.   Physica
harmonica, quatuor libellis methodice pro-
ponens I. Physicam Mosaicum. II. Physicam
Hebræorum. III. Physicam Peripateticam.
IV. Physicam chemicam. Tertiâ curâ ...
Herbornæ Nassoviorum: 1616.

  281 p.

91.   ALSTON, Charles.   A dissertation
on quick-lime and lime-water. Edinburgh:
W. Sands ..., 1752.
  iv, 60 p.

92.   ——.   Index medicamentorum simplicium triplex. Edinburgi: W. Sands ...,
1752.
  xi, 172 p.

ALTUS. *See* Mutus Liber.

93.   ALYON, Pierre Philippe.   Cours
élementaire de chimie théorique et pratique
suivant la nouvelle nomenclature ... Paris:
Le Normant, 1799.
  2 v. in 1.

94.   ——.   Essai sur les propriétés
médicinales de l'oxigène ... Paris: Cerioux
... [1794?].
  2 *l*., 159 p.

94a.   AMATUS LUSITANUS.   Curationum
medicinalium ... centvriae dvae, quinta videlicet ac sexta ... Venetiis: Valgrisius, 1560.
  8 *l*., 380 p., 2 *l*.

94b.   ——.   Curationum medicinalium ...
centvriæ qvatvor ... Venetiis: B. Constantinus,
1557.
  8 *l*., 645 p., 34 *l*.
  With his Curationum medicinalium ... 1560.

95.   AMELUNG, Peter.   Tractatvs nobilis
primvs, in quo alchimiæ seu chemicæ, artis
antiqvissimæ ... demonstratur ... Lipsiæ: M.
Lantzenberger excudebat, sumptibus I. Apelii,
1607.
  250 p.

96.   AMIDEI, Mattia.   Imerologio ouuero
Discordi divrni intorno alla confettione
iacintina ... Siena: E. Gori, 1643.
  8 *l*., 438 p., 1 *l*. illus.

97.   AMY, Joseph.   Observations experi-
mentales sur les eaux des rivieres de Seine
de Marne, d'Arcueil et de Puits, et sur les
filtres ... à purifier & à conserver l'eau ...
Paris: Morel le jeune, 1749.
  1 *l*., 61 p., 4 *l*.

98.   ANATOMIA et physiognomia simplicium,
das ist: Zween Tractat von der Signatura
aller Erdgewächsen ... Nürnberg: W. Endter,
1647.
  152 p., 11 *l*.

With Ritter, M.F., Astronomia inferior ... 1646.

99.   ANDREE, John.   An account of the Tilbury water ... London: M. Jenour [for] J. Clarke, 1737.
2 *l*., 38 p.

100.   ANDRENAS, Philippe.   Premier extrait d'vn livre intitvlé Or potable levain, ov Discovrs de l'or potable levain ... Paris: J. Bouillerot, 1674.
116 p., 1 *l*.

101.   ANDRY, Charles Louis François. Recherches sur la rage. Nouvelle edition, augmentée dans quelques endroits, & suivie du traitement fait à Senlis ... Paris: Didot, 1780.
4 *l*., 424, 142 p.

102.   ANDRY DE BOIS-REGARD, Nicolas. An account of the breeding of worms in human bodies: their nature and several sorts; their effects, symptoms, and prognostics ... Done from the French original, with figures. London: for H. Rhodes and A. Bell, 1701.
xl p., 2 *l*., 266 p., 12 *l*.   illus.

103.   ANGELI, Luigi.   Delle acque medicate di Riolo nel territoria Imolese ... Vicenza: Turra, 1783.
vii, 110 p., 1 *l*.

104.   L'ANGELIQUE, *le sieur de.*   La vraye pierre philosophale de medecine ... Paris: L. Boulanger, 1622.
400 p., 9 *l*.

105.   ANGELOCRATOR, Daniel.   Doctrina de ponderibus, mensuris, et monetis ... Marpurgi Cattorum: J. Saurius, 1617.
4 *l*., 81 p., 1 *l*.

ANGELUS DE FORTIBUS. *See* Forte, Angelo di.

106.   ANNOIES, Phesius Sanus de, *pseud.* Hermeticæ disciplinæ lvcifer quo fugatis errorum tenebris secretiora naturæ arcana reuelatur ... Bononiæ: hæredes A. Pisarii, 1680.
62 p.

ANNULUS PLATONIS.   *See* Kirchweger, Anton Joseph, *supposed author.*

ANTARVETUS, Joannes, *pseud. See* Riolan, Jean, 1580-1657.

107.   ANTHONIE, Francis.   Apologia veritatis illvcescentis pro avro potabili ... Londini: J. Legatt, 1616.
9 *l*., 112 p., 2 *l*.

108.   ——. The apologie, or defence of a verity heretofore pvblished concerning a medicine called avrvm potabile ... London: J. Legatt, 1616.
3 *l*., 126 p.

——. Arum-potabile: or the receit. *In* Collectanea chymica ... 1684.

109.   ——. Panacea aurea sive Tractatus duo de ipsius auro potabili, nunc primum in Germania ex Londinensi exemplari excusi, opera M.B.F.B. ... Hamburgi: Bibliopolus Frobenianus, 1618.
8 *l*., 205 p.

110.   ANTIDOTARIUM Collegii Medicorum Bononiensis. Editio altera juxta exemplar Bononiense ... Venetiis: J. Orlandelli, 1790.
2 *l*., 240 p.

111.   ANTIDOTARIVM Gandavense sive Medicamentorvm componendorvm a pharmacopeis Gandavensibvs observanda methodvs ... Gandavi: B. Manilius, 1656.
14 *l*., 278 p., 15 *l*.

112.   The ANTIDOTHARIUS, in the whiche thou mayst lerne howe thou shalte make many, and dyuers noble plasters, salues, oyntmēt, powders, bawmes, oyles, & wounde drynk, the whiche be very necessary, and behouefull, vtyle, & profytable, for euery surgyan, therin to be expert, and redy at all tymes of nede. [London: R. Wyer, ca. 1535?]
22 *l*.
Lacking leaves d₁ and f₁.

113.   APOCALYPSIS SPIRITUS SECRETI. A revelation of the secret spirit. Declaring the most concealed secret of alchymie. Written first in Latine by an vnknowne author, but explained in Italian, by Iohn Baptista Lambye ... translated into English, by R.N.E. ... London: I. Haviland for H. Skelton, 1623.
6 *l*., 80 p.

114.   APOTECK für den gmeynē man der die Ertzet zuersüchē ... Fleissig corrigiert ... [n.p.: 1529.]
2 *l*., xxv numb. *l*., 1 *l*.   illus.

115.   The APOTHECARY'S mirror; or, The present state of pharmacy explored; in a letter to J. H. Sequeira ... London: C. Macrae, 1790.
2 *l*., 31 p.

APULEIUS *Barbarus.* De herbarum virtutibus. *In* Galenus, Liber de plenitudine ... 1528.

116. ARANDA Y MARZO, José. Descripcion tripartita medico-astronomica ... Madrid: M. Fernandez, 1737.
11 *l.*, 183 p.

117. ARBUTHNOT, John. An essay concerning the effects of air on human bodies. London: for J. and R. Tonson ..., 1751.
xi p., 2 *l.*, 224 p.

118. ———. An essay concerning the nature of aliments, and the choice of them ... The second edition ... London: for J. Tonson, 1732.
12 *l.*, 430 p.

119. ARCANDAM, *pseud.* The most excellent, profitable, and pleasant book of the famous doctor ... Arcandam, or Alcandrin ... with an addition of physiognomy ... Now newly turned out of our French into our vulgar tongue. By William Warde. London: F. Kingston, 1649.
91 *l.* illus.

120. ARCE, Francisco de. A most excellent and compendiovs method of curing woundes in the head ... translated into English by Iohn Read, chirurgion. Wherevnto is added the exact cure of the caruncle ... with a treatise of the fistulæ ... translated out of Iohannes Ardern ... London: T. East for T. Cadman, 1588.
16 *l.*, 119 numb. *l.* illus.

ARCET, Jean d'. *See* Darcet, Jean

121. ARCHER, John. A compendious herbal, discovering the physical vertues of all herbs in this kingdome ... London: E.C. for the author, 1673.
143 p., 4 *l.*

ARDERNE, John. A treatise of the fistulæ. *In* Arce, F. de, A most excellent method ... 1588.

122. ARETAEUS. Libri septem nunc primum e tenebris eruti a Ivnio Pavlo Crasso Patavino accuratissime in latinum sermonem uersi. Rvffi Ephesii ... De corporis humani partium appellationibus libri tres ... Venetiis: Ivntae,1552.
4 *l.*, 90 numb. *l.*, 17 *l.*

123. ———. Περὶ αἰτίων καὶ σημείων ὀξέων

καὶ χρονίων παθῶν ... De causis et signis acutorum et diuturnorum morborum ... novamque versionem dedit, Johannes Wigan ... Oxoniæ: e Typographeo Clarendoniano, 1723.
2 *l.*, xxxiv p., 1 *l.*, 151 p., 49 *l.*; 168 p., 7 *l.* folio.
Lacks gathering A of the second part.

124. ARGENTERIO, Giovanni. In artem medicinalem Galeni, commentarij tres ... Parisiis: I. Poupy, 1578.
2 v. in 1.

125. The ARGUMENT of sulphur or no sulphur in waters discussed ... being the subjects of a correspondence between the author of the Methodical synopsis of mineral waters, and W.R. Esq. ... To which are annexed, two tracts: I. The analysis of milk ... by John Rutty ... II. A practical dissertation on the uses of goat's whey. Dublin: A. M'Culloh, 1762.
var. pag. chart.

126. ARISTOTLES. Contenta hoc volvmine. Problematum Aristotelis sectiones duæ de quadraginta: Theodoro Gaza interprete. Problematum Alexandri Aphrodisiei libri duo: eodem Theodoro interprete ... Parisiis: S. Colin, 1534.
29 *l.*, 123 numb. *l.*

127. ———. Problemata ... ac philosophorum, medicorumq́ue complurium. Marci Antonii Zimarae Sanctipetrinatis problemata ... Item Alexandri Aphrodisei, super questionibus nonnullis physicis, solutionum liber, Angelo Politiano interprete. [Venetiis: I. Variscus, 1569.]
176 numb. *l.*

———. ———. *In* Brasavola, A.M., Examen omnium simplicium medicamentorum ... 1539.

———. Tractat an Alexandrum Magnum. *In* Alchymistisch Sieben-Gestirn ... 1697.

128. ARNALDUS DE VILLANOVA. ... Vno çardino de ueritade rose de philosophie & de tutti secretilo maior secreto de vna uerace compositione de naturali philosophi ... [Venice: 1505?]
22 *l.* illus.

———. Rosarium philosophorum. *In* Ulsted, P., Coeluṃ philosophorum ... 1630.

———. Epistola de sanguine humano.

In Joannes de Rupescissa, De consideratione
... [1561].

129.   ———.   Omnia, qvæ exstant, opera
chymica: videlicet, Thesaurus thesaurorum
... Lumen nouum, Flos florum, & Speculum
alchimiæ ... edita ... Hieronymi Megiseri.
Francofvrti: J. Bratheringius, 1603.
     120, 76 p.
     Lacking pages 95-114.

130.   ———.   Praxis medicinalis ... Cui
accesserunt sub sinem tractatus eiusdem
aliquot ... Cathena avrea et Testamentvm
philosophicvm evisdem. Lvgdvni: I. Strativs,
1586.
     2 *l*., 245 p.; 314 p., 9 *l*.; 2 *l*., 47 p.
     Ten leaves (p. 313-314 and Index), ending
part two, misbound after part one.

131.   ———.   Speculum alchimiæ ... nvnc
primvm in lvcem editvs, operâ & impensis
Hieronymi Megiseri ... Francofurti: hæredes
Romani Beati, 1602.
     76 p.
     With his Omnia, qvæ exstant, opera ...
1603.

132.   ARNAUD, E.R.   Introdvction a la
chymie, ov a la vraye physiqve ... Lyon: C.
Prost, 1655.
     20 *l*., 112 p.

133.   ARNAULD, Pierre, *sieur de la cheval_
lerie, ed. and tr.*   Trois traitez de la philo-
sophie natvrelle non encore imprimez, sca-
voir, Le secret livre dv ... Artephivs ... Plvs
Les figvres hieroglyphiqves de Nicolas
Flamel ... Ensemble, Le vray liure du docte
Synesivs ... le tout traduit par P. Arnavld ...
Paris: G. Marette, 1612.
     103 p.   illus.

134.   ———, *ed. and tr.*   Philosophie natvrelle de trois anciens philosophes renommez
Artephius, Flamel, & Synesius, traitant de
l'art occulte, & de la transmutation metallique. Dernière edition. Augmentée d'un petit
traité du mercure, & de la pierre des philosophes de G. Ripleus, nouvellement traduit
en François. Paris: L. d'Houry, 1682.
     106 p.   illus.

135.   ARNAULT DE NOBLEVILLE, Louis
Daniel.   Description abrégée des plantes
usuelles, avec leurs vertus, leurs usages &
leurs propriétés ... Paris: Debure, 1774.
     xx p., 1 *l*., 562 p.

136.   ———.   Le manuel des dames de

charité, ou Formules de médicamens faciles
a préparer ... Nouvelle edition. Paris: Debure,
1750.
     3 *l*., xxxii, 256 p.

137.   ARNOBIO, Cleandro.   Tesoro delle
gioie trattato cvrioso, nel quale si dichiara
breuemente la virtù, qualitⱥ & proprietà
delle gioie ... lodate, stimate, & conosciute
saluteuole, & medicinali. Raccolto dall'
Academico Ardende Etereo ... Reuisto, &
accresciuto dell' Academico Casinense
inquieto ... Padova: P.P. Tozzi, 1626.
     12 *l*., 212 p., 1 *l*.

138.   ARNOLD, Guido Ferdinand.   Der un-
gelehrt-gelehrte Alchymist, darinnen vorgestellet wird die Bereitung des Lapidis
Philosophorum, auf metallische und vegeta-
bilische Art ... [Leipzig]: Leipziger Michael-
Messe, 1723.
     32 p.
     With Siebenstern, C.F.S. von, Practica ...
1721.

     ARRAIS, Edward Madeira.   Arbor vitae;
or A physical account of the tree of life. *In*
Bacon, R., The cure of old age ... 1683.

139.   L'ART hermetique à decouvert, ou
Nouvelle lumiere magique, où sont contenus
diverses mysteres des Egyptiens, des Hebreux
& des Caldéens. [n.p.] 1787.
     98 p.

140.   ARTEPHIUS.   Clavis majoris sapientiæ.
Primùm, in lucem prodiit Parisiis, nunc iterum
secundum exemplar istud recusa. Argentorati:
J.A. Dolhopff, 1699.
     1 *l*., 53 p.

     ———.   ———.   *In* Opuscula quædam
chemica ... 1614.

     ———.   De arte occulta. *In* Janua
patefacta thesauro ... 1678.

141.   ———.   [Liber secretus nec non
Saturni Trismegisti siue F. Helie de
Assisio libellus ... quibus accesserunt
alia nondum impressa ... Francofurti:
1685.]
     119 p.   illus.
     Imperfect: lacks the title-page, which
has been supplied in contemporary man-
script.

     ———.   His secret booke, of the
blessed stone. *In* Flamel, N., Nicholas
Flammel, his exposition ... 1624.

——. Le livre secret. *In* Arnauld, P., Trois traitez ... 1612.

142. ARTIS AURIFERAE. Avriferae artis, qvam chemiam vocant, antiqvissimi avthores ... Basileæ: P. Perna, 1572.
2 v. illus.

143. ——. Artis avriferae, qvam chemiam vocant ... Basileæ: C. Waldkirch, 1610.
3 v. in 2. illus.

144. ARTIS chemicæ principes, Avicenna atqve Geber, hoc volumine continentur ... Basileæ: P. Perna, 1572.
16 ℓ., 767 p., 20 ℓ. illus.

ARVIDSSON, Petrus Afzelius. Chemiae progressus. *See* Bergman, T.O., *praeses*.

145. ASCHAM, Anthony. A litle herball of the properties of herbes, newly amended & corrected ... [London: J. Kynge, 1561?]
80 ℓ.

146. ASHMOLE, Elias, *comp.* Theatrum chemicum Britannicum. Containing severall poeticall pieces of our famous English philosophers, who have written the hermetique mysteries in their owne ancient language ... London: J. Grismond for N. Brooke, 1652.
8 ℓ., 486 p., 5 ℓ. illus.

147. ——. The way to bliss. In three books ... London: J. Grismond for N. Brook, 1658.
4 ℓ., 220 p., 1 ℓ. port.

148. ASTRUC, Jean. Tractatus pathologicus. Genevae: haer. Cramer & fratres Philibert, 1743.
1 ℓ., vi, 232 p.

149. ——. A treatise of veneral diseases, in nine books ... Translated from the last Latin edition printed at Paris. London: W. Innys, 1754.
xiv, 9 ℓ., 404, 338 p.

150. ATREMONT, H. d'. Le tombeau de la pauvreté ... Par vn philosophe inconnu. Seconde edition, reveuë & augmentée de la clef ... Avec vn congo philosophiquo cur lo cujot de l'art. Paris: L. d'Houry, 1681.
17 ℓ., 163 p., 2 ℓ.

151. AUBERI, Jean. Les bains de Bovrbon Lancy et Larchanbav ... [Paris]: A. Perier, 1604.
228 numb. ℓ., 3 ℓ.

152. AUBERT, Jacques. De metallorum ortu & causis contra chemistas breuis & dilucida explicatio. Lvgdvni: I. Berion, 1575.
69 p.

153. AUBIGNÉ DE LA FOSSE, Nathan. Bibliotheca chemica contracta ex delectu & emendatione Nathanis Albinei ... Genevæ: I.A. & S. de Tournes, 1653.
3 pts. in 1 v.
Contents: *Augurello*, G., Chrysopoeia et vellvs avrevm; *Sendivogius* , M., Novvm lvmen chemicvm, accessit tractatus de svlphvre; *Espagnet*, J., Enchiridion physicæ restitvtæ, Arcanvm hermeticæ philosophiæ opvs.

154. ——. ——. [Coloniæ Allobrogum: I.A. & S. de Tournes, 1673.]
3 pts. in 1 v.
Lacking the first 8 leaves.

155. AUDA, Domenico. Breve compendio di maravigliosi secreti .. diviso in qvattro libri ... Cō vn trattato per cōseruarsi in sanità ... Con nova aggionta ... Venetia: B. Milocho, 1673.
10 ℓ., 316 p.

156. ——. ——. Venetia: G. Zini, 1676.
10 ℓ., 316 p.

157. ——. Les admirables secrets de la medecine chimique du Sr. Joseph Quinti, docteur Venetien ... Traduction nouvelle de l'Italien ... Venise: J.F. Broncart, 1711.
5 ℓ., 281 p., 3 ℓ. illus.

158. Die AUFFRICHTIG entdeckte Probier- und Scheide-Kunst derer Venetianer ... I. Ein Probier-Büchlein ... II. Besondere particulararbeiten ... III. Einige zur Verbesserung derer Metallen ... IV. Eine Collation der Schrifften Fr. Basil Valentini ... Saalfeld: J.M. Kauffmann, 1717.
1 ℓ., 126 p.

159. AUGENIO, Orazio. De ratione cvrandi per sangvinis missionem libri XVII ... Hac editione quinta ab innumeris propemodum erroribus ... expurgati ... Francofvrti: A. Wechel ..., 1598.
8 ℓ., 532 p., 13 ℓ. port.

AUGURELLO, Giovanni Aurelio. Chrysopoeia et vellus aureum. *In* Aubigné de la Fosse, N., Bibliotheca chemica ... 1653.

——. Chrysopoeiae compendium. *In* Opuscula quædam chemica ... 1614.

———. Les trois livres de la chrysopee. *In* Joly, G., Trois anciens traictez ... 1626.

160. AUGUSTIS, Quiricus de. Lumen apothecariorum cum nonnullis expositionibus nouiter impressum. [Venetijs: B. Vercellensis, 1504.]
xl numb. *l*.

———. ———. *In* Manliis, J.J. de, de Bosco, Luminare maius ... 1506, etc.

AUREA CATENA HOMERI ... *See* Kirch-weger, Anton Joseph.

161. AURELIANUS, Caelius. Tardarvm passionvm libri V. D. Oribasii Sardi ... Euporiston lib. III. Medicinæ compen: lib. I. Curationum lib. I. Trochiscorū confect: lib. I. Basileae: H. Petrvs, 1529.
10 *l*., 345 p.
With Galenus, De temperamentis ... 1549.

AURIFERAE ARTIS. *See* Artis auriferae.

AURIFONTINA CHYMICA ... 1680. *See* Houpreght, John Frederick.

162. AUSSGEBRENTE und disillierte wasser wie sie zů iedem gebresten des Menschen leibs ... Strassburg: C. Egenolph [1530].
4 *l*., xxvi numb. *l*.

AVELLAN, Nicolaus. De perspira-tione insensibili. *See* Linné, C. von, *praeses*. Entry 2469.

163. AVENZOAR. Liber teisir, sive Recti-ficatio medicationis et regiminis. Antidotarium. Venice: J. & G. de Gregoriis, 1490/91.
40 numb. *l*.
Stillwell A1253. Lacking four preliminary leaves and leaves 41-108.

164. AVERTIMENTI a tvtti qvelli che de-siderano regolatamente viuere. Nelli quali si dimostra, come l'huomo possa fuggir i mali temperamenti dell'aria, e secondo le quattro stagioni dell'anno regolarsi. Fiorenza: G. Ferioli, 1602.
4 *l*.

165. AVICENNA. Avicennæ ... [Canon medicinae]. Ex Gerardi Cremonensis ver-sione, & Andreæ Alpagi Belunensis castiga-tione. A Ioanne Costaeo, & Ioanne Paulo Mongio annotationibus iampridem illustratus ... Venetiis: Iuntae, 1608.
2 v.

166. ———. [Jacobus de Forlivio super primo Avicenne. Jacobi Froliviensis in primum Avicenne canonem expositio ... Huic etiam nove impressioni scrito additam fore ex-positionem preclari Jacobi de Partibus ...] [Venetijs: L. de Giunta, 1520.]
6 *l*., 233 numb. *l*.
Lacking the title page.

167. ———. Principis et philosophi sapientissimi libri in re medica omnes qui hactenus ad nos peruenere. Id est Libri canonis quinque ... Venetiis: V. Valgrisius, 1564.
2 v.

168. ———. Quarta fen primi, de vniuersali ratione medēdi per M. Iacob Mātinum medicum Hebreū latinitate donata ... Haganoæ: [V. Kob] 1532.
lxxxviii numb. *l*.
With Macer, Floridus, De herbarvm ... [1530].

———. *See also* Artis chemicæ ... 1572.

169. AXT, Johann Conrad. Tractatus de arboribus coniferis et pice conficienda, aliisque ex illis arboribus provenientibus ... Jenæ: impensis J. Bielkii, typis S. Krebsii, 1679.
131 p. illus.

B

B., A.C.   *See* Bentz, Adolph Christoph.

170.   B., L.A.   Mémoires sur la réforme des thermometres, avec des avis particuliers, & des notes justificatives, critiques & instructives. Tours: A. Vauquer, 1779.
   1 *l*., 202 p.

171.   BABINGTON, William.   A systematic arrangement of minerals, founded on the joint consideration of their chemical, physical, and external characters ... London: for the author by T. Bensley, 1795.
   iv, 25 p.   charts.

172.   BACCI, Andrea.   De thermis ... libri septem ... De balneis totivs orbis, & de methodo medendi per balneas ... Venetiis: V. Valgrisius, 1571.
   32 *l*., 509 p.   illus.

173.   ——.   Discorso delle acqve Albvle, bagni di Cesare Avgvsto à Tivoli, delle acqve acetose presso à Roma, & delle acque d'Anticoli ... Roma: A. Blado, 1564.
   15 *l*.

174.   ——.   —— delle acqve di S. Giovanni a Capo di Boue nuouamente venute in luce ... Roma: heredi di A. Blado, 1567.
   34 p.

175.   BACERNI, Giuseppe.   Breue narratione de mirabili, e naturali effetti della potentissima, et arcana medicina del'oro potabile senza corrosiuo ... Bologna: F.M. Sarti, 1659.
   186 p., 8 *l*.   port.

176.   BACHIMIUS, Arnoldus.   Pan-sophia enchiretica, seu Philosophia universalis experimentalis ... per ignem examinata & probata ... [Nuremberg]: J. Zieger, 1682.
   3 *l*., 221 p.   illus.
   Lacking pages 1-2.

BÄCK, Albertus.   Animalia composita. *See* Linné, C. von, *praeses*. Entry 2420.

BACK, Jacobus de.   The discourse in which he handles the nullity of spirits. *In* Harvey, W., The anatomical exercises ... 1673.

——.   Dissertatio de corde. *In* Harvey, W., Exercitatio anatomica ... 1648, etc.

177.   BACON, Francis, *viscount St. Albans*. Historia naturalis & experimentalis de ventis, &c. Ludg. Batavorum: F. Hackius, 1648.
   8 *l*., 232 p., 8 *l*.

178.   ——.   The naturall and experimentall history of winds, &c ... Translated into English by R.G. London: for H. Moseley and T. Dring, 1653.
   12 *l*., 384 p., 23 *l*.

179.   BACON, Roger.   The cure of old age, and preservation of youth ... Translated into Latin ... by Richard Browne ... Also A physical account of the tree of life, by Edw. Madeira Arrais. Translated likewise out of Latin by the same hand. London: for T. Flesher and E. Evets, 1683.
   20 *l*., 156 p.; 3 *l*., 108 p., 5 *l*.

180.   ——.   De arte chymiæ scripta. Cvi accesservnt opuscula alia eiusdem authoris. Francofurti: typis I. Saurii, sumptibus I.T. Schönvvetteri, 1603.
   408 p.

——.   De mirabili potestate artis et naturae. *In* Celestino, C., De his que mundo mirabiliter eveniunt ... 1542.

181.   ——.   De l'admirable povvoir et pvissance de l'art & de nature, ou est traicté de la pierre philosophale. Traduit en François par Iacqves Girard de Tovrnvs. Paris: C. Hulpeau, 1629.
   63, 39 p.
   Includes: *L'art transmvtatoire dv Pape Iean XXII de ce nom.*
   With Sendivogius,. M., Cosmopolite ...

14

1629, *as issued*.

182. ——. ——. Paris: P. Billaine, 1629.
63, 39 p.
With Sendivogius, M., Cosmopolite ...
1629, *as issued*.

183. ——. Epistola ... de secretis
operibus artis et naturæ, et de nullitate
magiæ. Operâ Iohannis Dee ... castigata
olim, et ad sensum integrum restituta. Nunc
verò a quodam veritatis amatore ... foras
emissa; cum notis quibusdam partis ipsius
Johannis Dee, partim edentis. Hamburgi:
Bibliopolus Frobenianus, 1618.
80 p.

184. ——. Le miroir d'alqvimie ... Tra-
duiet de Latin en François, par vn gentil-
homme du D'aulphiné ... Lyon: M. Bonhomme,
1557.
4 pts. in 1 v.
Contents: *Bacon, R.*, Le miroir d'alquimie;
Joannes XXII, L'elixir des philosophes;
Bacon, R., De l'admirable pouvoir et puis-
sance de l'art; *Celestino, C.*, Des choses
merveilleusis.

185. ——. Le miroir d'alqvimie de Iean
de Mehvn. Paris: C. Seveste, 1613.
With Trismosin, S., *pseud.*, La toyson
d'or ... 1613.

186. ——. The mirror of alchimy ... Also
a most excellent and learned discourse of
the admirable force and efficacie of art and
nature, written by the same author. With certaine other worthie treatises of the like
argument ... London: for R. Olive, 1597.
2 *l.*, 84 p.

——. Speculum alchymiæ; the true
glass of alchemy. *In* Collectanea chymica
... 1684.

——. Of the medicine or tincture of
antimony. *In* Basilius Valentinus, Of natural
and supernatural things ... 1671.

187. ——. Thesavrvs chemicvs ... Francofurti: J.C. Unckelius, 1620.
408 p.

188. BACON, William. A key to Helmont.
Or, A short introduction to the better under-
standing of the theory and method of the
most profound chymical physicians. London:
for J. Starkey, 1682.
2 *l.*, 34 p.

189. Die BÄDER zu Tepliz in Böhmen, in
einer kurzen physisch-medizinischen und
politischen Uebersicht. Dresden: Walther,
1792.
70 p.

190. BAGELLARDO, Paolo. Opvscvlvm
recens natvm de morbis pverorvm, cum
appendicibus Magistri Petri Toleti ... Lvgdvni: G. Rose, 1538.
8 *l.*, 238 p., 1 *l.*

191. BAGLIVI, Giorgio. De praxi medica
ad priscam observandi rationem revocanda.
Libri duo. Accedunt dissertationes novae.
Romae: D.A. Herculis, 1696.
10 *l.*, 259 p., 1 *l.*, 119 p. map.

192. ——. Maladies, traduites du latin
de Baglivi. Aux quelles on a ajoûté des remarques & des observations fondées sur la
théorie la plus claire & la plus reçue, &
sur la plus saine pratique. Par m.G. d'Aignan
... Paris: V. Delaguette, 1757.
2 *l.*, lv, 340 p., 1 *l.*

193. ——. Opera omnia medico-practica,
et anatomica. Editio postrema Veneta emen-
datissima ... Venetiis: typis Remondinianis,
1752.
xxxii, 496 p. illus.

194. ——. Tractatus de fibra motrice et
morbosa ... Editio tertia. Lugduni: A. & J.
Posuel, 1703.
4 *l.*, 295 p., 1 *l.* illus.

195. BAIER, Johann Jacob. Biographiae
professorvm medicinae qvi in academia
Altorfina vnqvam vixervnt ... Norimbergae:
haeredes I.D. Tavberi, 1728.
7 *l.*, 195 p., 2 *l.* ports.

196. BAILLIE, Matthew. The morbid
anatomy of some of the most important parts
of the human body. The first American edition. Albany: Barber & Southwick, for T.
Spencer, 1795.
2 *l.*, viii, 248 p., 6 *l.*

197. ——. A series of engravings, ac-
companied with explanations, which are
intended to illustrate the morbid anatomy
of some of the most important parts of the
human body ... London: W. Bulmer, sold by
J. Johnson, 1799.
205 p. illus.

198. BAILLOU, Guillaume de. Commen-

tarivs in libellvm Theophrasti de vertigine.
Editore M. Iacobo Thevart. Parisiis: I. Qvesnel, 1640.

2 *l*., 41 p., 1 *l*.
With his Epidemiorum et ephemeridum ...
1640.

199. ———. Consiliorum medicinalium
libri II. A Iacobo Thevart ... authoris pro-
nepote, scholiis nonnullis illustrati, digesti, ac in lucem primum editi ... Adjecta
est authoris vita ... Parisiis: I. Qvesnel,
1635.

2 v. in 1.

200. ———. De convvlsionibvs libellvs.
In quo solennis quaestio explicatur,
cur sauciatis dextrâ capitis parte conu-
ulsio sanae partis contingat. Editore M.
Iacobo Thevart ... Parisiis: I. Qvesnel,
1640.

8 *l*., 51 p., 2 *l*.
With his Epidemiorum et ephemeridum ...
1640.

201. ———. Definitionvm medicarvm liber
... Studio & operâ M. Iacobi Thevart ...
Parisiis: I. Qvesnel, 1639.

10 *l*., 108 p., 4 *l*.
With his Epidemiorum et ephemeridum ...
1640.

202. ———. Epidemiorvm et ephemeridvm
libri dvo, studio & operâ M. Iacobi Thevart
... Parisiis: I. Qvesnel, 1640.

10 *l*., 273 p., 9 *l*.

203. ———. Opera omnia in quatuor tomos
divisa, studio et opera M. Jacobi Thevart ...
cum praefatione Theodori Tronchin. Genevae:
fratres de Tournes, 1762.

4 v. in 2.

204. ———. Opera omnia medica. [Studio,
cura et diligentia Jacobi Thevart. Venetiis:
A. Jeremias, 1734-1736.]

4 v.

205. BAIRO, Pietro. Secreti medicinali ...
Venetia [F. Sansovino, 1561].

8 *l*., 262 numb. *l*., 1 *l*.

206. ———. ———. Con nuoua giunta posta
nel fine ... Venetia: N. Tebaldini, 1602.

8 *l*., 262 numb. *l*.

207. BAKER, George. Opuscula medica,
iterum edita. Londini: ex officina J. & H.
Hughs, apud P. Elmsly, 1771.

2 *l*., 228 p.

208. BAKER, Robert. Cursus osteologicus;
being a compleat doctrine of the bones; according to the newest, and most refin'd
notions of anatomy ... The second edition.
London: T. Leigh & D. Midwinter, 1699.

5 *l*., 125 p. chart.

209. BALBIAN, Joost van, *ed*. Tractatvs
septem de lapide philosophico, e vetustis-
simo codice desumti, ab infinitis repurgati
mendis, & in lucem dati ... [Leyden] Plantin
..., 1599.

96 p.

210. BALDASSARRI, Giuseppe. Delle acque
minerali di Chianciano, relazione. Siena: A.
Bindi, 1756.

7 *l*., 273, 56 p., 1 *l*. illus.

211. ———. Osservazioni ed esperienze
intorno al bagno di Montalceto. Siena: B.
Bindi, 1779.

8 *l*., 144 p. illus., port., chart.

212. BALDI, Baldo. Del vero opobalsamo
orientale ... Dato in luce da' Signori Antonio
Manfredi, Vincentio Panvtio. Roma: V. Mas-
cardi, 1646.

3 *l*., 118 p.

213. ———. Disqvisitio iatrophysica ad
textum 23. libri Hippocratis de aere, aquis,
& locis. ... In qva de calcvlorvm cavsis, ac
de aquae Tiberis bonitate strictim disseritur
... Romae: L. Grignani, 1637.

6 *l*., 69 p., 1 *l*.

214. BALDUIN, Christian Adolf. Aurum
auræ, vi magnetismi universalis attractum,
per inventorem anagrammatizomenum: Sic
(infra, supra) sol duplus abundat in auris.
Colonia ad Spream: R. Völcker, 1674.

53 p., 1 *l*.

215. ———. Aurum superius & inferius
auræ superioris & inferioris hermeticum ...
Amstelodami: J. Jansonius, 1675.

10 *l*., 96 p., 7 *l*. illus.

216. ———. ———. Francofurti: G.H. Fromann,
1675.

16 *l*., 173 p. illus.

217. ———. Phosphorus hermeticus, sive
magnes luminaris. Francofurti: G.H. Fromann,
1675.

10 *l*.
With his Aurum superius ... 1675.

BALGUY, Charles. Epistola de morbo

miliari. *In* Fordyce, J., Historia febris
miliaris ... 1758.

218. BALL, John. Pharmacopoeia domestica
nova ... Cum variis additamentis annexis.
Londini: J. Scott, 1758.
vi, 94 p., 4 *l*.

BANCKES, Richard. Banckes' herbal.
See Herbal.

219. BANYER, Henry. Pharmacopoeia
pauperum: or, The hospital dispensatory: containing the chief medicines now used in the
hospitals of London ... The fourth edition
much enlarged. London: T. Longman, 1739.
1 *l*., ix, 167 p.

220. BARBA, Alvaro Alonzo. A collection
of scarce and valuable treatises upon metals,
mines, and minerals ... Part I and II containing the art of metals ... Part III containing
that invaluable piece of Mr. G. Plattes ...
Part IV Houghton's compleat miner. London:
C. Jephson for O. Payne, 1738.
6 *l*., 215 p.; 2 *l*., 66 p., 1 *l*. illus.

221. ――. The first [second] book of the
art of mettals ... Translated in the year, 1669.
By the R.H. Edward Earl of Sandwich. London:
for S. Mearne, 1674.
2 pts. in 1 v. illus.

222. ――. Metallurgie, ou L'art de tirer
et de purifier les métaux ... Avec des dissertations ... sur les mines & les opération
métalliques ... Paris: Didot, 1751.
2 v.

223. ――. Traité de l'art métalique, extrait des oeuvres d'Alvare-Alfonse Barba ...
auquel on a joint un memoire concernant les
mines de France ... Paris: Saugrain père,
1730.
11 *l*., 264 p., 20 *l*. illus.

224. BARBAY, Pierre. Commentarii in
Aristotelis physicam ... Editio quarta ...
Parisiis: vidua G. Josse, 1686.
2 v. illus.

225. BARBETTE, Paul. The chirurgical and
anatomical works ... Together with a treatise
of the plague ... Translated out of Low-Dutch
into English. London: J. Darby, sold by M.
Pitt, 1672.
8 *l*., 342, 52 p., 8 *l*. illus.

226. ――. Oevvres chirvrgiqves et
anatomiqves ... avec vn traité de la peste ...

Lyon: I. Faeton, 1680.
13 *l*., 554 p., 11 *l*. illus.

227. ――. La pratique de medicine. Enrichie de quantité de notes, observations &
histoires medicales. Par Frederic Deckers
... Le tout nouvellement & fidellement traduit
en François. Lyon: J.B. Guillimin, 1692.
2 v. illus.
Volume two only.

228. BARBEYRAC, Charles. Medicamentorum constitutio, seu formulæ ... Lugduni:
P. Bruyset, 1751.
4 *l*., 526 p.

229. BARCHUSEN, Johann Conrad. Acro-
amata, in quibus complura ad iatro-chemiam
atque physicam spectantia, jocunda rerum
varietate, explicantur. Trajecti Batavorum:
J. Visch, 1703.
12 *l*., 376 p., 11 *l*.

230. ――. De medicinæ origine et progressu dissertationes. In quibus medicorum
sectæ, institutiones, decreta, hypotheses,
præceptiones, &c. ab initio medicinæ usque
ad nostra tempora traduntur. Trafecti ad
Rhenvm: G. Paddenburg et G. Croon, 1723.
8 *l*., 679 p.

231. ――. Elementa chemiæ, quibus sub-
juncta est confectura lapidis philosophici
imaginibus repræsentata. Lugduni Batavorum:
T. Haak, 1718.
6 *l*., 532 p., 10 *l*. illus.

232. BARICELLI, Giulio Cesare. Hortvlvs
genialis, siue Rerum iucundarum, medicarum,
& memorabilium compendium ... Huic accessit
liber De esculentorum potulentorumque facultatibus. Arnaldo Freitagio ... auctore. Genevæ:
P. Albert, 1620.
6 *l*., 339 p., 14 *l*.; 320 p., 4 *l*.

233. BARISANO, Francesco Domenico. La
piscina salvtare in Piemonte ne' bagni di
Valdieri, &c. historiati, e descritti ... Torino:
B. Zapatta, 1674.
16 *l*., 170 p., 4 *l*. port.

234. BARLET, Annibal. Le vray et methodiqve
covrs de la physiqve resolvtive, vvlgairement
dite chymie ... C'est à dire, L'art de Diev, en
l'ovvrage le l'vnivers. Seconde edition ...
Paris: N. Charles, 1657.
4 *l*., 626 p., 18 *l*. illus., charts.

235. BARNAUD, Nicolas. Commentariolum
in ænigmaticvm qvoddam epitaphivm. Bononiæ

stvdiorvm ... Huic additisunt processus
chemici non pauci ... Lvgdvni Batavorvm:
T. Basson, 1593.
   47 p.
   With Dorn, G., Artificii chymistici ... 1594.

236. ———. De occvlta philosophia,
.epistola cuiusdam patris ad filium ... nunc
primum in lucem edita ... Lugduni Batavorum:
T. Basson, 1601.
   16 *l*.

237. ———. Qvadriga avrifera, nunc primùm à Nicolao Barnavdo ... edita ... [Leyden]
ex officina Plantiniana, apvd C. Raphelen-
givm, 1599.
   95 p.

———. Quadriga aurifera. *See also*
Ripley, G., Chymische Schrifften ... 1624.

238. ———. Tractatvlvs chemicvs, theo-
sophiae palmarivm dictus, anonymi cuiusdam
philosophi antiqui ... nunc primum editus, &
Avriga ad quadrigam auriferam ... Lugduni
Batavorum: T. Basson, 1601.
   26 *l*.
   With his De occvlta philosophia ... 1601.

239. ———. Triga chemica: de lapide
philosophico tractatvs tres ... [Leyden] ex
officina Plantiniana, apud C. Raphelengium,
1599.
   40 p., 8 *l*.

240. BARNER, Jakob. Chymia philosophica
perfecte delineata ... cum brevi sed accurata
& fundamentali salium doctrina ... Noribergæ:
A. Otto, 1689.
   8 *l*., 560 p., 28 *l*. illus.

241. ———. Dissertatio epistolica ad ...
D.D. Joelem Langelott ... seu Prodromus
vindiciarum experimentorum ac dogmatum
suorum, quæ David von der Becke ... in
epistolâ de volitalisatione salis tartari ...
venditavit ... Augustæ Vindelicorum: apud
G. Gebelium, typis Koppmayerianis [1690?].
   23 *l*.
   With Maynwaring, E., Historia et mysterium
... 1675.

242. ———. Spiritus vini sine acido, hoc
est: In spiritu vini & oleis indistinctè non
esse acidum ... demonstratio curiosa cum
modo conficiendi salia volatilia oleosa,
eorumqve usu. Lipsiæ: sumptibus J. Fritzchii,
literis J.E. Hahni, 1675.
   40 p.
   With Maynwaring, E., Historia ... 1675.

243. BARRELIER, Jacques. Plantæ per
Galliam, Hispaniam et Italiam observatæ,
iconibus æneis exhibitæ ... Opus posthumum,
accurante Antonio de Jussieu ... in lucem
editum ... Cvi accessit ejusdem auctoris
Specimen de insectis quibusdam marinis,
mollibus, crustaceis & testaceis. Parisiis:
G. Ganeau, 1714.
   6 *l*., 140 p.; 335 *l*., xxvi p., 1 *l*. illus.,
port.

244. BARROUGH, Philip. The method of
physick, contaning the cavses, signes, and
cvres of inward diseases in mans body ...
The sixth edition. London: R. Field ..., 1624.
   8 *l*., 477 p., 3 *l*.

245. BARROW, John. Dictionarium medicum
universale: or, A new medicinal dictionary
... London: for T. Longman ..., 1749.
   1 *l*., iv p., 293 *l*.

246. BARRY, *Sir* Edward. Observations
historical, critical, and medical, on the
wines of the ancients ... With general observations on the principles and qualities
of water, and in particular on those of Bath
... London: for T. Cadell, 1775.
   xii, 479 p.

247. ———. A treatise on a consumption
of the lungs, with a previous account of
nutrition, and of the structure and use of
the lungs. The second edition with additions.
London: for W. and J. Innys, 1727.
   276 p., 2 *l*.

248. BARTHOLIN, Caspar. Institvtiones
anatomicae, novis recentiorum opinionibus
& observationibus, quarum innumerae hactenus
editae non sunt, figurisque auctae ab Thoma
Bartholino. Lvg[dvni] Batavorum: F. Hackius,
1641.
   10 *l*., 496 p., 22 *l*. illus.

249. BARTHOLIN, Thomas. Anatomia, ex
Caspari Bartolini parentis institutionibus ...
Tertiùm ad sanguinis circulationem reformata
cum iconibus novis accuratissimis: accessit
... appendix De lacteis thoracicis & vasis
lymphaticis. Hagae–Comitis: A. Vlacq, 1655.
   8 *l*., 592 p., 7 *l*. illus., port.

250. ———. Anatome quartum renovata:
non tantum ex institutionibus b.m. parentis,
Caspari Bartholini ... Lugduni: J.A. Huguetan,
1677.
   16 *l*., 807 p., 9 *l*. illus., port.

251. ———. Cista medica Hafniensis, variis

consiliis, curationibus, casibus rarioribus, vitis medicorum Hafniensium, aliisque ad rem medica, anatomicam, botanicam & chymicam spectantibus referta. Accedit ejusdam Domus anatomica brevissimè descripta. Hafniae: typis M. Godicchenii, impensis P. Hauboldi, 1662.

   10 *l*., 62 p.; 1 *l*., 645 p., 3 *l*.

252. ——. De insolitis partus humani viis dissertatio nova. Accedunt ... Johannis Veslingi, De pullitie Aegyptiorum & aliae ejusdem observationes anatomicae & epistolae medicae posthumae. Hagae Comitum: P. Gosse, 1740.

   1 *l*., 194 p., 4 *l*., 248 p.

253. ——. De nivis usu medico observationes variæ. Accessit D. Erasmi Bartholini de figura nivis dissertatio; cum operum authoris catalogo. Hafniæ: typis M. Godicchii, sumptibus P. Haubold, 1661.

   16 *l*., 42, 232 p., 4 *l*.   illus.

   This copy lacks the Catalogus operum, and has the tract by E. Bartholinus bound first.

254. ——. ——. Hafniæ: typis M. Godicchii, sumptibus P. Haubold, 1661.

   12 *l*., 232 p., 4 *l*.; 7 *l*.; 3 *l*., 42 p.   illus.

   With his Historiarum anatomicarum ... 1661.

255 ——. Defensio vasorum lacteorum et lymphaticorum adversus Joannem Riolanum ... Accedit Guilielmi Harvei De venis lacteis sententia expensa ab eodem Th. Bartholino. Hafniae: typis haeredum M. Martzanis, sumptibus G. Holst, 1655.

   3 *l*., 195 p.

   With his Vasa lymphatica ... 1653.

——. Dissertatio anatomica de hepate defuncto novis bilsianorum observationibus opposita. Hafniae: excudebat C. Wering, sumptibus P. Hauboldi, 1661.

   84 p.

   With his Cista medica Hafniensis ... 1662.

257. ——. Epistolarum medicinalium à doctis vel ad doctos scriptarum ... Hafniæ: typis M. Godicchenii, impensis P. Haubold, 1663-1667.

   3 v. in 2.   illus.

258. ——. ——. Hagae Comitum: P. Gosse, 1740.

   4 v.   illus.

259. ——. Historiarum anatomicarum

rariorum. Centuria I et II. Amstelodami: I. Henrici, 1654.

   8 *l*., 326 p., 5 *l*.   illus.

260. ——. Historiarum anatomicarum rariorum centuria III & IV. Ejusdem cura accessere observationes anatomicae ... Petri Pawi. Hafniae: typis P. Hakii, sumptibus P. Haubold, 1657.

   4 *l*., 45 p., 1 *l*., 430 p., 4 *l*.   illus.

   With his Historiarum anatomicarum ... 1654.

261. ——. Historiarum anatomicarum & medicarum rariorum centuria V & VI. Accessit ... Joannis Rhodii Mantissa anatomica. Hafniae: typis H. Gödiani, sumptibus P. Hauboldi, 1661.

   8 *l*., 386 p., 7 *l*., 32 p.   illus.

262. ——. Responsio de experimentis anatomicis bilsianis et difficili hepatis resurrectione, ad clarissimum virum Nicolaum Zas. Hafniae: P. Haubold, 1661.

   40 p.

   With his Cista medica Hafniensis ... 1662.

263. ——. Vasa lymphatica, nuper Hafniae in animantibus inventa, et hepatis exseqviae. Hafniae: sumptibus G. Holst, typis P. Hakii, 1653.

   4 *l*., 58 p., 1 *l*.   illus.

BARTHOLINUS, Erasmus. De figura nivis. *In* Bartholin, T., De nivis usu ... 1661.

264. BARTHOLOMAEUS ANGLICUS. De proprietatibus rerum. [Westminster: Wynkyn de Worde, c. 1495.]

   480 *l*.   illus.

   A few leaves in facsimile.

265. ——. ——. Londini: T. Berthelet, 1535.

   8 *l*., ccclxxxvi numb. *l*.

266. BARTOLI, Daniello. Del ghiaccio e della coagvlatione trattati ... Bologna: G. Recaldini, 1682.

   4 *l*., 230 p., 4 *l*.

267. BASEILLAC, Pascal. Observations nouvelles sur les propriétés de l'alkali fluor ammoniacal ... Paris: l'imprimerie de Monsieur, 1778.

   1 *l*., 49 p.

268. BASILIUS VALENTINUS. Chymische Schriften, aus einigen alten Msten aufs fleis-

sigste verbessert, mit vielen Tractaten ...
in Drey Theile verfasset ... begleitet von
Bened. Nic. Petræo. Fünfte Edition. Hamburg:
G. Richter, 1740.
    80 *l*., 1133 p., 78 *l*.   illus., port.

269.   ——. Les dovze clefs de philosophie
... Plus l' Azoth, or le moyen de faire l'or
caché des philosophes. Tradvction francoise.
Paris: P. Moët, 1659.
    176, 196 p.   illus.

270.   ——. ——. Paris: P. Moët, 1660.
    167 [i.e. 176] p.   illus.
    Lacking L'azoth.

    ——.   ——.   *In* Janua patefacta the-
sauro ... 1678.

271.   ——. Geheime Bücher oder letztes
Testament. Vom grossen Stein der Vralten
Weisen vnd andern verborgenen Geheimnussen der Natur ... Strassburg: C. Dietzel,
1645.
    8 *l*., 272 p.   illus.

272.   ——. The last will and testament
... To which is added two treatises, the first
declaring his manual operations. The second
shewing things natural and supernatural ...
London: S.G. and B.G. for E. Brewster, 1671.
    12 *l*., 534 [i.e. 504] p.   illus., chart.

273.   ——. Haliographia de præparatione,
vsu, ac virtutibus omnium salium, mineralium,
animalium, & vegetabilium, ex manuscriptis
... Basilii Valentini ... ad ... Ioannem Lvparvm
collegiat ... Bononiæ: [typis N. Tebaldini,
apud A. Salmincium] 1644.
    8 *l*., 102 p.   illus.

274.   ——. Ein kurtzer summarischer
Tractat ... von dem grossen Stein der
vhralten ... Hierbey ein sonderlicher Tractat
de Microcosmo ... Ingleichem von der Wissenschafft vnd verborgenen geheimnissen der
sieben Planeten ... publieiret ... durch
Iohannem Thölden ... [Zerbst: gedruck durch
J. Schleern, in vorlegung J. Apels] 1602.
    14 *l*., 240 p.   illus.

275.   ——. Tractat von dem grossen Stein
der Vhralten ... I. Nebenst seiner selbst
eigenen klaren repetition vnd kurtzen Wieder-
holung ... II. De Microcosmo ... III. Von der
grossen Heimligkeit der Welt ... IV. Von der
Wissenschafft vnd verborgenen Geheimnüssen der sieben Planeten ... publiciret
... durch Johann Thölden ... [Leipzig] B.
Voigt, 1626.

256 p.   illus.

276   ——. Von dem grossen Stein der
Vhralten ... Neben angehängten Tractätlein
... Strassburg: C. Dietzel, 1645.
    4 *l*., 156 p., 2 *l*.   illus.
    With his Geheime Bücher ... 1645.

277.   ——. ——. Strassburg: 1666.
    4 *l*., 156 p., 2 *l*.   illus.

    ——. Practica. *In* Maier, M., Tripus
aureus ... 1618.

278   ——. Revelation des mysteres des
teintvres essentieles des sept metavx & de
leurs vertus medicinales. Composée en Allemand ... et traduite par le Sieur I. I. ...
Paris: I. de Senlecqve, I. Henavlt, 1645.
    7 *l*., 64 p.   illus.

279.   ——. ——. Nouuelle edition, reueuë,
augmentée ... Paris: la veufve I. de Senlecqve,
et L. Rondet, 1668.
    7 *l*., 70 p.

280.   ——. Triumph-Wagen Antimonii ...
publiciret, vnd an Tag geben, durch Johann.
Thölden ... mit einer Vorrede Doctoris
Joachimi Tanckij ... Leipzig: J. Apel, 1611.
    17 *l*., 3–598 p., 12 *l*.

281.   ——. ... Triumphant chariot of
antimony, with annotations of Theodore Kirk-
ringius ... With the true book of the learned
Synesius ... concerning the philosopher's
stone. London: for D. Newman, 1678.
    8 *l*., 176 p.   illus.

282.   ——. Theodori Kerckringii ... Com-
mentarivs in Currem triumphalem antimonii
Basilii Valentini, à se latinitate donatum.
Amstæladami: H. Wetstenius, 1685.
    10 *l*., 342 p., 9 *l*.   illus.

283.   ——. Cvrrvs trivmphalis antimonii
... E Germanico in Latinum versum operâ ...
Petri Ioannis Fabri ... Tolosæ: P. Bosc, 1646.
    13 *l*., 398 p.

284.   ——. Von den natürlichen vnd vber-
natürlichen Dingen ... Trewlich eröffnet durch
Fratrem Basilium Valentinum ... Vnd nunmehr
aus seiner eigenen Handschrifft in Druck publiciret, durch Johann Tholden ... Leipzig: B.
Voigt, 1624.
    4 *l*., 119 p., 1 *l*.

285.   ——. Of natural & supernatural things
... Whereunto is added, Frier Roger Bacon, of

the medicine or tincture of antimony; Mr.
John Isaac Holland, his work of Saturn, and
Alex. Van Suchten, of the secrets of antimony.
Translated out of High Dutch by Daniel
Cable. London: M. Pitt, 1671.
    238 p.
    Lacking the treatise of Van Suchten.

286.   ——. Tractatus chymico-philosoph-
icus de rebus naturalibus & supernaturalibus
metallorum & mineralium. Francofurti ad
Moenum: J.G. Seyler, 1676.
    64 p.

287.   BASSI, Ferdinando. Delle terme Porrettane ... Roma: G. Zempel, 1768.
    vi p., 1 ℓ., 283 p.   illus., map.

288.   BASTIANI, Annibale. Analisi delle
acque minerali di S. Casciano de'bagni e
dell uso di esse nella medicina. Firenze:
G. Cambiagi, 1770.
    xviii, 126 p.

289.   BASTIANI, Jacopo Filippo. De' bagni
di S. Casciano, opera medica ... Montefia-
scone: 1733.
    10 ℓ., 478 p., 9 ℓ.

290.   BATE, George. Pharmacopoeia
Bateana ... Huic accessit Orthotonia medicorum observata: annexa item est in calce
tabula posologica ... Amstelodami: Janssonio-
Waesbergios, 1688.
    6 ℓ., 130, 12, 16 p.

291.   ——. ——. Huic accesserunt Arcana
Goddardiana ... Editio tertia ... Londini: S.
Smith & B. Walford, 1700.
    4 ℓ., 286 p., 1 ℓ.

292.   ——. ——. Editio quarta ... Amstelædami: Wetstenius, 1709.
    4 ℓ., 240 p.
    With Fuller, T., Pharmacopoeia extem-
poranea ... 1709.

293.   ——. ——. Editio quinta ... Amstelaedami: Wetstenius, 1719.
    4 ℓ., 240 p.

294.   ——. ——. Curâ & operâ Thomæ
Fuller. Londini: G. & J. Innys, 1719.
    12 ℓ., 219 p., 12 ℓ.; 6 ℓ., 77 p., 7 ℓ.

295.   ——. ——. Editio sexta ... Amstelaedami: R. & J. Wetstenius & G. Smith, 1731.
    4 ℓ., 240 p.

296.   ——. ——. Deinde adduntur Georgii

Hernesti Stahllii Fundamenta chemico-
pharmaceutica. Editio ceteris emendatior.
Venetiis: N. Pezzana, 1776.
    224 p.; viii, 214 p.; 48 p.
    Contains also: Juncker, Johann. Con-
spectus formularum medicarum.

297.   ——. Pharmacopoeia Bateana: or,
Bate's dispensatory ... The Arcana Goddardiana
... By William Salmon. London: for S. Smith
and B. Walford, 1694.
    8 ℓ., 965 p., 9 ℓ.   illus.

298.   ——. ——. The third edition ...
London: for S. Smith and B. Walford, 1706.
    8 ℓ., 747 p., 6 ℓ.

299.   ——. ——. The fourth edition ...
London: for W. Innys, 1713.
    8 ℓ., 744 p., 8 ℓ.

300.   ——. Pharmacopoea Batheana of
de apotheek van de Heer Georgius Bath ...
Uitgegeeven door den Heer Jac. Shipton ...
Tweede druk. Hoorn: T. Tjallingius, 1762.
    7 ℓ., 335 p., 35 ℓ.

301.   BATE, John. The mysteries of nature
and art. In foure severall parts ... The second edition; with many additions unto each
part. [London] for R. Mabb, 1635.
    6 ℓ., 288 p., 8 ℓ.   illus., port.

302.   ——. ——. The third edition. With
many additions. [London] for A. Crooke, 1654.
    1 ℓ. 221 p. 7 ℓ.   illus.

303.   Le BATIMENT des receptes, traduit
d'Italien en François. Et augmenté d'une
infinité de beaux secrets dupuis peu mis en
usage. Avec un autre petit traité des receptes
intitulé Le grand jardin. Troyes: J.A. Garnier
[n.d.].
    140 p., 1 ℓ.

    BATSDORFF, Heinrich von, pseud. See
Reibehand, Christoph.

304.   BATT, William. Pharmacopoea seu
Formulæ selectæ medicamentorum ad normam
medicinæ hodiernæ aptatorum ... Genuæ:
F. Repettus, 1785.
    96 p.

    BATTIMELLUS, Andrea. Auctuarium.
In Musitanus, C., Ad Had. à Mynsicht ...
1701.

305.   BATTINI, Domenico. Ricerche intorno
alle acque minerali epatiche ed alla analisi

chimica di diverse acque minerali dello
stato de Siena. Siena: P. Carli, 1793.
  xvi, 322 p.

306.   BATTLE, William.   A treatise on madness. London: for J. Whiston and B. White,
1758.
  vii, 99 p.

307.   BAUDERON, Brice.   Paraphrase svr
la pharmacopée.   Diuisée en deux liures ...
Reueuë, corrigée, & augmentée par l'autheur.
Ensemble vn traicté des eaux distilées ...
par Laurens Catelan ... Dernière edition.
Lyon: P. Rigaud, 1618.
  8 ℓ., 496 p., 6 ℓ.; 36 p.   port.
  With Bright, T., A treatise ... 1580.

308.   ——.   Pharmacopée de Bavderon.
Reveve, corrigee et augmentée de plusieurs
compositions necessaires ... Auec vn Traicté
des plus vsitez & celebres medicamens
chymiques. Par G. Savvageon ... Paris: I.
Lacqvehay, 1636.
  8 ℓ. 512 p., 8 ℓ.; 32 p.; 1 ℓ., 77 p., 3 ℓ

309.   ——.   ——.   Tolose: A. Colomiez,
1654.
  8 ℓ., 512 p., 8 ℓ.; 32 p.; 2 ℓ., 97 p., 4 ℓ.

310.   ——.   —— a laqvelle ... sont
adiovstées de nouueau, les remarqves, corrections et compositions ... par François
Verny ... Lyon: I.A. Hvgvetan & M.A. Ravavd,
1662.
  8 ℓ., 408, 294 p., 6 ℓ.

311.   ——.   ——.   Lyon: P. Bailly, 1670.
  8 ℓ., 785 p., 9 ℓ.; 51 p.; 2 ℓ., 97 p., 4 ℓ.

312.   ——.   ——.   Nouvelle edition, reveuë
& exactement corrigée ... Lyon: G. Chaunod
& C. Chappuis, 1681.
  8 ℓ., 785 p., 9 ℓ.; 51 p.; 2 ℓ., 97 p., 4 ℓ.

313.   ——.   ——.   Troisiéme edition ... par
François Verny ... Lyon: I. Girin & B. Riviere,
1681.
  10 ℓ., 1022 p., 8 ℓ.

314.   BAUHIN, Johann.   Historia plantarvm
vniversalis, nova, et absolvtissima cvm
consensv et dissensv circa eas. Auctoribus
Ioh. Bavhino ... et Ioh. Henr. Cherlero ...
Quam recensuit & auxit Dominicvs Chabrævs
... Iuris verò publici fecit Franciscvs Lvd. A
Graffenried ... Ebrodvni: 1650-1651.
  3 v.   illus.

315.   BAUHIN, Kaspar.   Appendix ad the-

atrvm anatomicvm sive explicatio ... Francofvrti: excudebat M. Becker, impensis I.T.
& I.I. de Brij, 1600.
  4 ℓ., 197 p., 23 ℓ.   illus., port.
  With his Theatrvm anatomicum ... 1605.

316.   ——.   De lapidis bezaar orient. et
occident. cervini item et germanici ortv,
natvra, differentijs, veroóue vsu ... Basileæ:
C. Waldkirch, 1613.
  12 ℓ., 288 p., 5 ℓ.

317.   ——.   Πίναξ theatri botanici sive
Index in Theophrasti Dioscorides, Plinii et
botanicorvm qui à seculo scripserunt ...
Basileæ: J. Regis, 1671.
  12 ℓ., 518 p., 11 ℓ.

318.   ——.   Πρόδρομος theatri botanici
in qvo plantæ supra sexgentæ ab ipso primum descriptæ cum plurimis figuris proponuntur. Editio altera emendatior. Basileae:
J. Regis, 1671.
  2 ℓ., 160 p., 6 ℓ.   illus.
  With his Πίναξ theatri botanici ... 1671.

319.   ——.   Theatrvm anatomicum, novis
fuguris aeneis illustratum et in lucem emis-
sum opera & sumptibus Theodori de Bry ...
Francofurti at Moenum: M. Berker, 1605.
  8 ℓ., 1314 p.   illus., port.

320.   ——.   Theatrvm anatomicum, infinitis
locis auctum, ad morbos accommodatum & ad
erroribus ab authore repurgatum ... [Basle]
I.T. de Bry, 1621.
  7 ℓ., 664 p., 8 ℓ.; 258, 21 p.   illus.
  The plates have a separate title page:
Vivae imagines partium corporis humani ...
1620.

321.   BAUMÉ, Antoine.   Chymie expérimentale et raisonnée. Paris: P.F. Didot,
1773.
  3 v.   illus., port., charts.

322.   ——.   Chimica sperimentale e
ragionata ... Ora per la prima volta tradotta
in Italiano. Coll'aggiunta del trattato dell'arte
vetraria di ... Antonio Neri ... Venezia: F. di
N. Pezzana, 1781.
  3 v.   illus.

323.   ——.   Élémens de pharmacie théorique
et pratique ... Seconde édition ... Paris: Lacombe, 1769.
  2 v.
  Lacking v. 2.

324.   ——.   ——.   Quatrieme édition ...

Paris: Samson, 1777.
  2 *l*., xl, 957 p., 1 *l*. illus.

325. ——. ——. Sixieme édition ... Paris:
Samson, 1790.
  2 *l*., xxxix, 894 p., 1 *l*. illus.

326. ——. Manuel de chymie, ou Exposé
des opérations de la chymie et de leurs
produits ... Seconde édition. Revue & augmentée. Paris: P. Fr. Didot, 1766.
  xvi, 501 p., 1 *l*.

327. ——. A manual of chemistry ...
Translated from the French ... Warrington:
W. Eyres for J. Johnson, 1778.
  vi p., 1 *l*., 400 p.

328. ——. Memoire sur les argilles ou
Recherches et experiences chymiques et
physiques sur la nature des terres les plus
propres l'agriculture ... Paris: Lacombe,
1770.
  xiv, 87 p., 2 *l*.

329. BAUMES, Jean Baptiste Timothée.
De la phthisie pulmonaire, ouvrage couronné
en 1783, sur la question proposée en ces
termes ... Montpellier: G. Izar et A. Ricard,
1795.
  2 v.

330. BAUSNER, Bartholomaeus. De consensu partium humani corporis libri III ...
Amstelodami: I. Ravesteynius, 1556 [i.e.
1656].
  12 *l*., 185 p. illus.
  With Fehr, J.M., Hiera picra ... 1668.

331. BAWIER, Johann. Kurze und grund-
liche Beschreibung dess weitberühmten,
heilsammen Saurbrunnen und Bads zu Fideris
in dem Thal Prettigöw ... Anjetzo ... aufs
neue nachgedruckt ... Chur: A. Pfeffer, 1744.
  71 p.

332. BAYEN, Pierre. Opuscules chimiques.
Paris: A. Dugour et Durand, 1798.
  2 v. charts.

333. ——. Recherches chimiques sur
l'étain ... ou Réponse a cette question: Peut-
on sans aucun danger employer les vaisseaux
d'etain dans l'usage économique? Par MM.
Bayen ... & Charlard ... Paris: P.D. Pierres,
1781.
  viii, 285 p.

334. BAYLE, François. Tractatus de apoplexia: in qvo hvfvs affectionis causa penitius

inquiritur & curatio exponitur ex doctrina
Hippocratis. Tolosae: B. Guillemette, 1677.
  6 *l*., 125 p., 3 *l*.

335. BAYLIS, Edward. A new and compleat
body of practical botanic physic, from the
medicinal plants of the vegetable kingdom
... London: for Stace & Maids, 1791.
  viii, 400 p. illus.
  Lacking p. 401-563 and 48 additional
pages at end.
  Vol. I only. All published?

  BAYNARD, Edward, *jt. auth.*
ψυχρολουσία, or, The history of cold bathing.
See Floyer, *Sir* John.

336. BEAUSOBRE, Louis de. Dissertations
philosophiques ... sur la nature du feu; et
... les differentes parties de la philosophie,
et des mathematiques. Paris: Durand, Pissot,
1753.
  3 *l*., 231 p. charts.

337. BECCAFUMI, Domenico. [The mys-
terious labors of alchemy. Siena, ca. 1540?]
  10 woodcuts without text, individually
mounted and boxed.

338. BECCARI, Jacopo Bartolomeo. De
quamplurimis phosphoris nunc primum de-
tectis commentarius. Bononiæ: L. a Vulpe,
1744.
  6 *l*., 85 p., 1 *l*.

339. BECHER, Johann Joachim. Actorum
laboratorii chymici Monacensis, seu Physicæ
subterraneæ libri duo ... accesserunt sub
finem mille hypotheses seu mixtiones chymicæ,
ante hâc nunquam visæ ... Francofurti: J.D.
Zunner, 1669.
  20 *l*., 633 p., 3 *l*. illus.

340. ——. Physica subterranea profundam
subterraneorum genesin, e principiis hucusque
ignotis ostendens ... Editio novissima. Præfatione utili præmissa ... libro tersius et
curatius edendo operam navavit et Specimen
Beccherianum ... subjunxit Georg Ernestus
Stahl ... Lipsiæ: ex officina Weidmanniana,
1738.
  2 pts. in 1 v. illus.

341. ——. Chymisches Laboratorium,
oder Unter-erdische Naturkündigung, darinnen
enthalten wird, I. Die tieffe Zeugung derer
unter-erdischen Dinge ... II. Neue chymische
Proben ... III. Ein nochmaliger Zusatz ... IV.
Ein chymischer Rätseldeuter ... Franckfurt:
P. Fievet, 1690.

4 pts in 1 v.

342. ——. Chymischer Glücks-Hafen,
oder Grosse chymische Concordantz und
Collection von funffzehen hundert chymischen
Processen ... Franckfurt: J.G. Schiele, 1682.
4 *l*., 810 p., 18 *l*.

343. ——. ——. Nebst einer neuen Vorrede oder Bedencken von der Gold-Macherey
Herrn Georg Ernst Stahls ... neue und viel
verbesserte Edition ... Halle: E.G. Krug, 1726.
15 *l*., 810 p., 14 *l*.   port.

344. ——. ——. Leipzig: J.P. Kraus, 1755.
15 *l*., 876 p., 14 *l*.   port.

345. ——. Experimentum chymicum novum
... Loco supplementi in physicam ... subter-
raneam et responsi ad D. Rolfincij schedas
de non entitate mercurij corporum ... Francofurti: sumptibus J.D. Zunneri, typis H. Friesii,
1671.
172 p.

346. ——. Institutiones chimicæ pro-
dromæ, i.e. ... Oedipus chimicus obscuriorum
terminorum & principiorum chimicorum, mysteria aperiens & resolvens ... Francofurti: H.
à Sande, 1664.
8 *l*., 192 p., 4 *l*.   illus.

347. ——. ——. Amstelodami: E. Weyerstraten, 1664.
8 *l*., 202 p., 4 *l*.   illus.

348. ——. Oedipus chymicus, seu Institutiones chymicæ ... Editio novissima ...
Supplementa Beccheriana, elementa chymiæ
methodo mathematica ... subjunxit Joh. Jacobus Rosenstengelius. Francofurti ad
Moenum: J.M. van Sande, 1716.
10 *l*., 228 p., 6 *l*.; 3 *l*., 156 p., 3 *l*.
With his Opuscula chymica ... 1719.

349. ——. Magnalia naturæ: or, The
philosophers-stone lately expos'd to publick
sight and sale ... London: printed by T.
Dawks, sold by L. Curtiss, 1680.
3 *l*., 31 p.

350. ——. Magnalia naturæ: or, The
truth of the philosophers-stone asserted ...
London: T. Dawks, 1680.
3 *l*., 31 p.

351. ——. Minera arenaria perpetua ...
Scriptum hoc inservire poterit lectori pro
continuatione Trifolii Hollandici, & Supplementi tertii in authoris Physicam subter-

raneam. Londini: typis T.N., apud M. Pardoe,
1680.
112 p., 4 *l*.

352. ——. Mineralisches A B C. oder
Vier und zwantzig chymische Theses ... aus
dem Lateinischen ins Teutsche übersetzet.
Nun aber auf vieler Begehren zum Druck
befördet durch Friederich Roth-Scholtzen ...
Nürnberg: J.D. Taubers seel. Erben, 1723.
150 p.   port.

353. ——. Natur- Kündigung der Metallen
... Franckfurt: J.W. Ammon und W. Serlin,
1661.
8 *l*., 347 p., 18 *l*.

354. ——. Opvscvla chymica rariora,
addita nova præfatione ... a Friderico Roth-
Scholtzio. Norimbergæ: hæredes J.D. Tau-
beri, 1719.
6 *l*., 50, 310 p.   illus.

——. Pantaleon delarvatus. *In*
Faust, J.M., Philaletha illustratus ... 1706.

355. ——. Tripus hermeticus fatidicus,
pandens oracula chymica, seu I. Laboratorium
portatile ... II. Magnorum duorum productorum
... III. Alphabetum minerale ... His accessit
concordantia mercvrii lvnæ ... Francofurti
ad Moenum: J.G. Shiele, 1689.
186 p., 5 *l*.   illus.

356. BECKE, David von der.   Barnerus
leviter & amicè castigatus ... Hamburgi: G.
Schultz, 1675.
64 p.
With Maynwaring, E., Historia et mysterium
... 1675.

357. ——. Experimenta et meditationes
circa naturalium rerum principia ... Hamburgi:
G. Schultz, 1674.
7 *l*., 335 p.   illus.
Bound in a sheet of 15th century Latin
liturgical manuscript of German origin.

358. BECKER, Dietrich David.   Der chymische Wahrsager oder Beschreibung eines
Rubinrothen ... Langensaltza: J.C. Martini,
1755.
78 p.

359. ——. Des chymischen Wahrsagers
Vertheidigung, wider die partheyische Recen-
sion der Verfasser der Erfurtischen gelehrten
Nachrichten ... Langensaltza: J.C. Martini,
1757.
88 p., 1 *l*.

With his Der chymische Wahrsager ...
1755.

360. BECKHER, Daniel. Medicus micro-
cosmus, seu Spagyria microcosmi exhibens
medicinam corpore hominis tùm vivo, tùm
extincte doctè eruendam ... Editio nova
triplo auctior & correctior. Londini: J. Martin ..., 1660.
16 *l*., 304 p., 12 *l*.

361. BECKHER, Daniel Christophorus,
praeses. Dissertatio medica de hemiplexia
... respondente Christophoro à Lohen ...
Regiomonti: Reusner [1686].
14 *l*.

362. BEDDOES, Thomas. Contributions to
physical and medical knowledge, principally
from the west of England ... Bristol: Biggs &
Cottle for T.N. Longman ..., 1799.
25, 539 p., 2 *l*. illus.

363. ———. Considerations on the medicinal use of factitious airs, and on the
manner of obtaining them in large quantities.
In two parts. Part I. by Thomas Beddoes ...
Part II. by James Watt ... Bristol: Bulgin &
Rosser for J. Johnson ..., [1794].
48, 32 p. illus.

364. ———. Essay on the causes, early
signs, and prevention of pulmonary consumption for the use of parents and pre-
ceptors. Second edition, much enlarged.
London: Longman and Rees, 1799.
2 *l*., 340 p.

365. ———. Observations on the nature
and cure of calculus, sea scurvy, consumption, catarrh, and fever: together with con-
jectures upon several other subjects of
physiology and pathology. Philadelphia: T.
Dobson, 1797.
xvi, 278 p., 1 *l*.

366. BEER, Georg Joseph. Beproefde
middelen en ernstige raadgevingen voor
allen, die hunne oogen, tot in eenen hoogen
ouderdom, gezond bewaren of het verzwakte
gezigt weer versterken willen ... Haage: J.
C. Leeuwestijn [1799].
xvi, 160 p.

367. BEGUIN, Jean. Novvm lvmen ad
tyrocinivm chymicvm ... Coloniæ Agrippinæ:
A. Boëtzerus, 1625.
385 p., 6 *l*.
Interleaved.

368. ———. Tyrocinivm chymicvm e
natvræ fonte et manvali experientia de-
promptvm ... Hac secvnda editione ...
Coloniæ: A. Boëtzerus, 1612.
8 *l*., 195 p.

369. ———. ——— antehac à ... Christophoro Glückradt & ... Jeremia Barthio ...
notis elegantibus illustratum ... Nunc verò
à Joh. Georgio Pelshofero ... utriusque notis
& medicamentorum formulis in unum systema redactis ... Wittebergæ: A. Hartmann,
1656.
40 *l*., 480 p., 22 *l*. chart.

370. ———. ———. Genevæ: B. Le Melais,
1659.
39 *l*., 480 p., 22 *l*. chart.
Lacking the engraved title page.

371. ———. ———. Venetiis: Baleonius,
1669.
20 *l*., 360 p., 12 *l*. illus., chart.

372. ———. ——— commentario illustratum.
A Gerardo Blasio ... Editio secunda ...
Amstelodami: C. Commelinus, 1669.
18 *l*., 314 [i.e. 332] p., 4 *l*. chart.

373. ———. Tyrocinivm chymicvm: or,
Chymical essays, acquired from the foun-
tain of nature and manual experience ...
London: for T. Passenger, 1669.
6 *l*., 136 p., 2 *l*.

374. ———. Les elemens de chymie ...
Reueuz, notez, expliquez, & augmentez, par
I.L.D.R.B.IC.E.M. ... Lyon: P. Rigavd & E.
Michalet, 1658.
8 *l*., 384 p., 24 *l*. illus., chart.

375. ———. ———. Reueuz, augmentez, &
illustrez ... par le sievr Ravlt. Nouuelle &
derniere edition. Rouen: L. Behourt, 1660.
6 *l*., 469 p., 24 *l*. illus., chart.

376. ———. ———. Reueuz ... par
I.L.D.R.B.IC.E.M. ... Lyon: C. Chancey,
1665.
8 *l*., 384 p., 24 *l*. illus., chart.

———. *See also* Hartmann, J., Opera
omnia medico-chymica ... 1684.

377. BEHR, George Heinrich. Zwey Bücher
von der Materia Medica. Oder vollständige
Beschreibung aller und jeder Artzeney-Mittel:
samt beygefügter wohleingerichteter und
höchst-nutzbarer Therapie. Strassburg:

J. Beck, 1748.
    5 *l*., xii, 608 p.

378.   BELIN, Jean Albert.   Apologie dv
grand oevvre, ov elixir des philosophes; dit
vulgairement pierre philosophale ... Par
Monsieur l'abbé D.B. Paris: P. de Bresche,
1659.
    6 *l*., 236 p [i.e. 136] p.

379.   ——. Les avantvres dv philosophe
inconnv, en la recherche & en l'inuention
de la pierre philosophale. Divisees en
qvatre liures ... Paris: E. Danguy, 1646.
    6 *l*., 225 p.

380.   ——. ——. Seconde edition. Paris:
J. de Laize-de-Bresche, 1674.
    6 *l*., 215 p.

381.   ——. Wunderliche Begebenheiten
eines unbekandten Philosophi, in Such- und
Findung dess Steins der Weisen ... Welchen
beygefüget ein Tractätlein von dergleichen
Materie, Das Hauss dess Liechts genandt
... übersetzet von Johanne Langen. Hamburg: G. Liebernickel, 1690.
    144, 38 p.

382.   ——. La povdre de sympathie
ivstifiee ... Paris: P. de Bresche, 1658.
    8 *l*., 88 p.
    With his Apologie ... 1659.

383.   ——. Traité des talismans ov figvres astrales ... Paris: P. de Bresche, 1658.
    6 *l*., 126 p.
    With his Apologie ... 1659.

384.   BELL, Benjamin.   A system of surgery.
Illustrated with copperplates. The third edition, corrected. Edinburgh: 1788.
    3 v. illus.
    Lacking volumes one and two.

385.   ——. ——. The fifth edition. Edinburgh: for Bell ..., 1791.
    4 v. illus., port.

386.   ——. ——. The first American edition ... Worcester, Mass.: I. Thomas, 1791.
    4 v. illus.

387.   ——. ——. Extracted ... by Nicholas
B. Waters ... Philadelphia: T. Dobson, 1791.
    viii, 570, xxix p. illus.

388.   ——. A treatise on the theory and
management of ulcers; with a dissertation
on white swellings of the joints. To which

is prefixed, an essay on the chirurgical
treatment of inflammation and its consequences. Boston: I. Thomas and E.T. Andrews,
1791.
    288 p. illus.

389.   ——. Abhandlung von den Geschwüren
und deren Behandlung, nebst einigen Ber-
merkungen über die weissen Geschwülste
der Gelenke und die chirurgische Behandlung der Entzündung und ihre Folgen. Aus
dem Englischen ... Leipzig: Weidmann, 1792.
    5 *l*., 316 p. illus.

390.   ——. Zusätze zu Benjamin Bells
Abhandlung von den Geschwüren und deren
Behandlung, gesammelt und herausgegeben
von D. Ernst Benjamin Gottlieb Hebenstreit.
Leipzig: Weidmann, 1793.
    viii, 336 p.
    With his Abhandlung von den Geschwüren
... 1792.

391.   BELL, *Sir* Charles.   A system of di-
sections, explaining the anatomy of the
human body, the manner of displaying the
parts, and their varieties in disease. With
plates. Edinburgh: for Mundell & Son ...,
1798—1830.
    2 v. illus., folio.

392.   BELL, John.   The general and particular principles of animal electricity and
magnetism ... [London] for the author, 1792.
    80 p.

393.   BELLEGINGUE, Pierre.   Philosophie
du chaud et du froid ... Besançon: Métoyer
[1798?].
    5 *l*., 62 p.

394.   BELLINI, Lorenzo.   Opera omnia.
Pars prima. Editio secunda Veneta ... Venetiis:
J.G. Hertz, 1732.
    13 *l*., 500 p., 9 *l*.

    BELLON, Peter.   Observationes. *In*
L'Ecluse, C. de, Exoticorum libri ... 1605.

395.   ——. Potable balsome of life. Being
a collection of the choicest preservatives
that are extant within the three natural families ... reduced into such essences and
tinctures by the scientifick art of chymie ...
London: printed for the author, 1675.
    1 *l*., 21 p.

    BEN-ADAM.   Traum-Gesicht. *In*
Jean de Meun, Der Spiegel der Alchymie ...
1771.

396.   BENEDETTO, *detto il Persiano*.
I maravigliosi et occvlti secreti natvrali.
Traddoti di lingua Persiana nella nostra
lingua Italica ... Roma: P. Malatesta, 1613.
    4 *l*.

397.   BENIVIENI, Antonio.   De abditis non-
nvllis ac mirandis morborvm et sanationvm
cavsis. [Florentiae: P. Giunta, 1507.]
    54 *l*.

    ——.   ——.   *In* Galenus, Liber de
plenitudine ... 1528.

    ——.   ——.   *In* Scribonius Largus,
De compositione medicamentorum ... 1529.

398.   BENNET, Christopher.   Tabidorvm
theatrum; sive pthisios, atrophiae, & hecticae
xenodochium. Londini: typis T. Newcomb,
impensis S. Thompson, 1656.
    12 *l*., 187 p., 2 *l*.   illus., port.'

399.   ——.   —— item vestibulum tabidorum.
Lugduni Batavorum: J. van Kerckem, 1733.
    6 *l*., 160 p., 2 *l*.   illus.

400.   BENTZ, Adolph Christoph.   Das in
der tieffesten Krufft vergrabene und nunmehro entdeckte Kleinod, welches is der
alleredelste Schatz der Philosophorum, nem-
lichen Lapis Philosophorum seu Medicina
universalis ... Nebst einem Anhang einer
Warnungs-Schrifft der falschen Gold-und
Silber-Tincturen ... ab avctore A.C.B. M.D.
... Franckfurt: J. Adolph, 1714.
    15 *l*., 112 p.

401.   ——.   [Ferne Anhang] von dem in
der gantzen Welt hochgepriesenem Menstruo
universali ... Nürnberg: J. Adolph, 1709.
    5 *l*., 19 p.
    Over the first two words of the title has
been pasted a label with the words, in contemporary printing: Curiores und nutzliches
Tractätlein.

402.   ——.   Philosophische Schau-Bühne,
bestehend aus mehrentheils lauter eigenen
und wahrhafften Experimentis ... Nebst einem
Anhang der chymischen Charactern ... von
einem Alchymiæ cultore sub spe benedic-
tionis divinæ vivente. Nürnberg: W. Michahelles & J. Adolph, 1706.
    8 *l*., 134 p., 4 *l*.   illus.

403.   ——.   Thesaurus processuum chimi-
corum. Oder: Schatz chimischer Processen
... Nürnberg: verlegts J. Adolph ..., druckts
J.E. Adelbulner, 1715.

    4 *l*., 178 p., 13 *l*.

404.   BÉRAUD, Laurent.   Dissertation sur
la cause de l'augmentation de poids, que
certaines matieres acquierent dans leur
calcination ... Bordeaux: P. Brun, 1747.
    1 *l*., 36 p.

405.   ——.   ——.   La Haye: J. Neaulme,
1748.
    98 p.

406.   BERENGARIO, Jacopo.   Isagogae
breves et exactissimae in anatomiam hvmani
corporis ... [Argentorati: 1530.]
    135 *l*.   illus.

407.   BERGIUS, Peter Jonas.   Materia
medica e regno vegetabili, sistens simplicia
officinalia, pariter atque culinaria ... Editio
secunda correctior. Stockjolmiæ: P. Hessel-
berg, 1782.
    2 v.

    ——.   Spiritus frumenti.   *See* Linné,
C. von, *praeses*.   Entry 2444.

    BERGMAN, Johan Gabriel.   De effectu
et cura vitiorum diaeteticorum generali. *See*
Linné, C. von, *praeses*.   Entry 2449.

408.   BERGMAN, Torbern Olof.   Analyse
du fer ... Traduite en françois avec des notes
& un appendice, & suivie de quatre mémoires
sur la métallurgie, par M. Grignon ... Paris:
Méquignon, 1783.
    1 *l*., xvi, 286 p.

409.   ——.   A dissertation on elective
attractions ... Translated from the Latin by
the translator of Spallanzani's Dissertations.
London: for J. Murray & C. Elliot, 1785.
    xiv p., 1 *l*., 382 p., 1 *l*.
    Lacking the folding charts.

410.   ——.   Traité des affinités chymiques,
ou attractions électives; traduit du Latin, sur
la derniere édition de Bergman. Augmenté d'un
supplément & de notes ... Paris: Buisson,
1788.
    4 *l*., 444 p., 1 *l*.   charts.

411.   ——.   An essay on the usefulness of
chemistry, and its application to the various
occasions of life. Translated from the original
... London: for J. Murray, 1784.
    2 *l*., 163 p.

    ——.   ——.   *In* Watson, R., Chemical
essays ... 1783.

412. ———. Geschichte des Wachsthums
und der Erfindungen in der Chemie in der
ältesten und mittlern Zeit. Aus dem Lateinischen übersetzt ... von Johann Christian
Wiegleb. Berlin: F. Nicolai, 1792.
    6 *l*., 260 p.

413. ———. Opuscula physica et chemica,
pleraque antea seorsim edita, jam ab auctore
collecta, revisa et aucta ... Holmiæ: M.
Sweder, 1779–1790.
    6 v.   illus., map, charts.
    Volume 2 has imprint Upsaliae: J. Edman,
1780.   Volumes 3–6 have imprint Lipsiae:
J.G. Müller.

414. ———. Physical and chemical essays;
translated from the original Latin ... by Edmund Cullen ... to which are added notes
and illustrations by the translator. London:
for J. Murray ..., 1784.
    2 v.   illus.
    Lacking volume 2.

415. ———. ———. London: for J. Murray
and W. Creech, 1788–1791.
    3 v.   illus.
    Lacking volume 3.

416. ———. Opuscules chymiques et
physiques ... Recueillis, revus et augmentés
par lui-même. Traduits par M. De Morveau,
avec des notes ... Dijon: L.N. Frantin, 1780–
1785.
    2 v.   illus., charts.

417. ———. Sciagraphia regni mineralis,
secundum principia proxima digesti ... Londini: J. Murray, 1783.
    165 p.

418. ———. Outlines of mineralogy, translated from the original ... By William Withering ... Birmingham: Piercy & Jones for T.
Cadell & G. Robinson ..., 1783.
    iv, 128 p., 2 *l*.
    With his An essay on the usefulness of
chemistry ... 1784.

419. ———. Manuel du minéralogiste, ou
Sciagraphie du règne minéral ... Traduite et
augmentée de notes par M. Mongez ... Paris:
Cuchet, 1784.
    lxxxviii, 343 p.

420. ———, *praeses.* Dissertatio gradualis
sistens chemiae progressus a medio sæc. VII
ad medium sæc. XVII ... Publice ventilandam
exhibet Petrus Afzelius Arvidsson ... Upsaliæ:
J. Edman [1782].

1 *l*., 40 p.

421. BERGMÜLLER, Johann Georg.
Anthropometria, sive Statura hominis ...
oder: Statur des Menschen von der Geburt
an nach seinem Wachsthum und verschiedenen
Alter ... Augspurg: J.J. Lotter, 1723.
    3 *l*., 13 plates.

422. BERKELEY, George, *bp. of Cloyne.*
The medicinal virtues of tar water fully explained ... London: M. Cooper, 1744.
    32 p.

423. ———. Recherches sur les vertus
de l'eau de Goudron, où l'on a joint des
reflexions philosophiques ... Traduit de
l'Anglois ... Amsterdam: P. Mortier, 1745.
    xxiv, 343 p.   '

423a. ———. Siris: a chain of philosophical reflexions and inquiries concerning the
wirtues of tar water ... The second edition,
improved and corrected by the author. London: for W. Innys ..., 1744.
    174 p., 1 *l*.

        ———. Two letters shewing the
medicinal properties of tar-water. *In* Prior,
T., An authentic narrative of the success of
tar-water ... 1746.

424. BERLU, John Jacob.   The treasury of
drugs unlock'd. Or, a full and true description of all sorts of drugs ... London: for J.
Ha[rris, 1690].
    3 *l*., 125 [i.e. 145] p., 7 *l*.

425. ———. ———. The second edition, with
additions. London: for S. Ballard, 1738.
    166 p., 1 *l*.

426. BERNARD, *of Trevisano.* Abhandlung
von der Natur des (philosophischen) Eyes.
Ein hermetisches Senschreiben. Aus einem
uralten ... lateinischen Manuscript ... ins
Deutsche übersetzt, und mit einem Vorbericht
und Anhang von des Verfassers Schriften und
deren verschiedenen Lesarten begleitet. Hilde-
scheim: Schröder, 1780.
    112 p.

427. ———. Bernhardus innovatus, das ist
... Chemische Schrifften, von der Hermetischen
Philosophia ... Anjetzo Theils gantz von newem
auss den Lateinischen Exemplarien verteutscht,
theils von sehr vielen groben Erroribus vnd
Verfälschungen ... corrigirt ... durch Casparum
Hornium ... Nürnberg: W. Endter [1643?]
    54 *l*., 215 p.

——. La parole delaissée. *In* Divers traitez ... 1672.

——. ——. *In* Trois traitez ... 1618.

——. Entdecktes Wort. *In* Tæda trifida chimica ... 1674.

——. Response à Thomas de Boulongne. *In* Joly, G., Trois anciens traictez ... 1626.

428. ——. Le texte d'alchymie, et le songe-verd. Paris: L. d'Houry, 1695.
115 p., 1 *l*. illus.

429. ——. Traicté de la natvre de l'oevf des philosophes ... Paris: J. & C. Perier, 1624.
64 p.

430. ——. ——. Paris: 1659.
64 p.
With Basilius Valentinus, Les dovze clefs ... 1659.

——. A treatise of the philosophers stone. *In* Collectanea chymica ... 1684.

431. ——. Von der Hermetischenn Philosophia ... Item, Dicta Alani ... Ex libris Doctoris Henrici Vuolffij. Ietz von newem widerumb mit fleiss corrigirt vnd vbersehen. Strassburg: A. Bertram, 1586.
95 *l*.

432. BERNARDI, Francesco. Prospetto storico-critico dell'origine, facolà, diversi stati, progressi, e vicendo dell Collegio Medico-Chirurgico e dell'Arte Chirurgica in Venezia ... Venezia: D. Costantini, 1797.
3 *l*., 76 p.

BERNARDUS DE GORDONIO. *See* Gordonio, Bernardo.

BERNARDUS TREVISANUS. *See* Bernard, *of Trevisano*.

433. BERNHARDT, Johann Christian. Chymische Versuche und Erfahrungen aus Vitriole, Salpeter, Ofenruss, Quecksilber, Arsenik, Galbano, Myrrhen, der Peruvianer Fieberrinde und Fliegenschwämmen ... Leipzig: B.C. Breitkopf, 1755.
15 *l*., 328 p., 4 *l*. illus.

434. BEROALDE DE VERVILLE, Francois. L'histoire veritable, ov Le voyage des princes fortvnez ... Paris: C. de la Tovr, 1610.

16 *l*., 793 p., 6 *l*. map.

435. ——. Le palais des cvrievx. Auquel sont assemblées plusieurs diuersitez pour le plaisir des doctes ... Paris: la veusue M. Gvillemot & S. Thibovst, 1612.
8 *l*., 584 p.

436. BERQUEN, Robert de. Les merveilles des Indes orientales et occidentales ov Nouueau traitté des pierres precieuses & perles ... Paris: C. Lambin, 1669.
4 *l*., 152 p. port.

BERTHIOLI, Antonio. *See* Ferrari, Giacomo, Idea theriacæ ... 1601.

437. BERTHOLLET, Claude Louis. Éléments de l'art de la teinture ... Paris: F. Didot, 1791.
2 v. viii, 1, 336 p.; vii, 404 p., 1 *l*.

438. ——. ——. Paris: F. Didot, 1791.
2 v. viii, xlviii, 311 p.; vii, 365 p.

439. ——. Essay on the new method of bleaching, by means of oxygenated muriatic acid ... From the French of Mr. Berthollet ... by Robert Kerr ... Edinburgh: for W. Creech, 1790.
xxvii, 139 p. illus.

440. ——. ——. To which is now added, Observations on the art of dying with madder ... Second edition. Edinburgh: for W. Creech, 1791.
350, 12 p.

441. BERTOSSI, Giuseppe. Delle terme padovane volgarmente dette bagni d'Abano. Venezia: S. Coleti, 1759.
11 *l*., 104 p. illus.

442. BERTRAND, *agregé au College des Medecins de Marseille*. Reflexions nouvelles sur l'acide et sur l'alcali ... Lyon: T. Amaulry, 1683.
10 *l*., 359 p.

BERTRUCIUS, Nicolaus. Methodi cognoscendorum morborum. *In* Heyl, C., Artificialis medicatio ... 1534.

BERWARD, Christian. Interpres phraseologiae metallurgicae. *In* Ercker, L., Aula subterranea ... 1736.

443. BESARD, Jean Baptiste. Antrum philosophicvm, in qvo pleraqve arcana physica ... reuelantur ... Atque huic, Tractatvs de rebvs

qvae hvmano corpori eximiam & venustam
formam inducunt. De variis mineralium &
metallorum præparat ... Augustæ Vindelicorum: imprimebat D. Franck, impensis
authoris, 1617.
12 *l*., 248 p.

444. BESLER, Basilius. Hortvs eystet-
tenis, sive Diligens et accvrata omnivm
plantarvm, florvm, stirpivm, ex variis orbis
terræ partibvs, singvlari stvdio collectarvm
... hoc tempore conspicivntvr delineatio et
ad vivvm repræsentatio. [Norimbergæ]:
1613.
422 *l*. illus., port., folio.

445. ———. Rariora Mvsei Besleriani quae
olim Basilivs et Michael Rvpertvs Besleri
collegerunt ... nunc commentariolo illustrata
a Johanne Henrico Lochnero ... [Nuremberg]
1716.
12 *l*., 112 p. illus., port.

BESSON, Jacques. De absoluta
ratione extrahendi olea & aquas. *In* Libavius,
A., Praxis alchymiæ ... 1604.

446. BEUGHEM, Cornelius à. Biblio-
graphia medica & physica novissima: per-
petuo continuanda sive Conspectus primus
catalogi librorum medicorum chymicorum,
anatomicorum, chyrurgicorum, botanicorum
ut & physicorum, &c. Amstelaedami: Janssonio-Waesbergios, 1681.
4 *l*., 503 p.

447. BEUTHER, David. Zwey rare chymische Tractate, darinnen nicht nur alle
Geheimnisse der Probier-Kunst derer Ertze
und Schmelzung derselben, sondern auch die
Mögligkeit der Verwandelung, der geringen
Metallen in bessere, gar deutlich gezeiget
werden ... Deme beygefüget ... Universal,
oder Volkommener Bericht von der wahren
Alchymie ... Leipzig: J.C. Martini, 1717.
8 *l*., 218 p., 6 *l*.; 58 p.

448. BEVERWIJCK, Jan van. All de wercken
soo in de medecyne als chirurgye ... [Amster-
dam: J.J. Schipper, 1652.]
var pag. illus., port.

449. BEVIS, John. An experimental enquiry
concerning the contents, qualities, and medicinal virtues, of the two mineral waters,
lately discovered at Bagnigge Wells, near
London ... The second edition, with additions
... London: for J. Newbery, 1767.
2 *l*., 64 p.

BEYERSTEN, Johan Georg. Obstacula
medicinæ. *See* Linné, C. von, *praeses*. Entry
2485.

450. BEYNON, Elias. Barmhertziger
Samariter, oder: Freund-Brüderlicher Raht
allerhand Kranckheiten und Gebrechern dess
menschlichen Leibs innerlich und eusser-
lich zu heilen ... nebst einen sehr nutzlichen Unterricht vor die Hebammen ... nebst
einem neuen Anhang von der Pest ... Nürnberg: J. Hoffmann, 1696.
346 p.; 49 p., 5 *l*.; 29 *l*.

451. BIANCHI, Giovanni Battista. Ductus
lacrymales novi, eorumque anatome, usus,
morbi, & curationes. Dissertatio epistolaris
ad ... Josephum Lanzoni ... Augustæ Taurinorum: J.F. Mairesse & J. Radix, 1715.
51 p.
With his Opera anatomica practica ...
1715.

452. ———. Historia hepatica ... tertia
editione ... Genevæ: G. de Tournes, 1725.
2 v.

453. ———. Opera anatomico-practica.
Augustae Taurinorum: J.F. Mairesse & J.
Radix, [1715].
8 *l*., 156 p., 9 *l*. illus.

454. BIASIO, *detto il Figadet*. Tesoro di
secreti raccolta da diversi valenti huomini
... Bologna: Benacci [n.d.].
4 *l*.

455. BICCHIERAI, Alessandro. Dei bagni
di Montecatini ... Firenze: G. Cambiagi,
1788.
4 *l*., 347 p. illus., maps, charts.

456. BIDLOO, Govard. Anatomia hvmani
corporis, centum quinque tabvlis, per arti-
ficiosiss. G. de Lairesse ad vivum delineatis
... Amstelodami: vidua J. à Someren ..., 1685.
67 *l*., 105 plates. port., folio.

457. ———. Ontleding des menschelyken
lichaams ... Uitgebeeldt ... door de Heer
Gerard de Lairesse. Utrecht: J. van Poolsum,
1734.
67 *l*., 105 plates. folio.
Lacking plates 1—4, 47—48, 54—57.

458. BIGGS, Noah. Matæotechnia medicinæ praxeos. The vanity of the craft of
physick. Or, A new dispensatory ... With an
humble motion for the reformation of the

universitites ... London: for G. Calvert,
1651.
    16 *l*., 232 p.

459.   BILGUER, Johann Ulrich.   Dissertation sur l'inutilité de l'amputation des mem-
bres. Traduite & augmentée de quelques
remarques, par M. Tissot. Paris: P.F. Didot,
1764.
    xvi, 151 p.

460.   BILLICH, Anton Guenther.   ... De
natvra et constitvtione spagyrices emendatæ.
Exercitatio. Helmæstadi: typis heredum I.
Luci, impensis Z. Raben, 1623.
    30 *l*.

461.   ——.   ... De tribus chymicorum
principiis, et quincta essentiâ exercitatio
... Bremæ: T. Villerianus, 1621.
    4 *l*., 69 p., 1 *l*.

462.   ——.   Observationum ac paradoxorum
chymiatricorum libri duo ... Lugduni Batavorum: J. Maire, 1631.
    173 p.

463.   ——.   Thessalus in chymicis redivivus: id est, De vanitate medicinæ chymicæ,
hermeticæ, seu spagiricæ dissertatio fundamentalis ... accessit Anatomia fermentationis
Platonicæ apodictica & paradoxologa ...
Francofurti ad Moenum: impensis J. Beyeri,
typis C. Rötelii, 1640.
    8 *l*., 318 p.

464.   BIRCH, Thomas.   The history of the
Royal Society of London for improving of
natural knowledge ... London: for A. Millar,
1756–1757.
    4 v.   illus.

465.   ——.   The life of the honourable
Robert Boyle. London: for A. Millar, 1744.
    3 *l*., 458 p.. 8 *l*.

466.   BIRELLI, Giovanni Battista.   Opere
... Tomo primo, nel qual si tratta dell'
alchimia, suoi membri, vtili, curiosi, et
diletteuoli. Con la vita d'Hermete ...
Fiorenza: G. Marescotti, 1601.
    18 *l*., 552 p., 8 *l*.   illus.
    All published.

467.   BIRINGUCCIO, Vannuccio.   De la
pirotechnia, libri X ... [Venetia: V. Roffinello,
ad instantia di C. Nauo] 1540.
    8 *l*., 168 numb. *l*.   illus.

468.   ——.   Pirotechnia. Li diece libri della

pirotechnia ... [Vinegia: G. Padoano, a
instantia C. di Nauò] 1550.
    8 *l*., 167 numb. *l*., 1 *l*.   illus.

469.   ——.   ——.   Nvovamente corretta,
et ristampata ... Venetia: P.G. Giglio, 1559.
    345 numb. *l*., 7 *l*.   illus.

470.   ——.   ——.   Bologna: G. Longhi, 1678.
    16 *l*., 630 p.   illus.

471.   ——.   La pyrotechnie, ov Art dv fev,
contenant dix livres ... Et traduite d'Italien
en Francois, par feu maistre Iaques Vincent.
Paris: C. Fremy, 1556.
    4 *l*., 228 numb. *l*.   illus.

472.   ——.   ——.   Paris: G. Jullian, 1572.
    4 *l*., 168 numb. *l*.   illus.

473.   BIRKHOLZ, Adam Michael, *ed*.   Die
ganze höhere Chemie und Naturwissenschaft
in allgemeinen Grundsätzen, nach den drei
Urfängen und Grundkräften der ganzen Natur.
Aus dem Lateinischen übersetzt, mit bei-
gefügten Anmerkungen von AdaMah Booz.
Leipzig: J.F. Junius, 1787.
    8 *l*., 366 p.

    BJERKEN, Per af.   Morbi expeditionis
classicæ MDCCLVI. *See* Linné, C. von,
praeses.   Entry 2482.

    BLACK, Joseph.   Directions for pre-
paring aerated medicinal waters. *See* Directions for preparing aerated medicinal waters
... 1787.

474.   ——.   Experiments upon magnesia
alba, quick-lime, and other alcaline substances ... To which is annexed, An essay
on the cold produced by exaporating fluids
... by William Cullen ... Edinburgh: W. Creech
and T. Cadell, 1782.
    137 p., 1 *l*.

475.   BLACKMORE, *Sir* Richard.   A treatise
of consumptions and other distempers belonging to the breast and lungs. London: for
J. Pemberton, 1724.
    xxxvii p., 1 *l*., 223 p.

476.   BLACKWELL, Elizabeth.   A curious
herbal, containing five hundred cuts of the
most useful plants which are now used in
the practice of physick ... London: for J.
Nourse, 1739.
    2 v.   illus., folio.

477.   ——.   Herbarivm Blackwellianvm

emendatvm et avctvm, id est ... Collectio
spirpivm qvæ in pharmacopoliis ad medicvm
vsvm asservantvr, qvarvm descriptio et
vires ex Anglico idiomate in Latinvm con-
versæ sistvntvr ... Norimbergæ: J.J. Fleisch-
mann, 1750–1773.
 6 v. illus., folio.
 Text in Latin and German.

478.   BLAGDEN, Charles. History of the
congelation of quicksilver. Read at the Royal
Society, June 5, 1783. London: J. Nichols,
1784.
 71 p.

479.   BLANE, *Sir* Gilbert. A lecture on
muscular motion, read at the Royal Society,
the 13th and 20th of November, 1788. London: J. Cooper [ca. 1788].
 1 *l*., 57 p.

480.   BLANKAART, Steven. Anatomia
practica rationalis, sive Rariorum cadaverum
morbis denatorum anatomica inspectio.
Accedit item tractatus novus de circulatione
sanguinis per tubulos, deque eorum valvulis
&c. Amstelodami: C. Blancard, 1688.
 12 *l*., 321 p., 6 *l*. illus.

481.   ———. Anatomia reformata, sive Con-
cinna corporis humani. Dissectio, ad neotericorum mentem adornata, plurimisque tabulis
chalcographicis illustrata. Accedit ejusdem
authoris De balsamatione, nova methodus ...
Lugduni Batavorum: C. Boutesteyn, J. Luchtmans, 1687.
 2 pts. in 1 v. illus.

482.   ———. Cartesianische Academie,
oder Grund-lere der Arzney-Kunst, worinnen
die völlige Arzney-lere auf den naturgemässen
Grunden des welt-berümten Cartesii aufge-
furet wird. Leipzig: T. Fritsch, 1699.
 4 *l*., 787 p., 26 *l*. illus.

483.   ———. Die neue heutiges Tages ge-
bräuchliche Scheide-Kunst, oder Chimia nach
den Gründen des fürtreflichen Cartesii und
des Alcali und Acidi eingerichtet ... Hannover: G.H. Grentz, 1689.
 179 p., 5 *l*. illus.

484.   ———. Neue und besondere Manier
alle verstorbene Cörper ... der Gestalt zu
balsamiren ... übersetzet von G.A.M. Hannover: G.H. Grentz, 1690.
 104 p.

485.   ———. Opera medica, theoretica,
practica et chirurgica ... Lugduni Batavorum:

C. Boutestein, 1701.
 2 v. in 1. illus.

486.   ———. A physical dictionary; in
which, all the terms relating either to anatomy, chirurgery, pharmacy, or chymistry,
are very accurately explain'd ... London:
printed by J.D., sold by J. Gellibrand, 1684.
 4 *l*., 302 p.

487.   ———. ———. The third edition, with
the addition of above a thousand terms ...
London: for S. Crouch, 1697.
 2 *l*., 212 p.

488.   ———. Lexicon medicum renovatum,
in quo totius artis medicae termini, in
anatome, chirurgia, pharmacia, chymia, re
botanica etc ... Editio novissima, caeteris
longe auctior & perfectior. Lugduni Batavorum:
S. Luchtmans, 1717.
 7 *l*., 688 p., 103 *l*.

489.   ———. ———. Lugduni Batavorum: S.
& J. Luchtmans, 1756.
 8 *l*., 1015 p., 126 *l*.   port, charts.

490.   ———. Theatrvm chimicvm, oder
Eröffneter Schau-Platz und Thür zu den
Heimligkeiten in der Scheide-Kunst, nebenst
einer Vermehrung wie die geringen Metallen
und gemeinen Steine zu verbessern sind,
durch Kenelm Digby. Leipzig: T. Fritsch,
1700.
 3 *l*., 472 p., 24 *l*.; 155 p., 2 *l*.
 Lacking frontispiece.

491.   BLASIUS, Gerardus. Anatome animalium, terrestrium variorum, volatilium,
aquatilium, serpentum, insectorum, ovorumque,
structuram naturalem ex veterum, recentiorum,
propriisque observationibus proponens. Amstelodami: viduae J. à Somerens. H. & T.
Boom, 1681.
 4 *l*., 494 p. illus.

492.   ———. Observationes medicæ rariores.
Accedit monstri triplicis historia. Amstelodami: A. Wolfgang, 1677.
 2 *l*., 120 p., 2 *l*.; 71 p. illus.

493.   BLAUENSTEIN, Salomon de. Inter-
pellatio brevis ad philosophos veritatis tam
amatores, quam scritatores pro laipde philosophorum contra antichymisticum Mundum
subterraneum P. Athanasii Kircheri ... Biennæ
apud Bernates: D. Suitz, 1667.
 14 *l*.

494.   BLÉGNY, Nicolas de. L'art de guerir

les hernies, ou Descentes de toutes expeces
dans les deux sexes ... Troisième edition,
corrigée & augmentée par l'autheur. Paris:
la veuve J. d'Houry et L. d'Houry, 1688.
    12 *l*., 297 p., 19 *l*.

495.   BLEULAND, Jan.   Experimentum
anatomicum, quo arteriolarum lymphaticarum
existentia probabiliter adstruitur, institutum,
descriptum, et icone illustratum ... Lugduni
Batavorum: A. et J. Honkoop, 1784.
    2 *l*., 36 p., 1 *l*.   illus.

496.   ———.   Icon tunicæ villosæ intestini
duodeni, juxta felicem vasculorum imple-
tionem ... Trajecti ad Rhenum: B. Wild et J.
Altheer, 1789.
    10 p.   illus.

497.   ———.   Observationes anatomico-
medicæ de sana et morbosa oesophagi
structura. Lugduni Batavorum: A. et J. Honkoop, 1785.
    120 p.   illus.

498.   ———.   Tractatus de difficili aut im-
pedito alimentorum ex ventriculo in duodenum
progressu ... Lugduni Batavorum: A. et J.
Honkoop, 1787.
    4 *l*., 144 p.   illus.

499.   BLOCHWICK, Martin.   Anatomia
sambuci: or, The anatomie of the elder ...
Gathered in Latine ... now translated ...
London: for T. Heath, 1655.
    6 *l*., 230 p.

500.   ———.   ———.   London: for H. Brome
and T. Sawbridge, 1677.
    8 *l*., 230 p.

BLOM, Carl Magnus.   ... Lignum
qvassiæ. *See* Linné, C. von, *praeses*. Entry
2436.

501.   BLUMENBACH, Johann Friedrich.
Anfangsgründe der Physiologie. Aus dem
Lateinischen übersetzt, und mit zusätzen
vermehrt von Joseph Eherel. Wien: C.F. Wappler, 1789.
    7 *l*., 418 p.   illus.

502.   ———.   Introdvctio in historiam medicinae litterariam. Goettingae: J.C. Dieterich,
1786.
    xvi, 462 p.

503.   ———, *ed*.   Medicinische bibliothek.
Göttingen: J.C. Dieterich, 1783–1788.
    3 v.

Volume 1 only.

504.   BOCK, Hieronymus.   De stirpivm ...
commentariorum libri tres, Germanica primum
lingua conscripti, nunc in Latinam conuersi,
interprete Davide Kybero. His accesservnt
... praefationes dvae: altera D. Conradi
Gesneri ... rei herbariæ scriptorum ...
catalogum complectens: altera ipsius
authoris, herbariæ cognitionis laudes ...
continens ... [Argentorati: V. Rihelius, 1552.]
    34 *l*., 1200 p., 32 *l*.   illus., port.

505.   ———.   Kreutterbuch darin Under-
scheidt, Nammen und Vurckung der Kreutter
... so inn Teutschen Landen wachsen, auch
der selben eigentlicher unnd wolgegründter
gebrauch inn der Artzney ... Jetzund aufs
new ... ubersehen ... durch ... Melchiorem
Sebizivm ... Strassburg: J. Rihel [1577].
    30 *l*., 450 numb. *l*., 23 *l*.   illus., port.

BOECLER, Christian Ernst.   De suturis
vulnerum in genere. *See* Linné, C. von, *praeses*.
Entry 2426.

505a.   BOECLER, Johann.   Cynosura materiæ
medicae continuata, ad cynosuræ materiæ
medicæ Hermannianæ imitationem collecta
... Argentorati: J. Beck, 1729–1731.
    2 v.

506.   BOECLER, Johann Heinrich.   ... Dissertatio medica inauguralis, De remediis
ex microscosmo ... Argentorati: J. Giesen,
1711.
    32 p.

BOEHM, Michael Friedrich. ᐧ Examen
acidi pinguis. *See* Spielmann, Jacob Reinhold, *praeses*.

507.   BOERHAAVE, Herman.   Academical
lectures on the theory of physic ... London:
for W. Inny, 1742–1746.
    6 v.
Volume one is of the second edition, London, W. Inny, 1751.

508.   ———.   Aphorismi de cognoscendis et
curandis morbis in usum doctrinae domesticae
digesti. Lugduni Batavorum: T. Haak ..., 1742.
    4 *l*., 370 p., 12 *l*.

509.   ———.   Consultationes medicæ: sive
Sylloge epistolarum cum responsis ... Hagæ-
Comitum: A. Johnson, 1743.
    2 *l*., 231, 34 p.

510.   ———.   Historia plantarum, quæ in

Horto Academico Lugduni-Batavorum crescunt ... Editio novissima ... Londini: sumptibus Societatis, 1738.
  2 v.

511. ——. Institutiones et experimenta chemiæ. Parisiis: 1724.
  2 v. in 1. illus.

512. ——. Elementa chimiæ ... Lugduni Batavorum: I. Severinus, 1732.
  2 v. illus.

513. ——. ——. Lipsiæ: C. Fritsch, 1732.
  2 v. illus.

514. ——. ——. Editio altera ... Cui etiam accessere ejusdem auctoris opuscula omnia ... Parisiis: G. Cavelier, 1733.
  2 v. illus.

515. ——. Elements of chymistry, faithfully abridg'd from the late genuine edition ... To which are added, curious and useful notes, rectifying several opinions, &c. of the learned author. By a physician. London: for J. Wilford, 1732.
  vi, 210; viii, 208 p., 5 ℓ., 17 p.

516. ——. Elements of chemistry: being the annual lectures of Herman Boerhaave ... Translated from the original Latin by Timothy Dallowe. London: for J. and J. Pemberton ... 1735.
  2 v. illus.

517. ——. A new method of chemistry; including the history, theory, and practice of the art; translated from the original Latin ... To which are added, notes; and an appendix ... by Peter Shaw. The second edition. London: for T. Longman, 1741.
  2 v. illus.

518. ——. Elemens de chymie ... Traduits du Latin par J.N.S. Allamand ... Leide: C. Haak, 1752.
  2 v. illus.

519. ——. Institutiones medicae, in usus annuae exercitationis domesticos, digestae ... Editio Leydensis quinta prioribus longe auctior. Lugduni: T. Haak ..., 1734.
  8 ℓ., 548 p., 18 ℓ.

520. ——. —— ab editionem Leydensem quintam curatius revisum & correctum. Norimburgae: Lochner & Mayer, 1740.
  8 ℓ., 548 p., 18 ℓ.

521. ——. ——. Editio Leydensis sexta prioribus longe auctior. Lugduni Batavorum: J. & H. Verbeek ..., 1746.
  8 ℓ., 548 p., 18 ℓ.

522. ——. Methodus studii medici, emaculata, & accessionibus locupletata ab Alberto ab Haller. Editio prima Veneta ... Venetiis: ex typographia Remondiniana, 1753.
  2 v. illus.

523. ——. Opera omnia medica, quorum series post praefationem subjicitur. Venetiis: L. Basilius, 1766.
  10 ℓ., 547 p., 1 ℓ. port.

524. ——. Opuscula omnia, quae hactenus in lucem prodierunt ... Hagae-Comitis: J. Neaulme, 1738.
  2 ℓ., 139 p. illus.

525. ——. Praxis medica Boerhaaveana, being a compleat body of prescriptions adapted to each section of the practical aphorisms ... To which is annexed Methodus præscribendi formulas secundum Archibaldum Pitcarnium. London: for B. Cowse and W. Innys, 1716.
  6 ℓ., 136 p.

526. ——. Meteria medica: or, A series of prescriptions. Adapted to the sections of his practical aphorisms concerning the knowledge and cure of diseases ... London: for W. Innys and R. Manby, 1741.
  4 ℓ., 208, xxix p., 1 ℓ.

527. ——. Materia medica, or The druggist's guide, and the physician and apothecary's table book ... London: for the author, sold by J. Hodges, 1755.
  vii, 280 p.

528. ——. Praelectiones academicae de morbis nervorum quae ex auditorum manuscriptis collectas edi curavit Jacobus van Eems ... Francofurti: sumptibus Societatis, 1762.
  2 v.

529. ——. Some experiments concerning mercury ... Translated from the Latin, communicated by the author to the Royal Society. London: for J. Roberts, 1734.
  55 p.

530. ——. Tractatus de viribvs medicamentorvm. Parisiis: G. Cavelier, 1723.
  6 ℓ., 352 p., 10 ℓ. illus.

531. ——. ——. Editio novissima. Juxta
exemplar Lutetiæ Parisiorum editum. [n.p.]
1742.
   256 p., 4 *l*. illus.

   ——. Traité du scorbut. *In* Lind, J.,
Traité du scorbut ... 1783.

532. BÖHME, Jakob. Kurtze und deutliche Beschreibung des Steins der Weisen
... deme noch beygefügt eine Schutz-Schrift
seiner Schriften. Amsterdam: 1747.
   91 p., 2 *l*.

533. BOHN, Johann. De officio medici
duplici, clinici nimirum ac forensis, hoc est
qua ratione ille se gerere debeat penes in-
firmos pariter, ac in foro, ut medici eruditi,
prudentis ac ingenui nomen utrinque tueatur.
Lipsiae: J.F. Gleditsch, 1704.
   4 *l*., 684 p., 13 *l*.

534. ——. De renvnciatione vvlnervm,
sev Vvlnervm lethalivm examen, cvi accesservnt Dissertationes binae de partv enecato,
et an qvis vivvs mortvvsve aqvis svbmersvs,
strangvlatvs avt vvlneratvs fverit. Lipsiae:
T. Fritsch, 1711.
   2 *l*., 198 p., 5 *l*.

535. ——. Dissertationes chymico-
physicæ, chymiæ finem instrumenta & operationes freqventiores explicantes ... Qvibus
accessit ... De aeris in sublunaria influxu.
Lipsiæ: sumptibus J.F. Gleditschii, literis
C. Gözl, 1685.
   146 *l*.

536. ——. —— et De alcali et acidi
insvfficientia. Lipsiæ: J.T. Fritsch, 1696.
   8 *l*., 554 p., 10 *l*.

537. ——. Epistola ad ... D. Joelem
Langelottum ... De alcali et acidi insuffic-
ientiâ pro principiorum seu elementorum
corporum naturalium munere gerendo ...
Lipsiæ: sumptibus J. Fritzschii, literis J.E.
Hahnii, 1675.
   64 p.
   With Maynwaring, E., Historia et mysterium ... 1675.

538. BOISSIEU, Barthélemy-Camille de.
Dissertations sur les antiseptiques ... Dijon:
F. Des Ventes, 1769.
   xiv p., 1 *l*., 416 p., 4 *l*. chart.

   A BOKE of the propertyes of herbes
... *See* Herbal.

539. BOLNEST, Edward. Aurora chymica:
or a rational way of preparing animals,
vegetables, and minerals for a physical
use ... London: T. Ratcliffe & N. Thompson
for J. Starkey, 1672.
   8 *l*., 146 p., 1 *l*.

540. ——. Aurora chymica. Sive Rationalis
methodus præparandi animalis, vegetabilia
& mineralia ad usum medicum ... Hamburgii:
J. Naumann & G. Wolff, 1675.
   5 *l*., 134 p.

541. ——. Medicina instaurata, or; A
brief account of the true grounds and principles of the art of physick ... Also an
epistolary discourse upon the whole by the
author of Medela medicinæ. London: for J.
Starkey, 1665.
   16 *l*., 151 p.

542. BOMBASTE, *comte de*. Le trompette
François, ou, Fidele François. [n.p.] 1609.
   112 p., 1 *l*., 113–184 p. illus.
   The second part has a separate title page:
Le miroir des alchimistes, ov l'on voit les
erreurs qui se font en la recherche de la
pierre philosophale ... Avec Instruction aux
dames ... Seconde edition ... Par le chevalier
imperial ... [n.p.] 1609.

543. BONAI, I.D., *supposed author*.
Abregé de l'astronomie inferievre, expliquant
le systeme des planetes; les douze signes
du zodiac & autres constellations du ciel
hermetique. Avec vn essay de l'astronomie
natvrelle ... Paris: I. de Senlecqve et I. Remy,
1644.
   19 *l*., 185 p.

544. BONDT, Jakob de. De medicina
indorv̄. Lib. IV. 1. Notae in Garçiam ab Orta.
2. De diaeta sanorum. 3. Meth. medendi
Indica. 4. Observationes e cadaveribus.
Lugduni Batavorum: F. Hackius, 1642.
   212 p., 2 *l*.

   ——. Medicina indorum. *In* Alpini,
P., Medicina Aegyptiorum ... 1719.

545. BONET, Théophile. Medicina septen-
trionalis collatitia, sive Rei medicæ, nvperis
annis à medicis Anglis, Germanis & Danis
emissæ, sylloge & syntaxis ... Genevæ: L.
Chovët, 1686–1687.
   2 v. in 1. illus.

546. ——. Sepulchretum sive Anatomia
practica, ex cadaveribus morbo denatis ...

Editio altera, quam novis commentariis ...
Lugduni: Cramer & Perachon, 1700.
  3 v. in 2.   port.

547.   BONNAUD. Dégradation de l'espace
humaine par l'usage des corps a baleine ...
Paris: Hérissant, 1770.
  xxiv, 219 p., 2 *l*.

548.   BONNEFOY, Jean Baptiste. Analyse
raisonnée des rapports des commissaires
chargés par le roi de l'examen du magnétisme
animal. [n.p.] 1784.
  1 *l*., 89 p.

549.   BÖNNEKEN, Johann Wolffgang Friederich. Kurtze jedoch auf Vernunfft und Erfahrung gegründete Abhandlung von denen
erdhaften Mittelns ... Wertheim: J.G. Nehr,
1742.
  13 *l*., 86 p.
  With Wahrsager, E., Höchst nöthige Anmerkungen über des Herrn ... 1742.

  BONNET, Théophile. *See* Bonet,
Théophile.

550.   BONTEKOE, Cornelis. Fundamenta
medica sive De alcali et acidi effectibus
per modum fermentionis & effervescentiæ.
Accedit item anonymi cujusdam authoris
Pharmacopæa ad mentem neotericorum
adornata. Amstelodami: C. Blancard, 1688.
  4 *l*., 228 p., 6 *l*.

  BONTIUS, Jacob. *See* Bondt, Jakob
de.

  BONUS, Petrus. *See* Lacinio, Giano.

551.   BONVICINO, Valeriano. Lanx peri-
patetica qva vetus arcani physici veritas
appenditur. Et avctoris mvndi svbterranei,
noua obiecta reuocantur ad pondus ... Patauij:
heredes P. Frambotti, 1667.
  15 *l*., 434 p.

552.   A BOOK of fruits & flowers. Shewing
the nature and use of them, either for meat
or medicine ... London: M.S. for T. Jenner,
1656.
  1 *l*., 51 p.   illus.

553.   The BOOKE of pretty conceits: taken
out of Latine, French, Dutch, and English ...
Newly inlarged, corrected and amended. London: J. Flescher [1628?].
  12 *l*.

  A BOOKE of the properties of herbes

... *See* Herbal.

554.   BOORDE, Andrew. The breuiary of
helthe, for all maner of sykenesses and
diseases the whiche may be in man, or
woman ... [London: W. Myddleton, 1547.]
  cxlii numb. *l*., 4 *l*.; xxix numb. *l*., 3 *l*.
port.

555.   ——. ——. [London: W. Powell]
1552.
  cxxiii numb. *l*., 4 *l*.; xxvii numb. *l*., 1 *l*.
port.
  The Britwell Court copy with the Miller
arms stamped in gold on the front and back
covers.

556.   ——. Here followeth a compendious
regiment, or dietarie of health ... London:
H. Jackson, 1576.
  64 *l*.

557.   BORCH, Oluf. Conspectus scriptorum
chemicorum illustriorum, libellus posthumus
cui præfixa historia vitæ ipsius ab ipso conscripta. Havniæ: S. Garmann, 1697.
  6 *l*., 48 p.

558.   ——. De ortu et progressu chemiæ
dissertatio. Hafniæ: typis M. Godicchenii,
sumptibus P. Haubold, 1668.
  6 *l*., 150 p., 1 *l*.

559.   ——. Hermetis Aegyptiorum et
chemicorum sapientia ab Hermanni Conringii
animadversionibus vindicata ... Hafniæ: P.
Haubold, 1674.
  4 *l*., 448 p., 4 *l*.

560.   ——. Lingua pharmacopoeorum, sive
De accuratâ vocabulorum in pharmacopoliis
usitatorum pronunciatione. Hafniae: typis M.
Godicchenii, sumptibus P. Hauboldi, 1670.
  49 *l*.

561.   BORDEU, Théophile. Lettres contenant
des essais sur l'histoire des eaux minerales
du Bearn, & de quelques-unes des provinces
voisines ... Adressées à Madame de Sorberio
... Amsterdam: les freres Poppé ..., 1746.
  221 p., 1 *l*.

562.   ——. Recherches sur le tissu muqueux;
ou L'organe cellulaire, et sur quelques maladies
de la poitrine ... On y a joint une dissertation
du même auteur, sur L'usage des eaux de
baréges, dans les ecrouelles ... Paris: P.F.
Didot, 1767.
  2 *l*., x p., 1 *l*., 227 p.; 2 *l*., x p., 4 *l*.,
228 p.

563.   BOREL, Pierre.   Bibliotheca chimica,
sev Catalogvs librorvm philosophicorvm
hermeticorvm ... Cum eiusdem bibliothecæ
appendice, & corollario ... Parisiis: C. de
Mesnil et T. Jolly, 1654.
    6 ℓ., 276 p.

564.   BORELLI, Giovanni Alfonso.   De
motv animalivm. Opus posthumum. Romae:
A. Bernabò, 1680—1681.
    2 v.   illus.

565.   ——.   ——.   Editio altera. Correctior
& emendatior. Lugduni Batavorum: P. van der
Aa, C. Boutesteyn ..., 1685.
    2 pts. in 1 v.   illus.

566.   BORN, Ignaz, *edler* von.   New process of amalgamation of gold and silver ores,
and other metallic mixtures ... Translated
into English by R.E. Raspe ... London: for T.
Cadell, 1791.
    xxxiv, 256 p.   illus.

567.   ——.   Ueber das Anquicken der gold-
und silberhältigen Ertze, Rohsteine, Schwarz-
kupfer und Hüttenspeise ... Wien: C.F. Wappler, 1786.
    8 ℓ., 227 p.   illus.

568.   BORSIERI, Giambattista.   Delle acque
di S. Cristoforo ... Seconda edizione con
aggiunte. Faenza: L. Genestri, 1786.
    2 ℓ., 147 p.   illus.

569.   ——.   Instivtionvm medicinae practicae qvas avditoribvs svis praelegebat ...
Editio nova. Lipsiae: C. Fritsch, 1787—1790.
    4 v.

570.   ——.   Nuovi fenomeni scoperti nell'
analisi chimica del latte memoria ... [Pavia:
Porro, Bianchi e comp.] 1772.
    104 p.

571.   BOSCH, Iman Jacob van den.   Verhandeling over den waaren aart der kinderpokjes ... Rotterdam: G.A. Arrenberg, 1791.
    1 ℓ., x, 224 p., 1 ℓ.

572.   BOSSCHE, Guilielmo van den.   Historia medica, in qva libris IV animalivm
natvra, et eorum medica utilitas ... tractan-
tur ... Brvxellæ: I. Mommart, 1639.
    7 ℓ., 422 [i.e. 434] p., 10 ℓ.   illus.

    BOSTRÖM, Andreas.   Febris Upsalien-
sis. *See* Linné, C. von, *praeses*. Entry 2475.

573.   BOTALLO, Leonardo.   Opera omnia

medica & chirurgica. Hac postrema editione
à mendis repurgata ... Joannis van Horne.
Lugduni Batavorum: D. & A. à Gaasbeeck,
1660.
    8 ℓ., 800 p., 12 ℓ.   illus.

574.   BOTTARELLI, Giovanni.   De bagni
di San Casciano, osseruazioni ... Firenze:
V. Vangelisti [1688?].
    308 p.   illus.

575.   BOTTONI, Domenico.   Pyrologia
topographica, id est, De igne dissertatio
juxta loca cum eorum descriptionibus ...
Neapoli: D. A. Parrino & M. A. Muzio, 1692.
    20 ℓ., 245 p.   illus.

576.   BOULES, R.   The queens royal closet,
newly opened. And the art of physick discovered ... London: for F. Cole, T. Vere ...
[n.d.].
    12 ℓ.

577.   BOULLANGER.   Expériences et observations sur la spath vitrieux, ou fluor
spathique ... [Paris] 1773.
    32 p.

578.   BOULTON, Samuel.   Medicina magica
tamen physica: Magical, but natural physick.
Or A methodical tractate of diastatical physick ... London: T.C. for N. Brook [1665?].
    4 ℓ., 195 p., 1 ℓ.

579.   BOURGELAT, Claude.   Matiere médicale raisonnée ou Précis des médicamens
considérés dans leurs effets ... Avec les
formules médicinales ... Lyon: J.M. Bruyset,
1765.
    2 ℓ., xxiv, 227, 56, 239 p.

580.   BOURRU, Edme Claude.   L'art de se
traiter soi-même dans les maladies vénér-
iennes, et de se guérir de leurs différens
symptômes ... Paris: J.P. Costard, 1770.
    2 pts. in 1 v.

581.   BOYLE, Robert.   The aerial noctiluca:
or Some new phoenomena, and a process of a
factitious self-shining substance ... London:
printed by T. Snowden, sold by N. Ranew,
1680.
    4 ℓ., 109 p.

582.   ——.   New experiments, and observations, made upon the icy noctiluca ... To
which is annexed a chymical paradox ...
London: R.E. for B. Tooke, 1681/2.
    7 ℓ., 150 p., 1 ℓ.
    With his The aerial noctiluca ... 1680.

583. ———. Die Lufftige Noctiluca, oder
Etliche neue Phoenomena, sampt einer Anleitung allerhand Phosphoros und selbst-
scheinende Wesen zu zubereiten ... in
Hochteutsch übersetzet durch J.L.M.C.
Hamburg: G. Schultz, 1682.
   1 *l*., 88 p.

584. ———. Noctilvca aeria sive nova
qvædam phænomena in substantiæ factitiæ
sive artificialis, sponte lucidæ, productione
observata ... Vnà adnectuntur ... Experimenta
nova & observata facta in glacialem nocti-
lucam. Quibus adjicitur Paradoxon chymicvm.
Genevæ: S. de Tournes, 1693.
   108 p.

585. ———. Certain physiological essays,
written at distant times, and on several occasions. London: for H. Herringman, 1661.
   2 *l*., 1–36 p., 1 *l*., 37–105 p., 6 *l*.,
107–249 p.

586. ———. Tentamina, quædam physiologica. Diversis temporibus, & occasionibus
conscripta. Amstelodami: C. Commelinus,
1667.
   194 p., 1 *l*.; 159 p.

587. ———. ——— cum ejusdem Historia
fluiditatis et firmitatis ... Amstelodami: D.
Elzevirius, 1667.
   4 *l*., 424 p.

588. ———. ———. Accessit De novo trac-
tavs de absolvta qviete in corporibvs ...
Genevæ: S. de Tovrnes, 1677.
   2 *l*., 60 p.; 3 *l*., 94 p.; 18 p.

589. ———. ———. Coloniæ Allobrogvm: S.
de Tovrnes, 1677.
   2 *l*., 60 p.; 3 *l*., 94 p.; 18 p.

590. ———. ———. Coloniæ Allobrogvm: S.
de Tovrnes, 1680.
   2 *l*., 60 p.; 3 *l*., 94 p.; 18 p.

591. ———. ———. Genevæ: S. de Tournes,
1680.
   2 *l*., 60 p.; 3 *l*., 94 p.; 18 p.

592. ———. A disquisition about the final
causes of natural things ... To which are subjoyn'd ... some uncommon observations about
vitiated sight ... London: H.C. for J. Taylor,
1688.
   8 *l*., 274 p., 3 *l*.

593. ———. ———. London: H.C. for J. Taylor, 1688.

   8 *l*., 274 p., 3 *l*.
   Another issue, with the author's name
in line ten of the title.

594. ———. An essay about the origine
& virtues of gems ... London: printed by W.
Godbid, sold by M. Pitt, 1672.
   8 *l*., 185 p.

595. ———. Specimen de gemmarvm origine
& virtvtibvs ... Genevæ: S. de Tovrnes, 1677.
   3 *l*., 58 p.

596. ———. ———. Genevæ: S. de Tovrnes,
1680.
   3 *l*., 58 p.

597. ———. An essay of the great effects
of even languid and unheeded motion. Whereunto is annexed an experimental discourse
of some little observed causes of the in-
salubrity and salubrity of the air and its
effects. London: S. Smith, 1690.
   4 *l*., 123 p.; 4 *l*., 158 p.

598. ———. Essays of the strange subtilty,
great efficacy, determinate nature of efflu-
viums. To which are annext new experiments
to make fire and flame ponderable: together
with a discovery of the perviousness of
glass ... London: W.G. for M. Pitt, 1673.
   var. pag.

599. ———. Essays of the strange subtelty,
determinate nature, great efficacy of efflu-
viums. To which are annext new experiments
to make fire and flame ponderable: together
with a discovery of the perviousness of
glass ... London: W.G. for M. Pitt, 1673.
   var. pag.

600. ———. ———. Another copy. Inscribed:
"For Mr. Isaac Newton from the author."

601. ———. Exercitationes de atmosphæris
corporvm consistentivm ... Subjunctis experimentis novis, ostendentibus, posse partes
ignis & flammæ reddi stabiles ponderabilesque
... Genevæ: S. de Tovrnes, 1677.
   var. pag.

602. ———. ———. Genevæ: S. de Tovrnes,
1680.
   var. pag.

603. ———. Examen dialogi physici Domini
T. Hobbs, de natvra aëris, in iis quæ refer-
unter in Dni Boyle libro de novis experimentis
circa aëris vim elasticam ... Genevæ: S. de
Tournes, 1695.

4 *l*., 64 p., 2 *l*.

——. Experiences curieuses ... sur les savevrs et sur les odeurs. *In* Recueil d'experiences et observations sur le combat ... 1679.

604.   ——. Experimenta & observationes physicæ: wherein are briefly treated of several subjects relating to natural philosophy in an experimental way. To which is added, a small collection of strange reports ... London: for J. Taylor and J. Wyat, 1691.
13 *l*., 158 p., 1 *l*., 28 p., 1 *l*.

605.   ——. Experimenta et notæ circa prodvcibilitatem chymicorvm principiorvm: quæ sunt totidem partes appendicis ad scepticvm chymicvm. Genevæ: S. de Tovrnes, 1694.
6 *l*., 92 p.

606.   ——. Experiments and considerations touching colours ... The beginning of an experimental history of colours ... London: for H. Herringman, 1664.
20 *l*., 423 p.   illus.

607.   ——. ——. London: for H. Herringman, 1670.
20 *l*., 423 p.

608.   ——. ——. Coloniæ Allobrogvm: S. de Tovrnes, 1680.
10 *l*., 168 p., 4 *l*.

609.   ——. ——. Genevæ: S. de Tovrnes, 1680.
10 *l*., 168 p., 4 *l*.

610.   ——. Experimenta et considerationes de coloribus ... nunc verò in lucem prodire passa, ceu initium historiæ experimentalis de coloribus ... Amstelodami: G. Schagen, 1667.
12 *l*., 371 p., 10 *l*.

611.   ——. ——. Roterodami: A. Leers, 1671.
12 *l*., 518 p., 15 *l*.

612.   ——. ——. Genevæ: S. de Tovrnes, 1676.
10 *l*., 168 p., 4 *l*.

613.   ——. Experiments, notes, etc. about the mechanical origine or production of divers particular qualities: among which is inserted a discourse of the imperfection of the chymist's doctrine of qualities ...

London: E. Flesher for R. Davis, 1675.
var. pag.

614.   ——. ——. London: E. Flesher for R. Davis, 1676.
var. pag.

615.   ——. Experimenta nec non observationes circa variarvm particvlarivm qualitatum originem, sive productionem mechanicam: quibus accesserunt tractatus quo imperfecta chymistarum doctrina de qualitatibus detegitur ... Genevæ: S. de Tournes, 1694.
xvi, 144 p.

616.   ——. A free enquiry into the vulgarly receiv'd notion of nature made in an essay, address'd to a friend ... London: H. Clark for J. Taylor, 1685/6.
12 *l*., 412 p., 1 *l*.

617.   ——. De ipsa natura, sive Libera in receptam naturæ notionem disquisitio ad amicum ... Ex Anglico sermone in Latinum traducebat ... Londini: typis H. Clark, impensis J. Taylor, 1687.
13 *l*., 193 p., 2 *l*.

618.   ——. Tractatvs de ipsa natura, sive Libera in receptam naturæ notionem disquisitio ad amicum ... Genevæ: S. de Tovrnes, 1688.
8 *l*., 111 p.

619.   ——. ——. Coloniæ Allobrogvm: S. de Tovrnes, 1688.
8 *l*., 111 p.

620.   ——. General heads for the natural history of a country, great or small; drawn out for the use of travellers and navigators ... London: for J. Taylor and S. Holford, 1692.
2 *l*., 134 [i.e. 138] p., 1 *l*.

621.   ——. Generalia capita pro historia naturali regionum majorum vel minorvm, deducta in peregrinatorum & navigatorum vsum ... Genevæ: S. de Tournes, 1696.
2 *l*., 39 p.

622.   ——. The general history of the air ... London: for A. & J. Churchill, 1692.
xii, 259 p.   illus., charts.

623.   ——. Hydrostatical paradoxes, made out by new experiments ... Oxford: W. Hall for R. Davis, 1666.
18 *l*., 247 p.   illus.
Lacking the last 2 preliminary leaves.

624. ———. Paradoxa hydrostatica novis
experimentis ... evicta ... Nuper ex Anglico
sermone in Latinum versa. Oxonii: typis H.
Hall, impensis R. Davis, 1669.
   24 ℓ., 209 p., 3 ℓ. illus.

625. ———. ———. Roterodami: A. Leers,
1670.
   23 ℓ., 240 p., 1 ℓ. illus.

626. ———. ———. Coloniæ Allobrogvm:
S. de Tovrnes, 1677.
   8 ℓ., 72 p. illus.

627. ———. ———. Coloniæ Allobrogvm:
S. de Tovrnes, 1680.
   8 ℓ., 72 p. illus.

628. ———. ———. Genevæ: S. de Tovrnes,
1680.
   8 ℓ., 72 p. illus.

629. ———. Medicina hydrostatica: or,
Hydrostaticks applyed to the materia medica
... To which is subjoyn'd, a previous hydrostatical way of estimating ores ... London:
for S. Smith, 1690.
   12 ℓ., 217 p., 3 ℓ.; 1 ℓ., 14 p. illus.

630. ———. Medicina hydrostatica, sive
Hydrostatica materiæ medicæ applicata ...
Accessit prævia methodvs hydrostatica
explorandi mineras. Genevæ: S. de Tournes,
1693.
   6 ℓ., 66 p., 2 ℓ.

631. ———. Medicinal experiments: or,
A collection of choice and safe remedies ...
The third edition. London: for S. Smith and
B. Walford, 1696-1698.
   3 v. in 1. port.
Volume three has a separate title page
with the imprint: London: for J. Taylor, 1698.

632. ———. ———. The fourth edition: enlarged with a supplement. London: for S.
Smith, 1703.
   3 pts. in 1 v.

633. ———. ———. The sixth edition corrected. London: for W. and J. Innys, 1718.
   3 pts. in 1 v.

634. ———. ———. The seventh edition
corrected. London: for W. Innys, 1731.
   3 pts. in 1 v.

635. ———. Memoirs for the natural history of humane blood, especially the spirit
of that liquor ... London: for S. Smith, 1684.

8 ℓ., 289 p., 3 ℓ.

636. ———. ———. London: for S. Smith,
1683/4.
   8 ℓ., 289 p., 3 ℓ.

637. ———. Apparatvs ad historiam naturalem
sangvinis hvmani, ac spiritvs præcipve eivsdem liqvoris ... Genevæ: S. de Tovrnes, 1685.
   4 ℓ., 91 p.

638. ———. ———. Genevæ: S. de Tovrnes,
1686.
   4 ℓ., 91 p.

639. ———. ———. Coloniæ Allobrogum:
S. de Tovrnes, 1686.
   4 ℓ., 91 p.

640. ———. New experiments and observations touching cold, or An experimental
history of cold, begun ... Whereunto is annexed an account of freezing ... by the
learned Dr. C. Merret ... London: for J.
Crook, 1665.
   30 ℓ., pp. 1-696, 2 ℓ., pp. 697-803, 2 ℓ.,
pp. 805-845, 5 ℓ., pp. 1-54. illus.

641. ———. ———. Together with an appendix, containing some promiscuous experiments ... London: for R. Davis, 1683.
   19 ℓ., 324 p., 2 ℓ.; 20 p.; 1 ℓ., 29 p.
illus.

642. ———. New experiments physico-
mechanicall, touching the spring of the air,
and its effects, (made, for the most part, in
a new pneumatical engine) ... Oxford: H.
Hall for T. Robinson, 1660.
   16 ℓ., 399 [i.e. 389] p. illus.

643. ———. ———. The second edition.
Whereunto is added a defence of the authors
explication of the experiments, against the
obiections of Franciscus Linus and Thomas
Hobbes. [Oxford: H. Hall for T. Robinson,
1662.]
   8 ℓ., 207 p.; 6 ℓ., 122 p.; 4 ℓ., 98 p.
illus.

644. ———. ———. London: M. Flesher for
R. Davis, 1682.
   8 ℓ., 203 p.; 6 ℓ., 117 p.; 4 ℓ., 102 p.,
1 ℓ. illus.

645. ———. Nova experimenta physico-
mechanica de vi aëris elastica & ejusdem
effectibus, facta maximam partem in nova
machina pneumatica ... Editio postrema.
Roterodami: A. Leers, 1669.

12 *l*., 351 p., 4 *l*.; 15 *l*., 176 p., 4 *l*.
illus.

646. ——. ——. Coloniæ Allobrogvm:
S. de Tovrnes, 1677.
　　6 *l*., 154 p., 3 *l*.; 6 *l*., 80 p., 3 *l*.; 2 *l*.,
19 p.　illus.

647. ——. ——. Coloniæ Allobrogvm:
S. de Tovrnes, 1680.
　　6 *l*., 154 p., 3 *l*.; 7 *l*., 80 p., 3 *l*.; 2 *l*.,
19 p.　illus.

648. ——. ——. Genevæ: S. de Tovrnes,
1680.
　　6 *l*., 154 p., 3 *l*.; 7 *l*., 80 p., 3 *l*.; 2 *l*.,
19 p.　illus.

649. ——. A continvation of nevv experiments physico-mechanical, touching the
spring and weight of the air, and their effects. The I. part ... Whereto is annext a
short discourse of the atmospheres of con-
sistent bodies. Oxford: H. Hall for R. Davis,
1669.
　　11 *l*., 198 p., 6 *l*.　illus.

650. ——. Novorvm experimentorvm
physico-mechanicorum continvatio prima,
de aeris elaterio et pondere, nec non eorundem effectibus ... Genevæ: S. de Tournes,
1694.
　　6 *l*., 118 p., 3 *l*.　illus.

651. ——. ——. Genevæ: S. de Tournes,
1695.
　　6 *l*., 118 p., 3 *l*.　illus.

652. ——. A continuation of new experiments physico-mechanical touching the
spring and weight of the air, and their effects. The second part ... London: M. Flesher
for R. Davis, 1682.
　　8 *l*., 198 p., 3 *l*.　illus.

653. ——. Experimentorum novorum
physico-mechanicorum continuatio secunda.
In qua experimenta varia ... continetur. Londini: M. Flesher pro R. Davis, 1680.
　　10 *l*., 223 p., 6 *l*.　illus.

654. ——. ——. Genevæ: S. de Tovrnes,
1682.
　　4 *l*., 130 p., 1 *l*.　illus.

655. ——. Nova experimenta pneumatica
respirationem spectantia. Genevæ: S. de
Tovrnes, 1686.
　　47 p.

656. ——. ——. Coloniæ Allobrogvm:
S. de Tovrnes, 1686.
　　47 p.

657. ——. Occasional reflections upon
several svbiects. Whereto is premis'd a
discourse about such kind of thoughts ...
London: W. Wilson for H. Herringman,
1665.
　　18 *l*., 1-80, 161-264 p.; 1 *l*., 229 p.,
5 *l*.

658. ——. Of a degradation of gold made
by an anti-exixir: a strange chymical narrative. London: T.N. for H. Herringman, 1678.
　　3 *l*., 17 p.

659. ——. An historical account of a
degradation of gold, made by an anti-elixir:
a strange chymical narrative ... The second
edition. London: for R. Montagu, 1739.
　　vi, 17 p.

——. An abridgment of Boyle's ac-
count of a degradation of gold. *In* Price, J.,
An account of some experiments on mercury
... 1782.

660. ——. Of the reconcileableness of
specifick medicines to the corpuscular
philosophy. To which is annexed A discourse
about the advantages of the use of simple
medicines ... London: for S. Smith, 1685.
　　8 *l*., 225 p., 7 *l*.

661. ——. De specificorum remediorum
cum corpusculari philosophia condordia. Cui
accessit Dissertatio de varia simplicium
medicamentorum utilitate, usuque. Ex Anglico
in latinum sermonem traducebat D.A.M.D.
Londini: S. Smith, 1686.
　　6 *l*., 180 p.

662. ——. ——. Genevæ: S. de Tovrnes,
1686.
　　4 *l*., 64 p.

663. ——. ——. Genevæ: S. de Tovrnes,
1687.
　　4 *l*., 64 p.

664. ——. ——. Coloniæ Allobrogvm:
S. de Tovrnes, 1687.
　　4 *l*., 64 p.

665. ——. Opera omnia, nunc primùm in
unum corpus redacta, ac tres in tomos distributa ... Venetiis: J.J. Hertz, 1696-1697.
　　3 v.　port.

666.   ——. Opera varia, quorum posthac
exstat catalogus ... Genevæ: S. de Tovrnes,
1680.
    2 v. illus., port.

667.   ——. The origine of formes and
qualities, (according to the corpuscular
philosophy,) illustrated by considerations
and experiments ... Oxford: H. Hall for R.
Davis, 1666.
    25 l., 269 p., 2 l., 271-433 p.

668.   ——. ——. The second edition,
augmented by a discourse of subordinate
formes ... Oxford: H. Hall for R. Davis,
1667.
    16 l., 363 [i.e. 361] p.

669.   ——. Origo formarum et qualitatum
juxta philosophiam corpuscularem considera-
tionibus & experimentis illustrata ... Ex
Anglico sermone in Latinum traducta ...
Oxoniæ: excudebant A. & L. Lichfield, impensis R. Davis, 1669.
    32 l., 291 p.
    Lacking pages 123-126, 141-142.

670.   ——. ——. Genevæ: S. de Tovrnes,
1688.
    16 l., 147 p.

671.   ——. The philosophical works ...
abridged, methodized, and disposed under
the general heads of physics, statics, pneu-
matics, natural history, chymistry, and
medicine ... By Peter Shaw. London: for W.
and J. Innys ..., 1725.
    3 v. illus.

672.   ——. ——. The second edition,
corrected. London: for W. Innys ..., 1738.
    3 v. illus., port.

673.   ——. The sceptical chymist: or
Chymico-physical doubts & paradoxes,
touching the spagyrist's principles commonly
call'd hypostatical ... London: J. Cadwell
for J. Crooke, 1661.
    10 l., 442 p.

674.   ——. ——. To which in this edition
are subjoyn'd divers experiments and notes
about the producibleness of chymical principles. Oxford: H. Hall for R. Davis and B.
Took, 1680.
    10 l., 440 p.; 14 l., 268 p.

675.   ——. Chymista scepticus vel dubia
et paradoxa chymico-physica, circa spagyricorum principia ... Roterodami: A. Leers, 1662.

9 l., 23 p., 1 l., 293 p.

676.   ——. ——. Editio secunda priori
emendatior. Roterodami: A. Leers, 1668.
    14 l., 392 p.

677.   ——. ——. Genevæ: S. de Tovrnes,
1677.
    6 l., 148 p.

678.   ——. ——. Coloniæ Allobrogvm:
S. de Tovrnes, 1680.
    6 l., 148 p.

679.   ——. ——. Genevæ: S. de Tovrnes,
1680.
    6 l., 148 p.

680.   ——. Short memoirs for the natural
experimental history of mineral waters ...
London: for S. Smith, 1684/5.
    9 l., 112 p., 7 l.

    ——. Specimina quædam historiæ
naturalis et experimentalis aqvarum mineralium. In Vallerius, N., Tentamina physico-
chymica ... 1699.

681.   ——. Some considerations touching the vsefvlnesse of experimental naturall
philosophy ... Oxford: H. Hall for R. Davis,
1663.
    10 l., 127 p., 3 l.; 1 l., 417 p., 9 l.

682.   ——. ——. Oxford: H. Hall for R.
Davis, 1663-1671.
    2 v. in 1.

683.   ——. ——. A second edition ... Oxford: H. Hall for R. Davis, 1664.
    8 l., 126 p., 2 l.; 416 p., 8 l.

684.   ——. ——. A second edition ... Oxford: H. Hall for R. Davis, 1664-1671.
    2 v. in 1.

685.   ——. Exercitationes de utilitate
philosophiæ naturalis experimentalis ... Una
cum ejusdem additionibus ... Lindaviæ: T.
& J.C. Hechten, 1692.
    8 l., 602 p., 4 l.

686.   ——. Considerationes circa utilitatem
philosophiæ natvralis experimentalis ...
Genevæ: S. de Tournes, 1694.
    4 l., 602 p., 4 l.

687.   ——. Tentamen porologicum sive ad
porositatem corporum tum animalium, tum
solidorum, detegendam. Londini: S. Smith, 1684.

4 *l*., 131 p.
With his De specificorum remediorum ...
Londini, 1686.

688. ——. ——. Genevæ: S. de Tovrnes, 1686.
   3 *l*., 46 p.

689. ——. ——. Coloniæ Allobrogvm:
S. de Tovrnes, 1686.
   3 *l*., 46 p.

690. ——. Tracts ... about The cosmicall qualities of things. Cosmical suspitions. The temperature of the subterraneall regions. The temperature of the submarine regions. The bottom of the sea. To which is præfixt, An introduction to the history of particular qvalities. Oxford: W.H. for R. Davis, 1671.
   var. pag.

691. ——. Tractatus de cosmicis rerum qualitatibus ... Quibus præmittitur introductio ad historiam qualitatum particvlarivm. Accedit denique tractatus de absoluta quiete in corporibus ... Amstelodami: J. Janssonius a Waesberge, G. Schultz, 1671.
   var. pag.

692. ——. Introdvctio ad historiam qvalitatvm particvlarivm. Cui subnectuntur tractatus de cosmicis rerum qualitatibus ... Genevæ: S. de Tovrnes, 1677.
   var. pag.

693. ——. ——. Coloniæ Allobrogvm:
S. de Tovrnes, 1680.
   var. pag.

694. ——. ——. Genevæ: S. de Tovrnes, 1680.
   var. pag.

695. ——. Tracts consisting of observations about the saltness of the sea: an account of a statical hygroscope and its uses: together with an appendix about the force of the air's moisture: a fragment about the natural and preternatural state of bodies ... To all which is premis'd A sceptical dialogue ... London: E. Flesher for R. Davis, 1674.
   var. pag.

696. ——. Observationes de salsedine maris. Genevæ: S. de Tovrnes, 1686.
   23 p.

697. ——. Tracts ... containing new experiments, touching the relation betwixt flame and air. And about explosions ... London:

for R. Davis, 1672.
   var. pag.

698. ——. Tractatvs varii continentes nova experimenta circa relationem inter flammam & aerem & circa explosiones ... Genevæ: S. de Tournes, 1696.
   2 *l*., 120 p.

699. ——. Tracts: containing I. Suspicions about some hidden qualities of the air ... II. Animadversions upon Mr. Hobbes's Problemata de vacuo. III. A discourse of the cause of attraction by suction ... London: printed by W.G., sold by M. Pitt, 1674.
   var. pag.

700. ——. Tractatus, in quibus continentur svspiciones de latentibvs qvibsdam qvalitatibvs aeris ... Animadversions in D. Hobbesii problemata de vacvo, et dissertatio de cavsa attractionis per svctionem ... Genevæ: S. de Tovrnes, 1679.
   2 *l*., 87 p.

701. ——. ——. Genevæ: S. de Tovrnes, 1680.
   2 *l*., 87 p.

702. ——. ——. Coloniæ Allobrogvm:
S. de Tovrnes, 1680.
   2 *l*., 87 p.

703. ——. Tracts ... of a discovery of the admirable rarefaction of the air. New observations about the duration of the spring of the air ... London: T.N. for H. Herringman, 1671.
   2 *l*., 28 p.

704. ——. Tractatus ... vbi I. Mira aeris ... rarefactio detecta. II. Observata nova circa dvrationem virtvtis elasticæ aeris expansi. III. Experimenta nova de condensatione aeris ... IV. Ejusdem quantitatis aeris rarefacti ... extensio. Genevæ: S. de Tournes, 1680.
   2 *l*., 19 p.

705. ——. The works ... in five volumes. To which is prefixed the life of the author. London: for A. Millar, 1744.
   5 v.   illus.
   Lacks the portrait.

706. ——. ——. A new edition. London: for J. and F. Rivington ..., 1772.
   6 v.   illus., port.

707. BRACESCO, Giovanni.   La espositione

di Geber philosopho ... nella qvale si
dichiarano molti nobilissimi secreti della
natura ... Vinetia: G. Giolito de Ferrarii,
1544.
  83 numb. *l*. illus.

708. ——. ——. Vinegia: G. Giolito de
Ferrarii, 1551.
  83 numb. *l*. illus.

709. ——. De alchemia dialogi II. Quorum prior genuinam librorū Gebri sententiam
... retegit, & certis argumentis probat. Alter
Raimundi Lullij ... Mysteria in lucem pro-
ducit. Quibus præmittuntur, propositiones
centum uiginti nouem ... Norimbergæ: I.
Petreius, 1548.
  64 *l*.

710. ——. De alchemia, dialogi duo
nunquam ante hac conjunctim sic editi,
correcti, & emaculati. Præmittuntur propositiones centum viginti novem ... Hamburgi:
J. Naumann & G. Wolff, 1673.
  8 *l*., 272 p.

711. BRADLEY, Richard. The plague at
Marseilles consider'd: with remarks upon
the plague in general ... The second edition.
London: W. Mears, 1721.
  8 *l*., 60 p., 3 *l*.

712. BRANDE, Augustus Everard. Experiments and observations on the Angustura
bark. London: G. Stafford for T. Payne, 1791.
  viii, 86 p.

713. BRASAVOLA, Antonio Musa. Examen
omnium catapotiorum uel pilularum ... [Con-
radi Gesneri] ... envmeratio medicamētorum
purgatium, uomitoriorum, & aluum bonam
facientium ... [Basileæ] Froben [1543].
  4 *l*., 166 p., 1 *l*.

714. ——. Examen omnium loch, idest
linctuum, suffuf, idest puluerum, aquarum,
decoctionum, oleorum, quorum apud Fer-
rarienses pharmacopolas vsus est ... Venetiis:
Ivnta, 1553.
  291 [i.e. 299] numb. *l*., 1 *l*.

715. ——. Examen omnium simplicium
medicamentorum, quorum in officinis usus
est. Addita sunt insuper Aristotelis problemata ... Venetiis: in officina Erasmiana,
1539.
  24 *l*., 542 p.

716. BRENDEL, Zacharias. Chimia in artis
formam redacta ... Editio secunda correctior,

& auctior ... consilio Werneri Rolfinck ...
Jenæ: J. Reiffenberger, 1641.
  8 *l*., 175 p., 7 *l*.

717. ——. ——. Lugduni Batavorum: A.
Doude, 1671.
  167 p., 6 *l*.

718. BRENTZ, Andreas. Farrago philosophorvm: hoc est, Varii modi, processus,
& sententiæ philosophorum, perveniendi ad
lapidem philosophicum, seu benedictum ...
[Ambergæ: M. Forster] 1606.
  1 *l*., 107 p.
  With Stupani, E., Vere avreorvm aphorismorum ... 1615.

719. BRESMAL, Jean François. Hidro-
analise des minerales chaudes & froides
de la ville imperiale d'Aix-la-Chapele ...
Liege: J.L. de Milst, 1703.
  xvi, 176 p., 2 *l*. illus.

720. ——. ——. Liege: J.L. de Milst, 1752.
  xvi p., 1 *l*., 176 p., 3 *l*.

721. BRESSY, Joseph. Essai sur l'élec-
tricité de l'eau. Paris: Fuchs, 1797.
  2 *l*., viii, 178 p., 1 *l*. illus.

722. BRETSCHNEIDER, Johann. Compendivm pharmacopoeæ Ioannis Placotomi.
Eiusdem Dispensatorivm vsitatissimorum
hoc tempore medicamentorum descriptiones
contines. Lvgdvni: G. Rouillius, 1561.
  421 p., 11 *l*.

723. BREVE trattato di fisionomia, per il
qvale si pvo cognoscere le qualità, com-
plessioni, & costumi di ciascuna persona
... Vi si contengono ancora alcuni secreti
da indouinare ... [n.p.: n.d.]
  4 *l*.

BREVIS tractatio de antiquissimo
atque certissimo illo particulari quod per
exaltationem seu gradationem solis s. auri
parari solet ... *In* Con- et dissensus chymicorum ... 1715.

724. BRIGHT, Timothy. A treatise of
melancholy ... Newly corrected and amended.
London: W. Stansby, 1613.
  11 *l*., 347 p.

725. ——. A treatise: wherein is declared
the sufficiencie of English medicines, for
cure of all diseases, cured with medicine.
London: H. Middleton for T. Man, 1580.
  48 p.

726. BRISSON, Mathurin Jacques. Pesan-
teur spécifique des corps ... Paris: Imprimerie Royale, 1787.
    1 *l*., xxiv, 453, xx p., 1 *l*.   charts.

727. ———. Principes élémentaires de
l'histoire naturelle et chymique des substances minérales ... Paris: F. Didot, 1797.
    viii, 345 p.

    BRODD, Sueno. Dissertatio de mor-
bis ex hyeme. *See* Linné, C. von, *praeses*.
Entry 2442.

728. BRODIN DE LA JUTAIS, Pierre.
L'abondance ou véritable pierre philosophale,
Qui consiste seulement à la multiplication
de toutes sortes de grains, de fruits, de
fleurs, & généralement de tous les végéta-
tifs ... Paris: Delaguette, 1752.
    xii, 67 p., 2 *l*.

    BROEN, Johannes. De somno &
somnifero opio. *See* Hulsius, A., *praeses*.

729. BROEKHUIZEN, Daniel van, *ed*.
Secreta alchimiæ magnalia D. Thomæ
Aqvinatis ... Item Thesaurus alchimiæ se-
cretissimus ... Accessit et Ioannis de
Rvpescissa Liber lucis, ac Raymundi Lullij
... Clavicula & Apertorium ... Cum præfa-
tione D. Ioannis Heurnij. Lugduni Batavorum:
T. Basson, 1598.
    71 p.

730. ———. ———. Editio tertia. Lugduni
Batavorum: T. Basson, 1602.
    71 p.

731. BROOKES, Richard. The general
dispensatory, containing a translation of
the pharmacopoeias of the Royal College of
Physicians of London and Edinburgh: together with that of the Royal Hospital of
Edinburgh ... London: for J. Newberry and
W. Owen, 1753.
    viii, 2, 408 p., 13 *l*.

732. ———. ———. The third edition. London: for J. Rivington ..., 1773.
    x p., 1 *l*., 388 p., 17 *l*.

733. ———. ———. The natural history of vegetables ... Together with the method of culti-
vating those planted in gardens ... London:
for J. Newbery, 1763.
    xii, 437, x p.   illus.

734. BROQUETAS, Juan. Luz de la verdad
y extincción de preocupaciones. Tratado de

las aguas thermales de la villa de Caldes
de Monbuy ... Barcelona: B. Pla, [1790].
    2 *l*., 52 p., 1 *l*.

735. BROTOFFER, Radtichs. Elucidarius
chymicus. Oder, Erleuchterung vnd deutliche
Erklerung, was die Fama fraternitatis vom
Rosencreutz, für chymische secreta de lapide
philosophorum, in ihrer Reformation der Welt,
mit verblümbten Worten versteckt haben ...
[Gosslar] 1617.
    74 p.

736. ———. Theophrastus non Theophrastus.
Oder Deutliche Endeckung was von Theo-
phrasto Paracelso zu halten sey, ob er seine
hohe Weissheit vnd Kunst von Gott oder dem
Teufel gehabt ... Gosslar: bey J. Vogt, in
verlegung H. und H. Stern, 1617.
    47 *l*.

737. BROUAUT, Jean. Traité de l'eav de
vie ov Anatomie theoriqve et pratiqve dv vin,
divisé en trois livres ... Paris: J. de Senlacque,
J. Henault, 1646.
    22 *l*., 115, 56 p.   illus.

    ———. *See also* Bonai, I.D., Abregé
de l'astronomie.... 1644.

738. BROUSSOUNET, François. Q.F.F.F.Q.S.
Quæstiones chemico-medicæ duodecim ...
Monspelii: J. Martel, 1759.
    36 p.
    With Venel, G.F., Quæstiones chemicæ
duodecim ... 1759.

739. BROWN, John. A compleat treatise
of preternatural tumours, both general and
particular ... London: S.R. for R. Clavel,
1678.
    9 *l*., 395 p., 2 *l*.   illus., port.

740. BROWN, John, 1735–1788. The elements of medicine; or, A translation of the
Elementa medicinae Brunonis. With large
notes, illustrations, and comments. By the
author of the original work. A new edition.
Philadelphia: T. Dobson, 1790.
    1 *l*., xiii, 390 p., 4 *l*.   chart.

741. ———. Grundsätz der Arzenenlehre.
Aus dem Lateinischen übersetzt von M.A.
Weikard ... Ofen: gedruckt auf Kosten der
Herausgeber in der königl. Pester Univer-
sitäts-Buchdruckerey, 1798.
    xvi, 392 p.

742. BROWN, Thomas. Nature's cabinet
unlock'd. Wherein is discovered the natural

causes of metals, stones ... the nature of
plants ... together with a description of
the individual parts and species of all
animate bodies ... London: for E. Farnham,
1657.
   3 *l*., 331 p., 1 *l*.

743.   BROWNE, John.   Myographia nova
sive Musculorum omnium (in corpore humano
hactenùs repertorum) accuratissima descriptio, in sex praelectiones distributa ...
Lugduni Batavorum: J. Mouckee, 1687.
   4 *l*., 56 p., 2 *l*.   illus., chart.

744.   ——.   Myographia Nova: or, A
graphical description of all the muscles in
the humane body, as they arise in dissection ... London: T. Milbourn for the author,
1698.
   4 *l*., viii p., 12 *l*., x, 9-186 p.   illus., port.

745.   BROWNE, Richard.   Prosodia pharmacopoeorum: or The apothecary's prosody ...
London: for B. Billingsley, 1685.
   24 *l*., 237 p.

746.   BROWNRIGG, William.   The art of
making common salt, as now practised in
most parts of the world; with several improvements proposed in that art, for the use
of the British dominions. London: C. Davis
..., 1748.
   xxiv, 295 p.   illus.

747.   ——.   Considerations on the means
of preventing the communication of pestilential contagion, and of eradicating it in in-
fected places. London: L. Davis, 1771.
   1 *l*., 40 p.

748.   BRUEL, Walter.   Praxis medicineae;
or The physicians practice ... London: J.
Norton for W. Sheares, 1632.
   2 *l*., 407 p., 2 *l*.

   BRUMMET, Christoph.   *See* Grummet,
Christoph.

749.   BRUNACCI, Gaudenzio, *supposed
author*.   La sferza de gl'alchimisti, diuisa
in quatro capitoli ... Lion: 1665.
   120 p.

750.   BRUNFELS, Otto.   Ονομαστικόν medi-
ciniæ. Continens omnia nomina herbarum,
fruticum ... Argentorati: I. Schottus, 1534.
   186 unnumb. *l*.   illus.

751.   ——.   Reformation der Apotecken,
welche inhaltet vil gůter stück, die eynem

yeglichen fast nützlich sein, so seiner
gesundtheyt gern acht haben will ... Strass
[burg]: W. Kiel, 1536.
   4 *l*., liiii numb. *l*.

752.   ——.   Theses sev commvnes, loci
totius rei medicæ. Item. De vsv pharmacorum
... Argentorati: G.V. Andlanus, 1532.
   8 *l*., 232 numb. *l*.
   Two leaves of Index misbound after leaf
228.

753.   BRUNSCHWIG, Hieronymus.   Liber
de arte distillandi de compositis. Das büch
der waren kunst zu distillieren die Composita vñ simplicia, vnd dz Büch thesaurus
pauperū ... [Strassburg: (J. Grüninger) 1512.]
   cccxliiii numb. *l*., 6 *l*.   illus.

754.   ——.   Die distellacien eñ virtuyten
der waterē. [Bruesele: (T. van de Noot)
1517.]
   103 *l*.   illus.
   Lacking leaf N_1.

755.   ——.   Das Buch zu Distilieren die
zusamen gethonen ding: Composita genant:
durch die einzigen ding, vñ das buch Thesaurus pauperum genant ... [Strassburg: B.
Grüninger, 1532.]
   8 *l*., cclxxx numb. *l*.   illus.

756.   ——.   The vertuose boke of distyl-
lacyon of the waters of all maner of herbes
... Fyrst made and compyled by ... Jherom
Bruynswyke, and now newly translate out
of Duyche into Englysshe ... [London: L.
Andrewe, 1527.]
   138 *l*.   illus.

757.   ——.   ——.   [London: P. Treveris?
ca. 1530.]
   138 *l*.
   Lacking 18 leaves, as follows: a_6, $d_{1,2,4}$,
E_1, P_{1-6}, R_6, V_{1-6}. Leaves I_{2-4} in facsimile.

   ——.   Ars destillandi, oder Diestellier
Kunst. *In* Dioscorides, P., Kräuterbuch ... 1610.

758.   ——.   The noble experyence of the
vertuous handy warke of surgeri ... [London:
P. Treueris, 1525.]
   78 *l*.   illus.

759.   ——.   Thesavrvs pavpervm. Einn
fürtrefliche vnd volkomne Haussapoteck ...
Franckfurt: C. Ege[nolff, 1537].
   4 *l*., lxxvi numb. *l*.   illus.

760.   ——.   Hauss apoteck zu yeden leibs

gebresten für den gemainen mañ und das
arm Landnolck ... [Augspurg: H. Stayner,
1539.]
3 *l*., lxxxi numb. *l*. illus.

761. ———. A most excellent and perfecte
homish apothecarye ... Translated out of the
Almaine ... by Jhon Hollybush. Collen: A.
Birckman, 1561.
45 numb. *l*.
With Turner, W., The first and seconde
partes of the herbal ... 1568.

762. BRY, Johann Theodor de. Emblemata
secvlaria, mira et ivcvnda varietate secvli
hvivs mores ita exprimentia ... mit artlichen
Lateinischen, Teutschen, Frantzösischen
... Carminibus und Reimen geziert ... Oppenhemii: H. Galleri, 1611.
56 p. illus.

763. BUCCI, Antonio. Saggio sopra il
flogisto, le differenti specie d'aria e il
calore ... Faenza: G. Archi, 1783.
84 p.

764. Das BUCH Amor Proximi geflossen
aus dem Oehl der goettlichen Barmhertzig-
keit ... Franckfurt: 1782.
159 p.

765. BUCHAN, William. Domestic medicine: or, A treatise on the prevention and
cure of diseases by regimen and simple
medicines ... The seventh edition, corrected:
to which is now added, a complete index.
London: for W. Strahan ..., 1781.
xxxvi, 754 p., 6 *l*.

766. ———. ———. Eighth edition; corrected
and enlarged. London: for W. Strahan ...,
1784.
xxxvi, 767 p., 18 *l*.

767. ———. ———. Fourteenth edition. London: for W. Strahan ..., 1794.
xliv, 712 p., 18 *l*.

768. ———. ——— revised and adapted to
the diseases and climate of the United
States of America, by Samuel Powel Griffitts
... Philadelphia: T. Dobson, 1795.
xxxi, 757 p., 1 *l*.

769. ———. Huislyke geneeskunde, of
Verhandeling over de verhoeding en geneezing
van ziektens ... Met eene voorreden en
eenige aantekeningen vermeerderd door J.E.
Lyklama à Nyholt ... Utrecht: G. van den
Brink, 1775.

2 *l*., vi, xxiv, 810 p., 7 *l*.

770. BUCHER, Urban Gottfried. Das
Muster eines nützlich-gelehrten in der
Person Herrn Doctor Johann Joachim Bechers
... nach seinen ... Schriften beurtheilet ...
Nürnberg: J.D. Taubers seel. Erben, 1722.
7 *l*., 160 p. illus., port., maps.

771. BUC'HOZ, Pierre Joseph. Recueil
de secrets surs et expérimentés, a l'usage
des artistes ... Seconde edition ... Paris:
l'auteur, 1783-1785.
2 v.

772. BULLEIN, William. Bulleins bul-
warke of defēce againste all sickness, sornes,
and woundes, that dooe daily assaulte man-
kinde ... London: J. Kyngston, 1562.
var. pag. illus.

773. BULLIARD, Pierre. Flora Parisiensis,
ou Descriptions et figures des plantes qui
croissent aux environs de Paris ... Paris:
P.F. Didot, 1776-1783.
6 v. illus.

774. ———. Herbier de la France. Paris:
l'imprimerie de Monsieur, et Leblanc, 1784-
1812.
4 v. in 6. illus.

775. BULSTRODE, Whitelock. An essay
of transmigration, in defence of Pythagoras:
or, A discourse of natural philosophy ...
London: E.H. for T. Basset, 1692.
28 *l*., 192 p. port.

776. BUNWORTH, Richard. Ὁμοτροπία
naturæ. A physical discourse, exhibiting the
cure of diseases by signature. Whereunto is
annexed, a philosophical discourse vindi-
cating the soul's prerogative in discerning
the truths of the Christian religion with the
eye of reason ... London: printed by J.C.,
sold by J. Hirons, 1656.
5 *l*., 90 p., 4 *l*.

777. BUONANNI, Filippo. Neuer Tractat
von Firniz-Laquir und Mahler-Künsten ... Mit
vielen neuen Arcanis, unterschiedlichen
Beschreibungen des Gummi Copals und Bern-
steins ... Zweyte und vermehrte Auflage.
Berlin: J.J. Rembold, 1730.
160 p. illus.
With Hellwig, C. von, Neu-vermehrtes
historisch-medicinisches ... 1726.

BUONO, Pietro. Margarita pretiosa.
See Lacinio, G., Margarita pretiosa ... 1608.

778. BURCKARD, Johann Jacob. Dissertatio medica inauguralis de radice senecka
... Argentorati: Pauschinger, 1750.
20 p.

779. BURCKHARD, Johann Heinrich. Mvsei
Bvrckhardiani ... complectens bibliothecam
in IV partes distribvtam ... Helmstadii: typis
Drimbornianis apud I.C. Meisnervm, 1750.
2 v. illus.

BURG, Hieronymus von. De acetariis.
See Linné, C. von, *praeses*. Entry 2448.

780. BURGGRAV, Johann Ernst. Achilles
πάνοπλος redivivus, seu Panoplia physico-
vulcania in praelio φίλοπλος in hostem
educitur sacer et inviolabilis. Cui praemissa est Marcelli Vranckheim ἐπίκρισις
στοχαστικὴ ad Achillem πανυπεροπλόμαχον.
Amsterodami: H. Laurentius [1612].
130 p., 2 *l*.

781. ——. Lampadem vitæ & mortis
omniumque graviorum in microcosmo παθῶν
indicem; hoc est: Biolychnium sive lucernam
... Antehâc quidem cura & studio J.E.B.
obscurè nimis ... traditam: nunc, dilucidiori
stylo, S E expositurum intimat G.F. ... Lugd.
Batav.: A. Doude, 1678.
72 p. illus.

782. BURGHART, Gottfried Heinrich. Iter
Sabothicvm, das ist: Ausführliche Beschrei-
bung einiger an. 1733 und ie folgenden
Jahre auf den Zothen-Berg gethanen Reisen
... Bresslau: M. Hubert, 1736.
9 *l*., 176 p. illus.
With his Zum allgemeinen Destillier-Kunst
... 1736.

783. ——. Zum allgemeinen Gebrauch
wohleingerichtete Destillier-Kunst ... Bresslau: J.J. Korn, 1736.
8 *l*., 402 p., 21 *l*. illus., tables.

784. BURNET, Duncan. Iatrochymicvs,
siue De praeparatione et compositione
medicamentorvm chymicorvm artificiosa,
tractatus ... Editio altera ... Stvdio ac opera
Ioannis Danielis Mylii. Francofvrti ad

Moenvm: typis E. Kempfferi, sumptibus L.
Jennis, 1621.
4 *l*., 111 p.

785. BURNET, Gilbert. A sermon preached
at the funeral of the honourable Robert Boyle;
at St. Martins in the fields, January 7,
1691/2. London: for R. Chiswell and J. Taylor, 1692.
40 p.

786. ——. ——. The second edition.
London: for R. Chiswell, 1704.
28 p.

787. BURTON, Robert. The anatomy of
melancholy ... and severall cvres of it ...
by Democritvs Iunior ... Oxford: I. Lichfield
and I. Short ... 1621.
2 *l*., 72 p., 4 *l*., 783 p., 4 *l*.

788. ——. ——. The seventh edition,
corrected and augmented ... London: H.
Cripps, 1660.
2 *l*., 77 p., 5 *l*., 646 p., 6 *l*.

789. BURTON, William. An account of
the life and writings of Herman Boerhaave
... In two parts. With an appendix. London:
for H. Lintot, 1743.
2 *l*., vii, 226 p. port.

790. BUTLER, Richard. An essay concerning blood-letting. Shewing the various
effects and peculiar advantages of bleeding
in different parts of the human body ...
London: for W. Mears, 1734.
1 *l*., vi p., 1 *l*., 148 p.

791. BUTTER, William. A treatise on the
kinkcough, with an appendix containing an
account of hemlock and its preparations.
London: T. Cadell, 1773.
1 *l*., ix, 206 p., 5 *l*.

792. BUTTNER, Johann. Catalogvs medicamentorvm tam simplicivm qvam compositorvm, ut et chymicorvm officinæ pharmacevticæ Bvttnerianæ ... [Gorlicii Lusa-
torum: J. Rhamba] 1629.
14 *l*., 107 p., 12 *l*. illus.

C

C***, *physician*. *See* [Caillot] *physician*.

793.   CABALÆ verior descriptio, das ist, Gründliche Beschreibung und Erweisung aller natürlichen und übernatürlichen Dingen ... Hamburg: G. Wolff, 1680.
   64 p.   illus.

794.   CABROL, Barthélemy.   Ontleedingh des menschelycken lichaems. Eertijts in't Latijn beschreven ... nu verduytscht en met by-voechselen als oock figuren verrijckt ... Amsterdam: G. Ioosten ..., 1648.
   8 ℓ., 262 p.   illus.

CADET DE GASSICOURT, Louis Claude, *jt. auth*. *See* Rouelle, G.F., Analyses ... 1755.

CAELIUS AURELIANUS. *See* Aurelianus, Caelius.

795.   CAËLS, Theodore Pierre.   Ratio occurrendi morbis a mineralium abusu produci solitis ... Amstelodami: J. van Harrevelt, 1781.
   3 ℓ., 117 p.

796.   ——.   De la cure des maladies produites par l'abus des minéraux. Ouvrage traduit sur l'original Latin publié en 1781 à Amsterdam & à Bruxelles. Paris: Lagrange, 1787.
   95 p.

797.   CAESAR, Theophilus.   Alchimy Spiegel: oder Kurz entworffene Practick, der gantzen chymischen Kunst ... Alles in zweyen lustigen Gesprächen verfasset: vnd das erste vor diesem auss dem Arabischen von Roberto Castrensi in Latein, nun aber ... in unser Teutsche Sprach vbergesetzt ... Franckfurt am Mayn: V. Steinmeyer, 1613.
   116 p.

798.   CAGLIOSTRO démasqué a Varsovie. Ou relation authentique de ses opérations alchimiques ... Par un témoin oculaire. [n.p.] 1786.
   3 ℓ., 62 p.

799.   CAILLEAU, André Charles.   Clef du grand oeuvre, ou Lettres du Sancelrien Tourangeau, a Madame L.D.L.B***. T.D.F.A.T. ... Corinte & Paris: Cailleau, 1777.
   94 p.

800.   [Caillot] *physician*.   Lettre sur les nouveaux bains medicinaux. Par M. C*** docteur en medecine. Paris: la veuve Quillau, 1752.
   84 p.

801.   CALDANI, Leopold Marco-Antonio. Institutiones physiologicae. Patavii: Cominianis, 1773.
   xvi, 477 p.

802.   CALMET, Augustin.   Traité historique des eaux et bains de Plombieres, de Bourbonne, de Luxeuil, et de Bains. Nancy: Leseure, 1748.
   2 ℓ., 333 p., 11 ℓ.   maps.

CALZOLARI, Francesco.   Iter Baldi civitatis Veronæ montis. *In* Mattioli, P.A., De plantis epitome ... 1586, etc.

CAMEL, Fridericus.   De salubritate febrium. *See* Hoffman, F., *praeses*.

CAMPESIUS, Joannes Antonius. Directorium summae summarum medicinae. *In* Ulsted, P., Coelum philosophorum ... 1553, etc.

803.   CANÀLS Y MARTÌ, Juan Pablo.   Memorias, que de orden de la real junta general de comercio y moneda, se dàn al público: sobre el albayalde, sal de Saturno, genuli, minio, y lithargirio ... Madrid: Sanchez, 1769.
   xxiv p.

804. ———. Memorias sobre la púrpura de los antiguos, restaurada en España, se dan al público ... Madrid: B. Roman, 1779.
18 *l*., 86 p., 1 *l*. illus.

805. CANDIDA, Giulio. Sulla formazione del molibdeno lettera ... al Signor Vincenzo Petagna. Napoli: G.M. Porcelli, 1785.
61 p.

806. CANDY, Louis. Discours touchant les merveilleux effets de la pierre divine ... à luy entierement cedée par le sieur d'Acqueville ... De nouveau revû & augmenté. Paris: J. Boüillerot, 1688.
5 *l*., 95 p.

807. CANEPARI, Pietro Maria. De atramentis cujuscunque generis ... In sex descriptiones digestum ... Londini: execudebat J.M., impensis J. Martin ..., 1660.
8 *l*., 568 p.

808. CANGIAMILA, Francesco Emmanuele. Abregé de l'embryologie sacrée, ou Traité des devoirs des prêtres, des médecins, des chirurgiens & des sages-femmes envers les enfants qui sont dans le sein de leurs meres. Seconde édition ... Paris: Nyon, 1774.
xxxi, 592 p. illus.

808a. ———. ———. Nouvelle edition ... Paris: Bailly, 1775.
vi, iii-xxvii, 596 p. illus.

809. ———. Embryologia sacra sive De officio sacerdotum, medicorum, et aliorum circa aeternam parvulorum in utero existentium salutem. Libri quatuor. Panormi: F. Valenza, 1758.
1 *l*., xxiv, 358 p. illus.

810. CANVANE, Peter. A dissertation on the oleum palmæ Christi, sive oleum rigini; or, (as it is commonly call'd) castor oil ... Bath: C. Pope for W. Frederick ... [1764].
2 *l*., vi, 88 p. illus.

811. CAPELLO, Arcadio. De vita ... Sanctorii Sanctorii ... Sermo habitus Venetiio ... XV kal. Novemb. anno sal. MDCCXLIX ... Venetiis: J. Thomasinus, 1750.
24 p.

812. CAPELLO, Giovanni Battista. Lessico farmaceutico-chimico contenente li rimedj piu' usati nella medicina ... Nova impressione ... Napoli: presso V. Orsini, a spese di S. Manfredi, 1770.
x p., 5 *l*., 252, 15 p.

813. CARANTA, Iago. Decadvm medicophysicarvm liber primvs [secundus] de natvra avri arte facti, & num sit pharmacum cordiale ... Saviliani: C. Strabella, 1623.
20 *l*., 288 p.

814. CARDANO, Girolamo. De rervm varietate libri XVII. Basileæ: [H. Petri] 1557.
6 *l*., 707 p., 6 *l*. illus.
Lacks last 15 leaves, comprising part of the index and the colophon.

815. ———. ———. Basileæ: [H. Petri] 1557.
15 *l*., 1194 p., 32 *l*. illus.
This edition is an octavo; the preceding edition is a folio.

816. ———. ———. A prima editione ab ipso denuò authore recogniti ... Avinione: M. Vincentivs, 1558.
7 *l*., 883 p., 24 *l*. illus.

817. ———. De svbtilitate libri xxi ... Norimbergæ: J. Petreius, 1550.
17 *l*., 371 p. illus.

818. ———. ———. Nunc demum ab ipso autore recogniti, atque perfecti ... Lugduni: G. Rouillius, 1559.
718 p., 27 *l*. illus.

819. ———. Les livres ... intitulez de la subtilité, & subtiles inuentions, ensemble les causes occultes, & raisons d'icelles. Traduits de Latin en François, par Richard le Blanc. Nouuellement reueuz, corrigez, & augmentez sur le dernier exemplaire Latin de l'auteur ... Paris: G. le Noir, 1584.
33 *l*., 478 numb. *l*. illus.

820. ———. La metoposcopie ... comprise en treize livres ... a laquelle a esté adjousté, le Traicté des marques naturelles du corps, par Melampvs ... Paris: T. Iolly, 1658.
4 *l*., viii, 225 p., 1 *l*. illus.

821. ———. Opera omnia ... curâ Caroli Sponii ... Lvgdvni: I.A. Hvgvetan & M.A. Ravavd, 1663.
10 v. in 5. illus., port.

822. ———. Somniorvm synesiorvm omnis generis insomnia explicantes, libri IIII ... Qvibvs accedvnt ... De libris proprijs. De curationibus ... Neronis encomium ... Basileæ: S. Henricpetri [1585].
22 *l*., 278 p.; 18 *l*., 413 p., 1 *l*.

823.   CARDILUCIUS, Johann Hiskias.
Heilsame Artzney-Kräffte des Nürnbergischen
Wild-Bades ... Nürnberg: W.M. Endter und
J. A. Endtero Seel. Söhne, 1681.
    12 *l*., 124 p., 4 *l*.

824.   ——, *ed*.   Magnalia medico-chymica, oder Die höchste artzney und feur-
künstige Geheimnisse ... zwar aus Paracelsi
Handschrift ... aufs neue verhochdeutschet
... nebenst ... dem unvergleichlichen Tractat
genannt: Offenstehender Eingang zu dem
vormals vorschlossenen königlichen Pallast
... Nürnberg: W.M. Endter und J.A. Endters
Sel. Erben, 1676.
    24 *l*., 409 p., 15 *l*., 32 p.
    Includes: Appendix introitus aperti ad
occlusum regis palatium ..., separately
paged at the end.

    CARERIUS, Alexander.   Quaestio an
arte metalla permutari possint. *In* Wittestein,
K., Disceptatio philosophica ... 1583?

825.   CAREY, Mathew.   A short account of
the malignant fever, lately prevalent in
Philadelphia: with a statement of the proceedings that took place on the subject in
different parts of the United States. Second
edition. Philadelphia: 1793.
    103 p., 4 *l*.

826.   ——.   ——. To which are added,
accounts of the plague in London and Marseilles; and a list of the dead from August 1,
to the middle of December, 1793. Fourth edition, improved. Philadelphia: 1794.
    164 p.

827.   CARL, Johann Samuel.   Armen-
Apotheck nach allen Grund-Theilen u. -Sätzen
der Medicin kürtzlich und einfältig eingerichtet und mitgetheilt ... Büdingen: J.F.
Regelein, 1721.
    161 p., 35 *l*.

828.   ——.   ——. Sechste und vielvermehrte Auflage. Büdingen: J.C. Stöhr, 1748.
    1 *l*., 250 p., 14 *l*.   port.

829.   ——.   Praxeos medicæ therapie
generalis et specialis ... [Halæ] impensis
Orphanotrophei, 1718.
    4 *l*., 147 p., 18 *l*.
    With his Specimen historiæ medicæ ...
1719.

830.   ——. Specimen historiæ medicæ
ex solidæ experientiæ documentis ... Halæ:

sumptibus Orphanotrophei, 1719.
    304 p.

831.   ——. Zeugnuss von chymischer
Storgerey, sonderlich in neuen Exempeln ...
Erweisen aus chymischen und medicinischen
Gründen und Erfahrungen. Samt einer Nach-
rede von Fatis chymicis. Franckfurt: J.C.
Göpner, 1733.
    8 *l*., 170 p., 7 *l*.

    CARLBOHM, Gustaf Jacob.   Censura
medicamentorum simplicium vegetabilium.
See Linné, Carl von, *praeses*. Entry 2422.

832.   CARLO, *detto il Franzosino*.   Segreti
bellissimi non piv dati in lvce ... Viterbo: G.
Discepolo, 1603.
    4 *l*.

833.   CARLUCII, Luca.   Lectiones medico
chemicæ. Neapoli: V. Ursini, 1770.
    32 p., 9 *l*.
    With Capello, G.B., Lessico farmaceutico-
chimico ... 1770.

834.   CARRÈRE, Joseph Barthélmy François.
Catalogue raisonné des ouvrages qui ont
été publies sur les eaux minérales en général et sur celles de la France en particulier
... Paris: C. Cailleau, 1785.
    viii, 584 p.

835.   CARTHEUSER, Johann Friedrich.
Elementa chymiae dogmatico-experimentalis
in vsvm academicvm conscripta. Editio
secvnda priori longe emendatior. Francofvrti
ad Viadrvm: J.C. Kleyb, 1753.
    viii, 228 p., 4 *l*.

836.   ——. Fvndamenta materiae medicae
tam generalis qvam specialis in vsvm
academicvm conscripta. Francofvrti ad Viadrvm: J.C. Kleyb, 1749-1750.
    2 pts. in 1 v.

837.   ——. Matiere médicale. Traduit du
Latin, augmentée d'une introduction à la
matiere médicinale. Paris: Briasson, 1765.
    2 v.   charts.

838.   ——. Pharmacologia theoretico-
practica rationi et experientiae svperstrvcta
in qva medicamentorvm officinalivm vsitatiorvm
præparatio ... Berolini: A. Havde, 1745.
    6 *l*., 756 p., 8 *l*.

839.   CARY, Walter.   Caries farewell to
physicke. First published in the yeere

1587. and now, in 1611. reuiewed and augmented. The VI. edition ... London: for the Companie of Stationers, 1611.

4 ℓ., 88 [i.e. 86] p.

Pages 67-88 have separate title-page: The hammer for the stone ... London: H. Lownes, 1611.

840. CASATI, Paolo. Dissertationes physicæ de igne ... Juxta exemplar Venetianum revisæ atqve curatius editæ. Francofurti: J.F. Gleditsch, 1688.

4 ℓ., 392 p., 11 ℓ.

841. ———. Pyrologia curiosa & experimentalis, i.e. Ignis scrutinium exactum ... Hanoviæ: J.C. Laurer, 1689.

3 ℓ., 393 p., 11 ℓ.

842. CASSIUS, Andreas. De extremo illo et perfectissimo naturæ opificio ac principe terrænorum sidere auro ... Hamburgi: G. Wolff, 1685.

4 ℓ., 152 p.

843. CASTAIGNE, Gabriel de. Les oevvres ... tant medicinales que chymiques, diuisées en quatre principaux traitez. I. Le paradis terrestre. II. Le grand miracle de la nature metallique. III. L'or potable. IV. Le thresor philosophique de la medecine metallique. Seconde edition ... adioustez les Aphorismes Basiliens, & la methode particuliere pour bien faire ... Manus Dei ... Paris: I. Dhovrry, 1661.

19, 93 p.; 1 ℓ., 78, 146, 15 p.

844. CASTELLI, Bartolommeo. Amaltheum Castello-Brunonianum, sive Lexicon medicum ... Accesserunt huic novae editioni Joannis Rhodii in Castelli Lexicon perutiles, & hoc signo notatae additiones ... Patavii: J. de Cadorinis, 1699.

7 ℓ., 827 p.

845. ———. Lexicon medicum Graeco-Latinum, ante a Jacobo Pancratio Brunone iterato editum ... Editio nova accuratissima. Genevae: fratres de Tournes, 1746.

2 ℓ., 788 p.

846. CASTELMONT, *sieur de.* Traité des bains de la ville d'Aix en Provence, et la maniere d'en user ... Aix: J. Tholosan ..., 1600.

8 ℓ., 28 p., 1 ℓ.

CASTIGLIONE, Branda Franciscus. De spiritbvs, extractis, salibvs. *In* Prospectus pharmaceuticus ... 1668.

CASTIGLIONE, Giovanni Onorato. *See* Prospectus pharmaceuticus ... 1668, etc.

847. CASTLE, George. The chymical Galenist: A treatise wherein the practise of the ancients is reconcil'd to the new discoveries in the theory of physick ... In which are some reflections upon a book, intituled, Medela medicinæ ... London: S. Griffin for H. & T. Twyford, 1667.

8 ℓ., 196 p., 6 ℓ.

A CATALOGUE of chymicall books ... *In* Cooper, W., The philosophical epitaph ... 1673.

848. CATELAN, Laurens. Demonstration des ingredians de la confection d'alkermes, & discours sur icelle, faite en la presence de Messieurs le Gouuerneur & gens du Roy ... Montpelier: A. Blanc, 1609.

5 ℓ., 247 p.

———. Traicté des eaux distillées. *In* Bauderon, B., Paraphrase sur la pharmacopée ... 1618, and editions of Bauderon's Pharmacopée.

849. CATTANI, Niccoló Antonio. Breve raggauaglio della natura, e qualità dell' acqua nomata dal Volgo in Assisi di Mojano ... Aggiuntavi in ultimo una compendiosa dissertazione epistolare, concernante il buon uso del non mai abbastanza lodato rimedio della dieta aquea. Assisi: A. Sgariglia, 1737.

136 p., 1 ℓ.

850. ———. Opuscoli o dissertazioni fisico-mediche d'intorno alle qualità salubri, ed insalubri dell'aere in genere, di ciascun paese, et ispicie di quello di Bevagna nell' Umbria ... Assisi: A. Sgariglia, 1745.

8 ℓ., 195 p.

851. CATTIER, Isaac. De la natvre des bains de Bovrbon et des abvs qvi se commettent à présent en la boisson de ces eaux. Avec vne instruction pour s'en seruir vtilment ... Paris: P. David, 1650.

4 ℓ., 148, 56 p., 2 ℓ.

With Desbrest, E.T., Traité des eaux minérales ... 1778.

CAVALLO, Francisco. Tractatus de animali theria. *In* Montagnana, B., Consilia ... 1514.

852. CAVALLO, Tiberius. A complete

treatise on electricity, in theory and practice ... The fourth edition ... Containing the
practice of medical electricity, besides
other additions and alterations ... London:
for C. Dilly, 1795.
    3 v.   illus.

853.   ——. Trattato completo d'elettricità
teorica e pratica con sperimenti originali
... Tradotto in Italiano ... Firenze: G. Cambiagi, 1779.
    xx, 511 p.   illus.

854.   ——. An essay on the theory and
practice of medical electricity. London: for
the author, 1780.
    xvi, 112 p.   illus.

855.   ——. The history and practice of
aerostation. London: for the author, sold by
C. Dilly ..., 1785.
    viii, 326 p., 4 *l*.   illus.

856.   ——. A treatise on the nature and
properties of air ... To which is prefixed,
an introduction to chymistry ... London: for
the author, 1781.
    xii, 835 p., 4 *l*.   illus., charts.

857.   CAVENDISH, Henry.   Expériences
sur l'air ... Mémoire lû à la Société Royale,
le 15 Janvier, 1784. Londres: E. Cox, 1785.
    viii, 68 p.

858.   ——. Observations on Mr. Hutch-
ins's experiments for determining the degree
of cold at which quicksilver freezes ... Read
at the Royal Society, May 1, 1783. London:
J. Nichols, 1784.
    1 *l*., 26 p.

859.   CELESTINO, Claudio.   De his quo
mundo mirabiliter evenivnt ... De mirabili
potestate artis et natvræ, vbi de philosophorum lapide, F. Rogerij Bachonis Anglici,
libellus. Hæc duo ... opuscula Orontius F.
... diligenter recognoscebat ... [Paris] S.
Colinæus, 1542.
    4 *l*., 52 numb. *l*.

        ——. Des choses merveilleuses en
nature. *In* Bacon, R., Le miroir d'alquimie ...
1557.

860.   CELSUS, Aulus Cornelius.   De re
medica, libri octo eruditissimi. Q. Sereni
Samonici Praecepta medica, uersibus hexa-
metris. Q. Rhemnij Fannij Palaemonis, De
ponderibus & mensuris ... Haganoæ: I.
Sec[erius], 1528.

288 numb. *l*., 16 *l*.; 29 numb. *l*., 2 *l*.

861.   ——. De re medicæ libri octo ...
Accessit ... liber Scribonii Largi, titulo
Compositionū medicamentorum: nunc primum
tineis ... industria Ioannis Rvellii ... Parisiis:
C. Vuechel, 1529.
    20 *l*., 131 numb. *l*.; 10 *l*., 31 numb. *l*.,
5 *l*.

862.   ——. De re medica libri octo. Accessere in primum eiusdem, Hieremiae Thriveri
Brachelii commentarij doctissimi: in reli-
quos verò septem, Baldvini Ronssei Ganden-
sis, enarrationes. Lvgdvni Batavorvm: ex
officina Plantiniana, apud F. Raphelengium,
1592.
    12 *l*., 752 p., 8 *l*.   illus.

863.   ——. De medicina libri octo ex fide
vetvstissimorvm librorvm recensvit innvmeris
depravationibvs partim alivnde partim a Lin-
denio invectis liberavit lectiones variantes
et animadversiones tvm aliorvm probatis-
simorvm avctorvm ... tvm svas nec non in-
dices copiosos aliaqve adiecit Car. Christian.
Kravse. Lipsiae: C. Fritsch, 1766.
    L, 777 p., 28 *l*.   port.

864.   ——. De medicina. Libri octo. Ad
optimas editiones collati praemittitur notitia
literaria Studiis Societatis Bipontinae. Editio
accurata. Biponti: ex typographia Societatis,
1786.
    1 *l*., xxiv, 553 p., 11 *l*.

865.   ——. Of medicine. In eight books.
Translated with notes critical and explanatory, by James Greive. London: for D. Wilson
and T. Durham, 1756.
    xxxii, 520 p., 3 *l*.

866.   ——. Traduction des ouvrages
d'Aurelius-Cornelius Celse, sur la médecine.
Par M. Ninnin. Paris: Desaint ..., 1753.
    2 v.

867.   CERASIO, Giovanni Pietro.   Methodo
dello spetiale ... Nel quale ... si tratta del
vero modo di perfettamente formare qual si
voglia composto medicinale ... Milano:
Iacomo de gli Antonii, 1611.
    4 *l*., 132 p., 10 *l*.

        CERMISOUS, Antonio. Consilia. *In*
Montagnana, B., Consilia ... 1514.

868.   CESALPINI, Andrea.   De metallicis
libri tres ... Noribergæ: C. Agricola, 1602.
    8 *l*., 222 p., 1 *l*.

869. ———. Peripateticarum questionum libri quinque. Venetiis: Iunta, 1571.
    14 *l*., 128 numb. *l*.

870. CHAMBON, Joseph. Principes de physique, rapportez à la medecine pratique, & autres traitez sur cet art ... Nouvelle edition. Paris: A. de la Roche ..., 1714.
    18 *l*., 473 p., 1 *l*.

871. ———. Traité des metaux et des mineraux, et des remedes qu'on en peut tirer; avec des dissertations sur le sel & le soulphre des philosophes ... Paris: C. Jombert, 1714.
    22 *l*., 547 p., 2 *l*.

872. ———. ———. Paris: C. Jombert, 1750.
    10 *l*., 547 p., 3 *l*.

873. CHAMPIER, Symphorien. ... Libelli duo. Primus de medicinae claris scriptoribus ... Secundus de legū divinarū conditoribus ... Dyalogus ... in legem machometicam ... De corporū animorieorumdeque remediis opusculum ... Aphorismi sive collectiones medicinales. Alexandri Benedicti Aphorismi ... Alexandri Aphrodisei de febribus. Opera parva Hippocratis noviter de greco in latinum traducta ... [Lyons: J. de Campis, 1506?]
    var. pag.

874. CHANDLER, John. Frauds detected: or, Considerations offered to the public; shewing the necessity of some more effectual provision against deceits, differences, and incertainties, in drugs, and compositions of medicines ... London: for G. Woodfall, 1748.
    1 *l*., 34 p.
    With A new method for the improvement ... 1747.

875. ———. A treatise of the disease called a cold; shewing its general nature, and causes ... London: A. Millar ..., 1761.
    1 *l*., 123 p.

    CHAPMAN, Henry. Thermæ redivivæ: The city of Bath described. *In* Guidott, T., A collection of treatises ... 1725.

876. CHAPTAL DE CHANTELOUP, Jean Antoine Claude. Elémens de chimie ... Montpellier: J.F. Picot, 1790.
    3 v.

877. ———. ———. Troisième édition, revue et augmentée. Paris: Deterville, 1796.
    3 v.

878. ———. Elements of chemistry ... Translated from the French. The second edition ... London: for G.G. & J. Robinson, 1795.
    3 v.

879. ———. Tableau analytique du cours de chymie ... Montpellier: J.F. Picot, 1783.
    2 *l*., 209 p.

880. CHARAS, Moyse. Histoire natvrelle des animavx, des plantes, & des mineraux qui entrent dans la composition de la Theriaque d'Andromachus ... Paris: O. de Varennes, 1668.
    14 *l*., 310 p., 5 *l*.

881. ———. Novvelles experiences svr la vipere ... Avec vne svite des novvelles experiences svr la vipere, et vne dissertation svr son venin ... Paris: l'avtevr ..., 1672.
    7 *l*., 245 p., 3 *l*. illus.

882. ———. New experiments upon vipers ... Originally written in French ... Now rendered English ... London: T.N. for J. Martyn, 1670.
    8 *l*., 223 p. illus.

883. ———. Opera tribus tomis distincta: I. Pharmacopoea regia galenica. II. Pharmacopoea regia chymica. III. Tractatus de theriaca & tractatus de vipera. [Genevæ: J.L. Du-Four, 1684.]
    3 v. in 2. illus.
    The title is taken from the half-title. There is no general title page, but each part has a separate title page with the above imprint.

884. ———. Pharmacopée royale galenique et chymique. Paris: 1676.
    7 *l*., 1060 p., 17 *l*. illus.

885. ———. ———. Nouvelle edition ... Paris: L. d'Houry, 1692.
    2 v. in 1. illus., port., chart.

886. ———. ———. Nouvelle edition ... avec les formules Latines & Françoises. Lyon: Anisson & Posuel, 1704.
    2 v. in 1. illus.

887. ———. ———. Lyon: Anisson & Posuel, 1717.
    4 *l*., 884 p., 24 *l*. illus.

888. ———. ——— augmentée par M.L.M. avec formules Latines & Françoises; le tarif des médicamens, & un traité extrêmement curieur sur les eaux minérales. Lyon:

F. Bruyset, 1753.
2 v. in 1. illus.

889. ———. The royal pharmacopoea,
galenical and chymical ... Faithfully Englished ... London: for J. Starkey and M. Pitt,
1678.
4 l., 272, 245 p., 7 l. illus., charts.

890. ———. Pharmacopoea regia, galenica
et chymica ... Genevae: J.L. Du-four, 1683.
2 v. in 1. illus.

CHARLARD, Louis Martin. See Bayen,
P., Recherches chimiques ... 1781.

891. CHARLETON, Rice. Three tracts on
Bath water ... A chymical analysis of Bath
water ... An inquiry into the efficacy of
Bath water in palsies ... Histories of hospital cases under ... Dr. Oliver; with additional cases and notes, by the editor. Bath:
R. Cruttwell for W. Taylor ..., 1774.
var. pag.

892. ———. A treatise on the Bath waters:
wherein are discover'd the several principles
of which they are compos'd; the cause of
their heat; and the manner of their production ... Bath: T. Bodley, sold by J. Leake ...,
1754.
2 l., 74 p., 1 l. illus.

893. CHARLETON, Walter. Enquiries into
human nature, in VI. anatomic prælections
in the new theatre of the Royal Colledge of
Physicians in London ... London: M. White
for R. Boulter, 1680.
21 l., 1-149, 369-544 p., 2 l. illus.

894. ———. Natural history of nutrition,
life and voluntary motion ... London: H.
Herringman, 1659.
9 l., 210 p., 7 l.

895. ———. Two discourses. I. Concerning the different wits of men ... II. The mys-
terie of vintners, or a discourse concerning
the various sicknesses of wines, and their
respective remedies ... London: R.W. for W.
Whitwood, 1669.
7 l., 230 p.

CHEMIA rationalis rationibus philosophicis ... See T., P.

CHERLER, Johann Heinrich, *jt. auth*.
Historia plantarum universalis. See Bauhin,
Johann.

896. CHESELDEN, William. The anatomy
of the human body. The VIIth edition with
forty copper plates engrav'd by Ger. Vander-
gucbt. London: C. Hitch & R. Dodsley, 1756.
5 l., 334 p., 8 l. illus.

897. ———. ———. The XIth edition ...
London: for J.F. Rivington, 1778.
1 l., v p., 1 l., 334 p., 8 l. illus.

898. ———. ———. The XIIth edition ...
London: J.F. Rivington ..., 1784.
2 l., v p., 334 p., 8 l. illus.

899. ———. Osteographia, or The anatomy
of the bones. London: 1733.
82 l. illus., folio.

900. ———. ———. London [n.d.].
1 l., 56 plates, 1 l. illus., port., folio.
Portrait dated 1753.

901. CHESNEAU, Nicolas. Observationum
... libri qvinqve ... Parisiis: F. Leonard,
1672.
8 l., 652 p., 6 l.

902. ———. La pharmacie theoriqve, nov-
vellement recveillie de diuers autheurs ...
Paris: F. Leonard, 1660.
3 l., 252 p., 4 l.

903. CHESTON, Richard Browne. Patho-
logical inquiries and observations in surgery, from the dissection of morbid bodies
... Glocester: R. Raikes ..., 1766.
6 l., 144 p. illus.

904. CHEYNE, George. The English malady:
or A treatise of nervous diseases of all kinds,
as spleen, vapours, lowness of spirits, hypo-
chondriacal, and hysterical distempers, &c.
In three parts ... London: for G. Strahan and
J. Leake, 1733.
3 l., xxxii p., 1 l., 370 p., 3 l.

905. ———. The natural method of cureing
the diseases of the body, and the disorders
of the mind depending on the body. In three
parts ... The second edition. London: G.
Strahan ..., 1742.
10 l., 316 p.

906. ———. Observations concerning the
nature and due method of treating the gout
... together with an account of the nature
and qualities of the Bath waters ... London:
for G. Strahan ..., 1720.
1 l., v p., 3 l., 98 p.

907. CHICOYNEAU, François. Traité des causes, des accidens, et de la cure de la peste, avec un recueil d'observations ... Paris: P.-J. Mariette, 1744.
3 *l*., 602, 272 p., 1 *l*. port.

CHIRURGIA. De chirurgia scriptores optimi ... *See* Gesner, Konrad, *ed.*

908. CHISHOLM, Colin. An essay on the malignant pestilential fever introduced into the West Indian Islands from Boullam on the coast of Guinea, as it appeared in 1793 and 1794. London: C. Dilly, [1794].
xvi, 279 p.

909. CHOMEL, Jacques François. Traité des eaux minerales bains et douches et de Vichy ... Clermont-Ferrand: P. Boutaudon, 1734.
6 *l*., cix p., 4 *l*., 348 p.

910. CHOMEL, Pierre Jean-Baptiste. Abrégé de l'histoire des plantes usuelles dans lequel on donne leurs noms differens, tant François que Latins ... Cinquiéme edition, revuë & corrigée. Paris: J. Clousier, 1737.
3 v.
Lacking volumes 1 and 2.

911. ——. ——. Paris: J. Clouzier, 1739.
3 v.

912. ——. ——. Nouvelle édition, revue corrigée & augmentée. Paris: Nyon, 1761.
3 v. port.

913. CHRYSOGONUS DE PURIS, *pseud.* Cynosura chemica, tincturam universalem per certos aphorismos succintè delineans ... [n.p.] 1689.
2 *l*.

914. ——. Statua mercurialis, ad tincturam particularem ex universali ortam, per certos aphorismos viam chemicam demonstrans ... [n.p.] 1689.
2 *l*.
With his Cynosura chemica ... 1689.

915. CHURCH, John. An inaugural dissertation on camphor: submitted to the examination of the Rev. John Ewing. The trustees & medical faculty of the University of Pennsylvania ... Philadelphia: J. Thompson, 1797.
70 p.

916. ... CHYMIA cvriosa variis, non solum ex regno vegetabili, sed etiam ex minerali

et animali, experimentis adornata ... Londini: H. Gellords et C. Wallich, 1687.
2 *l*., 16 p.
Lacking all after page 16.
At head of title: H.M.H.S.P.M.C.
With Helmont, F.M. van, Quaedam ... cogitationes ... 1697.

917. CHYMIÆ AURIFODINA incomparabilis quam recludit præludium prosimetricum magicarum noctium sortes Sibyllinæ chymicæ vanni granatum erutum, authoribus immortalibus adeptis cui subjungitur Commentatio de pharmaco catholico. Lugduni Batavorum: sumptibus authoris, 1696.
392 p.; 1 *l*., 76 p., 1 *l*. illus.
A reprint of the 1666 edition entitled Reconditorium ...

918. CHYMIPHILUS, J.J., *pseud.* Der wahren chymischen Weisheit Offenbahrung, das ist, Getreue und aufrichtige Entdeckung der Materie, welche genommen werden muss, wann man den wahren Weisen-Stein lapidem philosophorum tincturam universalem machen will ... [n.p.] 1720.
4 *l*., 219 p., 7 *l*.

919. CHYMISCHE Versuche, welche grössentheils aus alten Manuscripten hergenommen ... mit Anmerkungen ... an das Licht gestellet von I.H. ... Frankfurt und Leipzig: 1756.
2 pts. in 1 v.
Title page of second part: ... an das Licht gestellet von B.A.

920. Der CHYMISCHE Warsager, oder eine in zwanzig Wochen-Blättern herausgegebene Unterweisung ... Nebst einer kurz abgefassten gründlichen Vorrede, von A.D. CCC. S.F. EEE. P.H. JJJ. N.K. RRR. L.A. Hamburg: 1748.
50 *l*.
Issued as a periodical in 20 nos. from 11 Nov. 1747–23 March 1748.

CHYMISCHER Monden-Schein. *See* Siebenstern, Christian Friedrich Sendimir von.

921. CHYMISCHES Etwas in Nichts, das ist: Wie der hochberühmte Stein der Weisen als eine edle Gabe Gottes, entfernet, und in hohen Dingen vergeblich gesuchet, aber nahe, und in geringen, glücklich wird gefunden, in Etwas, doch gründlich entworffen ... von einem, der sich Mit In Gott BeLustiget. Dressden: G. Leschen, 1722.
38 p., 5 *l*.

922. CLAJUS, Johann. Altkumistica; das

ist, Die wahre Goldkunst aus Mist durch seine Operation vnd Process gut Gold zu machen ... Mülhausen: gedruckt durch J. Stangen, in Vorlegung J. Birckners, 1616.
28 *l.*

923. CLARKE, William. The natural history of nitre ... London: E. Okes for N. Brook, 1670.
8 *l.*, 93 p.

924. CLAUDER, Gabriel. Inventum cinnabarinum, hoc est, Dissertatio de cinnabari nativa Hungarica, longa circulatione in majorem efficaciam fixata et exaltata ... Jenæ: J. Bielk, 1684.
2 *l.*, 68 p.

925. ——. Dissertatio de tinctura universali, (vulgò lapis philosophorum dictâ) ... Altenburgi: G. Richter, 1678.
6 *l.*, 272 p., 12 *l.*

926. CLAUDINI, Giulio Cesare. Responsionvm et consvltationvm medicinalivm. Tomvs vnicvs. Nunc accurate recognitus, & ab omnibus erroribus ... repurgatus ... Hanoviae: typis Vvechelianis, apud C. Marnium & haeredes I. Aubrij, 1628.
16 *l.*, 602 p.

927. CLAVE, Estienne de. Novvelle lvmiere philosophiqve des vrais principes et elemens de natvre, & qualité d'iceux ... Paris: O. de Varennes, 1641.
6 *l.*, 493 p., 2 *l.*

928. ——. Paradoxes, ov Traittez philosophiqves des pierres et pierreries, contre l'opinion vulgaire ... Paris: la veufue P. Chevalier, 1635.
12 *l.*, 492 p., 1 *l.*

929. CLAVICULA hermeticae scientiae ab hyperboreo quodam horis subsecivis calamo consignata. Anno CIↃ CICC XXXII. Amstelaedami: P. Motier, 1751.
1 *l.*, 73 p., 2 *l.*
Text in Latin and French.

930. ——. ——. [n.p.] 1786.
76 p.

931. CLAVICULA Salomonis filii David. [n.p.: 1600?]
48 p. illus.

CLAVIS RAYMUNDI LULLII ... *See* Lull, Ramon.

932. CLEGHORN, George. Observations on the epidemical diseases in Minorca from the year 1744 to 1749. To which is prefixed, a short account of the climate, productions, inhabitants, and endemial distempers of that island. Second edition. London: for D. Wilson, 1762.
xix, 288 p.

CLEIDOPHORUS MYSTAGOGUS. *See* Conti, Luigi de'.

933. CLIFTON, Francis. The state of physick, ancient and modern, briefly consider'd: with a plan for the improvement of it ... London: W. Bowyer for J. Nourse, 1732.
20 *l.*, 192 p. charts.

934. CLINGE, Franz. Ein richtige Wegweiser zu der einigen Warheit in Erforschung der verborgenen Heimligkeiten der Natuhr ... Berlin: J.M. Rüdiger, 1701.
5 *l.*, 156 p., 40 *l.* illus.
Lacking p. 1-2.
Includes his: Antwort zu Theodorum Candidum, wegen des Cluvers fameuse Charteqve, wider den Wegweiser zu einigen Warheit ... [n.p.: 1701].

CLOPINEL, Jehan de Meun. *See* Jean de Meun.

CLUSIUS, Carolus. *See* L'Ecluse, Charles de.

935. CLUTTERBUCK, Henry. An account of a new and successful method of treating those affections which arise from the poison of lead ... London: T. Boosey, 1794.
69 p.

936. CLUTTON, Joseph. A true and candid relation of the good and bad effects of Joshua Ward's pill and drop ... The whole being an essay to discover how far this random practice of physic is really useful. London: F. Wilford, 1736.
2 *l.*, vi, 114 p.

937. COCCHI, Antonio. Dei bagni di Pisa ... Firenze: stamperia Imperiale, 1750.
6 *l.*, 415 p. illus., maps.

938. ——. Del vitto Pitagorico per uso della medicina. Firenze: F. Moucke, 1743.
84 p.

939. ——. Graecorvm chirvrgici libri, Sorani vnvs de fractvararvm signis, Oribasii

dvo de fractis et de lvxatis e collectione
Nicetae ... descripti conversi atqve editi
ab A. Cocchio ... Florentiae: ex typographio
Imperiali, 1754.
　　xix, 173 p.
　　Text in Greek and Latin.
　　Last leaf bound before page 1.

940.　COCKBURN, William.　Profluvia
ventris: or The nature and causes of loose-
nesses plainly discovered ... London: for B.
Barker and G. Strahan, 1701.
　　9 ℓ., 178 p.

941.　COCKE, Thomas.　Kitchin-physick:
or, Advice to the poor, by way of dialogue
... London: for J.B. [n.d.].
　　3 ℓ., 87 p.

942.　——.　Miscelanea medica: or, A
supplement to kitchin-physick; to which is
added, A short discourse on stoving and
bathing ... London: 1675.
　　4 ℓ., 52 p., 2 ℓ.
　　With his Kitchin-physick ... [n.d.].

943.　CODEX medicamentarius, seu Pharma-
copoea Parisiensis, ex mandato Facultatis
Medicinæ Parisiensis in lucem edita, M.
Hyacintho Theodoro Baron, Decano. Parisiis:
G. Cavelier, 1732.
　　7 ℓ., cxxvi p., 1 ℓ., 251, xxxvi p.

944.　—— edita ... M. Joanne Baptista
Boyer. Editio quinta. Parisiis: P.G. Cavelier,
1758.
　　xxiv, cxxxii, 320 p.

945.　——. Editio in Germania prima.
Francofurti ad Moenum: F. Varrentrapp, 1760.
　　11 ℓ., 176, 246 p., 10 ℓ.

946.　CODICE farmaceutico per lo stato
della serenissima repubblica di Venezia.
Compilato per ordine dell' eccellentissimo
magistrato della sanità. Padova: nella
stamperia del Seminario, presso T. Bettinelli,
1790.
　　xii, 274 p.

947.　CODRONCHI, Giovanni Battista.
De morbis veneficis ac veneficijs. Libri
qvattvor. In qvibvs non solvm certis rationibus veneficia dari demonstratur, sed eorum
species, caussae, signa, & effectus noua
methodo aperiuntur ... Venetiis: F. de F.
Senens, 1595.
　　8 ℓ., 199 numb. ℓ., 13 ℓ.

　　　COELLN, Johan von.　... Specifica

canadensium. See Linné, C. von, praeses.
Entry 2467.

948.　COELUM philosophorum. Die auf alle
Liebhaber der wahren hermetischen Weissheit
ihre Influenzen herabflössende ... Dressden:
Hübner, 1739.
　　8 ℓ., 143 p.

949.　COENDERS VAN HELPEN, Barend.
Thresor de la philosophie des anciens ou ...
la connoissance de tous les metaux &
mineraux ... Cologne: C. le Jeune, 1693.
　　3 ℓ., 240 p.　illus.

950.　COGAN, Thomas.　The haven of
health ... now of late corrected and augmented. Hereunto is added a preseruation
from the pestilence: with a short censure
of the late sicknesse at Oxford ... London:
T. Orwin for W. Norton, 1589.
　　8 ℓ., 276 p., 6 ℓ.

951.　COHAUSEN, Johann Heinrich.　Dissertatio satyrica physico-medico-moralis
de pica nasi, sive Tabaci sternutatorii
moderno abusu, & noxa. Amstelodami: J.
Oosterwyk, 1716.
　　10 ℓ., 177 p., 5 ℓ.

952.　——. Hermippus redivivus: or, The
sage's triumph over old age and the grave
... London: for J. Nourse, 1744.
　　4 ℓ., 168 p.

953.　——. ——. London: for J. Nourse,
1748.
　　1 ℓ., iii, 124 p.

954.　——. ——. The second edition carefully corrected and much enlarged. London:
J. Nourse, 1749.
　　4 ℓ., 248 p.

955.　——. Lumen novum phosphoris
accensum, sive Exercitatio physico-chemica,
de causa lucis in phosphoris tam naturalibus
quàm artificialibus ... Amstelodami: J. Ooster-
wik, 1717.
　　14 ℓ., 306 p., 11 ℓ.　illus.

956.　COITER, Volcher.　Externarvm et
internarvm principalivm hvmani corporis
partivm tabvlæ ... Noribergae: T. Gerlatzen,
1573.
　　7 ℓ., 133 p.　illus., charts.

957.　COLBATCH, Sir John.　A collection
of tracts, chirurgical and medical ... The
second edition ... London: for D. Brown, 1704.

1 *l.*, 568 p., 8 *l.*

958. ——. A dissertation concerning
misletoe ... The fourth edition. To which is
added, A second part ... London: D. Browne,
1725.
    viii, 30, 41 p.

959. ——. The doctrine of acids in the
cure of diseases farther asserted ... London:
for D. Brown and A. Roper, 1698.
    xvi, 128 p.

960. ——. A scheme for proper methods
to be taken, should it please God to visit us
with the plague. London: J. Darby, 1721.
    21 p.

    COLE, Abdiah. *See* Sennert, D., Thir-
teen books of natural philosophy ... 1661.

961. COLE, William. Novae hypotheseos,
ad explicanda febrium intermittentium symp-
tomata et typos excogitatae hypotyposis ...
Accessit Dissertatiuncula de intestinorum
motu peristaltico. Londini: D. Brown & S.
Smith, 1693.
    20 *l.*, 266 p.; 1 *l.*, 17 p.

    ——. Novae hypotheseos. *In* Morton,
R., Opera medica ... 1696.

    ——. Tractatus de secretione ani-
mali. *In* Morton, R., Opera medica ... 1696.

962. COLES, William. Adam in Eden: or,
Natures paradise. The history of plants,
fruits, herbs and flowers ... London: J.
Streater for N. Brooke, 1657.
    10 *l.*, 629 p., 12 *l.*

963. ——. The art of simpling. An introduction to the knowledge and gathering of
plants ... Whereunto is added, A discovery
of the lesser world ... London: J.G. for N.
Brook, 1656.
    8 *l.*, 175 p.

964. COLLECTANEA chymica: A collection
of ten several treatises in chymistry, concerning the liquor alkahest, the mercury of
philosophers, and other curiosities worthy
of perusal ... London: W. Cooper, 1684.
    3 *l.*, 193 p., 2 *l.*; 32 p.

965. COLLECTANEA chymico-metallurgica
curiosa; oder zusammen getragene chymisch
und metallurgische Processe von Gold-Kiesen,
Kobalt und Talck-Ertzen. Nebst einem Anhang
von vitris metallicis und Schmeltz-Flüssen

... Von einem Freunde der Chymie und Metallurgie am fruchtbaren Hartze. Leipzig: J.H.
Kloss, 1715.
    8 *l.*, 352 p.

966. COLLECTI processus de lapide philosophorvm præparando, aliisqve secretis non
vulgaribus ... Nebst einem curiösen Wein-
Büchlein. Jenæ: J. Bielck, 1704.
    274 p., 7 *l.*

967. COLLEGE OF PHYSICIANS OF PHILA-
DELPHIA. Facts and observations relative
to the nature and origin of the pestilential
fever, which prevailed in this city in 1793,
1797, and 1798. Philadelphia: T. Dobson,
1798.
    99 p.

968. COLLESSON, Jean. L'idée parfaite
de la philosophie hermetique, ou L'abregé
de la theorie & pratique de la pierre des
philosophes. Troisième edition. Augmentée
d'observations pour l'intelligence des principes & fondemens de la nature, & de la
philosophie hermetique ... Paris: L. d'Houry,
1719.
    3 pts. in 1 v.

    COLLIANDER, Johan Georg. De
spigelia anthelmia. *See* Linné, C. von,
praeses. Entry 2456.

969. COLLIN, Heinrich Joseph von. Nosocomii civici Pazmanniani annus medicus
tertius sive Observationum circa morbos
acutos et chronicos. Vindobonae: J.T. de
Trattner, 1764–1773.
    3 v.

970. COLOMBE, Etienne Guillaume, *called*
Sainte-Colombe. Lettre sur la pierre philosophale, contre les procédés ruineux des
souffleurs ... Adressée à un professeur de
Leipsic. Paris: Cailleau, 1756.
    68 p.

971. COLONNA, Francesco Maria Pompeo.
Abregé de la doctrine de Paracelse, et de ses
archidoxes. Avec une explication de la nature
des princpies de chymie ... Paris: d'Houry,
1724.
    9 *l.*, liv, 442 p., 1 *l.*

972. ——. Les secrets le plus cachés de
la philosophie des anciens, découverts et
expliqués, a la suite d'une histoire des plus
curieuses. Par M. Crosset de la Haumerie.
Paris: d'Houry fils, 1722.
    xvi, 336 p. illus.

973. ———. Suite des experiences utiles
et curieuses. Nouveau traité des dissolutions & coagulations naturelles ... Par M.
Le Crom. Paris: V. Jollet & J. Lamesle, 1725.
    6 ℓ., 177 p., 1 ℓ.

974. ———. Vade mecum philosophique,
en forme de dialogue ... Avec un petit traité
des dissolutions, et coagulations naturelles
& artificielles. Par le sieur Le Crom. Paris:
D. Jollet et la veuve Papillon, 1719.
    4 ℓ., 107, 40 p., 13 ℓ.

975.   COLSON, Lancelot. Philosophia
maturata: An exact piece of philosophy, containing the practick and operative part
thereof in gaining the philosophers stone
... Whereunto is added, a work compiled by
St. Dunstan, concerning the philosophers
stone ... London: for G. Sawbridge, 1668.
    5 ℓ., 142 p.

976.   COLUMBUS, Matthaeus Realdus.
De re anatomica. Libri XV. Venetiis: N.
Beuilacquae, 1559.
    4 ℓ., 169 [i.e. 269] p., 1 ℓ.   illus.

977.   COMBACH, Ludwig, ed. Tractatus
aliquot chemici singvlares summum philosophorum arcanum continentes. 1. Liber de
principiis naturæ, & artis chemicæ, incerti
authoris. 2. Johannis Belye Angli tractatulus
novus, et alius Bernhardi comitis Treveren-
sis, ex Gallico versus. Cum fragmentis
Eduardi Kellæi, H. Aquilæ Thuringi, & Joh.
Isaaci Hollandi. 3. Fratris Ferrarii tractatus
integer ... 4. Johannis Daustenii Angli
Rosarium ... Geismariæ: typis S. Schadewitz,
sumptibus S. Köhlers, 1647.
    var. pag.
    With Nolle, H., Discursus ... 1636.

978.   COMBRUNE, Michael. An essay on
brewing ... London: for R. and J. Dodsley,
1758.
    xvi, 214 p., 1 ℓ.

979. ———. The theory and practice of
brewing ... London: J. Haberkorn, 1762.
    vi, xii, 298 p., 1 ℓ.

COMITIBUS, Ludovico de. See Conti,
Luigi de'.

980.   COMMELIN, Caspar. Præludia
botanica ad publicas plantarum exoticarum
demonstrationes, dicta in horto medico ...
His accedent Plantarum rariorum ... Lugduni
Batavorum: F. Haringh, 1703.
    4 ℓ., 85 p., 1 ℓ. illus.

981.   A COMPENDIOUS system of anatomy
in six parts. Part I. Osteology. II. Of the
muscles, etc. III. Of the abdomen. Part.
IV. Of the thorax. V. Of the brain and nerves.
VI. Of the senses. Illustrated with twelve
large copperplates. Extracted from the American edition of the Encyclopaedia. Philadelphia
T. Dobson, 1792.
    438 p., 1 ℓ.   illus.

982.   CON- et dissensus chymicorum de
famigeratissimo rustici minoris particulari
... bestehende und vorgestellet in funfzehen
davon hendelnden Processen ... Nebst noch
zweyen andern ... Particularien de exalta-
tione solis ejusque animæ extractione in
über 30. der besten Processen bestehende
... durch einen Freund der edlen Chymie und
Metallurgie am grünen Hartze. Leipzig: J.H.
Klossen, 1715.
    4 ℓ., 70 p.; 4 ℓ., 76 p.

983.   CONCEPT einer Supplication an die
Röm. Keys. May. vnserm allergnädigsten
Herrn, von allen Eheweibern in gemein ...
vmb Abschaffung, zweyer schädlichen
Gesellschafften, deren die ein in gemein
Gelt auffnimpt, sich für einander Verburgt,
die ander der Alchymisten oder Goldmacher
genendt wird ... [Pressburg] 1621.
    13 p.

984.   CONCOREGIUS, Joannes. Practica
noua medicine ... Summula eiusdem de curis
febrium secundum hodiernum modum & vsum
cōpillata: nouissime recognite. infinitisque
erroribus castigate. [Venetiis: heredū Dñi
Octauiani Scoti, 1515.]
    101 numb. ℓ.

985.   CONDIE, Thomas. History of the
pestilence, commonly called yellow fever,
which almost desolated Philadelphia, in the
months of August, September & October,
1798. Philadelphia: R. Folwell [1799].
    108, xxxii p., 34 ℓ.

986.   CONRING, Hermann. De germanicorvm
corporvm habitvs antiqvi ac novi cavsis, dissertatio. Helmestadi: H. Muller, 1645.
    62 ℓ.

987. ———. De hermetica Aegyptiorvm
vetere et Paracelsicorvm nova medicina liber
vnvs ... Helmestadii: typis H. Mvlleri, sumptibus M. Richteri, 1648.
    4 ℓ., 404 p., 8 ℓ.

988. ———. De hermetica medicina libri
dvo ... Editio secvnda ... Helmestadii: H.

Muller, 1669.

11 *l*., 447 p., 31 *l*.

989. CONSIDERATIONS on the nature, causes, cure, and prevention of pestilences; being a collection of papers published on that subject by the Free-thinker. London: W. Wilkins for J. Peele, 1721.

viii, 198 p.

990. CONSPECTUS materiae medicae selectioris ... medicamenta usitatiora, tam simplicia, cum recta eorundem præparatione ... et communis normæ instar, pharmacopolis Ratisbonensibus ... cura et opera Collegii Medici ... Ratisbonae: J.C. Peezius, 1727.

6*l*., 218 [i.e. 128] p.

991. CONSTANT DE REBECQUE, Jacob. L'apoticaire francois charitable ... Lyon: J. Certe, 1683.

7 *l*., 543 p.

CONSTANTINUS AFRICANUS. Viaticum. *In* Muhammad ibn Zakariya Abu Bakr, *Al Razi*, Divisiones ... 1510.

992. CONTARENI, Gasparo. De elementis & eorum mixtionibus libri quinque. Diligintiss. denuo recogniti & emendati. Scipionis Capitij de principiis rerum poëma ... Parisiis: A. Wechelus, 1564.

128 numb. *l*.

993. CONTI, Luigi de'. Clara fidelisq. admonitoria disceptatio practicæ manualis experimento veraciter comprobata. De duobus artis & naturæ miraculis ... Venetiis: F. Nicolino, 1661.

4 *l*., 46 p., 2 *l*. illus.

At the end there is bound in a 17th century manuscript of 9 pages entitled: *Elixir solis Theophr. Paracelsi.*

994. ——. ——. Francofurti: H. à Sande [1661].

6 *l*., 116 p. illus.

Lacking five of the preliminary leaves, including the printed title page.

From Isaac Newton's library.

995. ——. ——. Francofurti: H. à Sande, 1664.

11 *l*., 116 p. illus.

996. ——. Discours philosophiques sur les deux merveilles de l'art et de la nature ... mis en François par Robert Preud'homme ... Seconde edition, reveuë & corrigée. Paris: J. d'Houry, 1678.

195 p., 4 *l*.

997. ——. Mercury's caducean rod: or, The great and wonderful office of the universal mercury, or God's vicegerent, displayed ... London: printed by W. Pearson, sold by T. Northcott, 1702.

4 *l*., 76 p., 1 *l*.; 32 p.

The second part has the caption title: A philosophical epistle, discovering the unrevealed mystery of the three fires of the sophi.

998. ——. Metallorvm ac metallicorvm natvræ opervm. Ex orthophysicis fundamentis recens elucidatio qua eorum omnium principia, causæ, proprietates, generationes, generationumque modi apertè ac fideliter enucleantur ... Coloniæ Agrippinæ: J. Busæus, 1665.

286 p.

999. ——. Trifertes sagani, or immortal dissolvent. Being a brief but candid discourse of the matter and manner of preparing the liquor alkahest of Helmont, the great hilech of Paracelsus, the sal circulatum minus of Ludovicus of Comit ... London: W. Pearson, 1705.

7 *l*., 53 p.

1000. COOKE, James, *of Warwick*. Mellificivm chirvrgiæ: or, The marrow of chirurgery ... The fourth edition, enlarged with many additions ... London: T. Hodgkin for W. Marshall, 1685.

9 *l*., 616 p., 6 *l*. illus., port.

1001. ——. ——. London: for W. Marshall, 1693.

8 *l*., 610 p.

Lacking all after page 610.

1002. COOPER, Ambrose. The complete distiller ... To which are added, accurate descriptions of the several drugs, plants, flowers, fruits, &c. used by distillers ... The second edition, with many additions. London: for P. Vaillant and R. Griffiths, 1760.

8 *l*., 283 p., 7 *l*. illus.

1003. COOPER, William. The philosophical epitaph of W.C. Esquire ... Also, A brief of the golden calf ... by Jo. Fr. Helvetius and, The golden ass well managed ... Written by Jo. Rod. Glauber. With Jehior ... or the daydawning or light of wisdom ... With a catalogue of chymical books. London: T.R. and N.T. for W. Cooper, 1673.

var. pag. illus.

1004. COPPONAY DE GRIMALDI, Denis de. Etablissement du laboratoire de S.A.R. et de son academie chymique, avec le combat de la medecine galenique, contre elle fait dans la sale de l'august senat de Savoye ... [Chambery] 1684.
429 p.

1005. ———. Oeuvres posthumes ... Avec une dissertation physique sur les sujets qui entrant dans le composition de ces remedes. Par M.*** editeur de ces oeuvres posthumes. Paris: Durand, 1745.
xiv, 224 p.

1006. CORBEIUS, Theodorius. Pharmacia simplicium et compositorum bipartita ... ex authoribus medicinæ celeberrimis ... Francofvrti: J.G. Schönwetter, 1656.
2 ℓ., 672 p.

1007 CORDUS, Valerius. Dispensatorivm, sive Pharmacorvm conficiendorvm ratio, a Petro Covdebergo ... erroribus liberata atque vindicata: adiecto Valerij Cordi nouo libello, aliisque paucis post præfationes annotatis. Antverpiæ: C. Plantin, 1568.
16 ℓ., 429 p.

1008. ———. ———. Lugdvni: L. Cloquemin, 1571.
5 ℓ., 473 p., 10 ℓ.

1009. ———. Dispensatorivm pharmacorvm omnium, quæ in usu potissimum sunt ... multo emendatius ... ex secunda editione publicatum ... Noribergæ: P. Kaufmann, 1598.
6 ℓ., 295 p., 3 ℓ.

1010. ———. [Le guidon des apothecaires. Lyon: 1578?]
7 ℓ., 518 p.
Lacks title page.

1011. ———. In hoc volvmine continentvr ... Annotationes in Pedacij Dioscoridis Anazarbei de medica materia libros V ... Eivsdem Va. Cordi Historiae stirpivm lib. IIII ... Sylva ... De artificiosis ... Compositiones medicinales aliquot ... Omnia summo studio atque industria ... Conr. Gesneri ... collecta ... [Argentorati: I. Rihelius] 1561.
8 ℓ., 301 numb. ℓ., 8 ℓ.   illus.

CORNACCHINI, Marco Antonio. *Methodus qua omnes humani corporis affectiones ab humoribus copia vel qualitate pecantibus genitæ curantur. In* Hartmann,

J., *Praxis chymiatrica* ... 1647, etc.

1012. CORNACCHINI, Tommaso. Tabvlae medicae. In quibus ea ferè omnia, quae à principibus medicis Graecis, Arabibus, & Latinis de cvrationis apparatv, capitis, ac thoracis morbis, febribvs, pvlsibvs, vrinis scripta sparsim reperiuntur ... Patauij: P.P. Tozzi, 1605.
6 ℓ., 368 p.   charts.

CORNARO, Luigi. *Discorsi della vita sobria. In* Regimen Sanitatis Salernitanum ... 1712.

1013. ———. Sure and certain methods of attaining a long and healthful life ... Written originally in Italian ... and made English. To which are added, Rules for health and directions for life, by Joseph Addison, esq. The fifth edition. London: for D. Midwinter and A. Ward, 1737.
2 ℓ., 197 p.

1014. ———. ———. Translated into English by W. Jones ... Edinburgh: A. McCaslan, 1771.
64 p.

1015. CORONA, Nicola. Saggio chimico medico ed economico delle qualità venefiche del rame e della salubrità del ferro. Roma: G. Puccinelli, 1796.
xx, 235 p.

1016. CORTÈS, Jerónimo. Fisonomia, y varios secretos de naturaleza ... Barcelona: P. Campins, 1769.
2 ℓ., 258 p., 9 ℓ.

1017. ———. ———. Barcelona: T. Piferrer [17——].
2 ℓ., 252 p., 4 ℓ.

1018. CORTES, Juan. Discvrso apologico, y excelencias de la medicina ... Madrid: la viuda de I. Goncalez, 1638.
2 ℓ., 14 numb. ℓ.

1019. CORTESE, Angelo. Tesoro di sanita, nel quale si contiene alcuni particolari, e marauigliosi secreti ... Milano: P. Malatesta [n.d.].
4 ℓ.

1020. CORTESE, Isabella. I secreti ... ne' qvali si contengono cose minerali, medicinali, arteficiose, & alchimiche ... Venetia: G. Bariletto, 1561.
8 ℓ., 88 numb. ℓ.   illus.

1021. ——. ——. Di nuouo ristampati, &
con diligenza corretti. Venetia: M. Bonibelli,
1595.
    8 *l*., 206 p.   illus.

1022. ——. Secreti varii ... ne' quali si
contengono cose minerali, medicinali, pro-
fumi, belletti, artifitij, & alchimia ... Venetia:
B. Miloco, 1677.
    12 *l*., 204 p.

1023. COSSON, Giovanni. Secreti novamente ritrouati ... non più da nissuno stam-
pati ne posti in luce ... Milano: P. Malatesta
[n.d.].
    4 *l*.

1024. COSTA, Christovam da. Aromatum
& medicamentorum in Orientali India nas-
centium liber: plvrimvm lucis adferens iis
quæ à Doctore Garcia de Orta in hoc genere
scripta sunt. Caroli Clvsii Atrebatis opera
... Antverpiæ: C. Plantin, 1582.
    88 p.   illus.
    With Orta, G. da, Aromatvm ... 1579.

1025. ——. Tractado de las drogas, y
medicinas de las Indias Orientales ...
Bvrgos: M. de Victoria, 1578.
    11 *l*., 448, 38 p., 1 *l*.   illus., port.

1026. ——. Trattato ... della historia,
natvra, et virtv delle droghe medicinali, &
altri semplici rarissimi, che vengono portati
dalle Indie Orientali in Europa ... Nuouamente recato dalla Spagnuola ... Venetia: F.
Ziletti, 1585.
    25 *l*., 342 p.   illus.

1027. COSTA, Filippo. Discorsi ... sopra
le compositioni de gli antidoti, & medica-
menti, che piv si costvmano di dar per bocca.
Di nuouo dal medesimo in questa seconda
impressione ricorretti, & ampliati ... Mantova:
F. Osanna, 1586.
    8 *l*., 108 numb. *l*.

1028. COSTE, Jean-François. De genre de
philosophie propre a l'étude et a la pratique
de la médecine ... Nancy: J.B.H. Leclerc,
1775.
    1 *l*., iv, 48 p.

1029. COTTA, John. A short discoverie of
the vnobserved dangers of seuerall sorts of
ignorant and vnconsiderate practisers of
physicke in England ... London: for W. Jones
and R. Boyle, 1612.
    4 *l*., 135 p.

1030. COTTEREAU DU CLOS, Samuel.
Observations sur les eaux minerales de
plusieurs provinces de France, faites en
l'Academie royale de sciences en l'année
1670 & 1671 ... [Paris] l'Imprimerie Royale,
1675.
    203 p., 4 *l*.

1031. COTUGNO, Domenico. De sedibvs
variolarvm σύνταγμα. Viennae: R. Graeffer,
1771.
    8 *l*., 274 p., 4 *l*.   illus.

1032. ——. Dello spirito della medicina,
discorso accademico letto nel teatro ana-
tomico del Regio Spedale degl' Incurabili
di Napoli ... Firenze: Moücke, 1785.
    30 p.
    With Batt, W., Pharmacopoea ... 1785.

1033. COUILLARD, Joseph. Le chirvrgien
operatevr ov Traicté methodiqve des principales operations en chirurgie ... Seconde
edition ... de plus ... Observations iatro-
chirvrgiqves ... Lyon: P. Ravavd, 1640.
    14 *l*., 256, 122 p., 24 *l*.

1034. [The COUNTRY-MANS physician ...
London: R. Chiswel, 1680?].
    7 *l*., 94 p.
    Lacking the title page.
    With Boules, R., The queens royal closet
... [n.d.].

1035. COUTAN. Le grand oeuvre dévoilé,
en faveur des enfans de la lumiere. Traduit
du chaldaïque ... Amsterdam: Delalin et
l'auteur, 1775.
    74 p.
    With Bernard, *of Trevisano*, Traicté de
la nature de l'oevf ... 1624.

1036. COWPER, William. Anatomia corporum
humanorum centum et quatuor-decim tabulis
... Accedunt ejusdem introductio in oeconomiam
animalium ... Omnia nunc primum latinitate
donata curante Guilielmo Dundass. Lugduni
Batavorum: J.A. Langerak, 1739.
    70 *l*., 114 plates.   folio.

1037. ——. ——. Ultrajecti: N. Muntenda,
1750.
    70 *l*., 114 plates.   folio.

1038. ——. The anatomy of humane bodies
... To which is added an introduction explain-
ing the animal oeconomij ... Oxford: for S.
Smith and B. Walford, 1698.
    70 *l*., 114 plates.   port., folio.

1039. ——. ——. Revised and publish'd
by C.B. Albinus ... The second edition. Leyden: for J.A. Langerak, 1737.
70 *l.*, 114 plates. folio.

1040. COXE, Thomas. A discourse, wherein the interest of the patient in reference to
physick and physicians is soberly debated
... London: for R. Chiswel, 1669.
10 *l.*, 333 p., 1 *l.*

1041. CRAMER, Johann Andreas. Elementa
artis docimasticæ duobus tomis comprehensa
... Lugduni Batavorum: C. et G.J. Wishoff,
1739.
2 pts. in 1 v. illus.

1042. ——. ——. Lugduni Batavorum: C.
et G.J. Wishoff, 1744.
2 v. illus.

1043. ——. Elements of the art of assaying metals ... Translated from the Latin ...
To which are added, several notes and observations not in the original ... London: for
T. Woodward and C. Davis, 1741.
6 *l.*, 470 p., 4 *l.* illus.

1044. ——. Elemens de docimastique, ou
De l'art des essais, divisés en deux parties
... Traduit du Latin ... Paris: Briasson, 1755.
4 v. illus.

CRASSELLAME CHINESE, Marcantonio,
pseud. See Tachenius, Otto.

1045. CRAWFORD, Adair. Experiments
and observations on animal heat, and the
inflammation of combustible bodies ... London: for J. Johnson, 1788.
8 *l.*, 491 p. illus.

1046. ——. Versuche und Beobachtungen
über die Wärme der Thiere und die Entzündung der verbrennlichen Körper ... übersetzt
von D. Lorenz Crell ... Leipzig: J.G. Müller,
1789.
xvi, 382 p. illus.

1047. CREILING, Johann Konrad. Abhandlung vom goldenen Vliess oder Möglichkeit
der Verwandlung der Metalle. Aus dem Lateinischen ... übersezt. Tübingen: J.C. Heerbrandt, 1787.
8 *l.*, 176 p.

1048. ——. Die edelgeborne Jungfer Alchymia, oder: Eine durch rationes, viele
exempla und experimenta abgehandelte Untersuchung, was von der Alchymia zu halten und

vor Nutzen daraus zu schöpffen seye, nebst
einem Zusatz von der Medicina universali,
Universal-Process und einigen Kunst-
Stücken ... Tübingen: die Gebrüder Cotta,
1730.
12 *l.*, 424 p.

1049. CRELL, Carl Justus Ludwig von.
Commentatio de optima extracta parandi
methodo ... Gottingae: J.C. Dieterich
[1793].
31 p. illus.

CREMER, John. Testamentum. *In*
Maier, M., Tripus aureus ... 1618.

CRESSONIÈRES, Antitus de. Epistola
ad magistrum Iosephum Quercetanum. *In*
Fenotus, J.A., Alexipharmacum ... [1575].

1050. CROLL, Oswald. Basilica chymica,
continens philosophicam propria laborum
experientia confirmatam descriptionem &
vsum remediorum chymicorum selectissimorum
è lumine gratiæ & natvræ desumptorum. In
fine libri additus est eiusdem autoris Tractatus nouus de signatvris rervm internis.
Coloniæ Allobrogvm: P. Marcellvs, 1610.
8 *l.*, 364 p., 30 *l.*; 7 *l.*, 92 p., 18 *l.*
illus.

1051. ——. ——. Francofvrti: G. Tampachiu
1620.
336 p., 24 *l.*; 100 p., 14 *l.*; 16 p. illus.

1052. ——. ——. Genevæ: P. Albertus,
1631.
20 *l.*, 364 p., 30 *l.*; 7 *l.*, 92 p., 18 *l.*
illus.

1053. ——. —— aucta a Ioan Hartmanno ...
Edita a Johanne Michaelis ... et Georg. Ever-
hardo Hartmanno ... Genevæ: P. Chouët,
1635.
8 *l.*, 220 p., 6 *l.*; 419 p., 6 *l.*; 114 p.,
19 *l.* illus.

1054. ——. ——. Genevæ: S. Chouët,
1658.
8 *l.*, 419 p., 6 *l.*; 114 p., 19 *l.*; 220 p.,
6 *l.* illus.

1055. ——. ——. Francofurti: G. Tampachiu
[n.d.]
8 *l.*, 283 p., 12 *l.*; 8 *l.*, 80 p., 8 *l.*; 24 p.
illus.

1056. ——. ——. Coloniæ Allobrogvm: in
officina Fabriana [16——].
20 *l.*, 364 p., 30 *l.*; 7 *l.*, 91 p., 18 *l.* illu

The printed date has been altered in ink to read MDCCX.

1057. ——. Basilica chymica oder Alchymistisch königlich Kleijnod ... Beneben angehengtem seinem newen Tractat von der innerlichen Signaturn ... Franckfuhrt: G. Tampach [1629?].

4 *l.*, 248 p., 8 *l.*; 72 p., 4 *l.*   illus.
Part 2 has separate pagination and a title page with the imprint: Franckfurt am Mayn: C. Rötel, in Verlegung G. Tampachs, 1629.

1058. ——. Hermetischer Probier-Stein, darauff nicht allein alle und jede in dess Osvvaldi Crollii intitulirten Alchymistischen königlichen Kleynod ... examiniret ... sondern dieselbe ... vermehret und verbessert worden. Von Johann Hartmann ... Neben angehengten Crollischen Tractätlein von den innerlichen Signaturen ... und dem Hermetischen Wunderbaum ... Franckfurt am Mayn: J.G. Schönwetter, 1647.

3 pts. in 1 v.   illus.
Lacking 20 *l.* after p. 368 of part 1.

1059. ——. La royalle chymie ... Tradvitte en Francois par I. Marcel de Bovlene. Paris: M. Henault, 1633.

3 pts. in 1 v.   illus.

1060. ——. ——. Rouen: J. Osmont, 1634.
1 *l.*, 460 p., 31 *l.*; 126 p., 16 *l.*   illus.

1061. ——. Philosophy reformed & improved in four profound tractates. The I. discovering the great and deep mysteries of nature ... The other III. discovering the wonderfull mysteries of the creation, by Paracelsus: being his philosophy to the Athenians. Both made English by H. Pinnell ... London: M.S. for L. Lloyd, 1657.

11 *l.*, 226 p.; 1 *l.*, 70 p.   port.
Lacking pages 161—186.

——. *See also* Hartmann, J., Opera omnia medico-chymica ... 1684.

1062. CRONENBURGIUS, Bernardus Dessenius.   Medicinae veteris et rationalis, adversvs ... Georgij Fedronis, ac vniuersæ sectæ Paracelsica imposturas, defensio ... Accesit præterà purgantium medicamentorum usitatorum ... Coloniae Agrippinae: I. Gymnicus, 1573.

16 *l.*, 246 p., 19 *l.*; 4 *l.*, 49 p., 2 *l.* port.
With Curio, J., Inscriptvs Hermotimi nomine ... 1570.

1063. CROOKE, Helkiah.   Μικροκοσμογραφία. A description of the body of man. Together with the controversies thereto belonging. Collected and translated out of all the best authors of anatomy ... The second edition corrected and enlarged. London: T. & R. Cotes, sold by M. Sparke, 1631.

14 *l.*, 1012 p.   illus., folio.

1064. ——. ——. London: R.C., sold by J. Clarke, 1651.

15 *l.*, 766 p.   illus., folio.

CROSSET DE LA HAUMERIE, *pseud.*
See Colonna, Francesco Maria Pompeo.

1065. CRUEGNER, Michael.   [Aenigmata philosophica chymica. Dressden: P.A. Hamann, 1675.]

3 pts. in 1 v.   illus.
Each part has separate pagination and half-title, as follows: Aenigmata philosophica chymica boreale; Aenigmata philosophica chymica zodiacale; Aenigmata philosophica chymica in plaga australi. Preceding the text is Emblema physicum spagiricum, with half-title, 2 leaves of text and folding copperplate, possibly belonging to the rest of the book. There is no general title page.

1066. ——. ... Chymischer aufgewickelter Gebrauch und Bereitung seiner Elixiren ... Dem beygefügt ein besonderer philo-medico chymischer Anhang, oder kurtzer Tractat ... [Dressden: in verlegung] C. Bergen, gedruckt in Seyfferts Druckerey, 1662.

12 *l.*, 242 p., 19 *l.*

1067. CRUIKSHANK, William.   The anatomy of the absorbing vessels of the human body. The second edition; considerably enlarged, and illustrated with additional plates. London: G. Nicol, 1790.

3 *l.*, 214 p.   illus.

1068. ——. William Cruikshank's und Paul Mascagni's Geschichte und Beschreibung der Saugadern des menschlichen Körpers. [Leipzig: Weidmann, 1789-1794.]

3 v. in 1.   illus.

1069. CRUSIUS, David.   [Theatrum morborum Hermetico-Hippocraticum, seu Methodica morborum et curationis eorundem dispositio: multis elegantissimis problematis ac Hermeticæ medicinæ flosculis illustrata ... Erfurti: Mechler, 1616.]

7 *l.*, 284 p., 6 *l.*   chart.
Part 2 only, of 2 pts.
Lacking the title-page.

CRUSIUS, Johannes.   Disputatio medica quam de aurea catena Jovis coelo demissa. *See* Major, J.D., *praeses.*

CULLEN, William.   An essay on the cold produced by evaporating fluids. *In* Black, J., Experiments upon magnesia alba ... 1782.

1070.   ——.   First lines of the practice of physic. A new edition ... Worcester, Massachusetts: I. Thomas, 1790.
    3 v.
    Volume 2 only.

1071.   ——.   Institutions of medicine. Part I. Physiology. For the use of the students in the University of Edinburgh. The third edition, corrected. Edinburgh: for C. Elliot and T. Cadell, 1785.
    240 p.

1072.   ——.   ——.   The fourth edition, corrected. Edinburgh, Boston: reprinted by J. Norman, 1788.
    126 p.

1073.   ——.   Lectures on the materia medica ... Philadelphia: R. Bell, 1775.
    viii, 512 p.

1074.   ——.   A treatise of the materia medica, in two volumes. Edinburgh: 1789.
    2 v.
    Volume two imprint: Dublin: L. White, 1789.

1075.   CULPEPER, Nicholas.   Culpeper's last legacy ... containing sundry admirable experiences in severall sciences, more especially, in chyrurgery, and physick ... with two particular treatises; the one of feavers; the other of pestilence ... [London] for N. Brooke, 1657.
    6 pts. in 1 v.   port.

1076.   ——.   The English physician enlarged; with three hundred sixty and nine medicines made of English herbs, that were not in any impression untill this ... London: for A. and J. Churchill, 1703.
    8 ℓ., 386 p., 5 ℓ.

1077.   ——.   ——.   London: J. Bruce ..., 1784.
    6 ℓ., 348 p.

1078.   ——.   A physical directory: or A Translation of the dispensatory made by the Colledg of Physitians of Lonon ... And in

this third edition is added A key to Galen's method of physick ... London: P. Cole, 1651.
    6 ℓ., 138 p., 8 ℓ., 139-167 p.   port.

1079.   ——.   Pharmacopoeia Londinensis: or The London dispensatory ... London: P. Cole, 1653.
    6 ℓ., 325 p., 7 ℓ.

1080.   ——.   ——.   Sixth edition ... London: P. Cole, 1659.
    13 ℓ., 377 p., 16 ℓ.

1081.   ——.   ——.   London: for G. Sawbridge, 1675.
    12 ℓ., 305 p., 19 ℓ.

1082.   ——.   ——.   London: for W. Churchill, 1718.
    13 ℓ., 382 p., 12 ℓ.

1083.   ——.   Treatise of aurum potabile. Being a description of the three-fold world ... To which is added Mr. Culpepper's ghost ... London: for G. Eversden, 1656.
    7 ℓ., 193 p., 3 ℓ.; 3 ℓ., 16 p.

1084.   ——.   ——.   London: for G. Eversden, 1657.
    7 ℓ., 193 p., 3 ℓ.

——.   *See also* Sennert, D., Thirteen books of natural philosophy ... 1661.

1085.   CURIO, Jakob.   Inscriptvs Hermotimi dialogvs, in qvo primùm de vmbratico illo medicinæ agitur genere, quod in scholis ad disputandum, non ad medēdum, comparatum videri potest. Deinde & de illo recens ex chymicis furnis nato eductoq́ue altero ... Accessit & querela medicinæ dogmaticæ, conscripta à Petro Reidano ... Basileæ: P. Perna, 1570.
    4 ℓ., 183 p., 2 ℓ.

1086.   CURRIE, William.   Observations on the causes and cure of remitting or bilious fevers. To which is annexed, an abstract of the opinions and practice of different authors; and an appendix ... relative to the synochus icteroides, or yellow fever. Philadelphia: W.T. Palmer, 1798.
    2 ℓ., 227 p.

1087.   ——.   A treatise on the synochus icteroides, or yellow fever; as it lately appeared in the city of Philadelphia ... Philadelphia: T. Dobson, 1794.
    viii, 85 p.
    With his Observations on the causes ... 179

D

D***, Monsieur. *See* Respour, P.M. de.

D., Mr. Traittez des barométres. *See* Alence, Joachim d'.

DACQUET, Gabriel. Qvaestio medica cardinalitiis. *See* Germain, C., *praeses*.

DAHLGREN, Johan Adolph. De maro. *See* Linné, C. von, *praeses*. Entry 2470.

1088. DALE, Samuel. Pharmacologia, seu Manuductio ad materiam medicam ... Quinta editio, ex scriptis Hermanni Boerhaave locupletata ... Lugduni Batavorum: G. Potvliet, 1751.
   2 *l*., vii p., 2 *l*., 459 p., 24 *l*.

1089. DALECHAMPS, Jacques. Histoire generale des plantes ... faite Françoise par M. Iean des Movlins ... Derniere edition ... Lyon: P. Borde ..., 1653.
   2 v. illus.

1090. DARAN, Jacques. Observations chirurgicales, sur les maladies de l'urethre ... Troisieme edition. Paris: de Bure, 1750.
   1 *l*., ccxx, 429 p., 1 *l*.

1091. ——. Réponse a la brochure portant pour titre, Pour la défense et la conservation des parties les plus essentielles à l'homme & à l'etat. Paris: de Bure, 1750.
   1 *l*., 76 p., 1 *l*.
   With his Observations chirurgicales ... 1750.

1092. DARCET, Jean. Memoire sur l'action d'un feu egal, violent, et continué pendant plusieurs jours sur un grand nombre de terres, de pierres & de chaux métalliques ... Lu à l'Académie Royale des Sciences les 16 & 28 Mai 1766 ... Paris: P.G.Cavelier, 1766.
   122 p.

DARELIUS, Johan Anders. Lignum colubrinum leviter delineatum. *See* Linné, C. von, *praeses*. Entry 2480.

DASTIN, John. Rosarium. *In* Alchymistisch Sieben-Gestirn ... 1697.

——. ——. *In* Combach, L., Tractatus aliquot chemici ... 1647.

1093. DAUBENTON, Louis Jean Marie. Tableau méthodique des minéraux, suivant leurs différentes natures, et avec des caractères distinctifs, apparens ou faciles à reconnoître ... [Paris: Demonville, 1784.]
   36 numb. *l*.

1094. DAVISON, William. Commentariorum in ... Petri Severini Dani Ideam medicinæ philosophicæ, propediem proditurorum prodromus ... Hagæ-Comitis: A. Vlacq, 1660.
   6 *l*., 708 p. illus., chart.
   With Severin, P., Idea medicinæ ... 1660.

1095. ——. Commentaria in Ideam medicinæ philosophicæ Petri Severini Dani ... Hagæ-Comitis: A. Vlacq, 1663.
   259 p.
   With Severin, P., Idea medicinæ ... 1660.

1096. ——. Philosophia pyrotechnica ... sev Cvrricvlvs chymiatricvs nobilissima illa & exoptatissima medicinæ parte pyrotechnica instructus ... Parisiis: J. Bessin, 1635.
   4 pts. in 1 v. illus., chart.

1097. ——. Les elemens de la philosophie de l'art du feu ou chemie ... Traduit du Latin ... par Iean Hellot ... Paris: F. Piot, 1651.
   9 *l*., 677 [i.e. 715] p. illus., chart.

1098. DAZILLE, Jean Barthélemy. Observations sur le tétanos ... Paris: Planche, 1788.
   2 *l*., 478 p., 3 *l*.

1099. DE ALCHEMIA. In hoc volvmine de alchemia continentur hæc. Gebri ... De inuestigatione perfectionis metallorum, liber I.

Summæ perfectionis metallorum, siue perfecti magisterij, libri II ... De inuentione
ueritatis seu perfectionis metallorum, liber
I. De fornacibus construendis, liber I. Item,
Speculum alchemiæ ... Rogerij Bachonis.
Correctorium alchemiæ ... Richardi Anglici
... Liber secretorum alchemiæ Calidis filij
Iazichi Iudæi. Tabula smaragdina de alchemia, Hermetis Trismeg. Hortulani philosophi, super Tabulam smaragdinam Hermetis
commentarius ... Norimbergæ: I. Petreius,
1541.
10 *l.*, 373 p., 2 *l.* illus.

1100. ———. De alchimia opvscvla com-
plvra vetervm philosophorum ... [Franco-
forti: Cyriacus Iacobus, 1550.]
3 *l.*, 168 numb. *l.*; 96 *l.* illus.
The second part has a separate title page
as follows: Rosarivm philosophorvm. Secvnda
pars alchimiæ de lapide philosophico vero
modo præparando ...

1101. DE ARTE CHEMICA libri dvo ... qvorvm
prior De veritate & antiquitate artis chemicæ
... testimonia & theoremata ex varijs autori-
bus per Robertvm Vallensem selecta. Posterior, Ioann. Chrysippi Faniani De arte
metallicæ metamorphoseos liber singularis.
Item de iure artis alchemiæ ... Montisbeli-
gardi: J. Foillet, 1602.
51 p., 3 *l.*, 67 p.

1102. DE BALNEIS omnia qvæ extant apvd
Græcos, Latinos, et Arabas, tam medicos
quàm quoscunque ceterarum artium probatos
scriptores ... Venetiis: Ivntae, 1553.
14, 497 numb. *l.* illus.

DE LA transformation metallique. *See*
Metallique.

1103. DEE, Arthur. Fascicvlvs chemicvs,
abstrvsæ Hermeticæ scientiæ, ingressvm,
progressvm, coronidem, verbis apertissimis
explicans, ex selectissimis & celeberrimis
authoribus ... Parisiis: N. de la Vigne, 1631.
10 *l.*, 172 p.

1104. ———. Fasciculus chemicus: or
chymical collections ... Whereunto is added,
The arcanum or grand secret of hermetick
philosophy. Both made English by James
Hasolle ... London: J. Flesher for R. Mynne,
1650.
25 *l.*, 268 p. illus.

1105. DEFOE, Daniel. The history of the
great plague in London, in the year 1665 ...
To which is added, a journal of the plague

at Marseilles, in the year 1720. London: for
F. and J. Noble, 1754.
2 *l.*, 376 p.

1106. DEGNER, Johann Hartmann. Historia
medica de dysenteria biliosocontagiosa quæ
MDCCXXXVI neomagi et in vicinis ei pagis
epidemice grassata fuit ... Accedit Relatio
historia cum responso facultatis medicæ
Halensis de morte per mercurium sublim.
in emplastro adplicatum, inducta. Editio
novissima, ab auctore ipso revisa & aucta.
Trajecti ad Rhenum: N. van Vucht, 1754.
3 *l.*, x, 389 p., 12 *l.*

1107. DEIDIER, Antoine. Chimie raisonnée.
Où l'on tâche de découvrir la nature & la
maniere d'agir des remedes chimiques les
plus en usage en medecine & en chirurgie
... Lyon: M. Duplain, 1715.
12 *l.*, 522 p.

1108. ———. Traité des tumeurs contre
nature ... Cinquieme edition, augmentée
d'une dissertation préliminaire sur la
chirurgie pratique ... du même auteur, avec
un discours académique sur la contagion
de la peste de Marseille. Paris: d'Houry,
1732.
1 *l.*, xlvi, 399 p., 5 *l.*

DEJEAN, distillateur, *pseud. See*
Hornot, Antoine.

1109. DELAVAL, Edward Hussey. An experimental inquiry into the cause of the
changes of colours in opake and coloured
bodies. With an historical preface ... London: for J. Nourse and P. Elmsly, 1777.
1 *l.*, lxxv, 138 p.

1110. ———. Ricerche sperimentali sulle
cagioni del cangiamento di colore ne' corpi
opachi, e coloratii ... trasportate in Italiano
da Gio. Francesco Fromond. Milano: A. Magg,
1779.
4 *l.*, 280 p.

DE-LEVIS, Giovanni Agostino. *See*
Levis, Giovanni Agostino.

1111. DEMACHY, Jacques François. L'art
du distillateur d'eaux-fortes ... [Paris]
1773.
1 *l.*, iv, 198 p. illus., folio.
With his L'art du distillateur liquoriste
... 1775.

1112. ———. L'art du distillateur liquoriste;
contenant le bruleur d'eaux-de-vie, le fabri-

quant de liqueurs, le débitantion le cafetier-
limonnadier ... [Paris] 1775.
   x, 153 p.   illus., folio.

1113. ——. Instituts de chymie, ou Principes élémentaires de cette science, pré-
sentés sous un nouveau jour ... Paris: Lottin
le jeune, 1776.
   2 v.

1114. ——. Précis de la table des principales combinaisons chymiques. [n.p.:
n.d.]
   40 p.   chart.

1115. ——. Procédés chymiques rangés
méthodiquement et définis. On y a joint le
précis d'une nouvelle table des combinaisons
ou rapports: pour servir de suite aux Instituts
de chymie ... Paris: Lottin le jeune, 1769.
   2 *l*., xxiv, 210 p.   chart.
   With Sage, B.G., Examen chymique ...
1769.

1116. ——. Recueil de dissertations
physico-chymiques présentées à differentes
académies ... Amsterdam: Monory, 1774.
   2 *l*., xvi, 489 p., 1 *l*.   charts.

1117. DÉMESTE, Jean. Lettres ... au
Docteur Bernard ... sur la chymie, la doci-
masie, la cristallographie, la lithologie, la
minéralogie & la physique en général ...
Paris: Didot ..., 1779.
   2 v.

   DEMOCRITUS *Abderites.* De arte
sacra, sive De rebus naturalibus. *In*
Mizauld, A., Memoralilium ... 1574.

   DEMOCRITUS, Christianus,*pseud*.
See Dippel, Johann Konrad.

   DEMOCRITUS JUNIOR,*pseud*. *See*
Burton, Robert.

1118. DERHAM, Samuel. Hydrologia philosophica or, An account of Ilmington waters
in Warwick-shire; with directions for drink-
ing the same. Together with some experimental observations touching the original
of compound bodies ... Oxford: L. Lichfield
for J. Howell, 1685.
   12 *l*., 162 p., 2 *l*.

1119. DESBOIS DE ROCHEFORT, Louis.
Cours élémentaire de matière médicale, suivi
d'un précis de l'art de formuler. Ouvrage
posthume ... Paris: Méquignon, 1789.
   2 v.

1120. ——. ——. Nouvelle édition. Paris:
Méquignon, 1793.
   2 v.

1121. DESBREST. Lettre à MM. les auteurs
du Journal de Medecine ... Clermont-Ferrand:
A. Delcros, 1779.
   35 p.
   With his Traité des eaux minérales ...
1778.

1122. ——. Nouvelles instructions sur
les eaux minérales de Chateldon en Boubon-
nois. [Clermont-Ferrand: A. Delcros, 1780.]
   24 p.
   With his Traité des eaux minérales ... 1778.
   Lacking title page. Caption title.

1123. ——. Traité des eaux minerales de
Chateldon, de celles de Vichy et Haute-Rive
en Bourbonnois, avec le détail de leurs propriétés médicinales & leur analyse ... Moulins:
la veuve Faure & Vidalin ..., 1778.
   xxiv, 301 p., 1 *l*.

1124. DESCARTES, René. Lettres ... où
sont traittées les plus belles questions de
la morale, physiqve, medecine, & des mathe-
matiqves. Paris: H. le Gras, 1657.
   14 *l*., 663 p.   illus.

1125. ——. Les passions de l'ame. Paris:
T. Girard, 1664.
   xlviii, 272 p.

1126. ——. The passions of the soule in
three books ... London: for A.C., sold by J.
Martin and J. Ridley, 1650.
   15 *l*., 173 p.

1127. DESCRIPTION de divers procédés
pour extraire la soude du sel marin, faite
en exécution d'un arrêté du Comité de Salut
public du 8 Pluvoise, an 2 de la République
Française ... Paris: l'Imprimerie du Comitè
de Salut public [1795].
   1 *l*., 80 p.   illus.

1128. DESJARDINS, Théodore. Lettre ... a
M. Sarrepuy ... au sujet de son or potable,
& sur son établissement à Paris ... [Paris?:
1692?]
   44 p.

   DESSENIUS VAN CROONENBURCH,
Bernard. *See* Cronenburgius, Bernardus
Dessenius.

1129. DETHARDING, Georg. Chymischer
Probir-Ofen, darinnen alle Processe und

Handgriffe, die in Johannis Agricolæ ...
Commentarijs und Notis, über Johan: Poppij
chymische Medicin enthalten, und von ihm
... für grosse, geheime, und gantz newe
Künste ausgeruffen werden ... [Stettin]
gedruckt bey G. Götzken, in verlegung J.
Mamphrasen, 1648.
    8 *l*., 38, 344 p., 19 *l*.
    With Kirsten, G., Adversaria ... 1648.

1130. ———. [Scriptum illusivm contra
Hauptmannianum famosum scriptum Collu-
sivum. Das ist: Vnumbgängliche Beand-
wortung und Wider-Rede, in welcher D.
Johannis Agricolæ phantastische Tinctura
... nach chymischen Grunden examiniret ...
Stettin: gedruckt bey G. Götzken, in verlegung J. Mamphrasen, 1647.]
    136 p.
    Lacking the first 4 preliminary leaves.
    With Kirsten, G., Adversaria ... 1648.

1131. DEVENTER, Hendrik van. Operationes
chirurgicae novum lumen exhibentes obste-
tricantibus ... Lugduni Batavorum: A. Dyck-
huisen, 1701.
    9 *l*., 274 p., 3 *l*. illus.

1132. ———. Neues Hebammen-Licht, bey
welchem die Hebammen-Kunst und was darzu
gehöret durch geschickte Handgriffe aufrichtig gelehret wird ... Jena: H.C. Cröker, 1717.
    6 *l*., 489 p., 11 *l*. illus.
    With Creiling, J.K., Die edelgeborne Jung-
fer Alchymia ... 1730.

1133. DEVÉZE, Jean. An enquiry into, and
observations upon the causes and effects of
the epidemic disease, which raged in Philadelphia from the month of August till towards
the middle of December, 1793. Philadelphia:
Parent, 1794.
    vii, 144 p.
    Parallel English and French texts.

1134. DIALOGUS CREATURARUM. Dialogus
creaturarum optime moralizatus, omni materie
morali iocundo modo applicabilis ... [Parr-
hisius: impēdio J. Parui, industria P. Pigou-
cheti, 1510.]
    lxiv numb. *l*., 7 *l*.

1135. ———. The dialogues of creatures
moralysed ... of late trāslated out of latyn
into our Englysshe tonge ... [Antwerp: M. de
Keyser, 1535.]
    163 *l*. illus.

1136. DIANA PALEOLOGO, Giovanni Battista.
Sacra universal filosofia dell'immacolata

concezione di Maria sempre vergine, madre
di Dio, divote speculazioni ... Lucca: P.
Frediani, 1713.
    8 *l*., 309 p. 2 *l*. illus.

1137. DICKINSON, Edmund. Edmundus
Dickinson ... et Theodorus Mundanus ...
de quintessentia philosophorum et vera
physiologia, unâ cum quæstionibus aliquot
de secretâ materiâ phisicâ. Editio altera.
Rotterodami: P. vander Slaart, 1699.
    1 *l*., 224 p.

    DICTIONAIRE hermetique. *See* Salmon,
William.

1138. DIDELOT, Nicolas. Avis aux personnes qui sont usage des eaux de Plom-
bières, ou Traité des eaux minérales ...
Bruyeres: Vivot, 1782.
    283 p.

1139. DIEMERBROECK, Ysbrand van. Opera
omnia, anatomica et medica ... Nunc simul
collecta, & diligenter recognita per Timannvm
de Diemerbroeck ... Genevae: S. de Tovrnes,
1687.
    3 *l*., xv p., 3 *l*., 844 p., 4 *l*.; 4 *l*., 183 p.
illus., port.
    Lacking the title page to the appendix.

1140. DIENERT, Alexandre Denis. Introduction a la matiere medicale, en forme de
thérapeutique ... Nouvelle edition. Paris:
P.F. Didot, 1765.
    6 *l*., 550 p., 1 *l*.

    DIENHEIM, Johann Wolffgang. Uni-
versal Artzney. *In* Taeda trifida chimica ...
1674.

1141. DIGBY, *Sir* Kenelm. Choice and experimented receipts in physick and chirurgery,
as also cordial and distilled waters and
spirits, perfumes, and other curiosities ...
Translated out of several languages by G.H.
... London: for the author, sold by H. Brome,
1668.
    3 *l*., 308 p., 6 *l*. port.

1142. ———. ———. The second edition corrected & amended. London: A. Clark for H.
Brome, 1675.
    2 *l*., 146 p., 4 *l*. port.

1143. ———. A choice collection of rare
chymical secrets and experiments in philosophy ... Now publishẹd for the good and benefit of the publick, by George Hartman. London: for the publisher, 1682.

8 *l*., 272 p.   illus.

1144. ———. Chymical secrets, and rare
experiments in physick & philosophy, with
figures ... Published since his death, by
George Hartman ... London: for W. Cooper,
1683.
7 *l*., 272 p.   illus.

1145. ———. Ausserlesene, seltsame,
philosophische Geheimnisse und chymische
Experimente ... bisshero ... verborgen ge-
halten, jetzo aber ... ans Tages Liecht
gebracht worden durch Georg Hartman. Aus
der Englischen in die Deutsche Sprache zum
ersten mahl übersetzet von J.L.M.C. ...
Hamburg: G. Schultz, 1684.
4 *l*., 269 p., 5 *l*.   illus., port.

1146. ———. Recviel des remedes et secrets, tirez des memoires de Mr. le chevalier
Digby ... Par Jean Malbec de Trefel. Paris:
l'auteur et M. de Beaujeu, 1669.
3 *l*., 359 p., 4 *l*.

1147. ———. Remedes souverains et secrets experimentez ... Avec plusieurs autres
secrets & parfums curieux pour la conservation de la beauté des dames. Paris: G. Cavelier, 1684.
2 *l*., 299 p., 13 *l*.

1148. ———. The closet of ... Sir Kenelm
Digby ... opened: whereby is discovered
several ways for making of metheglin, syder,
cherry-wine, &c. together with excellent
directions for cookery ... The third edition
corrected. London: H.C. for H. Brome, 1677.
2 *l*., 251 p., 4 *l*.
With his Choice and experimented receipts ... 1675.

1149. ———. Discovrs svr la vegetation
des plantes ... Tradvction Françoise. Paris:
la veuve Moet, 1667.
8 *l*., 89 p.

1150. ———. A late discourse made in a
solemne assembly of nobles and learned men
at Montpellier in France ... touching the cure
of wounds by the powder of sympathy ...
Rendered faithfully out of French into English by R. White ... The third edition corrected
and augmented ... London: for R. Lowndes
and T. Davies, 1660.
5 *l*., 152 p., 3 *l*.

1151. ———. Two treatises. In the one of
which, the natvre of bodies; in the other,
the natvre of mans solve; is looked into ...

Paris: G. Blaizot, 1644.
22 *l*., 466 p.

———. Vermehrung des Theatri
Chimici. *In* Blankaart, S., Theatrum chimicum ... 1700.

1152. DIGLIOLA, Giuseppe Donzelli, *barone
di*. Teatro farmacevtico dogmatico, e
spagirico ... in qvesta seconda impressione
dal dottor Tomaso Donzelli ... accresciuto
... con aggiunta ... Napoli: G.F. Paci ...,
1675.
44 *l*., 100, 299, 300 p.   illus., port.
The index lacking at the end has been
supplied in manuscript.

1153. ———. ——— in questa quarta impressione corretto, & accresciuto con vn catalogo
dell'herbe natiue del suolo Romano del signor
Gio. Giacomo Roggeri ... Venetia: G. Storti,
1681.
14 *l*., 811 p., 41 *l*.

1154. ———. ——— sesta impressione corretto ... Venetia: P. Baglioni, 1696.
12 *l*., 811 p., 42 *l*.   illus.

1155. ———. ———. Venezia: A. Bortoli,
1704.
12 *l*., 695 p., 38 *l*.

1156. ———. ———. Venezia: A. Poletti,
1713.
12 *l*., 695 p., 37 *l*.

1157. DIMSDALE, Thomas. The present
method of inoculating for the small-pox ...
sixth edition. London: 1772.
160 p.
Lacking the title page.

DIODORUS EUCHYON, *pseud. See*
Wolf, Kaspar.

1158. DIONIS, Pierre. L'anatomie de l'homme,
suivant la circulation du sang, & les derniéres
découvertes. Démontrée au Jardin Royal ...
Quatrieme edition ... avec une ample dissertation sur la génération ... Paris: L. d'Houry,
1705.
20 *l*., 710 p., 19 *l*.   illus., port.

1159. ———. A course of chirurgical operations, demonstrated in the Royal Garden at
Paris. Translated from the Paris edition. London: for J. Tonson, 1710.
8 *l*., 496 p., 8 *l*.   illus.

1160. ———. Dissertation sur la mort subite.

Avec l'histoire d'une fille cataleptique.
Paris: L. d'Houry, 1710.
　　6 *l.*, 189 [i.e. 201] p.

1161. DIOSCORIDES, Pedianus, *of Ana-
zarbos.* Alphabetvm empiricvm, sive,
Dioscoridis et Stephani Atheniensis ... De
remedijs expertis liber, iuxta alphabeti
ordinem digestus. Nunc primum à Casparo
Vuolphio ... in Latinam linguam conuersus,
& in lucem editus. [Zurich] 1581.
　　76 numb. *l.*

1162. ———. Pharmacorvm simplicium,
reique medicæ libri VIII. Io. Rvellio interprete . Vna cum Herm. Barbari Corollarijs,
& Marc. Vergilij, in singula capita cēsuris,
siue annotationibus ... Argentorato: I.
Schottus, 1529.
　　4 *l.*, 361 numb. *l.*, 12 *l.*
　　Lacks last leaf of index.

1163. ———. De medica materia libri sex,
Ioanne Ruellio ... interprete ... Parisiis: S.
Colinæus, 1537.
　　20 *l.*, 266 numb. *l.*, 20 *l.*

1164. ———. De medicinali materia libri
sex, Ioanne Rvellio interprete ... Additis
etiam annotationibus ... per Gvalthervm H.
Ryff ... Accessere in evndem avtorem scholia
noua ... Ioanne Lonicero autore. Franc[kfurt]:
C. Egenolphus [1543].
　　12 *l.*, 439 p.; 10 *l.*, 87 numb. *l.* illus.

1165. ———. De materia medica libri sex,
innumeris locis ab Andrea Matthiolo emendati ... Lvgdvni: I. Frellonius, 1554.
　　16 *l.*, 564 p., 72 *l.*

———. Simplicium medicamentorum.
In Du Pinet, A., Historia plantarum ... 1561.

1166. ———. Kräuterbuch ... von allerley
wolriechenden Kräutern, Gewürtzen ... vnd
andern ... Erstlich durch Ioannem Danzivm
... verteutscht, nun mehr aber von Petro
Vffenbach, bestelten ... Auch mit dess ...
Hieronymi Bravnschweig zweyen Büchern,
als der Kunst zu destillieren ... Franckfurt
am Mayn: gedruckt durch J. Bringern, in Verlegung C. Corthoys, 1610.
　　6 *l.*, 616 [i.e. 516] p., 17 *l.* illus.

1167. ———. Acerca de la materia medicinal, y de los venenos mortiseros, traduzido
de lengua Griega ... y illustrado con claras
y substantiales annotationes ... por el Doctor Andres de Laguna ... [Salamanca: M.
Gast, 1566.]

14 *l.*, 616 p., 14 *l.* illus., port.
Some leaves, including the title, mutilated.

1168. ———. ... Opera qvæ extant omnia.
Ex noua interpretatione Jani-Antonii Sara-
ceni ... [Franckofurti] hæredas A. Wechel
..., 1598.
　　18 *l.*, 479 p.; 1 *l.*, 144 p., 1 *l.*; 6 *l.*,
135 p., 4 *l.* port.
　　Text in Greek and Latin.

1169. DIPPEL, Johann Konrad. Weg-Weiser
zum verlohrnen Licht und Recht ... Samt einer
Vor-Rede worinnen Herrn Johannes Merckers
... dem Autori überschickte zwey Tractätlein
... Durch Christianum Democritum. [Berlin]
1704.
　　3 *l.*, 232, 198 p. illus.

1170. DIRECTIONS for preparing aerated
medicinal waters, by means of the improved
glass machines made at Leith glass-works.
Edinburgh: for W. Creech, 1787.
　　12 p., 1 *l.* illus.
　　Ascribed to Joseph Black.

DISCEPTATIO de lapide physico. *See*
Gassmann, Franz, *supposed author.*

1171. DISCORSO di fisionomia. [n.p.: n.d.]
　　4 *l.*
　　Caption title.
　　With Breve trattato di fisionomia ... [n.d.].

1172. DISDIER, Francois-Michel. Exposition exacte ou tableaux anatomiques en
tailles-douces des différentes parties du
corps humain ... [Paris] E. Charpentier,
1758.
　　68 numb. *l.* illus.

1173. DISPENSATORIUM medico-pharma-
ceuticum ... Succinctum in ordinem congestum, una cum taxa ... a Concilio Medico
Electorali Palatino. Mannhemii: ex typo-
graphejo Electorali Aulico, 1764.
　　10 *l.*, 208 p., 2 *l.*, 20, 20 p.

1174. DISPENSATORIUM AUSTRIACO-
VIENNENSE. Dispensatorium pharmaceuticum
Austriaco-Viennense, in quo hodierna die
usualiora medicamenta secundum artis regulas
componenda visuntur ... Sumptibus Collegii
Pharmaceutici Viennensis. Viennæ: G. Kurtzböck, 1729 reimpressum 1737.
　　16 *l.*, 273 p., 9 *l.*

1175. ———. Viennæ: G. Kurtzböck, 1729 reimpressum 1744.

16 *l*., 273 p., 9 *l*.   port.

1176. ——. Editio altera juxta exemplar
Bruxellense anni 1747 recusa, & nova rursus
appendice aucta. Lovanii: J.F. van Overbeke,
1774.
14 *l*., 395 p., 22 *l*., xxvi, ix p., 1 *l*.

——. *See also* Neue Apothecker Tax
... 1744, etc.

1177. DISPENSATORIUM BORUSSO-BRAN-
DENBURGICUM. Dispensatorium regium &
electorale Borusso-Brandenburgicum ...
Regii Collegii Medici Superioris cura &
opera denuo editum, revisum, emendatum et
auctum ... Berolini: J.G. Michaelis, 1731.
4 *l*., 302 p.

1178. ——. Nvnc vero insvper qvoqve
variis vtilissmis annotationibvs & observationibvs ... ab Ernesto Fagino. Erfordiae:
C.F. Jvngnicolius, 1734.
3 *l*., 278 p.

1179. ——. Wratislaviæ: I.I. Kornius,
1744.
2 *l*., 194 p.

1180. ——. Erfordiae: C.F. Ivngnicolius
filiae, 1747.
3 *l*., 210 p.

1181. DISPENSATORIUM BRUNSVICENSE.
Dispensatorivm pharmacevticvm Brvnsvicense
... et Pharmacopoeis dvcatvs Brnvsvico-
Wolfenbvttelani a Collegio Dvcali Svpremo
Sanitati Civivm dicato ... Brvnsvici: in officina Orphanotrophei, 1777.
3 *l*., 36, 378 p., 32 *l*., 63 p., 1 *l*.

1182. DIVERS TRAITEZ de la philosophie
naturelle. Sçavoir, La turbe des philosophes
... La parole delaissée de Bernard Trevisan.
Les deus traitez de Corneille Drebel ... avec
le tres-ancien duel des chevaliers. Nouvellement traduits en François, par un docteur en
medecine. Paris: J. d'Houry, 1672.
4 *l*., 298 p., 3 *l*.

1183. DOBSON, Matthew. A medical commentary on fixed air ... Chester: printed by
J. Monk, sold by T. Cadell ..., 1779.
3 *l*., 193 p.

1184. ——. ——. Third edition. With an
appendix on the efficacy of the solution of
fixed alkaline salts ... by William Falconer.
London: for T. Cadell, 1787.
vii, 172 p.; 126 p.

1185. DODOENS, Rembert. Crvydt-boeck
... met biivoeghsels achter elck capitel,
uyt verscheyden cruydt-beschrijvers: item,
in'talaetste enn beschrijvinghe van de
Indiaensche ghewassen, meest ghetrocken
uyt de schriften van Carolvs Clvsivs. Nu
wederom van nieuws oversien ende verbetert.
Antwerpen: B. Moretus, 1644.
18 *l*., 1492 p., 30 *l*.   illus.

1186. ——. A nievve herball, or historie
of plantes ... First set foorth in the Doutche
or Almaigne tongue ... and nowe first translated out of French into English, by Henry
Lyte ... London: G. Dewes, 1578.
12 *l*., 779 p., 12 *l*.   illus., port.

1187. ——. ——. London: 1586.
19 *l*., 916 p., 22 *l*.
Lacks title page and has other mutila-
tions.

1188. ——. ——. London: E. Bollifant,
1595.
20 *l*., 916 p., 24 *l*.

1189. ——. ——. London: E. Griffin,
1619.
12 *l*., 564 p., 15 *l*.

1190. ——. Florvm, et coronariarvm
odoratarvmqve nonnvllarvm herbarvm historia ... Altera editio. Antverpiæ: C. Plantin,
1569.
309 p., 4 *l*.   illus.
With his Pvrgantivm aliarvmqve ... 1574.

1191. ——. Historia vitis viniqve: et
stirpivm nonnvllarum aliarum. Item medicinalium observationum exempla ... Coloniae:
M. Cholinus, 1580.
8 *l*., 169 p., 3 *l*.

1192. ——. Medicinalivm observationvm
exempla rara. Accessere & alia quaedam,
quorum elenchum pagina post praefationem
exhibet. Hardervici: apud viduam T. Henrici, impensis H. Laurentij, 1521 [i.e. 1621].
8 *l*., 234 p., 3 *l*.

1193. ——. Pvrgantivm aliarvmqve eo
facientivm, tvm et radicum, conuoluulorum
ac deleteriarum herbarum historiæ libri IIII
... Accessit appendix variarū & quidem
rarissimarum nonnullarum stirpium ... breves
descriptiones continens. Antverpiæ: C.
Plantin, 1574.
505 p., 3 *l*.   illus.

1194. DOLAEUS, Johann. Opera omnia,

exhibentia non modò encyclopediam medicam dogmaticam, in qua affectus humani corporis interni; & encyclopaediam chirurgicam rationalem ... Francofurti ad Moenum: F. Knochius, 1703.
2 v. port.

1195. ——. Systema medicinale, a compleat system of physick, theoretical and practical ... Translated out of Latin into English ... Whereunto is annexed a prefatory discourse concerning the method of studying and practising physick ... Written by William Salmon ... London: for T. Passinger ..., 1686.
16 ℓ., 516, 360 p. port.

1196. DOLHOPFF, Georg Andreas, ed. Lapis animalis microcosmicus. Oder, Die höchste Artzney, aus der kleinen Welt des menschlichen Leibs. Samt einem Tractätlein vom Vrin oder Harn des Menschen. Strassburg: G.A. Dolhopff, 1681.
8 ℓ., 80 p.

1197. ——. Lapis mineralis oder Die höchste Artzney auss denen Metallen und Mineralien, absonderlich dem Vitriolo. Strassburg: G.A. Dolhopff, 1681.
6 ℓ., 116 p. illus.

DOMERQUE. Moyens faciles et assurez pour consever la santé. In Lessius, L., Le vray moyen ... 1705.

1198. DONATI, Marcello. De medica historia mirabili libri sex nunc primùm in lucem editi ... Venetiis: F. Valgrisivs, 1588.
10 ℓ., 96, 185-312 numb. ℓ.

1199. DONATO D'EREMITA. Dell'elixir vitæ ... libri qvattro ... Napoli: S. Roncagliolio, 1624.
25 ℓ., 182 p. illus.

DONZELLI, Giuseppe, barone di Digliola. See Digliola, Giuseppe Donzelli, barone di.

1200. DOPPET, François Amédée. Le médecin philosophe; ouvrage utile à tout citoyen, dans lequel on trouve une nouvelle manière de guérir, piusée dans les affections de l'ame, & la gymnastique. Turin et Paris: Reycends et Leroy, 1787.
xvi, 78 p., 1 ℓ.

1201. DORING, Michael. Μιθριδατειοτεχνία: hoc est, De mithridatii legitima constructione Nicolai Mutoni collectanea ... Prius exhibet

'Ακρόαμα medico-philosophicum ... Posterius Διατριβὴν de opobalsamo syriaco, judaico, ægyptio ... Jenæ: J. Beitmann, 1620.
3 pts. in 1 v.

1202. DORN, Gerhard. Chymisticvm artificivm naturæ, theoricum & practicum ... [n.p.] 1568.
156 p.

1203. ——. Artificii chymistici physici, metaphysicique, secunda pars & tertia ... Accessit etiam tertiæ parti, De præparationibus metallicis in vtroque lapidis philosophorū opere maiore minoreque ... [n.p.] 1569.
8 ℓ., 440 p., 4 ℓ.
With his Chymisticvm artificivm ... 1568, which forms part one of this work.

1204. ——. Artificii chymistici physici, metaphysiciqve, opvscvla ... Libri magno ingenii acumine ante 30. annos scripti ... & nunc primùm in lucem editi. [n.p.] 1594.
8 ℓ., 440 p., 4 ℓ.

1205. ——. Clavis totivs philosophiæ chymisticæ, per quam potissima philosophorum dicta referantur. Cui accessit iam recens artificium supernaturale ... Francoforti: C. Corvin, 1583.
429 p., 13 ℓ. illus.

1206. ——. Schlüssel der chimistischen Philosophy ... deme das Artificium supernaturale, sampt sein angehörigen Stucken vnnd Theilen ... hinzu gethan worden ... durch ein Liebhaber der edlen Philosophy in Teutschsprach gebracht, vnd ... mit etlichen Fragen gemehret. Strassburg: L. Zetzner, 1602.
8 ℓ., 414 p., 8 ℓ. illus.

1207. ——. Congeries Paracelsicæ chemiæ de transmvtationibvs metallorum, ex omnibus quæ de his ab ipso scripta reperire licuit hactenus. Accessit Genealogia mineralium atqve metallorum omnium, eiusdem autoris. Gerardo Dorneo interprete. Francofurti: A. Wechel, 1581.
277 p.

1208. ——. Lapis metaphysicvs, avt philosophicvs, qvi vniversalis medicina uera fuit patrum antiquorum ... [n.p.] 1570.
75 ℓ.
With his Chymisticvm artificivm ... 1568.

——. Monarchia triadis. In Paracelsus, Aurora thesaurusque ... 1577.

1209. ——, *ed.* Trevisanvs de chymico
miracvlo, qvod lapidem philosophiæ appel-
lant. Dionys. Zecharivs Gallus de eodem.
Auctoritatibus varijs principum huius artis,
Democriti, Gebri, Lvllii, Villanovani, con-
firmati & illustrati ... Basileæ: hæredes P.
Pernæ, 1583.
    3 *l.*, 198 p.
    With Nolle, H., Discursus ... 1636.

1210. DORTMANN, Nicolas. Libri duo. De
causis & effectibus thermarum Belilucanarum
paruo interuallo à Monspeliensi vrbe dis-
tantium. Lugduni: C. Pesnot, 1579.
    8 *l.*, 218 p., 19 *l.*

1211. DOSSIE, Robert. The elaboratory
laid open, or, The secrets of modern chemistry and pharmacy revealed ... London: for
J. Nourse, 1758.
    xi p., 1 *l.*, 375 p., 4 *l.*

1212. ——. The handmaid to the arts ...
London: for J. Nourse, 1758.
    2 v.

1213. ——. ——. The second edition ...
London: for J. Nourse, 1764.
    2 v.

1214. ——. Theory and practice of chirurgical pharmacy: comprehending a complete
dispensatory for the use of surgeons ... London: for J. Nourse, 1761.
    xviii p., 3 *l.*, 485 p., 1 *l.*

1215. DOUGLAS, James. Lateralis opera-
tionis historia seu Descriptio methodi cal-
culum extrahendi ... Accedit appendix de
ejusdem methodi apud Londinenses intro-
ductione & progressu. Lugduni Batavorum:
H. Mulhovius, 1728.
    102 p., 2 *l.*; 28, 38 p. illus.
    The appendix has a separate title page
with the imprint Lugduni Batavorum: C. Wishoff, 1733.

1216. ——. Myographiae comparatae
specimen: or, A comparative description of
all the muscles in a man and in a quadruped
... To which is added an account of the
muscles peculiar to a woman ... London:
W.B. for G. Strachan, 1707.
    xxxvi, 216, 16 p.

1217. ——. ——. A new edition, with
additions. Dublin: W. Sleater, 1777.
    xxxiv, 264 p.; iv, 110 p.
    Includes: An account of the blood vessels
and nerves.

    Les DOUZE PORTES d'alchymie. *In*
Trois traitez ... 1618.

1218. DOVER, Thomas. The ancient physician's legacy to his country. Being what he
has collected himself, in fifty-eight years
of practice: or, An account of the several
diseases incident to mankind described in
so plain a manner ... The eight edition ...
London: R. and H. Causton [1771].
    viii, 245 p., 1 *l.*

1219. ——. Encomium argenti vivi: A
treatise upon the use and properties of quicksilver ... With some remarks upon the animadversions of Dr. Turner upon Belloste. By
a gentleman of Trinity College, Cambridge.
London: for Stephen Austen, sold by J. Roberts
[1733?].
    1 *l.*, viii, 64 p.

1220. DREBBEL, Cornelis. Tractatus duo:
Prior de natura elementorum ... posterior de
qvinta essentia ... Editi curà Joachimi Morsi.
Accedit eiusdem epistola ad Britaniæ mon-
archum Iacobum, De perpetvi mobilis inventione. Hamburgi: H. Carsten, 1621.
    47 *l.*
    With Nolle, H., Discursus ... 1636.

1221. ——. Tractatvs dvo. I. De natvra
elementorvm. II. De qvinta essentia. Accedit
his de mobilis perpetvi inuentione epistola
... E Belgico idiomate in Latinum vertit D.
Petrvs Lavrembergivs ... [Geneva] J. de
Tournes, 1628.
    70 p.
    With Pleier, C., Medicus criticus-astro-
logus ... 1627.

    ——. Deux traitez philosophiques.
In Divers traitez ... 1672.

1222. ——. Gründliche Auflösung, von
der Natur und Eigenschafft der Elementen
... Mit einem Anhang und klaren Beweiss,
die von so vielen gesuchte Quint-Essenz
aus allen dreyen Reichen zu haben ...
sambt andern raren physicalischen Fragen,
von einem Liebhaber der Hermetischen
Kunst herausgegeben. Franckfurt am Mayn:
M.G. Ifingin, 1715.
    118 p.

1223. ——. Kort begrip der hoofdstoffelyke
natuurkunde, of Inleiding tot de kennis der
eigenschappen van der vier elementen ...
Vermeerderd met des auteurs leven ... Amsterdam: P.G. Geysbeek [n.d.].
    24, 108 p. illus.

1224. DRELINCOURT, Charles. Experimenta anatomica, ex vivorum sectionibus petita, edita per Ernestum Gottfried Heyseum. Lugd. Batav.: 1682.
70 p.
With Malpighi, M., Exercitatione de viscerum ... 1677.

1225. DREY CURIEUSE chymische Tractätlein, das erste betitult: Güldene Rose ... Das ander Bruñ der Weissheit und Erkäñtnis der Natur, von einem unvergleichichen Philosopho gegraben. Das dritte Blut der Natur ... Franckfurt und Leipzig: 1706.
70 p.; 1 *l*., 45 p.; 77 p.

1226. DREY KLEINE Schriften als Beyträge zur Naturlehre und der höheren Chymie, erstlich einzeln gedruckt, nun aber zusammen gezogen und herausgegeben von dem Verfasser selbst. [n.p.] 1778.
56 p.

1227. DRING, Rawlins. Dissertatio epistolica ad ... J.N. Armigerum conscripta: in qua crystallizationem salium in unicam & propriam, uti dicunt, figuram, esse admodum incertam, aut accidentalem, ex observationibus etiam suis, contra medicos & chymicos hodiernos, evincitur ... Amstelædami: 1688.
1 *l*., 73 p.

1228. DROYN, Gabriel. Le royal syrop de pommes, antidote des passions melancholiqves. Paris: J. Moreau, 1615.
4 *l*., 152 p.

1229. DUBÉ, Paul. Le medecin des pauvres ... Septiéme edition ... Paris: E. Couterot, 1713.
40 *l*., 444 p.; 12 *l*., 102 p., 1 *l*.
The second part has a separate title page: Le chirurgien des pauvres ... 1713.

1230. ———. The poor man's physician and surgeon ... with an addition of the true use of the quinquina or Jesuites pouder ... Translated from the eighth edition printed at Paris. London: 1704.
8 *l*., 420 p., 10 *l*.

DUBOIS, Gottfried. De taenia. *See* Linné, C. von, *praeses*. Entry 2494.

1231. DUBOIS, Jacques. De medicamentorum simplicivm delectv, praeparationibvs, mistionis moào, libri tres ... Parisiis: I. Gasellus, 1542.
4 *l*., 60 numb. *l*.
With Galenus, De temperamentis ... 1549.

1232. ———. La pharmacopee. Qui est la maniere de bien choisir & preparer les simples ... Faite Françoise par André Caille. Lyon: L. Cloqvemin, 1580.
13 *l*., 686 p., 3 *l*.

1233. ———. In Hippocratis elementa Iacobi Sylvii medici commentarivs. Parisiis: I. Gazellus, 1548.
9 numb. *l*.
With Galenus, De temperamentis ... 1549.

1234. ———. Opera medica ... Adivncta est eivsdem vita et icon, opera et stvdio Renati Moræi ... Genevæ: I. Chouët, 1635.
28 *l*., 892, 12 p., 16 *l*. port.

1235. DU BOYS, Joannes. In methodvm miscendorvm medicamentorvm, qvæ in qvotidiano sunt vsu obseruationes, ex Græcis, Arabibus, & neotericis ... Parisiis: I. Keruer, 1572.
8 *l*., 134 numb. *l*., 10 *l*.

1236. DUBUISSON. L'art du distillateur et marchand de liqueurs considérées comme alimens médicamenteux ... Paris: l'auteur ..., 1779.
2 v.

1237. DUCHANOY, Claude François. Essais sur l'art d'imiter les eaux minérales, ou, De la connoissance des eaux minérales & de la manière de se les procurer ... Paris: Méquignon, 1780.
vii, xxix, 402 p., 2 *l*. illus.

1238. DUCHESNE, Joseph. Ad Iacobi Avberti Vindonis de ortv et cavsis metallorvm contra chymicos explicationem ... responsio. Eivsdem De exqvisita mineralium, animalium, & vegetabilium medicamentorum spagyrica præparatione ... Lvgdvni: I. Lertot, 1575.
8 *l*., 186 p., 7 *l*.
With Aubert, J., De metallorum ... 1575.

1239. ———. Traicté familier de l'exacte preparation spagyriqve des medicamens, pris d'entre les mineraux, animaux & vegetaux. Avec vne breue response au liuret de Jacques Aubert ... Paris: C. Morel, 1624.
152 [i.e. 160] p., 7 *l*.

1240. ———. Ad veritatem Hermeticæ medicinæ ex Hippocratis veterúmque decretis ac therapeusi: necnon viuæ rerum anatomiæ exegesi, ipsiúsque naturæ luce stabiliendam, aduersus cuiusdam anonymi phantasmata responsio. Lutetiæ Parisiorum: A. Saugrain, 1604.
8 *l*., 312, 68 p., 4 *l*.

1241. ———. Conseils de medecine, dediez avx plvs celebres medecins de l'Europe ... Paris: C. Morel, 1626.
316 p., 1 ℓ.

1242. ———. Diæteticon polyhistoricon; opus utiqve varium, magnæ utilitatis ac delectationis, quòd multa historica, philosophica, & medica, tàm conservandæ sanitati, quàm variis curandis morbis necessaria contineat. Lipsiæ: T. Schurer & B. Voigt, 1607.
4 ℓ., 515 p.
With Ruland, M., Progymnasmata ... 1607.

1243. ———. Le povrtraict de la santé, où est au vif representée la reigle vniuerselle & particuliere de bien sainement & longuement viure ... Paris: C. Morel, 1606.
10 ℓ., 591 p., 2 ℓ.

1244. ———. Le grand miroir dv monde ... Lyon: B. Honorat, 1587.
8 ℓ., 206 p.

1245. ———. Liber de priscorum philosophorum veræ medicinæ materia, præparationis modo, atque in curandis morbis, præstantia ... His accesserunt ... de dogmaticorum medicorum legitima, & restituta medicamentorum præparatione ... S. Gervasii: hæredes E. Vignon, 1603.
12 ℓ., 432 p.
Lacking pages 241-272.

1246. ———. ———. [Lipsiæ] T. Schürer & B. Voigt, 1613.
11 ℓ., 480 p.

1247. ———. Traicté de la matiere, preparation et excellente vertu de la medecine balsamique des anciens philosophes. Avqvel sont adiovstez deux traictez, l'vn des signatures externes des choses, l'autre des internes & specifiques ... Paris: C. Morel, 1626.
4 ℓ., 215 p.
With his Conseils de medecine ... 1626.

1248. ———. Opera medica: scilicet, Ad Iacobi Avberti ... explicationem, breuis responsio. De exqvisita mineralivm, animalivm, et vegetabilium medicamentorum spagyrica preparatione & vsu, perspicua tractatio. Sclopetarivs ... Antidotarivm spagyricum aduersus eosdem ictus ... Francofurti ad Moenum: sumptibus L. Alberti, typis hæredum R. Beati, 1602.
8 ℓ., 152 p., 8 ℓ.; 8 ℓ., 175 p., 7 ℓ.

1249. ———. ———. Lipsiæ: T. Schürer & B.
Voigt, 1614.
8 ℓ., 152 p., 8 ℓ.; 8 ℓ., 175 p., 8 ℓ.
With his Liber de priscorum ... 1613.

1250. ———. Pharmacopee dogmaticorvm restitvta ... Francoforti: prælo Richteriano, impensis I.T. Schönvvetteri, 1607.
4 ℓ., 247 p., 4 ℓ.   port.

1251. ———. ———. Secunda editio ... Parisiis: C. Morellvs, 1607.
4 ℓ., 619 p., 13 ℓ.

1252. ———. ———. Venetiis: I. Antonius & I. de Franciscis, 1608.
12 ℓ., 269 p.

———. ———. In Renou, J. de, Dispensatorium ... 1631.

1253. ———. Quercetanus redivivus, hoc est, Ars medica dogmatico-hermetica. Tomis tribus digesta operâ Joannis Schröderi ... Francofvrti: hæeredes J. Beyer, 1679.
3 v. in 1.   illus.

1254. ———. La pharmacopee des dogmatiqves reformee ... Avec vn traicté familier le l'exacte preparation spagyrique des medicaments ... et vne breue response au liuret de Iacques Aubert ... Derniere edition ... Roven: O. Seignevré pour C. Pitreson, 1639.
4 ℓ., 548 p., 22 ℓ.; 150 p.
Second part incomplete.

1255. ———. Le ricchezze della riformata farmacopea ... nuouamente di fauelle Latina traportata in Italiana dal Sig. Giacomo Ferrari ... Venetia: G. Guerigli, 1619.
12 ℓ., 256 p.

1256. ———. ———. Venetia: Guerigli, 1646.
8 ℓ., 262 p.

1257. ———. The practise of chymicall, and Hermeticall physicke, for the preseruation of health ... translated into English, by Thomas Timme ... London: T. Creede, 1605.
102 ℓ.

1258. ———. Recveil des plvs cvrievx et rares secrets touchant la medecine metallique & minerale tirez des manuscripts ... Paris: S. Piget, 1648.
4 ℓ., 370 p., 7 ℓ.   port.

———. See also Fioravanti, L., Three exact pieces ... 1652, 1653.

1259. DUCLOS, Gaston.   Apologia chrysopoeiæ

et argyropoeiæ, adversvs Thomam Erastvm
... Cum nouo & recenter primùm edito eiusdem authoris ... opere ... de triplici avri et
argenti præparatione ... Ursellis: C. Sutorius,
1602.
8 *l.*, 267 p.

1260. ———. Claveus Germanicus, das ist:
Ein köstlichess Büchlein von dem Stein der
Weisen ... auss dem Latein ins Teutsch
versetzt ... Hall: P. Schmidt ..., 1617.
8 *l.*, 398 p.

1261. ———. Le filet d'Ariadne, pour entrer
avec seureté dans le labirinthe de la philosophie hermetique ... Paris: L. d'Houry,
1695.
4 *l.*, 176 p., 16 *l.* illus.

———. Traité philosophique de la
triple preparation de l'or et de l'argent. *In*
Salmon, W., Dictionaire hermetique ... 1695.

1262. DUCQUERIE, Jean Francis de la,
praeses. ... Quaestio medico-chymica
publicis agitanda disputationibus in scholis
medicorum academiæ Cadomensis pro licen-
tiatus gradu consequendo. Cadomi: A. Cavelier, 1709.
7 p.

1263. DUFOUR, Philippe Sylvestre. Traitez
nouveaux & curieux du café, du thé et du
chocolate ... Seconde edition. Lyon: J.B. De-
ville, 1688.
11 *l.*, 444 p., 4 *l.* illus.

1264. ———. ———. A quoy on a adjouté dans
cette edition, la meilleure de toutes les
methodes ... pour composer l'excellent chocolate par Mr. St. Disdier, troisiéme edition.
La Haye: A. Moetjens, 1693.
404 p., 1 *l.* illus.

1265. ———. Drey neue curieuse Tractätgen
von dem tranck Cafe, sinesischen The, und
der Chocolata ... nunmehro in die hochteutsche Sprache übersetzet von dem welcher
sich iederzeit nennet Theæ Potum Maxime
Colentem. Budissin: J. Wilisch, 1701.
5 *l.*, 247 p. illus.

1266. DUFRESNE, Pierre Jean Esnault.
Theoria gasorum, quam ... in augustissimo
Ludoviceo Medico Monspeliensi, tueri cona-
bitur ... [Montpelier?: 1788?].
15 p.
Caption title.

1267. DU HAMEL, Jean Baptiste. De con-

senv veteris et novæ philosophiæ libri dvo
... Parisiis: C. Savreux, 1663.
14 *l.*, 280 p. illus.

1268. ———. ———. Editio nova multo auctior
& emendatior ... Rothomagi: J. Lucas, 1675.
12 *l.*, 572 p., 1 *l.* illus.

1269. ———. De corporvm affectionibus
cum manifestis tum occultis, libri dvo ...
Parisiis: M. Le Petit & S. Michallet, 1670.
6 *l.*, 556 p., 9 *l.* illus.

1270. DUJARDIN, François. Histoire de
la chirurgie, depuis son origine jusqu'à nos
jours. Paris: l'Imprimerie Royale, 1774–
1780.
2 v. illus.
Volume 2 by Bernard Peyrilhe.

1271. DU LAURENS, André. Historia anatomica hvmani corporis et singvlarvm eivs
partivm mvltis controuersys & obseruationibus nouis illustrata. Francoforti: apud M.
Beckerum, impensis T. de Brij viduæ, [1600].
12 *l.*, 442 p., 14 *l.* illus., port.

1272. ———. ———. Francofurti: I. Rhodius,
1602.
9 *l.*, 996 p., 22 *l.* illus., port.

1273. ———. L'anatomie universelle de
toutes les parties du corps humain ... Paris:
Crépy, 1761.
28 *l.* illus.
With Piles, R. de, Abregé d'anatomie ...
[1765?]

1274. ———. Les oevvres de Mᵉ André Dv
Lavrens ... Tradvites de latin en françois par
Mᵉ Theophile Gelée ... Reveües, corrigées,
et avgmentées en cette derniere edition,
par G. Savvageon ... Paris: N. & I. de la
Coste, 1646.
8 *l.*, 597 p., 9 *l.*; 4 *l.*, 395 [i.e. 295] p.
illus.

1275. DU MONCHAUX, P.J. Anecdotes de
médecine. [Paris] 1762.
1 *l.*, xi, 343 p.

DUNANT, Charles Guillaume, *jt. auth.*
Pharmacopoea Genevensis. *See* La Roche,
Daniele.

1276. DUNCAN, Daniel. La chymie naturelle
ou L'explication chymique et mechanique de
la nourriture de l'animal ... Paris: L. d'Houry,
1683.
16 *l.*, 339 p.

1277. ——. ——. Montauban: L. d'Houry, 1682-1687.
4 v.
Imprint varies within the four volumes.

1278. ——. Wholsome advice against the abuse of hot liquors, particularly of coffee, chocolate, tea, brandy, and strong-waters ... Done out of French. London: for H. Rhodes and A. Bell, 1706.
4 ℓ., 280 p.

1279. DU PINET, Antoine. Historia plan-tarvm ... Quibus accessere simplicium medicamentorū facultates ... ex Dioscoride. Lvgdvni: G. Coterius, 1561.
640, 229 p., 13 ℓ. illus.

1280. DUPORTAL, Antoine Simon. De l'application de la chimie a quelques points de l'hygiène. Essai présenté à l'école de médecine de Montpellier, le troisième jour complémentaire, an 6 ... Montpellier: J.G. Tournel [1798].
62 p., 1 ℓ.

1281. DURADE, J. Georg. Traite physio-logique et chymique sur la nutrition ... Paris: Lottin, 1767.
xii, 158 p., 1 ℓ., 6 p.

1282. DURANTE, Castore. Herbario novo ... Venetia: appresso li Sessa, 1617.
5 ℓ., 492 p., 26 ℓ. illus., port.
Lacks pages 3-10, 59-64, 145-146, 287-289.

1283. ——. Il tesoro della sanita ... Venetia: G. Sarzina, 1611.
8 ℓ., 324 p.

1284. DURANTE, Giulio. Tratto di dodici bagni singolari della illustre città di Viterbo ... Perugia: P.P. Orlando, 1595.
46 ℓ.

1285. DU SOUCY, François, *sieur de Ger-zan*. A Ferdinand II. grand dvc de Toscane

... Bourdeaux: G. de la Court, 1655.
1 ℓ., 15 p.
With his Le grand or-potable ... 1653.

1286. ——. Le grand or-potable des anciens philosophes ... Paris: l'autheur, 1653.
3 ℓ., 292 [i.e. 284] p.

1287. ——. Sommaire de la medecine chymiqve ... Auec un recueil de diuers secrets de medecine. Paris: P. Billaine, 1632.
8 ℓ., 433 p.

1288. ——. Le vray tresor de la vie hvmaine ... Premiere partie. Paris: l'autheur, 1653.
4 ℓ., 252 p.
All published?
With his Le grand or-potable ... 1653.

——. *See also* Lettres envoyées à Mr. de Gerzan ... [n.d.].

1289. DUSSEAU, Michel. Enchirid, ov Manipvl des miropoles. Sommairement traduit & commenté suiuant le texte Latin ... Lion: I. de Tovrnes, 1561.
194 p., 5 ℓ.

1290. ——. ——. Lyon: J. Champion & C. Fourmy, 1655.
400 p., 12 ℓ.

1291. DUVERNEY, Guichard Joseph. Ana-tomie de la tête, en tableaux imprimés ... Paris: Gautier ..., 1748.
2 v. illus., folio.

1292. ——. Tractatus de organo auditus, continens structuram, usum et morbos omnium auris partium. Norimbergae: impensis J. Ziegeri, typis J.M. Spörlini, 1684.
10 ℓ., 48 p. illus.

1293. ——. Traité des maladies des os. Paris: de Bure, 1751.
2 v.

E

1294. An EASY WAY to prolong life, by a little attention to what we eat and drink: containing a chemical analysis: or, An enquiry into the nature and properties of all kinds of food ... By a medical gentleman. Dublin: J. Potts, 1773.
2 *l*., 72 p., 2 *l*.

1295. EBERHARD, Johann Peter. Abhandlung von dem Ursprung der Perle worin deren Zeugung, Wachsthum und Beschaffenheit erklärt, und eine Nachricht von verschiedenen Perlenfischereien gegeben wird. Halle: Renger, 1751.
7 *l*., 172 p., 2 *l*. illus.
With his Gedenken vom Feuer ... 1750.

1296. ———. Gedenken vom Feuer und denen damit verwandten Körpern dem Licht und der elektrischen Materie, nebst einem Anhang vom alchimistischen Feuer worin ein rares Sendschreiben des Pontanus mitgetheilt und erklärt wird. Halle: Renger, 1750.
7 *l*., 208 p. illus.

EDINBURGH. Royal College of Physicians. *See* Royal College of Physicians of Edinburgh.

EDINBURGH. Royal Hospital. *See* Brookes, R., The general dispensatory ... 1753.

1297. EDWARDS, John. A select collection of one hundred plates; consisting of ... exotic and British flowers ... and a short account of ... their uses in medicine ... London: for S. Hooper, 1775.
1 *l*., 50 p., 1 *l*. illus., folio.

EGLINUS ICONIUS, Raphael. *See* Thor, George.

1298. EGUIA Y HARRIETA, Félix Fermin. Formulario de medicamentos ... Reimpresso ... Madrid: G. Ramirez [1759].
8 *l*., 175 p.

EHRHARD, Johannes David. De tinctura bezoardica essentificata. *See* Wedel, Georg Wolfgang, *praeses*.

1299. EHRMANN, Friedrich Ludwig. Essai d'un art de fusion a l'aide de l'air du feu, ou air vital ... Traduit de l'allemand par M. de Fontallard ... Suivi des mémoires de Mr. Lavoisier ... sur le même sujet. Strasbourg: J.G. Treuttel ..., 1787.
xxxii, 366 p., 1 *l*. illus.

1300. EINES SCHARFSINNIGEN CHYMICI hinterlassene Gedanken von verbesserung der Metallen ... Hermanstadt: G. Bauer, 1757.
32 p.
With Leursen, J., Chymischen Schau-Platzes ... 1708.

1301. EINES WAHREN ADEPTI besondere Geheimnisse von der Alchymie ... Dressden: J.N. Gerlach, 1757.
6 *l*., 276 p., 10 *l*. illus.

1302. EINFÄLTIGER iedoch deutlicher und verhoffentlich nützlicher Unterricht von der Luna compacta et fixa, bestehende in einen kurtzen General-Bericht von derselben und dann in einer Collection von hundert Special-Processen davon ... Durch einen Freund der edeln Chymie une Metallurgie am grünen Hartze. Leipzig: J.H. Klossen, 1715.
8 *l*., 152 p.
With Cassius, A., De extremo illo ... 1685.

1303. EISENMANN, Georg Heinrich. Quatre tables anatomiques representant une observation tres rare d'une double matrice, mis au jour par ordre de la Faculte de Medicine de Strasbourg ... Traduit du Latin. Strasbourg: A. König, 1752.
7 *l*. illus., folio.

———. Theses medicæ de medicamentis martialibus. *See* Henninger, J.S., *praeses*.

1304. EIZAT, Edward. Apollo mathemati-
cus: or the Art of curing diseases by the
mathematicks ... to which is subjoined, A
discourse of certainty, according to the
principles of the same author ... [Edinburgh?]
1695.
    142, 26 p.

    ELFF, Eric. De haemorrhagiis uteri.
See Linné, C. von, *praeses.* Entry 2450.

1305. ELSHOLTZ, Johann Sigismund. The
curious distillatory: or The art of distilling
coloured liquors, spirits, oyls, etc. ... Put
into English by T.S. ... London: J.D. for R.
Boulter, 1677.
    8 *l.*, 111 p. illus.

1306. ———. De phosphoris observationes:
quarum priores binæ antea jam editæ, tertia
vero prima nunc vice prodit. Berolini: G.
Schultz, 1681.
    13 p., 1 *l.* illus.

    ELVERT, Johann Philipp. Dispvtatio
medica sistens millepedas. *See* Henninger,
J.S., *praeses.*

1307. ELYOT, *Sir* Thomas. The castel of
helth corrected and in some places augmented ... [Londini: T. Berthelet] 1541.
    8 *l.*, 94 [i.e. 96] numb. *l.*

1308. ELZEVIER, Kornelis. Lexicon galeno-
chymico-pharmaceuticum universale, of
groot-algemeen apothekers woordenboek ...
Amsterdam: H. Gartman ..., 1790.
    2 v. illus.

1309. ENAUX, Joseph. Méthode de traiter
les morsures des animaux enragés et de la
vipere; suivie d'un précis sur la pustule
maligne. Dijon: A.M. Defay, 1785.
    xlci, 275 p.

1310. ENGEL, Samuel. Bibliotheca selectis-
sima sive Catalogus librorum in omni genere
scientiarum rarissimorum. Bernae: F.S. Faet-
scherin, 1743.
    2 pts. in 1 v.

    ENGSTRÖM, Peter. Dissertatio fun-
damenta valetudinis sistens. *See* Linné, C.
von, *praeses.* Entry 2446.

1311. ENTZELT, Christoph. De re metallica,
hoc est, De origine, varietate & natura corporum metallicorum, lapidum, gemmarum atque
aliarum, quæ ex fodinis eruuntur, rerum, ad
medicinæ usum deseruientium libri III ...

Francofurti: C. Egenolph [1551?].
    8 *l.*, 271 p. illus., charts.
    At the end is bound a ms. of some 70
leaves, written in a 16th century hand and
apparently containing extracts from a medical work of Johannes Gorræus, *Definitionum
medicarum libri XXIIII* relating to stones
and minerals.

1312. ERASTUS, Thomas. De occvltis
pharmacorvm potestatibvs ... Accessit hvic
tractatvi disputatio alia eiusdem fere argumenti, de medicamentorvm purgantium facul-
tate ... Basileæ: P. Perna, 1574.
    4 *l.*, 194 p., 7 *l.*

1313. ———. Dispvtatio de avro potabili
... Adiectum est ad calcem libri Iudicium ...
de indicatione cometarum ... Baileæ: ex
officina Pernea, per C. Vvaldkirch [1584].
    6 *l.*, 144, 23 p., 3 *l.*

1314. ———. Dispvtationvm de medicina
nova Philippi Paracelsi pars prima: in qva,
qvae de remediis svperstitiosis & magicis
curationibus ille prodidit, præcipuè examinan-
tur ... Basileæ: P. Perna [1572].
    8 *l.*, 267 p., 8 *l.*

1315. ERBEN VON BRANDAU, Matthias.
Warhaffte Beschreibung von der Universal-
Medicin, und güldnen Tinctur Ursprung,
Anfang, Mittel und Ende ... Aus des ...
Autoris MSto zum Druck befördert und com-
municiret durch T.P.G.L.M.S. Leipzig:
Lanckisch, 1689.
    6 *l.*, 148 p.
    With his XII. Grund-Säulen ... 1689.

1316. ———. XII. Grund-Säulen der Natur
und Kunst, worauf die Verwandelung der
Metallen gebauet, benebst V. vornehmer
Artisten wahrhafften Processen, worunter
einer des Th. Paracelsi, welcher noch niemahlen in Druck gesehen worden ... nebst
einer kurtzen Beschreibung Johannis Potani
Secreten philosophischen Feuers ... [n.p.]
1689.
    50 p. illus.

1317. ERCKER, Lazarus. Aula subterranea
domina dominantium subdita subditorum. Das
ist: Untererdische Hofhaltung ... Fünffte
auflage. Franckfurt am Mayn: J.D. Jung,
1736.
    6 *l.*, 208 p., 2 *l.*; 36 p. illus.
    The last 36 pages have a separate title-
page: Interpres phraseologiæ metallurgicæ,
oder Erklärung derer fürnehmsten terminorvm
... durch ... Christianum Berwardum ...

1318. ——. Beschreibung allerfurnemisten
mineralischen ertzt unnd bergkwercks arten
... Auffs newe an vielen orten mit besserer
aussführung und mehren Figurn erklärt ...
Franckfurt am Mayn: J. Feyerabendt, 1598.
4 *l.*, 134 numb. *l.*, 3 *l.* illus.

——. *See also* Pettus, *Sir* John,
Fleta minor ... 1686.

1319. ERLÄUTERUNGEN der neuen österreichischen Militär-Pharmakopöe zum Be-
brauche der österreichischen Feldärtze ...
Wien: A.A. Patzowsky, 1795.
2 *l.*, 300 [i.e. 268] p.

ERNESTI, Joannes. De oleis variis
arte chymica destillatis. *In* Hartmann, J.,
Praxis chymiatrica ... 1647, etc.

1320. ERÖFFNETES philosophisches Vatter-
hertz, so bey heutiger Ausbreitung ... dess
sternflüssigen Blumengeruchs der hohen
Göttlichen Gnadengab der universal medicin
nicht länger hat können verschlossen blei-
ben ... Strassburg: G.A. Dolhopffen, 1676.
2 *l.*, 76 p.

1321. ERXLEBEN, Johann Christian Polykarp.
Anfangsgründe der Chemie ... Göttingen: J.
C. Dieterich, 1775.
16 *l.*, 472 p., 26 *l.*

1322. ESPAGNET, Jean d'. Enchiridion
physicæ restitvtæ ... Tractatus alter in-
scriptus Arcanvm Hermeticæ philosophiæ
opvs ... Vtrumque opus eiusdem authoris
anonymi, Spes mea est in agno. Quarta
editio emendata & aucta. Parisiis: vidua N.
de Sercy, 1642.
199, 105 p.

——. ——. *In* Aubigné de la Fosse,
N., Bibliotheca chemica ... 1653, etc.

——. Arcanum: or, The grand secret
of hermetick philosophy. *In* Dee, A., Fasciculus chemicus ... 1650.

1323. ——. Enchiridion physicae restitutæ;
or, The summary of physicks recovered ...
London: W. Bentley ..., 1651.
12 *l.*, 167 p.

1324. ——. La philosophie natvrelle
restablie en sa pvreté ... Auec le traicte de
l'ouurage secret de la philosophie d'Hermez
... Spes mea est in agno. Paris: E. Pepingué,
1651.
16 *l.*, 378 p., 3 *l.*

1325. ——. Das geheime Werck der Hermetischen Philosophie ... Leipzig: V. Adler,
1685.
6 *l.*, 90 p.

1326. An ESSAY on the use and abuse of
tea. Being a mechanical account of its action
upon human bodies ... by a physician. The
second edition. London: J. Clarke, 1725.
1 *l.*, 63 p. illus.

1327. ESTIENNE, Charles. De dissectione
partium corporis humani libri tres, à Carolo
Stephano, editi. Vnà cum figuris & incisionum
declarationibus, à Stephano Riuerio cōpositis.
Parisiis: S. Colineaus, 1545.
12 *l.*, 375 p. illus.

1328. ——. Pratum, lacvs, arundinetum.
Parisiis: S. Colinænus & F. Stephanus, 1543.
36 numb. *l.*

1329. ESTIENNE, Henri. Dictionarivm
medicum, vel, Expositiones vocum medi-
cinaliū, ad verbum excerptæ ex Hippocrate,
Aetio, Aretaeo, Alex. Tralliano, Galeno,
Pavlo Aegineta, Oribasio, Actvario, Rufo
Ephesio, Corn. Celso. Cum Latina interpretatione ... [Paris] excudebat H. Stephanus,
H. Fuggeri typographus, 1564.
608 p., 14 *l.*

1330. ——. Medicæ artis principes, post
Hippocratem & Galenum. Græci Latinitate
donati, Aretæus, Ruffus Ephesius, Oribasius,
Paulus Aegineta, Aetius, Alex. Trallianus,
Actuarius, Nic. Nyrepsus. Latini, Corn. Celsus, Scrib. Largus, Marcell. Empiricus ...
[Paris] excudebat H. Stephanus, H. Fuggeri
typographus, 1567.
var. pag.

ETSCHENREUTER, Gallus. Epistola
ad Guilielmum Gratarolum. *In* Opuscula
quaedam chemica ... 1614.

ETTEILLA. *See* Alliette.

1331. ETTMÜLLER, Michael. Methode de
consulter et de prescrire les formules de
medecine ... Lyon: T. Amaulry, 1698.
7 *l.*, 656 p., 34 *l.*

1332. ——. Nouveaux instituts de medecine. Lyon: T. Amaulry, 1693.
8 *l.*, 620 p., 43 *l.*

1333. ——. Nouvelle chymie raisonée ...
Lyon: T. Amaulry, 1693.
12 *l.*, 443 p., 30 *l.*

1334. ———. Opera omnia theoretica et
practica, in quibus universa praxis medica
sive Omnium totius humani corporis morborum dilucida descriptio ... Accedit Chirurgia medica ... Lvgdvni: 1685.
    6 *l.*, 428, 436, 212, 362 p.

1335. ———. Opera pharmaceutico-chymica.
Ejus scilicet I. Schröderus dilucidatus ...
II. Commentarius in Danielis Ludovici Dis-
sert. de pharmacia moderno ... III. Pyrotechnia rationalis ... Ejusdem dissertationes
selectæ academiæ ... Lugduni: 1686.
    var. pag.

1335a. ———, *praeses.* Dissertationem
medicam de chirurgia infusoria ... respondente Georgio Friderico Stirio ... Lipsiæ:
N. Scipionus, 1668.
    32 *l.*

1336. ———, *praeses.* Exercitatio medica
sistens ideam praescribendarum formularum
... Respondens Johannes Matthaeus Merckell
... Lipsiae: vidua G. Niemann [1683].
    56 *l.*

1337. ETTNER, Johann Christoph von. Des
getreuen Eckharts entlauffener Chymicus ...
Mit Beyfügung Sinn- und Lehr-reicher er-
schrecklicher und lustiger Begebenheiten ...
Augspurg: L. Kroniger & G. Göbels, 1697.
    7 *l.*, 1120 p. illus.

1338. ———. Dess getreuen Eckharts un-
würdiger Doctor, in welchem wie ein Medicus, der rechtschaffen Handeln will be-
schaffen seyn soll ... Augspurg: L. Kroniger
und G. Göbels, 1697.
    5 *l.*, 958, 207 p.

1339. ———. Manes Poteriani, i.e., Petri
Poterii ... Inventa chymica ... secundum
mentem autoris elaboranda ex autoris ...
textu combinata, exhibente editione Franco-
furtensi Wilh. Richardi Stockii anno. M.DC.
LXVI. adjunctis enchirisibus accuratissimis
... Francofruti: hæredes M. Rolachii [n.d.].
    20 *l.*

1340. ———. Rosetum chymicum, oder:
Chymischer Rosen-Garten, aus welchem der
vorsichtige Kunst-Beflissene Vollblühende
Rosen, der unvorsichtige Laborant aber
Dornen und verfaulte Knospen abbrechen
wird ... Franckfurt: M. Rohrlachs Wittib und
Erben, 1724.
    6 *l.*, 564 p. illus.

1341. ———. Vade et occide Cain, oder:

Gehe und schlage den Cain todt. Franckfurt:
M. Rohrlachs Wittib und Erben, 1724.
    70 p.
    With his Rosetum chymicum ... 1724.

1342. ETZLER, August. Isagoge physico-
magico-medica, in qva signatvræ non
pavcorvm vegetabilivm et animalivm tam
internæ quàm externæ accuratè depinguntur
... Argentinæ: C. Dietzel, 1631.
    3*l.*, 176 p., 5 *l.*

1343. EUGALENUS, Severinus. De scorbvto
morbo liber, in qvo omnia qvae de signis
eius diagnosticis dicipossunt ... Lipsiæ:
M. Lantzenberger, 1604.
    8 *l.*, 321 p., 5 *l.*

    EUGENIUS PHILALETHES. *See* Vaughan,
Thomas.

1344. EUSTACHI, Bartolomeo. Bernardi
Siegfried Albini ... Explicatio tabularum
anatomicarum Bartholomaei Eustachii, ana-
tomici summi ... Leidae Batavorum: J.A.
Langerak et J. & H. Verbeek, 1744.
    4 *l.*, 28, 277 p. illus.

1345. ———. ———. Leidae: J. & H. Verbeek,
1761.
    2 *l.*, 295 p. illus., folio.

1346. ———. A compleat system of the blood-
vessels and nerves, taken from Albinus's edition of Eustachius, also from Ruysch, Vieussens, Du Verney, Haller, Trew and J.B. ...
Translated into English ... London: H. Woodfall for J. & P. Knapton, 1750.
    18 *l.*, 11 plates. folio.
    With Albinus, B.S., Tables of the
skeleton and muscles of the human body
... 1749.

1347. ———. Opvscvla anatomica. Quorum
numerum & argumenta auersa pagina indica-
bit ... Venetiis: 1563.
    6 *l.*, 323 p., 4 *l.*, 95 p., 102 *l.* illus.

1348. ———. Tabulae anatomicae ... praefatione, notisque illustravit ... Jo. Maria
Lancisius. Romae: F. Gonzaga, 1714.
    xliv p., 1 *l.*, 115 p., 6 *l.* illus.,
charts.

1349. ———. ——— novis explicationibus
illustratae ab Andrea Maximino ... Romae:
P. Junchius, 1783.
    lx, 130 p., 47 plates.

1350. EYQUEM, Mathurin, *seigneur du*

Martineau.   Le pilote de l'onde vive, ou le secret du flux et reflux de la mer; contenant xxj. mouvemens; et du point fixe ... Paris: J. d'Houry et l'autheur, 1678.

    8 *ℓ.*, 221 p.   illus.

1351.   ——. —— Seconde edition reveuë & augmentée de devs traitez novveavx svr la philosophie naturelle. Paris: L. d'Houry, 1689.

    8 *ℓ.*, 221, 84 p.   illus.

F

1352. FABRE, Antcine. Traitté des eavx minerales dv Vivarez ... Avignon: J. Piot, 1657.
12 ℓ., 124 p., 2 ℓ.

1353. FABRE, Pierre. Réflexions sur la chaleur animale, pour servir de supplement à la seconde partie des Recherches sur différens points de physiologie, &c. ... Paris: T. Barrois, 1784.
31 p.

1354. FABRE, Pierre Jean. L'abregé des secrets chymiqves ... Avec les vertvs et proprietez des principes, qui composent & conseruent leur estre; & vn traitté de la medecine generale ... Paris: P. Billaine, 1636.
8 ℓ., 392 p.

1355. ———. Alchymista Christianvs ... in qvo Devs ... & quamplurima fidei Christianæ mysteria, per analogias chymicas & figuras explicantur ... Tolosæ Tectosagum: P. Bosc, 1632.
16 ℓ., 236 p., 2 ℓ.

1356. ———. Alle in zwey Theile verfassete chymische Schriften ... Hamburg: in Verlegung L. Eding, gedruckt durch G.F. Schultzen, 1713.
24 ℓ., 976 p.
Volume 1 only of 2 v.

1357. ———. Chirvrgia spagyrica ... in qva de morbis cvtaneis omnibus spagyricè & methodicè agitur, & curatio eorum cita, tuta, & iucenda tractetur. Tolosæ: P. Bosc, 1626.
176 p., 4 ℓ.
With his Palladivm spagyricvm ... 1624.

1358. ———. ———. Tolosæ: P. Bosc, 1638.
132 p., 2 ℓ.
With his Palladivm spagyricvm ... 1638.

1359. ———. Die hell-scheinende Sonne am alchymistischen Firmament ... Das ist ... Manuscriptum, oder sonderbares noch

niemahlen Teutsch herausgegebenes Buch ... Nürnberg: W. Moritz, 1705.
32 ℓ., 240 p. illus.
With Manget, J. J., Bibliotheca chemico-curiosa ... 1707.

1360. ———. Hercvles piochymicvs ... in qvo penitissima, tvm moralis philosophiæ, tum chymicæ artis arcana, laboribus Herculis ... obruta deteguntur ... Tolosæ Tectosagum: P. Bosc, 1634.
8 ℓ., 191 p.
With his Alchymista Christianvs ... 1632.

1361. ———. Hydrographvm spagyricvm ... in qvo de mira fontium essentia, origine ... tractatur ... Tolosæ Tectosagum: P. Bosc, 1639.
4 ℓ., 260 p., 6 ℓ.
With his Palladivm spagyricvm ... 1638.

1362. ———. Myrothecivm spagyricvm; sive, Pharmacopoea chymica, occvltis natvræ arcanis, ex Hermeticorum medicorum scrinijs depromptis abundè illustrata ... Tolosæ Tectosagum: P. Bosc, 1628.
448 p., 11 ℓ.

1363. ———. ———. Item: Insignes curationes variorum morborum ... Cum Chirurgia spagyrica ... Argentorati: heredes L. Zetzneri, 1632.
2 pts. in 1 v.

1364. ———. Palladivm spagyricvm ... Tolosæ: P. Bosc, 1624.
7 ℓ., 394 p., 9 ℓ.

1364a. ———. ———. Editio secunda. Argentorati: heredes L. Zetzneri, 1632.
5 ℓ., 326 p., 7 ℓ.
With his Myrothecium spagyricum ... 1632.

1365. ———. ———. Editio altera ab autore recognita & aucta. Tolosæ: P. Bosc, 1638.
7 ℓ., 276 p., 7 ℓ.

1366. ———. Panchymici sev Anatomiæ

totivs vniversi ... opvs in quo de omnibus
quæ in coelo & sub coelo sunt spagyrice
tractatur ... Tolosæ: P. Bosc, 1646.
  2 v.

1367. ——. ——. Accessit Propugnaculvm
alchymiæ ejusdem authoris. Francofurti ad
Moenum: J. Beyer, 1651.
  14 ℓ., 740 p., 22 ℓ.; 71 p.

1368. ——. Traicté de la peste, selon la
doctrine des medecins spagyriques ...
Tolose: R. Colomiez, 1629.
  5 ℓ., 162 p.

      ——. See also Salmon, W., Poly-
graphice ... 1685.

1369. FABRE-DUBOSQUET. Mes idées sur
la nature et les causes de l'air déphlogis-
tiqué; d'après les effets qu'il produit sur les
animaux, en prolongeant leur force & leur vie.
Londres: 1785.
  1 ℓ., 110 p., 1 ℓ.

      FABRICIUS, Georg. De metallicis
rebus. In Agricola, G., De otru & causis
subterraneorum ... 1612.

1370. FABRICIUS, Hieronymus, ab Aqua-
pendente. Opera chirurgica. Quorum pars
prior pentateuchum chirurgicum, posterior
operationes chirurgicas ... Lugduni Batavorum:
ex officina Boutestaeniana, 1723.
  6 ℓ., 744 col., 12 ℓ. illus.

1371. ——. Opera omnia anatomica &
physiologica ... nunc ... in unum volumen
redacta ... cum praefatione Johannis Bohnii.
Lipsiae: J.F. Gleditsch, 1687.
  6 ℓ., 452 p., 12 ℓ. illus.

1372. ——. —— cum praefatione Bernardi
Siegfried Albini. Editio novissima. Lugduni
Batavorum: J. van Kerckhem, 1738.
  24 ℓ., 452 p., 11 ℓ. illus., port.

1373. ——. Tractatvs de respiratione &
eius instrumentis, ventriculo intestinis, &
gula, motu locali animalium, secundum
totum, musculi artifiio, & ossium de articula-
tionibus ... Paravii: A. Meglietti, 1625.
  var. pag.

1374. ——. Tractatvs qvatvor. Qvorvm: I.
De formato fetu. II. De locvtione & eius
instrumentis. III. De loqvela brutorum. IV. De
venarvm ostiolis, loquitur ... Francofvrti: I.
Zetter, 1624.
  6 ℓ., 158 p., 5 ℓ. illus.

1375. FABRICIUS VON HILDEN, Wilhelm.
Opera quæ extant omnia ... Francofvrti ad
Moenvm: J. Beyer, 1646.
  12 ℓ., 1044 p., 10 ℓ. illus.

1376. ——. Wund-Artzney, gantzes Werck
und aller Bücher ... in das Teutsche übersetzt durch Friderich Greissen ... Hanaw:
getruckt bey J. Aubry, in Verlegung J. Beyers,
1652.
  14 ℓ., 1338 p., 14 ℓ. illus.

1377. FABRONI, Giovanni Valentino Mattia.
Elogio di Francesco Redi ... Firenze: Societa
Stecchi e Del-Vivo, 1781.
  136 p.

1378. FACHS, Modestin. Probier Büchlein, darinne gründlicher Bericht vermeldet,
wie man alle Metall, und derselben zuge-
hörenden metallischen Ertzen und Getöchten
ein jedes auff sein Eigenschafften und
Metall recht probieren sol ... Leipzig: G.
Gross, 1622.
  12 ℓ., 236 p., 5 ℓ. illus.

1379. FAGE, John. Speculum ægrotorum.
The sickemens glasse: or, A plaine introduction wherby one may giue a true, and infallible iudgement, of the life or death of
a sicke bodie ... London: for W. Lugger,
1606.
  64 ℓ.

      FAGRAEUS, Jonas Theodor. Medi-
camenta graveolentia. See Linné, C. von,
praeses. Entry 2496.

      FAIER, Thomas. See Phayer, Thomas.

1380. FALCK, N.D. A treatise on the medical qualities of mercury in three parts ...
London: B. Law, 1776.
  1 ℓ., iv p., 1 ℓ., 328 p.

      FALCONER, William. Appendix on
the efficacy of the Aqua Mephitica Alkalina.
In Dobson, M., A medical commentary ...
1787.

1381. ——. An essay on the Bath waters,
in four parts: containing a prefatory introduction on the study of mineral waters in
general ... London: for T. Lowndes ..., 1772.
  iv, 454 p., 1 ℓ.

1382. ——. Experiments and observations,
in three parts ... London: for W. Goldsmith,
1776.
  2 ℓ., 136 p.

1383. ——. Observations and experiments on the poison of copper ... London: for J. Johnson, 1774.
116 p.

1384. FALLOPPIO, Gabriello. De hvmani corporis anatome, compendivm. Venetiis: P. & A. Meietos, 1571.
88 numb. *l.*

1385. ——. De morbo Gallico liber absolutissimus ... additus etiam est ... De morbo Gallico tractatus Antonii Francanciani ... Secunda editio. Venetiis: F. Laurentinius, 1565.
8 *l.*, 98 numb. *l.*, 1 *l.*; 24 numb. *l.*

1386. ——. Lectiones ... de partibvs similaribvs hvmani corporis, ex diversis exemplaribvs a Volchero Coiter svmma cvm diligentia collectae ... Noribergæ: T. Gerlach, 1575.
38 *l.* illus., charts.
Some leaves mutilated.
With Coiter, V., Externarvm et internarvm principalivm ... 1573.

1387. ——. Observationes anatomicae. Venetiis: M.A. Vlmus, 1561.
8 *l.*, 222 numb. *l.*, 1 *l.*

1388. ——. Secreti diversi et miracolosi ... Novamente ristampati, & ricorreti ... Distinti in tre libri ... Venetia: Milochi, 1650.
16 *l.*, 366 p.

1389. ——. Neu eröffnete vortreffliche und rare Geheimnüsse der Natur, darinnen in dreyen Büchern gehandelt wird ... Geheimnüssen aus der Chymia, vormahls vom Authore in Italiänischer Sprache publiciret, itzo aber ... ins Teutsche übersetzet und vermehret mit einem Anhange von gifftigen Fiebern ... Franckfurt am Mayn: H. Grossen, 1690.
3 *l.*, 6 p., 16 *l.*, 1072 p. illus.

1390. FALSCHER und wahrer Lapis Philosophorum, oder Eines vornehmen und Christlichen Philosophi unschätzbarer Unterricht von allem demjenigen was ihm bey kostbarster Suchung des Steins der Weisen begegnet ist ... Franckfurt: D.C. Hechtel, 1752.
12 *l.*, 416 p., 1 *l.* illus.

1391. FAMA MYSTICA HERMETICA von dem grossen Universal-Stein ... als eine Antwort auf desjenige Avertissement, das eine unbekannte ... in dem Monat Hornung, des

Jahres 1765. durch das Frankfurter und Erlanger Wochenblat an die ... Societäten Londen, Paris, Berlin ... abgegeben und offentlich bekannt gemacht hat ... Frankfurt: J.P. Krauss, 1772.
88 p.

1392. FANIANUS, Joannes Chrysippus. De arte metallicæ metamorphoseos liber singularis ... Parisiis: G. Guillard, 1560.
4 *l.*, 20 numb. *l.*

——. ——. *In* De arte chemica ... 1602.

1393. FARMACOPEA CERUSICA. Farmacopea Cerusica ovvero scelta d'efficaci rimedj universali e particolari alle diverse malattie Cerusiche adattari ... Vercelli: C. Panialis, 1772.
viii, 218 p., 5 *l.*

1394. FARMACOPEA OFICIAL ESPAÑOLA. [Pharmacopoea Hispana] [n.p.: 1797?]
2 *l.*, vii p., 3 *l.*, 211 p., 12 *l.*
Lacking title page.

1395. FARNAUD, Jean. Considérations générales sur les abus de la chimie appliquée à la médicine ... Montpellier: G. Izar & A. Ricard, 1798.
55 p.

1396. FARNER, Christoph. Glauberus nondum vivus. Das ist: Nicht dem lebendigtodten Glauber zur Antwort: sondern nur dem günstigen Leser zur Kurtzweil oder Nachdencken gegebener Appendix ... Stuttgart: J.W. Rösslin, 1657.
30 p.

1397. FAUST, Bernhard Christoph. The catechism of health; selected and translated from the German ... Edinburgh: for W. Creech ..., 1797.
8 *l.*, 146 p.

1398. FAUST, Johann Michael, *ed.* Philaletha illustratus, sive Introitus apertus ad occlusum regis palatium, novis quibusdam animadversionibus explanatus ... Accessit his Narratio de vita et scriptis Starckii, nec non ... Becheri Pantaleon delarvatus. Operâ Joh. Michaelis Faustii ... Francofurti ad Moenum: J.P. Andreas, 1706.
32 *l.*, 122 p., 3 *l.* illus.

1399. FEHR, Johann Michael. Hiera picra, vel De absinthio analecta, ad normam & formam Academiæ Naturæ Curiosorum selecta ...

Lipsiæ: impensis viti J. Trescheri, literis
J.E. Hahnii, 1668.
   8 *l*., 176 p., 2 *l*. illus.

1400. FEIJOO Y MONTENEGRO, Benito
Jerónimo. An exposition of the uncertainties
in the practice of physic. Written originally
in Spanish ... translated from the seventh
edition. London: J. Tonson ..., 1751.
   viii, 64 p.

1401. ——. Rules for preserving health,
particularly with regard to studious persons.
In three treatises. Translated from the
Spanish. London: for R. Faulder [1799?].
   1 *l*., ii, 125 p.

1402. FELD-MEDICAMENTEN-KATALOG mit
beygesetzter neuen Taxe vom Jahre 1795 ...
Wien: A.A. Patzowsky, 1795.
   20 p.
   With Erläuterungen der neuen österreichischen ... 1795.

1403. FELDTAW, Anonymus von. Hermetischer Wunderbaum, worinen zu ersehen, wie
die Wunderbahre Wercke Gottes, von Liebhabern wahrhaffter chymischer Artzney,
recht zu verstehen, vnnd zu erkennen ...
Auss dem grosen Hermetischen Lustgarten
zusamen getragen vnd in sieben Büchlein
abgetheilet ... Franckfurt am Mayn: getruckt
bey A. Hummen, in Verlegung J. G. Schön-
wetters, 1635.
   6 *l*., 66 [i.e. 68] p. illus.
   With Croll, O., Basilica chymica ...
[1629].

   ——. Crollius redivivus, das ist,
Hermetischer Wunderbaum. *In* Croll, O.,
Hermetischer Probier-Stein ... 1647.

   FELGENHAUER, Paul. Anthora, das
ist: Gifft-Heil. *In* Beynon, E., Barmhertziger
Samariter ... 1696.

1404. FENOTUS, Joannes Antonius. Alexipharmacum, sive Antidotvs apologetica, ad
virulentias Iosephi cuiusdam Quercitani ...
euomitas in libellum Iacobi Auberti, de ortu
& causis metallorum contra chymistas ...
Addita est ... Epistola M. Antiti de Cres-
sonieres, ad eundem Quercitanum ... Basileæ
[1575].
   5 *l*., 101 p.

   FERNEL, Jean. Beschryvinghe der
deelen des menschelijcken lichaems. *In*
Paré, A., De chirurgie ... 1610.

   ——. Select medicinal counsels.
In Riviere, L., Four books ... 1658.

1405. ——. Therapevtices vniversalis
seu Medendi rationis libri septem ... Lvgdvni:
S. Honoratus, 1571.
   552 p., 27 *l*.

1406. ——. Universa medicina, cum notis,
observationibus, et remediis secretis Iohannis et Othonis Heurni ... Traiecti ad Rhenum:
G. á Zyll et T. ab Ackersdijck, 1656.
   48 *l*., 490 p., 2 *l*., 536 p., 1 *l*., 28 p.

1407. FERRARA, Camillo. Nvova selva
di cirvrgia divisa in tre parti ... Di nuouo
in questa terza impressione ampliato, &
acresciuto di molti secreti dall'istesso
autore ... Venetia: S. Combi, 1605.
   16 *l*., 565 p. illus.

1408. ——. ——. Et aggiuntoui la quarta
parte, che tratta della qualità, & rimedij
della peste ... Venetia: G.B. Combi, 1627.
   16 *l*., 565 p.; 8 *l*., 86 p. illus.

1409. FERRARI, Giacomo. Idea theriacæ
et mithridatii, ex optima, atque omnium
excellentissima Antonii Berthioli Pragmatia
... nunc demùm a Iacobo Ferrario ... partim
ex doctissimi olim Flamminii Evoli scriptis,
partim ex proprijs excerpta, & ad commune
commodum edita. Venetijs: I. Antonius & I.
de Franciscis, 1601.
   8 *l*., 24 numb. *l*.

1410. FERRARIUS, *monachus*. Bruders
Ferrarii sehr fürtrefflicher chimischer Tractat
viel vermehret, auffs neue ins Teutsch über-
setzet, und ... in den Truck gegeben von
Johann Langen. Hamburg: C. Guth [1674].
   1 *l*., 72 p.
   Lacking pages 71-72.
   This is part two only of Johann Lange's
Chymisches Zwey-Blat ... Franckfort, 1674.
   With Philosophisches Licht und Schatten
... 1738.

   ——. Tractatus chemicus. *In* Combach, L., Tractatus aliquot chemici ... 1647.

1411. FERRIAR, John. An essay on the
medical properties of the digitalis purpurea
or foxglove. Manchester: Sowler and Russell,
1799.
   2 *l*., iv, 66 p.

1412. FERRIS, Samuel. A dissertation on
milk. In which an attempt is made to ascer-

tain its natural use ... and to explain its
effects in the cure of various diseases ...
[London] J. Abraham ... [1785].
    4 ℓ., vii, 206 p.

1413. FICINO, Marsilio. De vita libri
tres, recensiam à mendis sitúque uindicati,
ac summa castigati diligentia ... Parisiis:
T. Richardus, 1550.
    288 p.

    ——. Regiment des Lebens. In Ul-
sted, P., Coelum philosophorum ... 1551.

1414. FICTULD, Hermann. Abhandlung von
der Alchymie, und derselben Gewissheit. Erlang: J.C. Tetzschner, 1754.
    3 ℓ., 226 p.

1415. ——. Azoth et ignis, das ist, Das
wahre elementarische Wasser und Feuer
oder Mercurius Philosophorum, als das
einige nothwendige der Fundamental-Uran-
fänge und Principiorum des Steins der Weisen. Avrevm Vellvs oder Goldenes Vliess
was dasselbe sey, sowohl in seinem Ursprunge, als erhabenen Zustande ... Leipzig:
M. Blochburger, 1749.
    1 ℓ., 379 p. illus.

1416. ——. Chymische Schriften, darinnen
in zwölff königlichen Palästen, von dem
Stein der Weisen gehandelt wird. Samt einer
kurtzen Vorrede ans Licht gestellet, durch
Friederich Roth-Scholtzen. Franckfurt: J.C.
Göpner, 1734.
    4 ℓ., 230 p.

1417. ——. Hermetica victoria, das ist:
Vollkommen erfochtener Sieg und Triumph,
des Welt-beruffenen und gleichwohl verach-
tenen Herma-phroditi, über die gantze Schaar
der Götter und Patronen des metallischen und
mineralischen Reichs ... Leipzig: M. Blochburger, 1750.
    224 p.
    With his Hermetischer Triumph-Bogen ...
1741.

1418. ——. Hermetischer Triumph-bogen,
auf zweyen Wunder-Säulen der grossen und
kleinen Welt bevestiget; das ist: Zwey Tractätlein von der wahren und einigen Weisheit
... das erste, genennt Cabbala mystica
naturæ ... und das zweyte, Occulta occultis-
sime ... Petersburg: bey Veraci Orientali
Wahrheit und Ernst Lügenfeind, 1741.
    37 ℓ., 112, 103 p.

1419. ——. Des längst gewünschten und

versprochenen chymisch-philosophischen
Probier-Steins erste Classe, in welcher der
wahren und ächten Adeptorum und anderer
würdig erfundenen Schrifften nach ihrem
innerlichen Gehalt und Werth vorgestellt
und entdecket worden ... Dritte Auflage.
Dresden: Hilscher, 1784.
    viii, 164 p., 2 ℓ.

1420. ——. Tvrba philosophorvm, das
ist: Gesammlete Sprüche der Weisen zur
Erläuterung der hermetischen Schmaragd-
Tafel, oder von dem Stein der Weisen ...
[n.p.] 1763.
    184 p.

1421. ——. Wege zum grossen universal,
oder Stein der alten Weisen, von einem Nach-
folger und Discipel der Hermetischen Adepty
... [n.p.] 1731.
    48 p.
    With Siebenstern, C.F.S. von, Practica
... 1721.

1422. FIGULUS, Benedictus. Rosarivm
novvm olympicvm et benedictvm. Das ist:
Ein newer gebenedeyter philosophischer
Rosengart ... Basel: in verlegung des autoris,
1608.
    2 parts in 1 v. illus.

1423. ——. Thesaurinella olympica aurea
tripartita. Das ist: Ein himmlisch güldenes
Schatzkämmerlein von vielen ausserlesenen
Clenodien zugerüstet darinn der uhralte grosse
und hochgebenedeyte Carfunckelstein und
Tincturschatz verborgen ... Franckfort am
Mayn: getrucke durch W. Richtern, in Verlegung N. Steinii, 1608.
    224, 63 p.
    There are special title pages for the other
two parts, as follows: Hortvlvs olympicvs
avreolus ...; Paradisvs avreolvs hermeticvs
... The third part is in latin and has separate
pagination.

1424. ——. ——. Franckfurt am Mayn:
gedruckt durch J. Görlin, in Verlegung G.
Wolffii, 1682.
    7 ℓ., 402 [i.e. 392] p. illus.

1425. FILTER, Franciscvs Ernestvs. Dissertatio inavgvralis medica De cortice
angvstvrae eivsqve vsv medico ... Jenæ:
Goepferdt [1791].
    27 p.

1426. FINKE, Leonhard Ludwig. Versuch
einer allgemeinen medicinischpraktischen
Geographie, worin der historische Theil der

einheimischen Völker- und Staaten-Arzeney-
kunde vorgetragen wird. Leipzig: Weidmann,
1792.
  2 v.

1427. FIORAVANTI, Leonardo. De' capricci
medicinali ... libri qvattro ... Di nvovo ...
in molti luoghi, di secreti importantissimi
ampliati ... Venetia: C. Gallina, 1617.
  18 ℓ., 230 numb. ℓ. illus.

1428. ——. ——. Venetia: Il Cestare,
1647.
  20 ℓ., 267 numb. ℓ. illus.

1429. ——. Les caprices ... touchant la
medicine ... Traduites d'Italien en François,
par M. Clavde Recard ... Paris: P. Cavellat,
1586.
  8 ℓ., 136 p., 4 ℓ.
  With his Miroir vniversel ... 1586.

1430. ——. Del compendio de secreti
rationali ... libri cinqve ... Venetia: Z. Conzatti, 1660.
  15 ℓ., 320 p.
  With his Della fisica ... 1629.

1431. ——. Della fisica ... diuisa in libri
quattro ... di nvovo ristampata ... Venetia:
il Spineda, 1629.
  12 ℓ., 391 p.

1432. ——. Miroir vniversel des arts et
sciences ... mis en François par Gab. Chap-
pvys ... reueu & augmenté en céte seconde
edition ... Paris: P. Cavellat, 1586.
  8 ℓ., 526 p.

1433. ——. ——. Plus les Caprices, qui
sent plusieurs & diuerses medecines nou-
uelles de grande efficace ... Paris: R. Chau-
diere, 1598.
  8 ℓ., 526 p.; 8 ℓ., 136 p., 4 ℓ.

1434. ——. Il tesore della vita hvmana
... diuiso in libri quattro ... Di nuouo posto
in luce ... Venetia: M. Sessa, 1582.
  32 ℓ., 327 numb. ℓ. port.

1435. ——. ——. Venetia: L. Spineda,
1603.
  32 ℓ., 327 numb. ℓ.

1436. ——. Three exact pieces of Leonard
Phioravant ... His rationall secrets, and
chirurgery ... Together with a book of excellent experiments and secrets ... Whereunto is annexed Paracelsus his one hundred
and fourteen experiments: with certain ex-

cellent works of B.G. à Portu Aquitano, also
Isaac Hollandus his secrets ... With Quercetanus his spagyrick antidotary for gun-
shot. London: printed by G. Dawson, sold
by W. Nealand, 1652.
  var. pag.

1437. ——. An exact collection of the
choicest and most rare experiments and
secrets in physick & chyrurgery ... Viz. Of
Leonard Phioravant ... His rational secrets
and chyrurgery, &c. Whereunto is annexed
Paracelsus's one hundred & fourteen experiments, with certain excellent works of B.
G. à Portu Aquitano. Also Isaac Hollandus
his secrets ... With Quercetanus his spagyrick antidotary for gun-shot. Also certain
collections out of some manuscripts of Dr.
Edwards ... London: printed by G. Dawson,
sold by J. Saywell, 1653.
  var. pag.

1438. FISCHER VON WALDHEIM, Gotthelf.
Mémoire pour servir d'introduction a vn
ouvrage sur la respiration des animaux,
contenant la bibliographie ... Paris: J.
Drisonnier, 1798.
  106 p. illus.

1439. FITZGERALD, Robert. Salt-water
sweetned: or, A true account of the great
advantages of this new invention both by
sea and by land ... Likewise a letter of
the Honourable Robert Boyle to a friend
upon the same subject ... The fourth edition, with additions. London: Harefinch,
1684.
  1 ℓ., 13 p.

1440. FIVE TREATISES of the philosophers
stone. Two of Alphonse king of Portugall ...
Translated out of the Portuguez into English.
One of John Sawtre a monke, translated into
English. Another written by Florianus Raudorff ... translated ... into English. Also a
treatise of the names of the philosophers
stone, by William Gratacolle, translated
into English. To which is added the Smarag-
dine table. By the paines and care of H.P.
London: printed by T. Harper, sold by J.
Collins, 1652.
  4 ℓ., 72 p.

1441. FLAMEL, Nicolas. Chymische Werke,
als 1. Das güldene Kleinod der Hieroglyphisch
Figuren. 2. Das Kleinod der Philosophiæ.
3. Summarium Philosophicum ... aus dem Französischen in das Teutsche übersetzt ... Wienn:
J.P. Kraus, 1751.
  290 p. illus.

1442. ——. Le grand esclairsissement de
la pierre philosophale pour la transmutation
de tous les metaux ... Paris: L. Vendosmes,
1628.
    8 *l.*, 99 p., 2 *l.*

1443. ——. ——. Amsterdam: Lamy, 1782.
    2 *l.*, 66 p.
    With Philovite, *pseud.*, La verité ... 1753.
Forms *Supplément à la Bibliothèque des
philosophes chymiques.* [By J.M. de Riche-
bourg] *Seconde partie.*

——. Le livre des figures hiero-
glifiques. *In* Arnauld, P., Trois traites ...
1612.

1444. ——. Nicholas Flammel, his exposition of the hieroglyphicall figures which
he caused to bee painted vpon an arch in
St. Innocents church-yard in Paris. Together
with the secret booke of Artephivs, and the
epistle of Iohn Pontanus ... Faithfully done
into English out of the French and Latine
copies. By Eirenævs Orandvs ... London:
T.S. for T. Walkley, 1624.
    6 *l.*, 240 p., 4 *l.*   illus.

——. Le sommaire philosophique.
In Metallique, De la transformation metallique ... 1561.

1445. FLANDES, Luis de. El antiguo
academico, contra el moderno sceptico, ò
dudoso, rigido, ò moderado ... Madrid: Imprenta del Reyno [1742].
    18 *l.*, 265 p.

FLEMYNG, Malcolm. Dissertation
sur les decouvertes de François Solano. *In*
Fouquet, H., Essai sur le pouls ... 1767.

1446. FLOYER, *Sir* John. The ancient
ψυχρολουσία revived: or, An essay to prove
cold bathing both safe and useful. In four
letters ... London: for S. Smith and B. Walford, 1702.
    12 *l.*, 328 p., 1 *l.*

1447. ——. Φαρμακο-Βασανος: or, The
touch-stone of medicines. Discovering the
vertues of vegetables, minerals, & animals,
by their tastes & smells ... London: for M.
Johnson, 1687-1691.
    2 v. in 1.

1448. ——. ψυχρολουσία: or, The history
of cold bathing: both ancient and modern. In
two parts. The first written by Sir John
Floyer. The second ... by Dr. Edward Baynard.

The second edition, with large additions ...
London: for S. Smith and B. Walford, 1706.
    17 *l.*, 192, 240 p., 12 *l.*

——. Inqvisitio in usum & abusum
calidorum, frigidorum & temperatorum balneorum. *In* Vallerius, N., Tentamina physico-
chymica ... 1699.

1449. ——. Traitè de l'asthme, contenant
la description, les causes & le traitement de
cette maladie. Traduit de l'Anglois. Paris:
P.F. Didot, 1761.
    1x, 286 p., 1 *l.*

1450. FLUDD, Robert. Tractatvs apolo-
geticvs integritatem societatis de Rosea
Crvce defendens ... Lugduni Batavorum: G.
Gasson, 1617.
    196 p.

1451. ——. Tractatus secundus, de natvræ
simia seu technica macrocosmi historia, in
partes undecim divisa ... Editio secunda.
Francofvrti: sumptibus haeredum J. T. de Bry,
typis C. Rotelii, 1624.
    788 p., 5 *l.*   illus.
    With his Utriusque cosmi maioris ...
1617.

1452. ——. Tractatvs theologo-philosophi-
cus, in libros tres distributus; quorum I. de
vita. II. de morte. III. de resurrectione ... a
Rudolfo Otreb ... Oppenheimii: typis H. Galleri,
impensis J.T. de Bry, 1617.
    126 p.   port.

1453. ——. Utriusque cosmi maioris scilicet et minoris metaphysica, physica atqve
technica historia in duo volumina secundum
cosmi differentiam diuisa ... Tomus primus
De macrocosmi historia in duos tractatus
diuisa. Quorum primus de Metaphysico macrocosmi ... Secundus de Arte naturæ simiain
macrocosmo producta ... Oppenhemii: ære J.
T. de Bry, typis H. Galleri, 1617.
    1 *l.*, 206 p., 5 *l.*   illus.
    Lacks pages 3-6.
    Volume one, part one only. Part two, in the
second edition, is bound with this.

FONTAINE, Jacques. *See* Fontanus,
Jacobus.

1454. FONTANA, Andrea. Fontana dove
n'esce fuori acque di secreti, doue leggendo
ne cauerai acqua chiara, de restituire la
sanita & scuotere la sete à qualunque in-
fermo ... Venetia [n.d.].
    8 *l.*

1455. FONTANA, Felice. Opuscoli scientifici ... Firenze: G. Cambiagi, 1783.
4 *l.*, 219 p.

1456. ——. Opuscules physiques et chymiques. Traduits de l'Italien par M. Gibelin. Paris: Nyon, 1784.
4 *l.*, 264 p.

1457. ——. Physische Untersuchungen über die Natur der Salpeterluft; der vom Brennbaren beraubten Luft; und der fixen Luft. Aus dem Französischen und Italienischen übersetzt von F. von Wasserberg. Wien: Gräffer, 1777.
2 *l.*, 228 p.

1458. ——. Traité sur le vénin de la vipere sur les poisons Americains sur le lauriercerise et sur quelques autres poisons végetaux ... Florence: 1781.
2 v. illus.

1459. ——. Treatise on the venom of the viper; on the American poisons; and on the cherry laurel, and some vegetable poisons ... Translated from the original French ... by Joseph Skinner ... London: for J. Murray, 1787.
2 v. illus.
Volume one only.

1460. FONTANUS, Jacobus. Practica cvrandorvm morborvm corporis humani, in quatuor libros distincta. Nunc primum in lucem edita. Parisiis: A. Beys, 1611.
5 *l.*, 572 p.
Lacking pages 569-570.

1461. FONTE, Lelius à. Consvltationes medicinales in qvibvs vera, vivaq. consvltandi effigies elucet, plurimorumque difficilium, & notatu dignorum affectuum agnitio, tractandique ... Venetiis: I. Guerilius, 1608.
20 *l.*, 459 p., 1 *l.*

1462. FOOT, Jesse. The life of John Hunter. London: for T. Becket, 1794.
2 *l.*, 287 p.

1463. FORDYCE, John. Historia febris miliaris, et de hemicrania dissertatio ... Accedit De morbo miliari epistola Caroli Balguy. Londini: D. Wilson & T. Durham, 1758.
1 *l.*, 106 p.

1464. FOREEST, Pieter van. The arraignment of vrines: wherein are set downe the manifold errors and abuses of ignorant vrine

monging empiricks ... collected and gathered ... and written first in the Latine tongue, and diuided into three bookes ... newly epitomized, and translated into our English tongue by Iames Hart ... London: G. Eld for R. Mylbourne, 1623.
11 *l.*, 122 p.

1465. ——. Observationvm et cvrationvm medicinalivm sive Medicinae theoricae & practicae, libri XXVIII ... Francofurti: e Paltheniana officina, 1602.
var. pag.

1466. FORMEY, Johann Ludwig. Versuch einer medicinischen Topographie von Berlin. Berlin: E. Felisch, 1796.
1 *l.*, xii, 382 p. charts.

1467. FORMULÆ medicamentorum usitatiores Editio altera auctior. Neapoli: 1791.
501 p.

1468. FORMULES de médicamens, usitées dans les différens hopitaux de Paris ... Nouvelle édition ... Paris: M. Païné, 1792.
xii, 498 p., 3 *l.*

1469. FORSTEN, Rudolph. Disquisitio medica cantharidum historiam naturalem chemicam et medicam exhibens ... Editio altera priori accuratior. Argentorati: A. König, 1776.
4 *l.*, 240 p., 4 *l.*

1470. FORSTER, Johann Reinhold. An easy method of assaying and classing mineral substances ... to which is added, a series of experiments on the fluor spatosus, or sparry fluor, abstracted from the Memoirs of the Royal Swedish Academy of Sciences for the year 1771 ... London: for E. & C. Dilly, 1772.
1 *l.*, 44 p.

1471. FORTE, Angelo di. Incomincia lo libro nominato Verita de la alchimia in loquale ragioneuolmente se narrano quasi tutti li modi ... per fare lo elexire o vero lapis philo. & medicina ... [Venetia: S. de Sabio, 1525.]
14 *l.*

1472. FOSTER, William. Hoplocrismaspongvs: or, A sponge to wipe away the weapon-salve ... London: T. Cotes for J. Grove, 1631.
8 *l.*, 56 p.

1472a. FOTHERGILL, John. A complete collection of the medical and philosophical works ... With an account of his life; and

occasional notes; by John Elliot. London: for
J. Walker, 1781.
4 *l*., xx, 661 p., 1 *l*. illus.

1473. FOUET, Claude. Le secret des
bains et eaux minerales de Vichy en Bourbonnois ... Paris: la veufve d'O. de Varennes,
1679.
12 *l*., 148 p.

1474. FOUQUET, Henri. Essai sur le pouls
... Ouvrage augmenté d'un abregé de la doctrine & de la pratique de Solano ... & d'un
Dissertation sur la théorie du pouls, traduit
du Latin de Mr. Fleming ... Montpellier: la
veuve J. Martel, 1767.
6 *l*., lxiv, 399 p.; viii, 38 p., 3 *l*.

1475. FOURCROY, Antoine François de.
Analyse chimique de l'eau sulfureuse d'Eng-
hien, pour servir à l'histoire des eaux sul-
fureuses en général. Par MM. de Fourcroy &
Delaporte ... Paris: Cuchet, 1788.
xx, 385 p.

1476. ———. Leçons élémentaires d'histoire
naturelle et de chimie ... Paris: 1782.
2 v. illus., charts.

1477. ———. Élémens d'histoire naturelle
et de chimie. Cinquième édition. Paris:
Cuchet, 1793.
5 v. and atlas. charts.

1478. ———. Elements of natural history,
and of chemistry: being the second edition
of the elementary lectures on those sciences,
first published in 1782, and now greatly enlarged ... Translated into English ... London:
for G.G.J. and R. Robinson, 1788.
4 v. charts.

1479. ———. Supplement to the elements of
natural history and of chemistry ... carefully
extracted from the edition of 1789, and
adapted to the English ... London: for G.G.J.
and J. Robinson, 1789.
viii, 381 p. charts.

1480. ———. Mémoires et observations de
chimie ... pour servir de suite aux Elémens
de chimie, publiées en 1782 ... Paris: Cuchet,
1784.
xvi, 447 p. illus.

1481. ———. Philosophie chimique, ou
Vérités fondamentales de la chimie moderne,
disposées dans un nouvel ordre. Paris:
1792.
128 p.

1482. ———. ———. Seconde édition. Paris:
Du Pont, 1795.
174 p.

1483. ———. ———. Nouvelle édition. Paris:
Du Pont, 1797.
8, 157 p.

1484. ———. ... Principes de chimie ...
Paris: 1787.
2 v. in 1.
Series: Bibliothèque universelle des
dames.

1485. FOUQUET, Marie (de Maupeou)
vicomtesse de Vaux. Recueil des remedes
faciles et domestiques, choisis, experimentez,
& trés-approuvez pour toutes sortes de
maladies ... Paris: J. Musier, 1712.
2 v.

1486. FOWLER, Thomas. Medical reports
of the effects of bloodletting, sudorifics,
and blistering, in the cure of the acute and
chronic rheumatism. London: J. Johnson,
1795.
xxi, 287 p., 6 *l*.

FRACANZANO, Antonio. De morbo
Gallico. *In* Falloppio, G., De morbo Gallico
... 1565.

FRACASSATI, Carlo, *joint author*.
Epistolae anatomicae. *See* Malpighi, Marcello.

1487. FRACASTORO, Girolamo. Hieronymi
Fracastorii ... Adami Fumani ... Nicolai Ar-
chii Comitis carminum editio II ... Patavii:
J. Cominus, 1739.
2 v. port.

1488. ———. Hieronymi Fracastorii, et
Marci Antonii Flaminii carmina, quibus in
hac editione accessere alia quamplurima
ex illustribus aliquoe poetis desumpta ...
Venetiis: ex typographia Remondiniana,
1759.
428 p.

1489. ———. Homocentrica. Eivsdem de
cavsis criticorvm diervm per ea qvae in nobis
svnt ... [Venetiis: 1538.]
3 *l*., 78 numb. *l*. illus.

1490. ———. Opera omnia ... Ex tertia editione. Venetiis: Ivntae, 1584.
22 *l*., 213 numb. *l*., 1 *l*. illus., port.

1491. ———. Operum pars prior [-posterior].

Philosophica & medica continens ... Lvgdvni:
F. Fabrus, 1591.
2 v. in 1. illus.

1492. ———. Syphilis, ou, Le mal vénérien,
poeme latin. Avec la traduction en françois,
& des notes [par P. Macquer et J. Lacombe].
Paris: J.F. Quillau, 1753.
1 *l*., 200 p., 2 *l*.

1493. FRANCE. Commission chargés de
l'examen du magnétisme animal. Rapport
des commissaires chargés par le Roi, de
l'examen du magnétisme animal ... Paris:
l'imprimerie royale, 1784.
1 *l*., 66 p.

1494. FRANCIOTTI, Giorgio. Tractatvs de
balneo Villensi in Agro Lvcensi posito. Lucæ:
Busdracus, 1552.
150 p., 1 *l*.

1495. FRANÇOIS, Jean. La science des
eavx, qui explique en quatre parties leur
formation, communication, mouuemens, &
meslanges; avec les arts de conduire les
eaux, & mesurer la grandeur tant des eaux
que des terres ... Paris: S. Piquet, 1654.
6 pts. in 1 v. illus.

1496. FRANCOLINO, Tomaso da. Tesoro
di secreti natvrali ... Roma: G. Cassiani:
[n.d.].
4 *l*.

1497. FRANK, Johann Peter. De curandis
hominum morbis epitome praelectionibus
academicis dicata ... Venice, Mannheim &
Tubingen: 1794–1811.
v.1–v.6, pt. 1.
A set made up of three different editions.

1498. ———. Geneeskundige staatsregeling
... Naar de tweede druk uit het Hoogduitsch
vertaald ... door H.A. Bake. Leyden: F. de
Does, 1787–1794.
4 v. in 6.

1499. ———. System einer vollständigen
medicinischen Polizey ... Manheim: C.F.
Schwan, 1780–1788.
4 v. illus., port.
Vol. 1 is in the second edition.

1500. FRANK, Joseph. Ratio Instituti
Clinici Ticinensis a mense Januario usque
ad finem Junii anni MDCCXCV. Praefatus est
Joannes Petrus Frank. Viennae: Camesina,
1797.
cxiii, 299 p., 1 *l*. illus., charts.

1501. FRANKENBERG, Abraham von. Gemma
magica oder Magisches Edelgestein, das ist,
Eine kurtze Erklärung des Buchs der Natur,
nach dessen sieben grösten Blättern ... zum
Druck übergeben und befördert durch einen
Liebhaber des sel. Autoris ... Amsterdam:
1688.
159 p.

1502. ———. Raphael oder Artzt-Engel. Auff
ehmahliges Ersuchen eines Gottliebenden
Medici A.S. ... Jetzo aber durch zuthum guter
Hertzen und Forderer verlegt und ans Licht
gebracht. Amsterdam: J. von Felsen, 1676.
2 *l*., 46 p., 1 *l*. illus.

1503. FRANKFURT AM MAIN. Ordinances,
etc. Reformation oder ernewerte Ordnung
des heyl. Reichs Statt Franckfurt am Mayn,
die Pflege der Gesundheit betreffend ...
Franckfurt am Mayn: T.M. Gössen, 1669.
190 p.

1504. ———. ———. Franckfurt am Mayn:
J.D. Zunner, 1687.
184 p.

1505. FRATA ET MONTALBANO, Marco
Antonio. Dell'acqve minerali del regno
d'Vngheria relatione ... Venetia: G. Albrizzi,
1687.
4 *l*., 27 p.

1506. ———. Pratica minerale trattato ...
Bologna: Li Manolessi, 1678.
4 *l*., 183 p.; 1 *l*., 39 p.
Part 2 has separate pagination and special
title-page: *Catascopia minerale* ...

1507. FRAUNDORFFER, Philipp. Tabula
smaragdina medico-pharmacevtica, in qua
sexcentorum contra omnis generis morbos
probatissimorum selectissimorumque medicamentorum ... fidelis & accurata descriptio
... Norimbergæ: J. Zieger & G. Lehmann,
1699.
10 *l*., 340 p., 24 *l*.

———. ———. *In* Fuller, T., Pharmacopoeia extemporanea ... 1790.

1508. FREDERICK, Johann Arnold, *praeses*.
Ταβακογια sive Tabaco dissertatio ... Adamus
Hahn autor. Jenæ: Werther [1667].
32 p.

1509. FRÉGEVILLE, Antoine de, *sieur du
Gault*. Palinodie chimiqve: ov Les errevrs
de cest art sont non moins plaisamment, que
serieusement refutez ... Paris: P. Sevestre, 1588

39 numb. *l.*, 1 *l.*

1510.   FREHER, Paulus.   Theatrum vivorum
eruditione clarorum ... Noribergæ: impensis
J. Hofmanni, typis hæredum A. Knorzii, 1688.
   1 v. in 2.   illus., port.
   Pages 1039—1222 and plates 48-54 misbound to follow page 1406.

1511.   FREIND, John.   Emmenologia in qua
fluxus muliebris menstrui phænomena,
periodi, vitia, cum medendi methodo, ad
rationes mechanicas exiguntur ... Huic editioni accedunt ejusdem authoris Prælectiones chymicæ. Parisiis: G. Cavelier, 1727.
   3 pts. in 1 v.   illus.

1512.   ——.   The history of physick; from
the time of Galen, to the beginning of the
sixteenth century ... London: for F. Walthoe,
1725-1726.
   2 v.

1513.   ——.   ——.   The third edition. London: for J. Walthoe, 1726—1727.
   2 v.
   Volume two is the second edition.

1514.   ——.   Nine commentaries upon
fevers: and two epistles concerning the
small-pox addressed to Dr. Mead. Written
in Latin ... Translated into English by Thomas
Dale. London: T. Cox, 1730.
   4 *l.*, 143 p.; 1 *l.*, 137 p.

1515.   ——.   Opera omnia medica. Editio
altera, Londinensi multo correctior et accuratior. Parisiis: G. Cavelier, 1735.
   xvi [i.e. lvi], 232, 388 p., 2 *l.*

1516.   ——.   Prælectiones chymicæ, in
quibus omnes fere operationes chymicæ ad
vera principia et ipsius naturæ leges redigun-
tur, Oxonii habitæ ... Amstelodami: Jansson-
Waesberg, 1710.
   8 *l.*, 93 p., 1 *l.*
   With Helmont, F.M. van, Quædam cogitationes ... 1697.

1517.   ——.   Chymical lectures: in which
almost all the operations of chymistry are
reduced to their true principles and the laws
of nature. Read in the Museum at Oxford,
1704 ... Englished by J.M. To which is
added, An appendix ... The second edition.
London: J.W. for C. Bowyer, 1729.
   8 *l.*, 200 p.

1518.   FREKE, John.   A treatise on the nature and property of fire. In three essays ...

London: for W. Innys and J. Richardson, 1752.
   viii, 196 p.

1519.   FRENCH, John.   The art of distillation, or A treatise of the choisest spagyricall
preparations performed by way of distillation ... London: printed by R. Cotes, sold by
T. Williams, 1651.
   12 *l.*, 199 p., 8 *l.*   illus.

1520.   ——.   ——.   The second edition. To
which is added, The London-distiller ... London: E. Cotes for T. Williams, 1653.
   8 *l.*, 191, 64 p., 8 *l.*   illus.

1521.   ——.   ——.   To which is added in
this third impression Calcination and sub-
limation: in two books ... London: E. Cotes
for T. Williams, 1664.
   8 *l.*, 250 p., 11 *l.*; 1 *l.*, 46 p., 2 *l.*   illus.

1522.   ——.   ——.   Fourth impression ...
London: E. Cotes for T. Williams, 1667.
   1 v. in 2.   illus.

1523.   ——.   The York-shire spaw, or A
treatise of four famous medicinal wells ...
London: for E. Dod & N. Ekins, 1652.
   4 *l.*, 124 p., 1 *l.*

1524.   FRIES, Lorenz, *of Colmar*.   Spiegl
der Artzny des gleichē vormals nie von keinē
doctor in tütsch vssgangē ist nützlich vñ
gütt allē denen so d'artzt radt begerent auch
dē gestreiffeltē leyē welche sich vnd erwindē
mit artznei vmb zegō ... [Strassburg: J. Grieninger, 1519.]
   clxxvi numb. *l.*   illus.

1525.   FRIGIMELIZA, Francesco.   De balneis
metallicis artificio parandis, liber postumus
novi argumenti e bibliotheca Joannis Rhodii
... Norimbergæ: J. Zieger, 1679.
   44 p., 2 *l.*

   FRITSCHIUS, Johann Christian.   The
grounds of pyrotechnical metallurgy.   *In*
Pyrotechnical discourses ... 1705, etc.

   FROMSCHMIDT VON HUGENFELSS,
Israel, *pseud.   See* Grimmelshausen, Hans
Jacob Christoffel von.

1526.   FRYDAU, Ferdinand von.   Licht des
Lichtes, das ist Beschreibung und Beleuch-
tung des fürstlichen und monarchischen grossen Geheimnisses aller Geheimnisse, des
Schatzes aller Schätze, des Steins der
Weisen ... Quedlinburg: Biesterfeld, 1763.
   136 p.

1527. ――. Sendschreiben an einen durch-
lauchtigsten Prinz eines hochfürstlichen
Hauses des Deutschen Reichs in welchem
von dem grossen hermetischen Geheimniss
dem Stein der Weisen gehandelt wird ...
Quedlinburg: Biesterfeld, 1762.
			64 p.
			With his Licht des Lichtes ... 1763.

1528. FUCHS, Leonhart. De componendorvm
miscendorvmqve medicamentorum ratione
libri quatuor ... Lvgdvni: I. Frellonius, 1556.
			48 *l.*, 910 p.

1529. ――. ――. Lvgdvni: I. Frellonius,
1561.
			48 *l.*, 910 p., 1 *l.*

1530. ――. De historia stirpivm commentarii insignes ... adiectis earvndem vivis
plvsqvam quingentis imaginibus ... Basileæ:
Isingrinius, 1542.
			14 *l.*, 896 p., 2 *l.*

1531. ――. Den nieuwen herbarius, dat
is, dboeck van den cruyden, int welcke ...
bescreuen is niet alleen die gantse historie ... van meesten deel de cruyden ... maer
oock alle de wortelen, stelen ... Basel: M.
Isingrinius [1550?].
			278 *l.* illus., port.

1532. ――. De sanandis totivs hvmani
corporis ... libri quinque ... Basileae [I.
Oporinus, 1542].
			8 *l.*, 608 p., 10 *l.*

1533. ――. Methodvs sev Ratio compen-
diaria perueniendi ad ueram solidamque
medicinā ... Eivsdem de vsitata hvivs tem-
poris componendorum miscendorumque
medicamentorum ratione libri III ... Basileae:
M. Isingrinius, 1541.
			40 *l.*, 540 p.

1534. ――. Paradoxorvm medicinae libri
tres, in qvibvs sanè mvlta à nemine hactenvs
prodita, Arabum ætatisque nostræ medicorum
errata non tantum indicantur, sed ... confu-
tantur ... Obiter deniqve hic Sebastiano
Montuo ... respondetur, eiusque annotatiun-
culæ ... exploduntur ... Basileae: I. Bebelius,
1535.
			10 *l.*, 122 numb. *l.*, 1 *l.*
			With Hippocrates, Epidemion ... 1537.

1535. FUENTE PIEROLA, Geronimo de la.
Tyrocinio pharmacopeo methodo medico, y
chimico ... Segvnda impresion ... Alcala:
F.G. Fernandez, 1673.

			6 *l.*, 236 p., 5 *l.*

1536. FULLER, Francis. Medicina gymnas-
tica: or, A treatise concerning the power of
exercise, with respect to the animal oeconom?
and the great necessity of it in the cure of
several distempers. The second edition, with
additions. London: R. Knaplock, 1705.
			18 *l.*, 284 p.

1537. ――. ――. The fourth edition. London: R. Knaplock, 1711.
			19 *l.*, 271 p., 5 *l.*

1538. FULLER, Thomas. Pharmacopoeia
extemporanea sive Præscriptorum sylloge
... Una cum viribus, operandi ratione, dosibus & indicibus annexis. Editio altera emendatior ... Londini: S. Smith & B. Walford, 1702
			6 *l.*, 288 p.
			Pages 253-263 misbound before page 1.

1539. ――. ――. Editio quarta ... Londini:
B. Walford, 1708.
			12 *l.*, 298 p., 13 *l.*

1540. ――. ――. Editio sexta ... Amstelædami: Wetstenios, 1709.
			8 *l.*, 319 p.

1541. ――. ――. Editio quinta ... Londini: G. Innys, 1714.
			18 *l.*, 340 p., 28 *l.*

1542. ――. ――. Editio decima ...
Lovanii: J.F. van Overbeke, 1752.
			20 *l.*, 346 p., 25 *l.*

1543. ――. ――. Editio decima & ultima
... Amstelædami: F. Grasset, 1761.
			42, 486 p.

1544. ――. ――. Cui adjectum est Enchiridion medicum practicum Josephi Jacksonii. Editio Veneta quarta ... Venetiis: A.
Perlini, 1763.
			xxxii, 303, 112 p.

1545. ――. ――. Editio castigatior curante
Theod. Baron. Parisiis: T. Barrois, 1768.
			xlix p., 1 *l.*, 600 p.

1546. ――. ――. Cui adduntur Tabula
smaragdina Philippi Fraundorffer, Thesaurus
Ludovicianus, ac Enchiridion medicum practicum Josephi Jacksonii. Venetiis: J. Orlandelli, 1790.
			xxxii, 264, 112, 152, 66 p.

1547. ――. Pharmacopoeia extemporanea:

or, A body of prescripts ... Done into English out of Latin by the author. With large additions and emendations. London: B. Walford, 1710.
    8 *l*., 443 p., 14 *l*.

1548. ——. ——. The third edition with additions ... London: for W. and J. Innys, 1719.
    9 *l*., 536 p., 16 *l*.

1549. ——. ——. The fourth edition. London: W. Innys, 1730.
    9 *l*., 528 p., 15 *l*.

1550. FUSCH, Remaclus. Historia omnivm aqvarvm quæ in communi hodie practicantium sunt usu ... Accessit preterea conditorum ... & specierum aromaticorum ... tractatus ... [Venetiis: V. Rossinelli, 1542.]
    61 *l*.

1551. FUZY, Antoine. Le mastigophore, ov Precvrsevr dv zodiaqve. Auquel, par maniere apologetique, sont brisées les brides à veaux de Maistre Ivvain Solanicqve ... Traduit de Latin en François par Maistre Victor Grévé ... [n.p.] 1609.
    4 *l*., 330 p.
    Lacking pages 95–96.

G

1552. GAEBELKHOUER, Osswaldt. The boock of physicke ... Faithfullye translated out of High-duche by ... Charles Battus ... And now neuelye translatede out of Low-duche into Englishe by A.M. Dorte: I. Caen, 1599.
22 *l.*, 393 p., 1 *l.*

1553. GAFFAREL, Jacques. Cvriositez inovyes, svr la scvlptvre talismaniqve des Persans, horoscope des patriarches, et lectvre des estoilles ... [n.p.] 1650.
8 *l.*, 315 p. illus.

1554. ———. Vnheard-of curiosities: concerning the talismanical sculpture of the Persians; the horoscope of the Patriarkes; and the reading of the stars ... Englished by Edmund Chilmead ... London: G.D. for H. Moseley, 1650.
20 *l.*, 433 p., 4 *l.* illus.

GAHN, Nils. Plantas officinales.
See Linné, C. von, *praeses.* Entry 2465.

1555. GALASSO, Mario. Giardino medicinale di nuouo dato in luce ... a beneficio de i corpi humani. Bologna: V. Benacci, 1587.
16 p.

1556. ———. Novo recettario ilqvale, e intitvlato Thesoro de poueri ... Date nouamente in luce ... Reuisto, & approbato per diuersi collegii d'Italia. [Milano: M. Tini, 1584.]
8 *l.*

1557. GALENUS. De compositione pharmacorum localium, libri decem Iano Cornario medico interprete. Lvgdvni: G. Rouillius, 1549.
16 *l.*, 831 p.

1558. ———. De differentiis febrivm libri dvo, Lavrentio Lavrentiano Florentino interprete. Parisiis: S. Colinaeus, 1523.

28 numb. *l.*
With Celsus, A.C., De re medicæ ... 1529.

1559. ———. De ratione cvrandi ad glavconem libri II. Martino Acakia ... interprete ... Lvgdvni: G. Rouillius, 1551.
412 p., 10 *l.*

1560. ———. De temperamentis libri III. De inaeqvali intemperie liber I. Thoma Linacro Anglo interprete ... Parisiis: I. Gazellus, 1549.
4 *l.*, 81 p., 3 *l.*

1561. ———. In Hippocratis librvm De hvmoribvs, commentarij tres ... Io. Baptista Rasario interprete. Venetiis: V. Valgrisius, 1562.
15 *l.*, 549 p., 1 *l.* illus.

1562. ———. Liber de plenitudine. Polybvs De salubri victus ratione priuatorum. Gvinterio Ioanne Andernaco interprete. Apvleivs Platonicvs De herbarvm uirtutibus. Antonii Benivenii Libellvs de abditis nonnullis ac mirandis morborū & sanationum causis. [Paris]: C. Wechel, 1528.
42, 21 numb. *l.*, 1 *l.*
With Celsus, A.C., De re medicæ ... 1529.

1563. ———. [Omnia quæ extant opera] Prima classis ... [Septima classis] Venetiis: hæredes L. Iuntæ, 1541.
7 v.
A supplemental volume contains three titles, as follows: Introdvctorii libri ...; Extra ordinem classium libri ...; Ascripti libri ...
The index is by Bartholomaeus Sylvanius and is dated 1542.

1564. ———. Omnia, qvae extant, in Latinvm sermonem conversa ... His accedvnt nvnc primvm Con. Gesneri praefatio & prolegomena tripartita, de uita Galeni, eiusque libris & interpretibus. [Basileae]: Froben, 1562.

3 pts. in 1 v.

1565.   ———.   Omnia qvae extant opera in
Latinum sermonem conuersa ... qvinta editio.
Venetiis: Ivntae, 1576–1577.
    7 v.

1566.   GALLARATI, Giuseppe.   Diatriba
medico sceptica de alacali, & acido ...
Bononiæ: J. Montius, 1688.
    81 p.

        GALLUS, Friedrich.   Reise nach der
Einöde St. Michael. *In* Jean de Meun, Der
Spiegel der Alchymie ... 1771.

1567.   GALVANI, Camillo.   Della pietra
fosforica Bolognese. [Bologna: Longhi, 1780.]
    91 p.   illus.

1568.   GANS, Johann Ludwig.   Corallorvm
historia, qva mirabilis eorvm ortvs, locvs
natalis, varia genera, præparationes chymicæ
quàmplurimæ, viresque eximiæ proponuntur.
Francofurti: L. Jennisius, 1630.
    8 *l*., 174 p.   illus.

1569.   GARENGEOT, René Jacques Croissant
de.   Traité des operations de chirurgie,
fondé sur la méchanique des organes de
l'homme, & sur la théorie & la pratique la
plus autorisée ... Troisieme edition ... Paris:
Cavelier, 1748.
    2 v.   illus.

        GARLANDUS, Joannes.   *See* Joannes
de Garlandia.

1570.   GAROFILO, Biagio.   De antiqvis avri,
argenti, stanni, aeris, ferri, plvmbiqve
fodinis ... opvscvlvm. Viennæ: I.T. Trattner,
1757.
    xx, 152 p., 1 *l*.

1571.   GASSMANN, Franz.   Bifolium metal-
licum, seu Medicina duplex, pro metallis &
hominibus infirmis, â proceribus artis Hermeticæ, sub titulo Lapidis philosophici, in
venta, elaborata & posteritati transmissa ...
à Pantaleone, Hermeticæ sophiæ perito.
Noribergæ: P. Fürst, 1676.
    55 p.
    With his Examen alchymisticum ... 1676.

1572.   ———.   ———.   Noribergæ: P. Fürst,
1676.
    55 p.

1573.   ———.   Examen alchymisticum, quo ...
adeptus à sophistâ & verus philosophus ab

impostore dignoscuntur ... Authore Pantaleone,
Hermeticæ sophiæ adepto. Noribergæ: P.
Fürst, 1676.
    44 p.
    Bound in a leaf from a manuscript written
ca. 1400 and containing a portion of a Psalter,
including an illuminated capital drawn in
gold leaf.

1574.   ———.   ———.   Noribergæ: P. Fürst,
1679.
    44 p.
    With his Bifolium metallicum ... 1679.

1575.   ———.   Tumulus Hermetis apertus, in
quo ad solem meridianum sunt videndæ,
antiquissimorum sophorum absconditæ verita-
tes physicæ & recentiorum quorundam erroneæ
opiniones de laudatissimo illo liquore mercurio philosophorum ... illuminatus ab anonymo
Pantaleone, sophiæ Hermeticæ adepto. Noribergæ: P. Fürst, 1676.
    2 *l*., 49 p., 1 *l*.
    With his Examen alchymisticum ... 1676.

1576.   ———.   ———.   Noribergæ: P. Fürst,
1684.
    2 *l*., 49 p., 1 *l*.
    With his Bifolium metallicum ... 1679.

1577.   ———, *supposed author*.   Disceptatio
de lapide physico, in qua Tumbam Semiramidis
ab anonymo phantasticè, non hermeticè sigil-
latam, ab anonymo reclusam, si sapiens in-
spexerit ipsam, promissis regum thesauris
vacuam inveniet. [n.p.] 1678.
    1 *l*., 95 p.; 1 *l*., 28 p.
    Part two has special title-page: *Tumba
Semiramidis hermeticè sigillata* ...
    With Basilius Valentinus, De rebus naturali-
bus ... 1676.

        GASTON LE DOUX. *See* Duclos, Gas-
ton.

1578.   GATAKER, Thomas.   Observations on
the internal use of the solanum or nightshade.
The fourth edition. To which is added, a supplement. [London] for R. and J. Dodsley, 1757.
    1 *l*., 92 p.   illus.

1579.   GAUBIUS, Hieronymus David.   Commentaria in institutiones pathologiae medicinalis. Collecta, digesta à Ferdinando Dejean. Viennae: R. Graeffer, 1792–1794.
    3 v. in 4.

1580.   ———.   Institutiones pathologiae medicinalis. Leidae Batavorum: S. et J. Luchtmans,
1758.

5 *l*., 493 p.

1581. ——. ——. Editio altera in Germania.
Lipsiae: J.P. Kravsii, 1771.
    12 *l*., 512 p.

1582. ——. Pathologie. Traduite du latin
en françois par M.P. Sue. Nouvelle édition ...
Paris: T. Barrois, 1788.
    8, xviii p., 1 *l*., 553 p., 1 *l*.

1583. ——. Libellus de methodo concinnandi formulas medicamentorum. Lugduni
Batavorum: C. Wishoff, 1739.
    6 *l*., 388 p.

1584. ——. De methodo concinnandi formulas medicamentorum libellus. Editio quarta
... Francofurti ad Mænum: F. Varrentrapp,
1750.
    14 *l*., 363 p.

1585. ——. L'art de dresser les formules
de medecine. Traduit du Latine ... Paris:
Desaint & Saillant & P.A. le Prieur, 1749.
    1 *l*., xvi, 529 p., 2 *l*.

1586. ——. Sermones II. Academici de
regimine mentis quod medicorum est. Accessit Abr. Kaau Boerhaave Sermo academicus
de iis, quae virum medicum perficiunt et
exornant. Editio tertia prioribus accuratior.
Argemtorati: A. König, 1776.
    2 *l*., 188 p.
    With Batt, W., Pharmacopoea ... 1785.

1587. GAUGER, Nicolas. Le mecanique du
feu, ou L'art d'en augmenter les effets, &
d'en diminuer la dépense ... Paris: C.A. Jombert, 1749.
    6 *l*., 267 p., 4 *l*.   illus.

1588. GAUTIER D'AGOTY, Jacques. Anatomie
des parties de la génération, et de ce qui
concerne la grossesse et l'accouchement,
jointe a l'angéologie de tout le corps humain
... Seconde édition, augmentée de la coupe
de la symphise. Paris: Demonville, 1778.
    3 *l*., 34 p.   illus., port.

1589. ——. Exposition anatomique de la
structure du corps humain, en vingt planches
imprimées avec leur couleur naturelle ...
Marseille: M. Vail ..., 1759.
    19 *l*.   illus., folio.

1590. ——. Exposition anatomique des
maux vénériens, sur les parties de l'homme
et de la femme ... Paris: J.B. Brunet & Demonville, 1773.

1 *l*., 26 p.   illus., folio.

GEBER. *See* Jābir ibn Haiyān, al-
Tarasūsī.

1591. GEHEIME FIGUREN der Rosenkreuzer,
aus dem 16ten und 17ten Jahrhundert ...
Altona: J.D.A. Eckhardt, 1785.
    3 pts. in 1 v.   illus.

1592. GEHEIME UNTERREDUNGEN zwischen
zweyen vertrauten Freunden, einem Theologo
philosophizante und philosopho theologizante,
von Magia naturali ... Zum Druck gegeben
vom Collegio curiosorum in Deutschland.
Cosmopoli: 1702.
    8 *l*., 144 p.   illus.

1593. Das GEHEIMNIS ALLER GEHEIMNISSE
ex Macrocosmo et microcosmo, oder Der
güldene Begriff der geheimsten Gehemnisse
der Rosen- und Gülden-Kreutzer mit ihren
drey Steinen der Wunder. Leipzig: A.F. Böhme,
1788.
    104 p.   illus.

1594. Das GEHEIMNISS DER HERMETISCHEN
PHILOSOPHIE, in welchem die Verborgenheit
der Natur und der Kunst, die Materie und
Weise zu würken betreffende, vom Steine
der Weisen, durch gewisse Regeln ordentlich
geoffenbaret wird. Aus der dritten vermehrten
und verbesserten Lateinischen Ausfertigung
Parischen Drucks ins Hochdeutsche übersetzt.
Frankfurt: Fleischer, 1770.
    88 p.

1595. GEHEIMNISSE EINIGER PHILOSOPHEN
und Adepten, aus der Verlassenheit eines
alten Mannes. Erstes Theil. Leipzig: C.G.
Hilscher, 1780.
    1 *l*., 187 p.   illus.
    No more published.

1596. סור ליקבה ושרפה i.e. Das GEHEIM-
NUSS DER VERWESUNG und Verbrennung aller
Dinge ... Dritte und mit vielen curiösen Observationibus vermehrte Auflage. Franckfurt
am Mayn: Fleischer, 1759.
    109 p.

1597. ——. ——. Vierte und mit vielen
curiösen Observationibus vermehrte Auflage.
Franckfurt am Mayn: Flesicher, 1771.
    109 p.

1598. GEISSLER, Friedrich. Baum des Lebens
das ist: Gründlicher Bericht vom wahrhafftigen
Auro potabili, wie ingleichen vom wunder-
bahren Stein der Weisen, oder grossen Elixir

derer Philosophen &c. ... Bresslau & Jena:
auff Verlag Veit J. Treschers, druckts J.
Nisius, 1683.
64 p. illus.

1599. GELLERT, Christlieb Ehregott. Anfangsgründe zur metallurgischen Chymie, in
einem theoretischen und practischen Theile
nach einer in der Natur gegründeten Ordnung
... Zweyte, vermehrte und verbesserte Ausgabe. Leipzig: C. Firtsch, 1776.
14 ℓ., 498 p. illus., chart, port.

1600. ——. Metallurgic chymistry. Being
a system of mineralogy in general, and of
all the arts arising from this science ... In
two parts. Translated from the original German ... by I.S. ... London: for T. Becket,
1776.
2 ℓ., iii, xv, 416 p. illus., chart.

1601. ——. Chimie métallurgique, dans
laquelle on trouvera la théorie & la pratique
de cet art ... Ouvrages traduits de l'Allemand
... Paris: Briasson, 1758.
2 v. illus., charts.

1602. GENERAL RULES to be observed in
raising and continuing a salivation: with the
method of cure, and treatment of such dan-
gerous symptoms as may accidentally occur.
London: 1775.
17 p.
With Birch, J., Pharmacopoeia chirurgica
... 1803.

1603. GEOFFROY, Etienne François. A
treatise of the fossil, vegetable, and animal
substances, that are made use of in physick
... Translated from a manuscript copy of the
author's lectures, read at Paris. By G. Douglas. London: for W. Innys ..., 1736.
xxiv, 387 p., 6 ℓ.

GEORGII, Georg Eberhard. Opium.
See Linné, C. von, praeses. Entry 2486.

1604. GERARD, John. The herball or generall historie of plantes ... London: J. Norton,
1597.
10 ℓ., 1392 p., 36 ℓ. illus., port., folio.

1605. ——. ——. Very much enlarged and
amended by Thomas Johnson ... London: A.
Islip ..., 1633.
19 ℓ., 1630 p., 24 ℓ. illus., folio.

1606. GERHARD, Johann. Decas qvæs-
tionum physico-chymicarum selectiorum &
graviorum ... de metallis. Cui adjuncta est

Medulla Gebrica de lapide philosophorum
... Tubingæ: P. Brunn, 1643.
8 ℓ., 143 p.

1607. GERMAIN, Claude. Icon philosophiæ
occultæ, sive Vera methodus componendi
magnum antiquorum philosophorum lapidem
... Parisiis: E. Couterot, 1672.
26 ℓ., 98 p., 1 ℓ.

1608. ——, praeses. Qvæstio medica
cardinalitiis dispvtationibvs mane discvtienda
in scholis medicorvm die Iovis xxii. Martij.
M. Clavdio Germain ... præside. [Paris?:
1668.]
6 p.
Lacking title page. Caption title.
Dissertation at Paris with Gabriel Dacquet
as respondent.

1609. GERMERIO, Gulielmo. Gioia pre-
ciosa ... Opera à chi brama la sanità vtilissima, & necessaria. Diuisa in quattro parti
... Venetia: N. Polo, 1604.
19 numb. ℓ., 1 ℓ. illus.

1610. GERON, T.F. Clavicule de la philosophie hermetique, ou Les misteres les plus
cachés des anciens & modernes sont misse
au jour en faveurs des enfans de l'art ...
[n.p.] 1753.
124 p.

1611. GERSDORFF, Hans von. [Feldtbuch
der Wundartzney. Strassburg: 1526?]
clxxvi p. illus.
Lacking title-page and last leaves.

1612. GERSTEN, Christian Ludwig. Tentamina systematis novi a d mvtationes baro-
metri ... Francofvrti: F. Varentrapp, 1733.
4 ℓ., 222 p., 1 ℓ. illus.

1613. GERTZ, P. Neu-eröffnete Kunst-
Kammer, oder Theophrastische Geheimnüsse
insonderheit vor Weinhändler, Goldschmiede
Mahler und Zobelfärber ... Deme noch beygefüget P. Kertzenmachers Alchimia und eines
anonymi Tractat, Sol sine veste & Sol non
sine veste. Constantinopel: 1720.
var. pag. illus.

1614. GESNER, Konrad. De omni rervm
fossilivm genere, gemmis, lapidibvs, metallis et hvivsmodi, libri aliquot, pleriqve nvnc
primvm editi ... Tiguri: I. Gesnerus, 1565.
8 pts. in 1 v. illus., port.

——. Enumeratio medicamentorum.
In Brasavola, A.M., Examen omnium cata-

potiorum ... 1543.

———. Horti Germaniae. *In* Cordus,
V., In hoc volumine continentur ... 1561.

1615. ———. Thesavrvs Evonymi Philiatri,
de remedii secretis ... nunc primū in lucē
editus ... Tiguri: A. Gessner & R. Wyssen-
bach, 1552.
   580 p., 24 *l.*   illus.

1616. ———. ———. Tiguri: A. Gessner,
1554.
   580 p., 20 *l.*

1617. ———. ———. Lugduni: B. Arnoullett,
1555.
   4 *l.*, 498 p., 19 *l.*   illus.

1618. ———. Evonymvs ... de remediis
secretis, liber secundus, nunc primùm opera
& studio Caspari VVolphii ... in lucem editus.
[Tiguri: C. Froschouer, 1569.]
   8 *l.*, 237 numb. *l.*, 11 *l.*   illus.

1619. ———. The treasure of Evonymvs,
conteyninge the vvonderfull hid secretes of
nature, touchinge the most apte formes to
prepare the destyl medicines ... Translated
... out of Latin, by Peter Morvvyng ... London: I. Daie [1559].
   10 *l.*, 408 p.   illus.

1620. ———. A new book of destillatyon
of waters called the treasure of Evonymvs
... Translated ... out of Latin, by Peter Mor-
wyng ... London: J. Day [1565].
   10 *l.*, 408 p., 7 *l.*   illus.

1621. ———. Tresor de Evonime Philiatre
des remedez secretz ... Lyon: B. Arnoullet,
1555.
   14 *l.*, 325 p., 1 *l.*   illus.

1622. ———. Tesavro di Evonomo Filiatro
de remedii secreti ... Aggiontovi molte et
diverse figvre de fornaci. Tradotto di Latino
in Italiano per M. Pietro Lauro. [Venetia:
G.B. & M. Sessa, 1556.]
   152 numb. *l.*, 16 *l.*   illus.

1623. ———. ———. [Venetia: G.B. & M.
Sessa, 1560.]
   152 numb. *l.*, 16 *l.*   illus.

1624. ———. The newe iewell of health,
wherein is contayned the most excellent
secretes of phisicke and philosophie, deuided
into fower bookes ... Faithfully corrected
and published in Englishe, by George Baker

... London: H. Denham, 1576.
   12 *l.*, 258 numb. *l.*   illus.

1625. ———. The practise of the new and
old phisicke, wherein is contained the most
excellent secrets of phisicke and philosophie
deuided into foure bookes ... Newly corrected
and published in English, by George Baker
... London: P. Short, 1599.
   11 *l.*, 256 numb. *l.*   illus.

1626. ———, *ed.*   Chirvrgia. De chirvrgia
scriptores optimi qviqve veteres et recentiores ... nvnc primvm in vnvm conivncti
volvmen ... Tigvri: A. Gessnervs et I. Gessnervs, 1555.
   10 *l.*, 408 numb. *l.*, 21 *l.*   illus.

1627. GESPRÄCHE in dem Reiche derer Welt-
Weisen, in acht verschiedenen Theilen
zusammen gefasset und mit einer Vorrede
von dem Vorzuge der neuern Welt-Weisen
vor den Alten begleitet ... Halle: J.C. Hendel, 1722.
   7 *l.*, 360 p., 6 *l.*   illus.

1628. GEYER, Johann Daniel.   Müssiger
Reise-Stunden gute Gedancken, von der Gold-
macher-Sucht ... Sechszehender discours.
Dresden: G.C. Hilschern, 1735.
   32 p.

1629. GHERLI, Fulvio.   Il proteo metallico
o sia Delle transformazioni superficiali de'
metalli ... opera filosofico-medico-chimica
... Venezia: G. Corona, 1721.
   8 *l.*, 261 p.

1630. GIBSON, Edmund, *bp. of London.*
The causes of the discontents, in relation
to the plague, and the provisions against it,
fairly stated and consider'd. London: for J.
Roberts, 1721.
   14 p.

1631. GIBSON, William.   The farriers dispensatory, in three parts ... To which is
also added, a compleat index ... London:
for W. Taylor, 1721.
   6 *l.*, 306 p., 9 *l.*, 16 p.

1632. GINÆCEVM CHIMICVM seù Congeries plvrivm avthorvm qui in artem
Hermeticam de lapide philosophico scripserunt, quorum tractatus nec in Theatro,
aut alio volumine vsque adhuc simul im-
pressi fuerunt ... Volvmen primvm. Lugduni:
J. de Trevis, 1679.
   2 *l.*, 727 p.
   All published.

1633. GIOANETTI, Victor Aime. Analyse des eaux minérales de S. Vincent et de Courmayeur dans le Duché d'Aoste avec une appendice sur les eaux de la Saxe, de Pré S. Didier et de Fontane-More ... Turin: J.M. Briolo, 1779.
viii, 119 p.

1634. GIOBERT, Giovanni Antonio. Des eaux sulphureuses et thermales de Vaudier avec des observations physiques, économiques et chimiques sur la Vallée de Gesse et des remarques sur l'analyse des eaux sulphureuses en général ... Turin: J. Fea, 1793.
4 *l.*, 277 p.

1635. GIROLAMI, Flavio. Nvova minera d'oro ... nella quale ... si dimostra, l'arte chimica esser verissima, e con la piera filosofica potersi far l'oro ... Venetia: B. Barezzi, 1590.
4 *l.*, 171 p., 6 *l.*

1636. GIRTANNER, Christoph. Anfangsgründe der antiphlogistischen Chemie. Berlin: J.F. Unger, 1792.
x, 470 p., 1 *l.*

1637. GLASER, Christophe. Traite de la chymie enseignant par vne brieve et facile methode toutes ses plus necessaires preparations ... Paris: l'autheur, 1663.
8 *l.*, 378 p., 2 *l.* illus.

1638. ——. ——. Troisième edition ... Lyon: J. Thioly, 1670.
10 *l.*, 394 p., 2 *l.* illus.

1639. ——. The compleat chymist, or, A new treatise of chymistry ... Written in French ... and from the fourth edition revised and augmented by the author. Now faithfully Englished by a fellow of the Royal Society ... London: for J. Starkey, 1677.
8 *l.*, 285 p., 1 *l.* illus.

1640. ——. Novum laboratorium medicochymicum, das ist: Neu-eröffnete chymische Artzney- und Werck-Schul, in drey Bücher abgetheilet ... Anjetzo ... in das Hoch-Teutsche übersetzet von Johann Marschalck ... Nürnberg: M. & J.F. Endter, 1677.
27 *l.*, 666 p., 7 *l.* illus.

1641. GLASS, Samuel. An essay on magnesia alba ... Oxford: for R. Davis & J. Fletcher, 1764.
6, 38 p.

1642. GLAUBER, Johann Rudolf. Apologia oder Verthaidigung gegen Christoff Farners Lügen und Ehrabschneidung. Franckfurt: T.M. Götzen, 1655.
80 p., 1 *l.*

1643. ——. ——. [Amsterdam?] 1655.
88 p.
With his Explicatio ... 1656.

1644. ——. Apologia sive Defensio ... contra Christophori Farnneri mendacia & calumnias ... Francofurti: T.M. Götzen, 1655.
86 p., 1 *l.*
Title page misbound at end.

1645. ——. Apologia contra mendaces Christophori Farnneri calumnias, ex Germanico in Latinum idioma trans-fusa. Amstelodami: 1655.
94 p.
With his Tractatus de tribus principiis ... 1667.

1646. ——. Zweyte Apologia, oder Ehren-Rettung gegen Christoff Farnern ... Lugen und Ehrabschneidung. Franckfurt am Mayn: T.M. Götzen, 1656.
40 p.
With his Apologia ... 1655.

1647. ——. Arca thesavris opvlenta, sive Appendix generalis omnium librorum hactenus editorum, quæ non solùm cuncta tam in philosophicus & medicis, quàm chymicis scriptis loca obscura illustrat ... Amstelædami: J. Jansson, 1660.
189 p.

1648. ——. Opulenti thesauri, et arcæ thesaurariæ, sive appendicis generalis centuria secunda ... Amstelodami: J. Jansson, 1661.
149 p.
With his Arca thesavris opvlenta ... 1660.

1649. ——. De auri tinctura sive Auro potabili vero ... Amsterodami: J. Jansson, 1651.
22 p.

1650. ——. De auri tinctura sive Auro potabili vero was solche sey, vnd wie dieselbe von einem falschen vnnd sophistischen auro potabili zu vnterscheiden vnd zu erkennen ... Amsterdam: J. Jansson, 1662.
32 p.
With his Furni novi philosophici ... 1661.

1651. ———. De Elia artista. Oder Wass
Elias Artista für einer sey, vnd wass er in
der Welt reformiren, oder verbesseren werde,
wann er kombt? ... Amsterdam: J. Waesberge
& der Witwe E. Weyerstraet, 1668.
71 p.

1652. ———. De igne secreto philosophorum.
Oder Geheimen Fewr der Weisen ... Amsterdam: J. Jansson à Waesberge & Wittwe von
E. Weierstraet, 1669.
54 p., 1 ℓ.

1653. ———. De lapide animali, oder Von
dieser animalischen Materi, oder Subjecto
... Was es eigentlich für ein Materi sey,
unnd wie eine wahre universal Medicin
darauss bereitet werden könne ... Amsterdam: J. Jansson à Waesberge & Witwe E.
Weierstraet, 1669.
60 p.

1654. ———. De tribus lapidibus ignium
secretorum. Oder von den drey alleredelsten
Gesteinen, so durch drey secrete Fewer
gebohren werden ... Amsterdam: J. Waesberge & der Wittwe E. Weyerstraet, 1668.
94 p.

1655. ———. Explicatio oder Ausslegung
über die Wohrten Salomonis: in herbis, verbis, & lapidibus, magna est virtus ... Amsterdam: J. Jansson, 1663.
101 p. illus.

1656. ———. Explicatio verborum Salomonis:
In herbis, verbis & lapidibus magna est virtus. Unà cum adjuncta tractatiuncula de
quinta essentia metallorum ... Amsterdami:
J. Jansson, 1664.
88 p.
With his Tractatus de tribus principiis ...
1667.

1657. ———. Explicatio oder Vber dass
vnlängst, von Joh. Rud. Glaubern aussge-
benes (Miraculum mundi, intitulirtes) Tractätlein aussfuhrliche Erklährung ... Amsterdam: J. Jansson, 1656.
110 p.

1658. ———. Explicatio tractatuli, qui
Miraculum mundi inscribitur ... Amstelodami:
J. Jansson, 1656.
70 p.
With his Miraculum mundi ... 1658.

1659. ———. Furni novi philosophici, sive
Descriptio artis distillatoriæ novæ ... Amsterodami: J. Jansson, 1658.

5 pts. and appendix to pt. 5 in 2 v.
illus.
Part 5 has the date 1651.
The appendix has the title: Annotationes
in appendicem quintæ partis formacum phil-
sophicarum.

1660. ———. A description of new philosophical furnaces, or a new art of distilling,
divided into five parts. Whereunto is added
a description of the tincture of gold ... also,
the first part of the mineral work ... Set
forth in English, by J.F. ... London: R. Cotes
for T. Williams, 1651.
8 ℓ., 452 p., 6 ℓ. illus.

1661. ———. Furni novi philosophici oder
Beschreibung einer New-erfundenen Distillir-
Kunst ... Amsterdam: J. Jansson, 1661.
6 pts. in 1 v. illus.
Parts 2-5 have title: Furni philosophici,
oder Philosophischer Oefen ...
Part 6 has title: Annotationes vber den
Appendicem welcher zu Ende des fünfften
Theils.

1662. ———. Glauberus concentratus. Oder
Laboratoriu·n Glauberianum; darinn die Spe-
cification, vnd Taxation dehren medicina-
lischen, vnd chymischen Arcanitäten, welche
in ermeldtem Laboratorio, von viel Jahren
zu Jahren nach einander bereitet ... Amsterdam: J. Waesberge & der Wittwe E. Weyerstraet, 1668.
75, 15 p.

1663. ———. Glauberus ridivivus, dass ist:
Der von falschen und gifftigen Zügen ermorte
... Glauber. Oder Klarer beweiss das Farners
Speyrischen Dohm-Stiffts Schaffners falsch-
genante Apologia nichts anders alss lauter
auss Neit und Hass erdichte Lügen sein.
Amsterdam: J. Jansson, 1656.
109 p.
With his Gründliche und warhafftige Be-
schreibung ... 1654.

———. The golden ass well managed.
In Cooper, W., The philosophical epitaph
... 1673.

1664. ———. Gründliche und warhafftige
Beschreibung wie man auss der Weinhefen
einen guten Weinstein in grosser Menge
extrahiren sol ... Amsterdam: 1654.
32 p.

1665. ———. Vera ac perfecta descriptio,
qua ratione ex vini fecibus bonum plurimumqu·
tartarum sit extrahendum ... Amstelodami:

J. Jansson, 1655.
28 p.

1666. ———. Kurtze Erklährung uber die
höllische Göttin Proserpinam, Plutonis
Haussfrawen, was die philosophische Poeten,
als Ovidius, Virgilius, und andere darduch
verstanden haben ... Ambsterdam: J. Jansson
von Waesberge und der Witwe E. Weyerstraet, 1667.
56 p.

1667. ———. Libellus dialogorum oder
Gespräch-Buchlein zwisschen einigen Liebhabern der hermetischen Medicin, tincturam
universalem betressend, den wahren Liebhabern guther Medicin, zu gefallen beschrieben ... Amsterdam: J. Jansson, 1663.
91 p.

1668. ———. Libellus dialogorum, sive
colloquia, nonnullorum Hermeticæ medicinæ
ac tincturæ universalis studiosorum ...
Amstelodami: J. Jansson, 1663.
91 p. illus.
With his Tractatus de tribus principiis
... 1667.

1668a. ———. Libellus ignium: oder Feur
Büchlein darinnen von unterschiedlichen
Frembden und biss Dato noch gantz unbe-
kandten Feuern gehandelt ... Amsterdam: J.
Jansson, 1663.
61 p.

1669. ———. Miraculum mundi, oder Aussführliche Beschreibung der wunderbaren
Natur, Art, vnd Eigenschafft des grossmäch-
tigen Subjecti, von den Alten Menstruum
universale oder Mercurius philosophorum
genandt ... Amsterdam: 1653.
1 ℓ., 105 p.
With his Furni novi philosophici ... 1661.

1670. ———. Miraculum mundi, sive Plena
perfectaque descriptio admirabilis naturæ
... ab antiquis menstruum universale sive
Mercurius philosophorum dicti ... Amsterodami: J. Jansson, 1653.
87 p.

1671. ———. ———. Amsterodami: J. Jansson,
1658.
64 p.

1672. ———. Miraculi mundi continuatio.
Darinnen die gantze Natur entdecket, vnd
der Weldt nackent vnd bloss vor Augen gelegt
... dass auss dem Salpeter aller Vegetabilien,
Animalien vnd Mineralien höchste Medicin

zu bereiten, müglich ... Amsterdam: J. Jansson, 1657.
133 p.
With his Explicatio ... 1656.

1673. ———. Miraculi mundi continuatio,
in qua tota natura denudatur, & toti mundi
nudè ob oculos ponitur ... Amstelodami: J.
Jansson, 1658.
133 p. illus.
With his Miraculum mundi ... 1658.

1674. ———. Miraculi mundi ander Theil
... Ambsterdam: J. Jansson, 1660.
10 ℓ., 113 p.
With his Furni novi philosophici ... 1661.

1675. ———. Miraculi mundi pars altera
in quâ adventus jam dudum prædicti Eliæ
artistæ magnificus describitur ... Amstelodami: J. Jansson, 1660.
101 p.
With his Miraculum mundi ... 1658.

1676. ———. Annotationes, uber dessen
Jüngst-herauss gegebenes (Continuatio
miraculi mundi intitulirtes) Tractätlein, in
welchem die darin begriffene Secreta, sambt
angezogenem Auro potabili vero, expliciret,
und defendiret werden ... Amsterdam: J. Jansson, 1659.
39 p.

1677. ———. Annotationes in nuper editam
Continuationem miraculi mundi ... cvm brevi
admonitione seu significatione incognitarum
quidem, sed omnibus hominibus utilissimarum
inventionum & secretorum ... Amstelodami:
J. Jansson, 1659.
37 p.
With his Miraculum mundi ... 1658.

1678. ———. Novum lumen chimicum. Oder
eines new-erfundenen vnd der Weldt noch
niemahlen bekandgemachten hohen Secreti
offenbahrung ... Ambsterdam: J. Jansson vom
Waesberge vnd E. Weyerstraet, 1664.
43 p., 1 ℓ.

1679. ———. Novum lumen chymicum. Hoc
est, Cujusdam recens inventi & mundo nondum unquam patefacti secreti ardui revelatio
... Amstelodami: J. Jansson à Waesberge, et
E. Weyerstraet, 1664.
45 p.
With his Arca thesavris opvlenta ... 1660.

1680. ———. Operis mineralis oder Vieler
künstlichen vnd nützlichen metallischen
Arbeitten Beschreibung erster[-dritter] Theil

... Amsterdam: 1651–1652.
3 pts. in 1 v.
With his Furni novi philosophici ... 1661.

1681. ——. ——. Prag: C. Wussin, 1705.
324 p.

1682. ——. Operis mineralis pars prima
[-tertia] ... Amsterodami: J. Jansson, 1659.
3 pts. in 1 v.
With his Fornacum philosophicarum pars
qvinta ... 1651.

1683. ——. Pharmacopæeæ spagyricæ,
oder Gründlicher Beschreibung wie man aus
den Vegetabilien, Animalien und Mineralien
... gute kräfftige bereiten soll. Erster [-Sie-
bender Theil] ... Amsterdam: J. à Waesberge
und der Witwe E. Weyetstraet, 1656–1668.
10 pts. in 1 v. illus.
Includes: Erster [-Dritter] Appendix ...

1684. ——. Pharmacopoea spagyrica ...
Pars prima [and pars tertia] ... Amsterodami:
J. Jansson, 1654–1657.
3 pts. in 1 v.
Lacking part 2.

1685. ——. Reicher Schatz- vnd Sammel-
kasten oder Appendix generalis vber alle
dessen heraussgegebene Bücher ... In decem
centuriis ... beschrieben ... Amsterdam: J.
Jansson, 1660–1668.
3 pts. in 1 v.
Includes *Centuria erste-fünfte* only. All
published?

1686. ——. Des Teutschlandts Wohlfart
... Amsterdam: J. Jansson, 1656–1661.
6 pts. in 1 v. illus.

1687. ——. Prosperitatis Germaniæ pars
prima[-sexta] ... à philochymico quodam
Latinitate donata. Amstelodami: J. Jansson,
1656–1661.
6 pts. and appendix to pt. 5 in 2 v. illus.

1688. ——. Tractatus de medicina universali, sive Auro potabili vero ... Amstelodami: J. Jansson, 1658.
75 p., 1 *l.*
With his De auri tinctura ... 1651.

1689. ——. Traitté de la medecine vni-
verselle, ov Le vray or potable ... mis en
françois par le Sr. Dv Teil. Paris: T. Iolly,
1659.
62 p.

1690. ——. Tractatus de natura salium ...

Item Tractatulus ... de salium, metallorum,
& planetarum signaturâ ... Amsterodami: J.
Jansson, 1659.
8 *l.*, 96, 44 p.
With his Pharmacopoea spagyrica ...
1654–1657.

1691. ——. Trost der Seefahrenten: darinnen gelehret und angewisen wirt wie sich
die Seefahrende vor Hunger und Durst, wie
auch solchen Kranckheiten so ihnen auff
langwiriger Reise begegnen möchten, ver-
sorgen und bewahren können ... Amsterdam:
J. Jansson, 1657.
102 p., 3 *l.*

1692. ——. Consolatio navigantium: in
quâ docetur ... quomodo per maria pere-
grinantes à fame ac siti immò etiam morbis,
qui longuinquo ab itinere ipsis contingere
possunt, sibi providere ac suppetiari liceat
... Amstelodami: J. Jansson, 1657.
96 p.
With his Pharmacopoea spagyrica ...
1654–1657.

1693. ——. Von den dreyen Anfangen der
Metallen, alss Schwefel, Mercurio, vnd Saltz
der Weisen ... Amsterdam: J. Waesberge &
E. Weyerstraet, 1666.
1 *l.*, 119 p.

1694. ——. Tractatus de tribus principiis
metallorum, videlicet sulphure, mercurio &
sale philosophorum ... Amstelodami: J. Jansson & vidua E. Weyerstraet, 1667.
109 p.

1695. ——. The works of ... John Rudolph
Glauber: containing, great variety of choice
secrets in medicine and alchymy ... Translated into English ... by ... Christopher
Packe ... London: T. Milbourn for the author
..., 1689.
6 *l.*, 440 p.; 2 *l.*, 220 p.; 92 p., 6 *l.*
illus.

1696. GLEDITSCH, Johann Gottlieb. Alpha-
betisches Verzeichnis der gewöhnlichsten
Arzeneygewächse ihrer Theile und rohen
Produkte ... Berlin: A. Wever, 1769.
8 *l.*, x, 480 p., 7 *l.* illus.

1697. GLISSON, Francis. Anatomia hepatis.
Cui praemittuntur quaedam ad rem anatomicam universe spectantia et ad calcem operis
subjiciuntur nonnulla de lymphae-ductibus
nuper repertis. Editio nova, caeteris emendatior. Amstelodami: J.J. à Waesberge & E.
Weyerstraten, 1665.

23 *l*., 423 p., 9 *l*. illus.

1698. GMELIN, Johann Friedrich. Abhandlung über die Wurmtroknis. Leipzig: Crusius, 1787.
1 *l*., 176 p. illus.

1699. ――. Anhang zu der Abhandlung von der Wurmtroknis ... Leipzig: Crusius, 1787.
2 *l*., 269 p. tables.
With his Abhandlung über die Wurmtroknis ... 1787.

1700. ――. Apparatvs medicaminvm, tam simplicivm quam præparatorvm et compositorvm in praxeos adivmentvm consideratvs P. II. Regnvm minerale complectens ... Goettingæ: J.C. Dieterich, 1795–1796.
2 v.

1701. ――. Einleitung in die Chemie zum Gebrauch auf Universitäten. Nürnberg: G.N. Raspe, 1786.
xvi, 528 p., 11 *l*.

1702. ――. Einleitung in die Pharmacie. Nürnberg: G.N. Raspe, 1781.
7 *l*., 392 p., 7 *l*.

1703. ――. Geschichte der Chemie seit dem Wiederaufleben der Wissenschaften bis an das Ende des achtzehenden Jahrhunderts. Göttingen: J.G. Rosenbusch, 1797–1799.
3 v.

1704. ――. Grundriss der pharmacie zum Gebrauche bei seinen Vorlesungen. Göttingen: J.C. Dieterich, 1792.
xii, 493 p., 12 *l*.

1705. GMELIN, Philipp Friedrich, *praeses*. Botanicam et chemiam ad medicam applicatam praxin per illvstria qvaedam exempla dissertation inavgvrali d. V. Avgvsti MDCCLV. ventilanda ... respondente Christiano Lvdovico Bilfinger ... Tubingæ: Erhardt [1755].
1 *l*., 30 p.

GÖCKEL, Christopher Ludwig. De serpentaria virginiana. *See* Wedel, Georg Wolfgang, *praeses*.

1706. GODFREY, Ambrose. Proposals for printing by subscription a compleat course of chemistry, in one volume quarto ... London: 1740.
2 *l*., 4 p. illus.

1707. GODFREY, Boyle. Miscellanea vere utilia: or Miscellaneous experiments and observations on various subjects. In three parts ... London: for J. Robinson [1735?].
5 *l*., 138 p.

1708. GOEUROT, Jehan. The regiment of life, whereunto is added a treatise of the pestilence, with the Booke of children, newly corrected and enlarged by Thomas Phaire. [London: E. Whitchurche, 1560.]
168 *l*.

1709. ――. ――. London: T. Este & H. Myddleton, 1567.
240 *l*.

1710. ――. ――. London: E. Allde, 1596.
87 *l*.

1711. GOGUET, Antoine Yves. De l'origine des loix, des arts, et des sciences; et de leurs progrès chez les anciens peuples ... Paris: Desaint & Saillant, 1758.
3 v. illus., charts.

1712. ――. The origin of laws, arts, and sciences, and their progress among the most ancient nations ... Edinburgh: A. Donaldson and J. Reed for the translator, 1761.
3 v.

1713. GOHORY, Jacques. Livre de la fontaine perillevse, avec la chartre d'amours: autrement intitulé, le songe du verger ... Auec commentaire de I.G.P. ... Paris: J. Ruelle, 1572.
1 *l*., 48 numb. *l*.

1714. ――. Theophrasti Paracelsi ... Compendivm, ex optimis quibusque eius libris, cum scholiis in libros IIII. eiusdē De vita longa ... auctore Leone Suauio ... Vita Paracelsi, Catalogus operum & librorum ... Parisiis: Roville [1567].
80 p., 4 *l*., 81–376 p., 11 *l*. port.

1715. GOLDMAYER, Andreas. Harmonia chymica, de novem lapidum philosophicorum artificiosa preparatione et usu ... Onoltzbach: gedruckt durch J. Lentzen, in Verlegung dess Autoris, 1656.
4 *l*., 69 p.

1716. GONTARD, J.A. Cours de chymie de Montpellier. Par J.A.G.D.M. ... [n.p.] 1749.
viii, 191 p.

1717. GOOD, John Mason. The history of

medicine so far as it relates to the profession of the apothecary, from the earliest accounts to the present period ... London: for C. Dilly, 1795.

viii, 239, 16 p.

1718. GOODALL, Charles. The Royal College of Physicians of London founded and established by law ... and an historical account of the college's proceedings ... London: M. Flesher for W. Kettilby, 1684.

6 ℓ., 472 p., 6 ℓ.

1719. GOODWIN, James. Reasons, against the bill for viewing, searching, and examining of all drugs, medicines, &c. Address'd to the Parliament of Great Britain ... To which is added, Mr. Goodwin's Case. By Philanthropos. London: for the author, 1731.

1 ℓ., 60 p., 1 ℓ.

1720. GORDONIO, Bernardo. Practica Gordinij dicta lilium medicine. Venetijs: J. & G. de Gregorijs, 1496.

4 ℓ., 271 numb. ℓ.

1721. GORIS, Gerhard. Mercurius triumphator continens argenti vivi historiam ... prærogativas & noxas in morborum chronicorum, præsertim in luis venereæ curatione. Accedit nova huic morbum per selectiora specifica curandi methodus, cum litteris nonnullis ad autorem conscriptis ... Quibus ... annectitur de curationibus sympatheticis tractatulus. Lugduni Batavorum: T. Haak, 1717.

12 ℓ., 252 p., 10 ℓ.

GORRIS, Pierre de. Formula remediorum. In Morescotti, A., Compendium medicinae ... 1604.

1722. GORTER, David de. Materies medica, exhibens virium medicamentorum simplicium catalogos in tres libros divisa ... Amstelodami: hæredes J. Ratelband, 1740.

11 ℓ., 447 p., 4 ℓ.

1723. GORTER, Johannes de. De perspiratione insensibili. Editio altera ... Lugduni Batavorum: J. vander Aa, 1736.

10 ℓ., 560 p., 22 ℓ. illus., port.

1724. ———. Exercitationes medicae quatuor ... Amstelaedami: haeredes J. Ratelband, 1737.

2 ℓ., 56, 56, 34, 40 p., 7 ℓ.

1725. GOSSET, le sieur. Revelations cabalistiques d'une medecine universelle

tirée du vin: avec une maniere d'extraire le sel de rosée: et une dissertation sur les lampes sepulchrales ... Amiens: l'auteur, 1735.

213 p., 1 ℓ.

1726. GÖTTLING, Johann Friedrich August. Description of a portable chest of chemistry; or Complete collection of chemical tests ... Translated from the original German. London: for C. & G. Kearsley, 1791.

vii, 191 p.

1727. ———. Praktische Vortheile und Verbesserungen verschiedener pharmaceutisch-chemischer Operationen für Apotheker. Weimar: C.R. Hoffmann, 1783.

8 ℓ., 159 p.

1728. ———. ———. Zweyte ... Auflage. Wiemar: C.L. Hoffmans Wittwe und Erben, 1789.

9 ℓ., 299 p.

1729. GOUTTARD. Traité des eaux minerales d'Abbecourt ... Avec l'explication des maladies chroniques ausquelles elles conviennent, & les observations des personnes qui ont été gueries par leur usage ... Paris: L. d'Houry, 1718.

16 ℓ., 171 p.

1730. GRAAF, Reinier de. De virorum organis generationi inservientibus, de clysteribus et de usu siphonis in anatomia. Ludg. Batav.: Hack, 1668.

16 ℓ., 234 p., 7 ℓ. illus., port.

1731. ———. Opera omnia. Lvgd.: I.A. Hvgvetan, 1678.

xx p., 2 ℓ., 390 p. illus., port.

1732. ———. Tractatus anatomico-medicus de succi pancreatici natura & usu. Lugd. Batavorum: Hack, 1671.

11 ℓ., 216 p., 7 ℓ. illus.

GRÄBERG, Johan Martin. De haemoptysi. See Linné, C. von, praeses. Entry 2459.

GRAEBNER, Godofr. Lebrecht. De melancholia vera. See Alberti, M., praeses.

1733. GRAHAM, James. A short treatise on the all-cleansing, all-healing, and all-invigorating qualities of the simple earth, when long and repeatedly applied to the naked human-body and lungs ... to which are added, A description of the best kinds

of soil ... and of the best methods of con-
ducting this most efficacious, and most
salutary practice of earth-bathing ... New-
castle upon Tyne: Hall & Elliot ..., 1790.
  1 *l*., 21 p.

1734. GRAMAN, Georg. Ein sonderliche
chymische Reise vnd Hauss Apoteca, sampt
ausführlichem Bericht, was für Vnterscheid
zwischen der Galenischen vnd Paracelsi-
schen Medicin sey ... [Ahrdruff?] gedruckt
bey J. Melchers Erben, in Verlegung J. Birckners, 1618.
  20 *l*., 160 p., 4 *l*.

1735. Le GRAND LIVRE de la nature, ou
l'apocalypse philosophique et hermetique
... Vù par une Société de Ph... Inc... &
publié par D....... Depuis I, jusqu'à l'an
1790. Au Midi: l'imprimerie de la vérité
[n.d.].
  115 p.

1736. GRANDI, Lazaro. Alfabeto di secreti
medicinali, et altri cvriosi e diletteuoli
d'ogni materia ... Et in questa seconda impressione aggiontoui dallo steso auttore
numerosi altri secreti di consideratione.
Milano: F. Vigone, 1670.
  4 *l*., 243 p.

1737. GRANGER, Guillaume. Paradoxe,
qve les metavx ont vie ... Paris: M. Soly,
1640.
  4 *l*., 96 p.
Pages 95-96 supplied in manuscript.

1738. ——. ——. Paris: M. Soly, 1640.
  4 *l*., 96 p.
With a different printer's device.

1739. GRASHUIS, Joannes. Dissertatio de
generatione puris. Editio nova priori auctior.
Accedit morbi non satis descripti hactenus
brevis delineatio eodem auctore. Neapoli:
J.M. Porcelli, 1783.
  85 p.
With Batt, W., Pharmacopoea ... 1785.

1739a. GRASSHOFF, Johann. Aperta arca
arcani artificiosissimi. Das ist: Eröffneter
vnnd offenstehender Kasten der allergrösten
vnd künstlichsten Geheimnüssen der Natur,
dess grossen und kleinen Bawers ... Franckfurt am Mayn: J.D. Zunner, 1643.
  7 *l*., 236 p.

1740. ——. Dyas chymica tripartita. Das
ist: Sechs herrliche Teutsche philosophische
Tractätlein ... Franckfurt am Mayn: L.

Jennis, 1625.
  150, 24 p. illus.

1741. ——. Harmoniæ inperscrvtabilis
chymico-philosophicæ, sive Philosophorvm
antiqvorvm consentientivm ... decas I[-II]
... Collectæ ab H.C.D. Francofurti: C.
Eifrid, 1625.
  2 pts. in 1 v.

1742. ——. Philosophia Salomonis oder:
Geheimes Cabinet der Natur und Kunst des
weisen Königes Salomons ... Augsburg: J.J.
Lotters sel. Erben, 1753.
  8 *l*., 207 p.

1743. ——. Ein philosophischer vnd
chemischer Tractat: genannt Der kleine Baur
... Sampt beygefügten Commentarijs Ioannis
Walchii ... Auch angehengter Epistel ad
cunctos Germaniæ Philosophos ... Strassburg: E. Zetzner, 1618.
  8 *l*., 376 p., 8 *l*.

1744. GRATAROLI, Guglielmo. A direction
for the health of magistrates and studentes
... Englished, by T.N. London: W. How for
A. Weale, 1574.
  86 *l*.

  ——. The names of the philosophers
stone. *In* Five treatises ... 1652.

1745. ——. Opvscuvla. Quorum cathalogum
versa pagella indicat. Ab ipso autore denuò
correcta & aucta. Lvgdvni: G. Coterius, 1558.
  5 *l*., 374 p.

1746. ——. Tvrba philosophorvm, das ist,
Das Buch von der güldenen Kunst, neben
andern Auctoribus, welche mit einander 36
Bücher ausmachen ... übersetzt und heraus
gegeben durch Philippum Morgenstern. Wienn:
J.P. Krauss, 1750.
  2 v. illus.

1747. ——. Veræ alchemiæ artisqve
metallicae, citra aenigmata, doctrina, cer-
tvsqve modus ... comprehensus ... Basileae:
[H. Petrus & P. Pernas] 1561.
  8 *l*., 244, 299 p.

1748. ——. Alchemiæ, qvam vocant, artisqve
metallicæ, doctrina, certusǴue modus, scriptis
tùm nouis, tùm veteribus ... comprehensus
... Basileæ: P. Perna, 1572.
  8 *l*., 686 p., 15 *l*.; 733 p., 12 *l*.

1749. GRAVEL, Carl Herrmann. Fontina Bernhardi revelata; oder: das ... königliche Wunder-

Baad ... in ganz reelen-und zuverläsigen Gedancken über die Bereitung des Steins der Weisen ... Erlang [J.C. Tetzschner, 1750].

136 p., 8 *l*. illus.

1750. GREAT BRITAIN. Parliament. House of Commons. Report from the committee appointed to examine the physicians who have attended his majesty, during his illness ... London: for J. Debrett, 1789.

1 *l*., 259 p.

1751. GREATRAKES, Valentin. A brief account of Mr. Valentine Greatrak's, and divers of the strange cures by him lately performed. Written by himself in a letter addressed to the honourable Robert Boyle ... London: for J. Starkey, 1666.

96 p.

1752. GREENHILL, Thomas. Νεκροκηδεία: or, The art of embalming ... London: for the author [1705].

3 *l*., viii, v p., 4 *l*., 367 p., 6 *l*. illus., port., maps.

1753. GREGOIRE, Pierre. Syntaxes artis mirabilis, in libros septem digestae ... Venetiis: D. Zenarius, 1586.

2 v. in 1. charts.

1754. GREGORINI, Gerasimo Constantini de. De hydrope uteri et de hydatidibus in utero visis aut ab eo exclusis ... Halae: Renger, 1795.

4 *l*., 72 p. illus.

1755. GREGORY, John. Lectures on the duties and qualifications of a physician. A new edition, corrected and enlarged. London: for W. Strahan ... 1772.

4 *l*., 238 p., 1 *l*.

1756. GREN, Friedrich Albrecht Carl. Grundriss der Naturlehre in seinem mathematischen und chemischen Theile neu bearbeitet. Halle: Hemmerde und Schwetschte, 1793.

4 *l*., 794 p., 9 *l*. charts.

1757. ——. System der pharmakologie; oder Lehre von den Arzneymitteln ... Zweyte ganz umgearbeitete Auflage. Halle: Waisenhaus, 1798-1800.

2 v. in 3.

1758. ——. Systematisches Handbuch der gesammten Chemie. Zweyte, ganz umgear-

beitete, Auflage: Halle: Waisenhaus, 1794-1795.

3 v.

1759. GRETE HERBALL. The greate herball whiche geueth parfyt knowlege and vnderstandyng of all maner of herbes & there gracyous vertues ... [London: P. Treveris, 1526.]

174 *l*. illus.

This volume, once owned by an English physician Richard Seymer in 1576, includes a 90-page manuscript of medical formularies and prescriptions written by him.

1760. ——. ——. Newlye corrected and diligently ouersene ... [London: J. Kynge] 1561.

141 *l*. illus.

1761. GREVIN, Jacques. Devx livres des venins ... Ensemble, Les oeuvres de Nicandre ... traduictes en vers François. Anvers: C. Plantin, 1568.

4 *l*., 333 p., 2 *l*.; 90 p.

The title page to the work by Nicander is dated 1567.

GREW, Nehemiah. The comparative anatomy of stomachs and guts. *In* Royal Society of London. Musæum Regalis Societatis ... 1681.

1762. ——. A discourse made before the Royal Society, Decemb. 10. 1674, concerning the nature, causes, and power of mixture ... London: for J. Martyn, 1675.

9 *l*., 120 p.

1763. ——. Dissertatio, quæ complectitur nova experimenta utilesque observations circa aquam marinam ... Londini: J. Gain [1684?].

24 p.

——. Experiences sur le combat que arrive du mélange de diverses liqueurs. *In* Recueil d'experiences ... 1 679.

——. Musæum Regalis Societatis. *See* Royal Society of London.

1764. GRIFONI, Teofilo. Osservazioni intorno all'acque del Bagno di Vignone ... Siena: Bonetti, 1705.

67 p.

GRIGNON, Pierre Clément. Quatre mémoires sur la métallurgie. *In* Bergman,

T.O., Analyse du fer ... 1783.

1765. GRIMALDI, Giacinto. Dell'alchimia
opra ... Palermo: A. dell'Isola, 1645.
  8 *l.*, 206 p.   chart.

1766. GRIMMELSHAUSEN, Hans Jacob
Christoffel von. Simplicissimi Galgen-
Männlin, oder Ausführlicher Bericht, woher
man die so genannte Allräungen oder Geld-
männlin bekoṁt, und wie man ihrer warten
und pflegen soll ... mit nutzlichen Anmerck-
und Erinnerungen erläutert durch Israël
Fromschmidt von Hugenfels ... [n.p.: 1673?]
  72 p.
  With Cardilucius, J.H., Heilsame Artzney-
Kräffte ... 1681.

  GRONOVIUS, Laurentius Theodorus.
Auctuarium in bibliothecam botanicam. *In*
Séguier, J.F., Bibliotheca botanica ... 1760.

1767. GROSMAN, J. A treatise for the service of chemistry in general; exhibiting the
universal and specific principles of body;
the simple and uniform proceedure of nature,
in petrification, in producing minerals, and
the generation of gold ... London: for J.
Millan, 1766.
  1 *l.*, 106 p.   illus.

1768. GROSSCHEDEL, Johann Baptist.
Proteus mercurialis geminus, exhibens naturam metallorvm, id est, Operis philosophici theoriam & eiusdem praxin ... Francofurti: L. Jennis, 1629.
  195 p.

1769. ――. ――. Hamburgi: M. Grocian,
1706.
  8 *l.*, 192 p.
  With Faust, J.M., Philaletha illustratus
... 1706.

1770. GRUMMET, Christoph. Das Blut der
Natur, aus eigener Erfahrung handgreifflich
angewiesen ... [n.d.] 1678.
  1 *l.*, 36 p.

1771. ――. Sol non sine veste, oder: Das
unüberwundene Gold in seiner Tapfferkeit
triumphirende aufgeführet ... Rothenburg:
1685.
  49 p.
  With Orschall, J.C., Sol sine veste ...
1685.

  ――. ――. *In* Gertz, P., Neu-eröffnete Kunst-Kammer ... 1720.

1772. GRÜNDLICHER UNTERRICHT von dem
wahren menstruo universali, als einem
Mittel, vermittelst welches das Gold wahr-
hafftig aufzuschliessen ... Leipzig: J.S.
Heinsio, 1731.
  56 p.
  With Philosophisches Licht und Schatten
... 1738.

  GRYSSELIUS, Johan. De medico sui
ipsius. *See* Linné, C. von, *praeses*. Entry
2452.

1773. GUELFO, Giovanni Battista. Amirabil
discorso circa la natvralezza, et influenza
delli dodici segni celesti, e de' sette pianeti.
Per saper conoscere l'infermità di ciascheduno,
& applicarni li rimedij necessarij ... Madrid
[n.d.].
  4 *l.*

1774. GUIBERT, Nicolas. Alchymia ratione
et experientia ita demvm viriliter impvgnata
& expugnata, vnâ cum suis fallacijs & de-
liramentis, quibus homines imbubinârat: vt
nunquam imposterum se erigere valeat ...
Item De balsamo, eivsqve lachrymæ quod
opobalsamvm dicitur, natura, viribus &
facultatibus admirandis ... Argentorati: L.
Zetzner, 1603.
  8 *l.*, 104 p.; 2 *l.*, 18 p.

1775. ――. De interitv alchymiæ metallorvm transmvtatoriæ tractatvs aliqvot ...
Adiuncta est ... Apologia in sophistam Li-
bauium ... Tulli: S. Philippe, 1614.
  8 *l.*, 88, 141 p.

1776. GUIBERT, Philbert. Le medecin
charitable ... Augmenté d'un discours du
bezoard ... Auec vn traicté de la peste. Lyon:
I.A. Candy, 1635.
  6 *l.*, 684 p.

1777. ――. Les oevvres charitables ...
Reueuës & augmentées de nouueau par luy-
mesme. Sçauoir, Le medecin charitable. Le
prix et valevr des medicamens. L'apotiqvaire
charitable. La maniere d'embavmer les corps
morts. Et les tromperies dv bezoard des-
covvertes. Paris: I. Iost, 1630-1629.
  2 pts. in 1 v.

1778. ――. Tovtes les oevvres charitables
... Reueues, corrigées & augmentées en cette
derniere edition. Paris: I. Iacqvin, 1653.
  6 *l.*, 880 p., 15 *l.*   port.

1779. GUIDI, Giovanni. De mineralibvs

tractatus in genere ... libri quatuor ...
Venetiis: T. Ballionus, 1625.
20 *l*., 208 p.

GUIDOTT, Thomas. An appendix
concerning Bathe. *In* Jorden, E., A discourse
of natural bathes ... 1669.

1780. ———. De thermis Britannicis tractatus, accesserunt observationes hydristaticæ,
chromaticæ, & miscellaneæ uniuscujusque
balnei apud Bathoniam ... Londini: F. Leach,
1691.
14 *l*., 412 p.; 1 *l*., 28 p., 8 *l*. illus.

1781. ———. A collection of treatises relating to the city and waters of Bath ... To
which is added, Thermæ redivivæ ... By Henry Chapman ... London: for J. Leake, 1725.
14 *l*., 430 p. illus.

1782. GUILANDINI, Melchior. Papyrvs,
hoc est Commentarivs in tria C Plinij maioris
de papyro capita. Accessit Hieronymi Mer-
cvrialis Repugnantia, qua pro Galeno strenuè
pugnatur. Item Melchioris Gvilandini Asser-
tio sententiæ in Galenum â se pronunciatæ
... Venetiis: M.A. Vlmus, 1672.
8 *l*., 280 p.

1783. GÜLDENFALK, Siegmund Heinrich.
Die himmlische und hermetische Perle oder
Der göttliche und natürliche Tinctur der
Weisen ... Frankfurt: Fleischer, 1785.
3 *l*., 298 p. illus.

1784. ———. Sammlung von mehr als hundert wahrhaften Transmutations-geschichten,
oder ... Beyspiele von Verwandlung der
Metallen in Gold oder Silber ... Frankfurt:
J.G. Fleischer, 1784.
xxxvi, 443 p.

1785. GULICHIUS, Abrahamus. Oratio inauguralis de natura hominis admiranda ...
Franequeræ: J. Gyselaer, 1679.
72 p.
With Queitsch, A.P., Ιατρομαθηματογραφία
synoptica ... 1737.

1786. GUYTON DE MORVEAU, Louis Bernard.

Allgemeine theoretische und praktische
Grundsätze der chemischen Affinität oder
Wahlanziehung zum gemeinnützen Gebrauch
... Aus dem Französischen übersetzt von
David Joseph Veit·... Mit Anmerkungen be-
gleitet und herausgegeben von D. Siegis-
mund Friedrich Hermbstädt ... Berlin: H.A.
Rottmann, 1794.
xvi, 320 p.

1787. ———. Allgemeine theoretische und
praktische Grundsätze über die sauren Salze
oder Säuren zum Gebrauch für Chemisten
... übersetzt ... von David Ludewig Bourguet
... Mit einer Vorrede begleitet von Dr. Sigismund Friedrich Hermbstädt. Berlin: G.A.
Lange, 1796-1804.
3 v.

1788. ———. Description de l'aérostate
l'Académie de Dijon ... Dijon: Causse et T.
Barrois, 1784.
1 *l*., v, 224 p. illus.

1789. ———. Discours sur l'état actuel
de la jurisprudence, prononcé à l'ouverture
des audiences, &c. Par M.***, Avocat Général. Paris: P.G. Simon, 1768.
59 p.
With Durade, J.G., Traite physiologique
... 1757.

1790. ———. Elémens de chymie, théorique
et pratique, rédigés dans un nouvel ordre,
d'après les découvertes modernes ... Dijon:
L.N. Frantin, 1777-1778.
3 v. charts.

1791. ———. Méthode de nomenclature
chimique, proposée par MM. de Morveau,
Lavoisier, Bertholet, & de Fourcroy. On y
a joint un nouveau systême de caractères
chimiques ... Paris: Cuchet, 1787.
2 *l*., 314 p. charts.

1792. ———. A translation of the table of
chemical nomenclature proposed by De
Guyton ... Lavoisier, Bertholet, and De
Fourcroy ... Second edition ... London: Cooper
and Wilson, 1799.
viii, 156, 4 p. charts.

H

1793. H., A.C.V. Ars chimica naturæ
æmula. Das ist, Die auss der edlen Chimie
hervor-blickende wundersame Natur ...
[n.p.] 1684.
24 *l*.
With Hanstein, P.H. von, Wasser und
Geist ... 1756.

1794. H., E. Ein ausführlicher Tractat,
von philosophischen Werck des Steins der
Weisen, durch eine Jungfer E.H. genannt,
anno 1574. geschrieben. Samt einer gründt-
lichen Untersuchung und Entdeckung, der
Art und Eigenschafft des Goldes ... Dabey
angefüget: Ein Catalogus librorum Kabal-
isticorum. Hamburg: G. Liebezeit, 1702.
4 *l*., 3-102 p.
With Quadratum alchimisticum ... 1705.

1795. [H., I.C.] Von der Natur und Kunst.
Ein Danksagungsschreiben an den erleuch-
teten Verfasser des hermetischen A.B.C. von
eInem Christlich gesinnten Hermetischen
Lehrjünger. Nebst einem Auszuge aus ...
Werken ... Hermann Fictulds. Als ein Ergän-
zungsstück zum Hermetischen A.B.C. von
Adamah Booz. Leipzig: A.F. Böhme, 1781.
8 *l*., 208 p.

1796. ———. Des Hermes Trismegists
wahrer alter Naturweg ... Leipzig: A.F. Böhme,
1782.
viii p., 1 *l*., 100 p. illus.

1797. HAAN, Andreas Leopold. Libellus,
in quo demonstratur quod non solum vegetabilia, animalia, & mineralia menstruo simplici paucis horis possint solvi, verum etiam
extracta purissima, & salia essentialia
educi. Vindobonnæ: J.T. de Trattner, 1766.
61 p. illus.

1798. HAASE, Johann Gottlob. De vasis
cutis et intestinorum absorbentibus plexi-
busque lymphaticis pelvis humanae annotationes anatomicae cum iconibus. Lipsiae:
I.F. Iunius, 1786.

5 *l*., 34 p., 4 *l*. illus., folio.

1799. HACKEL, Johann Christoph. Kurzgefasste Beschreibung und practische Erläuterung der in die Pharmakopäe für öster-
reichische Staaten neu aufgenommenen
Arzeneykörper ... Wien: C.F. Wappler, 1795.
118 p.

1800. HADLEY, Henry. Dissertatio medica
inauguralis de balsamo peruviano ... Ex
auctoritate magnifici rectoris D. Johannis
Jacobi Rau ... Lugduni Batavorum: Boutes-
tenian, 1718.
13 p.

1801. HAEN, Anton de. De magia liber.
Lipsiae: I.P. Kravs, 1775.
xxviii p., 2 *l*., 316 p., 1 *l*.

1802. ———. Opuscula quaedam inedita.
Accedunt Historiae morbum a stollio in collegio clinico Haenii annis 1770-72 con-
signatae. Editionem curavit, et praefatus
est Josephus Eyerel. Vindobonae: J. Camesina, 1795.
xxiv, 368 p.; 1 *l*., 368 p.

1803. ———. Prælectiones ... in Hermanni
Boerhaavii Institutiones pathologicas. Col-
legit, recensuit, additamentis auxit, edidit
F. de Wasserberg. Editio nova ... Coloniæ
Allobrogum: Societatis Bibliopolar, 1784.
2 v.

1804. ———. Ratio medendi in nosocomio
practico, quod in gratiam, et emolvmentvm
medicinae stvdiosorvm ... Vindobonae: I.T.
Trattner, 1757-1771.
15 v. in 8. illus.
Imprint varies.

1805. ———. Ratio medendi continuatae
in nosocomio practico ... Viennae: H.J.
Krüchten, 1771-1779.
3 v. in 2.
Imprint varies.

1806. HAGEN, Karl Gottfried. Grundriss
der Experimentalchemie zum Gebrauch bey
dem Vortrage derselben ... Zweyte vermehrte
und abgeänderte Auflage. Königsberg: G.L.
Hartung, 1790.
    xvi, 448 p.   charts.

1807. ———. Lehrbuch der Apothekerkunst.
Dritte, rechtmässige und verbesserte Ausgabe. Königsberg: G.L. Hartung, 1786.
    xx, 984 p., 1 ℓ.   illus.

    HAGSTRÖM, Johan Otto. De gen-
eratione calculi. See Linné, C. von, praeses.
Entry 2429.

    HAHN, Adam. Ταβακολογία sive
Tabaco dissertatio. See Frederick, Johann
Arnold, praeses.

1808. HAHNEMANN, Samuel. Apotheker-
lexikon. Leipzig: S.L. Crusius, 1793-1798.
    2 v.   illus.

1809. ———. Ueber die Arsenikvergistung
ihre Hülfe und gerichtliche Ausmittelung.
Leipzig: S.L. Crusius, 1786.
    xx, 276 p.

1810. HALES, Stephen. An account of a
useful discovery to distill double the usual
quantity of sea-water, by blowing showers
of air up through the distilling liquor ...
London: for R. Manby, 1756.
    59 p.   illus.

1810a. ———. An account of some experiments and observations on tar-water: wherein is shown the quantity of tar that is therein
... Which was read before the Royal Society.
London: for R. Manby & H.S. Cox, 1745.
    1 ℓ., 29 p.
    With Berkeley, G., Siris ... 1744.

1811. ———. Philosophical experiments:
containing instructions for such as under-
take long voyages at sea ... London: for W.
Innys ..., 1739.
    2 ℓ., xxx p., 1 ℓ., 163 p., 11 ℓ. illus.
    With his A description of ventilators ...
1743.

1812. ———. Vegetable staticks; or, An
account of some statical experiments on the
sap in vegetables ... Also, a specimen of an
attempt to analyse the air ... read at several meetings before the Royal Society ...
London: for W. & J. Innys & T. Woodward,
1724.
    4 ℓ., vii p., 1 ℓ., 376 p.   illus.

1813. ———. ———. London: for W. & J.
Innys, 1727.
    8 ℓ., 376 p.   illus.

1814. ———. Statical essays; containing
vegetable statics; or, An account of some
statical experiments on the sap in vegetables ... Also a speciment of an attempt
to analyse the air, by a great variety of
chymio-statical experiments ... The fourth
edition, with amendements. London: Wilson
and Nicol, 1769.
    2 v.   illus.

1815. ———. La statique des vegetaux, et
l'analyse de l'air. Lûes à la Societè Royale
de Londres ... traduit de l'Anglois, par M.
De Buffon ... Paris: Debure, 1735
    xviii p., 4 ℓ., 408 p., 1 ℓ.   illus.

1816. HALL, John. Select observations
on English bodies: or, Cures both empericall
and historicall, performed upon very eminent
persons in desparate diseases. First written
in Latine ... Now put into English ... by
James Cooke ... London: for J. Sherley, 1657.
    12 ℓ., 316 p.

1817. HALLÉ, Jean Noël. Recherches sur
la nature et les effets du méphitisme des
fosses d'aisance. Paris: P.D. Pierres, 1785.
    2 ℓ., 184 p.

1818. HALLE, Johann Samuel. Gifthistorie
des Thier- Pflanzen- und Mineralreichs,
nebst den Gegengiften, und der medicinischen
Anwendung der Gifte, nach den neuesten
Toxicologen. Frankfurt und Leipzig: 1787.
    1 ℓ., 301 p.

1819. HALLER, Albrecht von. Bibliotheca
anatomica, qua scripta ad anatomen et
physiologiam facientia a rerum initiis recensentur. Tiguri: Orell, Gesner, Fussli,
1774-1777.
    2 v.

1820. ———. Bibliotheca chirurgica qua
scripta ad artem chirurgicam facientia a
rerum initiis recensentur. Basileæ & Berne:
J. Schweighauser & E. Haller, 1744-1755.
    2 v.

    ———. De diaphragmatis musculis
dissertatio anatomica. In Swammerdam, J.,
Tractatus physico-anatomico-medicus ...
1738.

1821. ———. Deux memoires sur le mouve-
ment du sang, et sur les effets de la saignée;

fondés sur des experiences faites sur des animaux ... Lausanne: M.M. Bousquet et David, 1756.
  1 ℓ., viii, 343 p.   illus.

1822. ——. Disputationes ad morborum historiam et curationem facientes ... Lausannæ: M.M. Bousquet, 1757-1760.
  7 v.   illus.

1823. ——. Elementa physiologiae corporis humani. Lausannae: 1757-1778.
  8 v.   port.
  Imprint varies. Volumes 6-8 are in the second edition.

1824. ——. Icones anatomicae quibus praecipuae aliquae partes corporis humani delineatae proponutur & arteriarum potissimum historia continetur. Gottingae: vidua B.A. Vandenhoeck, 1756-1782.
  8 pts. in 1 v.   illus., folio.

1825. ——. Memoires sur la nature sensible et irritable, des parties du corps animal ... Contenant une seconde édition de la Dissertation sur l'irritabilité ... Lausanne: M. Bousquet ..., 1756-1760.
  4 v.   illus.
  Imprint varies.

1826. ——. Opera minora emendata, aucta, et renovata ... Lausannae: F. Grasset, 1763-1768.
  3 v.   illus.

1827. ——. Opuscula pathologica. Partim recusa partim inedita: quibus sectiones cadaverum morbosorum potissimum continentur. Accedunt experimenta de respiratione, quarta parte aucta. Lausannae: M.M. Bousquet, 1755.
  304 p.   illus.

1828. ——. Opuscula sua anatomica de respiratione de monstris aliaque minora recensuit, emendavit auxit aliqua inedita novasque icones addidit. Gottingae: J.W. Schmidt, 1751.
  13 ℓ., 358 p.   illus.

1829. ——. Primae lineae physiologiae. In usum praelectionum academicarum. Nunc quarto conscriptae emendatae et pluribus animadversionibus. Auctae ab Henrico Augusto Wrisberg. Goettingae: vidua A. Vandenhoeck, 1780.
  11 ℓ., 526 p., 2 ℓ.

1830. ——. First lines of physiology ...

Translated from the correct Latin edition. Printed under the inspection of William Cullen ... Edinburgh: for C. Elliot, 1779.
  vi, 530 p., 1 ℓ.

1831. HALMAAL, Jacob van. Ontleding over d'Amsterdamsche apotheek ... Tweede druk. Amsterdam: J. Hartig, 1739.
  8 ℓ., 246 p., 4 ℓ.   illus., charts.

1832. HAMILTON, James, jun. Reply to Dr. Gregory. Edinburgh: 1793.
  86 p.

1833. HAMILTON, Robert. Observations on scrophulous affections, with remarks on schirrus, cancer, and rachitis. London: for C. Dilly, 1791.
  xii, 236 p.

1834. HANCOCKE, John. Febrifugum magnum: or, Common water the best cure for fevers, and probably for the plague ... The fifth edition. London: for R. Halsey, sold by J. Roberts, 1723.
  2 ℓ., 80 p.

1835. ——. ——. The seventh edition, with additions. London: J. Roberts and R. Halsey, 1724.
  2 ℓ., 128 p.

1836. HANDY, Hast. An inaugural dissertation on opium ... Philadelphia: T. Lang, 1791.
  28 p.

1837. HANNEMANN, Johann Ludwig. Cato chemicus tractatus quo veræ ac genuinæ philosophiæ Hermeticæ, & fucatæ ac sophisticæ pseudo chemiæ & utriusque magistrorum characterismi accurate delineantur. Hamburgi: apud G. Liebernickel, literis Brendekii, 1690.
  48 ℓ.

1838. HANSTEIN, Philipp Heinrich, *baron* von. Wasser und Geist als die geoffenbahrte Natur-Grund-Anfänge der geheimnissvollen hermetischen Weisheit der Adepten ... von F.C.P.H. von Mondenstein genannt Schwefelbach. Erlangen: J.C. Müller, 1756.
  78 p., 1 ℓ.

1839. HARRIS, Walter. Pharmacologia anti-empicira: or A rational discourse of remedies both chymical and galenical ... London: for R. Chiswell, 1683.
  16 ℓ., 332 p., 6 ℓ.

——. Tractatus de morbis acutis
infantum. *In* Morton, R., Opera medica ...
1696.

1840. HART, James. Κλινική, or the diet
of the diseased. Divided into three bookes
... Collected as well out of the writings of
ancient philosophers, Greeke, Latine, and
Arabian, and other moderne writers, as out
of divers other authours ... London: J. Beale
for R. Allot, 1633.
7 *l.*, 27, 411 p., 8 *l.*

1841. HARTLIB, Samuel, *ed.* Chymical,
medicinal, and chyrurgical addresses made
to Samuel Hartlib ... London: G. Dawson for
G. Calvert, 1655.
16 *l.*, 181 [i.e. 159] p.

1842. HARTMANN, Johann. Opera omnia
medico-chymica. In quibus praxis ejvs
chymiatrica, Notæ in Basilicam Crollii &
Beguinii tyrocinium, Disputationes chymico
medicæ, Tractatus de opio, Miscellanea
medico chymica & Introductio in vitalem
philosophiam continentur ... In unum volumen
congesta ... a Conrado Johrenio ... Francofurti ad Moenum: impensis viduæ Seylerianæ,
typis B.C. Wustii, Jr., 1684.
var. pag.

1843. ——. Praxis chymiatrica edita à
Johanne Michaelis ... & Georgio Euerhardo
Hartmanno ... Huic postremæ editioni adiecti
sunt ... tres tractatus noui ... Genevæ: P.
Chouët, 1647.
631 p., 16 *l.*; 112 p., 7 *l.*   charts.

1844. ——. ——. Nvnc avctior, addita
Pathologia J. Fernelii ... cura Theop. Boneti
... Genevæ: L. Chouet, 1682.
6 *l.*, 494 p., 17 *l.*; 329 p., 15 *l.*
illus., charts.

1845. HARVET, Israel. Animadversiones
in Ioannis Antarveti ... apologiam pro iudicio
scholæ Parisiensis, de alchymia. Francoforti: C. Marnius & hered. I. Aubrius, 1604.
172 p.

1846. ——. Demonstratio veritatis doctrinæ chymicæ. Adversus Ioan. Riolani com-
parationem veteris medicinæ cum noua ...
Hanoviæ: typis Wechelianis, apud C. Marnium ..., 1605.
123 p.
With his Animadversiones ... 1604.

1847. HARVEY, Gideon. Archelogia philosophica nova, or New principles of philos-

ophy ... London: J.H. for S. Thomson, 1663.
2 pts. in 1 v.   illus.

1848. ——. The art of curing diseases
by expectation: with remarks on a supposed
great case of apoplectick fits ... London:
for J. Partridge, 1689.
2 *l.*, 224 p.

1849. ——. Ars curandi morbos expectatione; item De vanitatibus, dolis, & mendaciis medicorum ... [n.p.: n.d.]
1 *l.*, 312 p.
With Stahl, G.E., Sileni alcibiadis ...
1730.

1850. ——. Morbus Anglicus: or The
anatomy of consumptions ... The second
edition. London: T. Johnson for N. Brook,
1674.
3 *l.*, 154 p.
Includes: A discourse of the plague ...
The second edition. London: 1673.

1851. ——. The vanities of philosophy
& physick: together with directions and
medicines easily prepared by any of the
least skill, whereby to preserve health and
prolong life, as well in those that live
regularly, as others that live irregularly
... London: for A. Roper, R. Basset & W.
Turner, 1699.
4 *l.*, 184 p.

1852. ——. The third edition of the vanities of philosophy and physick: enlarg'd
to more than double the number of sheets
... London: for A. Roper, R. Basset & W.
Turner, 1702.
14 *l.*, 381 p.

HARVEY, William.   De lacteis venis
sententia. *In* Bartholin, T., Defensio vasorum
... 1655.

1853. ——. Exercitatio anatomica de motu
cordis & sanguinis. Cum praefatione Zachariae
Sylvii ... Accessit Dissertatio de corde Jacobi
de Back. Roterodami: A. Leers, 1648.
20 *l.*, 215 p.; 1 *l.*, 219 p., 4 *l.*   illus.

1854. ——. ——. Roterodami: A. Leers,
1671.
16 *l.*, 285 p., 9 *l.*; 252 p., 12 *l.*

1855. ——. The anatomical exercises ...
concerning the motion of the heart and blood.
With the preface of Zechariah Wood ... To
which is added, Dr. James de Back, his discourse of the heart ... London: for R. Lowndes

& M. Gilliflower, 1673.
12 *l*., 107 p.; 10 *l*., 172 p.

1856. ――. Exercitationes de generatione
animalivm. Quibus accedunt quaedam de
partu: de membranis ac humoribus vteri: &
de conceptione. Amstelodami: L. Elzevirius,
1651.
2 *l*., 568 p., 3 *l*.

1857. ――. ――. Editio novissima a
mendis repurgata. Hagae Comitis: A. Leers,
1680.
18 *l*., 582 p., 2 *l*.
With Marchetti, D. de, Anatomia ... 1656.

1858. ――. Anatomical exercitations,
concerning the generation of living creatures:
to which are added particular discourses, of
births, and of conceptions, &c. ... London:
J. Young for O. Pulleyn, 1653.
23 *l*., 566 p., 1 *l*. port.

1859. ――. Opera omnia: a Collegio Medicorvm Londinensi edita: MDCCLXVI. [Lon-
dini: G. Bowyer, 1766.]
4 *l*., xxxviii p., 1 *l*., 673 p. port.

1860. HASLAM, John. Observations on in-
sanity: with practical remarks on the disease,
and an account of the morbid appearances
on dissection. London: F. and C. Rivington,
1798.
xi, 147 p.

HASSELQUIST, Fredrik. Vires planta-
rum. *See* Linné, C. von, *praeses*. Entry 2498.

1861. HAUDICQUIER DE BLANCOURT, Jean.
De l'art de la verrerie. Où l'on apprend à
faire le verre, le cristal, & l'email ... Paris:
J. Jombert, 1697.
8 *l*., 602 p., 3 *l*. illus.

1862. ――. The art of glass ... To which
is added, the method of painting on glass
and enameling ... now first translated into
English. With an appendix, containing exact
instructions for making glass-eyes ... London: for D. Brown ..., 1699.
7 *l*., 355 p., 6 *l*. illus.

1863. HAUPTMANN, August. Neues chymisches Kunst Project und sehr wichtiges
Bergk Bedencken ober die allergrösten Haupt-
mängel des Bergckwercks ... Leipzig: A.
Löfflers, bey J. Bauern, 1658.
6 *l*., 98 p. illus.

1864. HAUSERUS, Joannes Jacobus. Dis-

pvtatio medica inavqvralis de ischvria integra vrinae svppressione ... Basileae: J.
Bertsch [1690].
8 *l*.

1865. HAUTNORTHON, Josaphat Friedrich.
Lucerna salis philosophorum. Hoc est:
Delineatio nuda desiderati illius principis
tertii mineralium Sendivogiani ... Amstelodami: H. Berk, 1658.
212 p.

1866. HAY, Alexander. Tyrocinium pharmaceuticum: sive Collectanea Galeno-Spagyrica,
Scoto-Britannica, medicamentorum simplicium
& compositorum ... Edinburgi: haeredes A.
Anderson [1697].
4 *l*., 180 p., 2 *l*.

1867. HEADRICH, John, *ed*. Arcana philosophia or Chymical secrets, containing the
noted and useful chymical medicines of Dr.
Wil. and Rich. Russel chymists ... London:
H. Hills, 1697.
8 *l*., 128 p., 4 *l*.

1868. HECQUET, Philippe. La medecine,
la chirurgie, et la pharmacie des pauvres;
nouvelle edition, revûë, corrigée sur le
manuscrit de l'auteur, & augmentée de notes
par M. Boudon ... On y a joint la vie de
l'auteur, avec un catalogue raisonné de ses
ouvrages. Paris: Clousier ..., 1742.
3 v. port.

1869. ――. Reflexions sur l'usage de
l'opium, des calmants, et des narcotiques,
pour la guerison des maladies. En forme de
lettre ... Paris: G. Cavelier, 1726.
4 *l*., 374 p., 7 *l*.

HEDIN, Sven Anders. Cannones
medici. *See* Linné, C. von, *praeses*. Entry
2421.

1870. HEER, Henri de. Spadacrene, hoc
est Fons Spadanus ... et Observationvm
medicarum oppido rarum liber univus ...
Editio correctior, & auctior cum indice.
Lugduni Batavorum: A. Wyngaerden & F.
Moiardus, 1645.
11 *l*., 159 p., 8 *l*.
Lacking the Observationum medicarum ...

1871. ――. ――. Editio novissima, prioribus emendatior cum indice. Lugd. Batav.:
P. vander Aa, 1685.
159 p., 8 *l*.; 3 *l*., 254 p., 10 *l*. illus.

HEIDENSTAM, Ernst Joachim Magnus

von. De haemorrhagiis ex plethora. *See*
Linné, C. von, *praeses.* Entry 2447.

1872. HEISTER, Lorenz. L'anatomie
d'Heister, avec des essais de physique sur
l'usage des parties du corps humain ...
enrichie de nouvelles figures ... Seconde
edition ... Paris: J. Vincent, 1735.
    xiv p., 3 *l.*, 852 p. illus.

1873. ——. Compendium anatomicum
totam rem anatomicam brevissime complectens. Editio sexta Veneta juxta quartam
altorfinam prioribus longe auctior atque
emendatior. Accedit ejusdem auctoris Compendium institutionum medicinae. Venetiis:
S. Coletius, 1755.
    xxviii, 486 p. illus.

1874. ——. Institvtiones chirvrgicae in
qvibvs qvicqvid ad rem chirvrgicam pertinet,
optima et novissima ratione pertractatvr ...
Amstelaedami: Janssonio-Waesbergios,
1739.
    11 *l.*, 715 p. illus.

1875. ——. Chirurgie, in welcher alles,
was zur Wundarzney gehöret ... Neue viel
vermehrte und verbesserte Auflage ... Nürnberg: G.N. Raspe, 1763.
    8 *l.*, 1078 p., 12 *l.* illus., port.

1876. ——. ——. Nürnberg: G.N. Raspe,
1779.
    8 *l.*, 1078 p., 12 *l.* illus., port.

1877. ——. La methode de tailler au petit
appareil, et ses avantages. Traduite du
Latin ... par Mr. M.S. ... Paris: Durand,
Pissot, 1751.
    8, 189 p. illus.

1878. HELCHER, Hans Heinrich. Aurum
potabile, oder Gold-Tinctur, dessen Præparation dass sie sicher, samt des Goldes
Vortrefflichkeit und Analogie mit unserm
Cörper, Würckung und Gebrauch curative so
wohl als præservative, nebst andern Medicamenten vor allerley Kranckheiten deutlich
beschrieben, und auff viele Einwürffe aus-
führlich geantwortet wird ... Zum andern
Mahl vermehrter auffgelegt. Bresslau: J.H.
Kloss, 1718.
    16 *l.*, 309 p., 5 *l.*

    HELIAS. Speculum alchymiae. *In*
Opuscula quaedam chemica ... 1614.

    HELLENS, Carl Niclas. Hypericum.
See Linné, C. von, *praeses*. Entry 2478.

1879. HELLOT, Jean. L'art de la teinture
des lains et des étoffes de laine, en grand
et petit teint: avec une instruction sur les
débouillis ... Paris: Didot, 1786.
    371 p.

1880. ——. The art of dying wool, silk
and cotton. Translated from the French of
M. Hellot, M. Macquer, and M. Le Pileur
d'Apligny. London: for R. Baldwin, 1789.
    ix p., 3 *l.*, 508 p. illus.

1881. HELLWIG, Christoph von. Der
curieuse und wohl-erfahrne Chymist ... Aus
berühmter Chymicorum Schrifften, theils
auch aus eigener Praxi zusammen getragen,
mit nöthigen Registern versehen, von Valentino Kräutermann. Andere Auflage. Leipzig:
J.J. Beumelberg, 1738.
    5 *l.*, 480 p., 10 *l.* illus.

1882. ——. Curieuses Reise- und Hauss-
Apotheckchen ... Nebst einer Zugabe derer
zweyen weltberühmten Medicamenten, dem
Theriac und Mithridat ... Franckfurth: zu
finden bey H.P. Ritscheln, gedruckt bey
H.A. Meurern, 1711.
    4 *l.*, 87 p.

1883. ——. Dreyfacher als Thüringisch-
Meissnischer und Niedersächsischer Teutsch-
und Lateinischer Apothecker-Tax ... Franckfurt: H.P. Ritschel, 1714.
    5 *l.*, 127 p.

1884. ——, *ed.* Fasciculus unterschied-
licher alten raren und wahren philosophischen
Schrifften vom Stein der Weisen, aus einem
alten Lateinischen Manuscripto übersetzet,
nebst einer curiosen Epistel, von denen
Duum Viriṣ Hermeticis Foederatis, und einer
Vorrede von einem wunderbaren vermischten
uncorrosivischen Menstruo ex Macro- &
Microcosmo die Metallen zu solviren ...
Leipzig: J.A. Grimin, 1719.
    8 *l.*, 302 p., 9 *l.*

1885. ——. Neu-vermehrtes historisch-
medicinisches Regnvm minerale, oder Metal-
len- und Mineralien-Reich, und zwar anietzo
in II. Haupt-Theilen ... Nebst einem Anhang,
in welchem alle zum Scheiden und Probiren
gehörige Sachen ... beschrieben werden ... Von
Valent. Kräutermann ... Franckfurt: E.L. Niedt, 17
    8 *l.*, 472 p., 4 *l.* illus.

1886. ——. Send-Schreiben vom Aurô
mercuriali, oder Mercurial-Golde, und dessen
Wirckungen ... Jean: J. Bielcken, 1704.
    16 *l.*

1887. HELMONT, Franciscus Mercurius
van. One hundred fifty three chymical
aphorisms. Briefly containing whatsoever
belongs to the chymical science. Done by
the labour and study of Eremita Suburbanus.
Printed in Latin at Amsterdam, Octob. 1687.
To which are added, some other phylosophick
canons ... made English and published ... by
Chr. Packe ... London: for the author, sold
by W. Cooper ... 1688.
    8 *l.*, 63 p.

1888. ———. The paradoxical discourses
... concerning the macrocosm and micro-
cosm ... Set down in writing by J.B. and now
published. London: J.C. and F. Collins for
R. Kettlewel, 1685.
    8 *l.*, 127, 215 p.   illus.

1889. ———. Quædam præmeditatæ & con-
sideratæ cogitationes super quatuor priora
capita libri primi Moysis, Genesis nominati
... Amstelodami: H. Wetsten, 1697.
    4 *l.*, 115 [i.e. 127] p.

1890. HELMONT, Jean Baptiste van. De-
liramenta catarrhi: or, The incongruities,
impossibilities, and absurdities couched
under the vulgar opinion of defluxions ...
The translator and paraphrast Dr. Charleton
... London: E.G. for W. Lee, 1650.
    6 *l.*, 75 p.
    With his A ternary of paradoxes ... 1650.

1891. ———. Les oevvres ... traittant des
príncipes de medecine et physiqve ... de la
tradvction de M. Iean Le Conte ... Lyon:
J.A. Huguetan & G. Barbier, 1671.
    4 *l.*, 396 p.

1892. ———. Opera omnia. Additis his de
novo tractatibus aliquot posthumis ejusdem
authoris, maximè curiosis pariter ac perutilis-
simis, antehac non in lucem editis ... Francofurti: J.J. Erythropilius, 1682.
    20 *l.*, 275 p., 22 *l.*; 8 *l.*, 765 p., 36 *l.*

1893. ———. Opvscvla medica inavdita.
I. De lithiasi. II. De febribus. III. De humoribus Galeni. IV. De peste. Editio secunda
multò emendatior. Amsterodami: L. Elzevirius,
1648.
    4 *l.*, 110, 115, 88 p.
    With his Ortus medicinae ... 1648.

1894. ———. Ortvs medicinae. Id est,
Initia physicae inavdita. Progressus medicinae novus, in morborum ultionem, ad vitam
longam. Edente authoris filio, Francisco
Mercvrio van Helmont. Amsterodami: L.

Elzevirius, 1648.
    17 *l.*, 800 p.   illus., ports.

1895. ———. ———. Editio nova ... Amsterodami: L. Elzevirius, 1652.
    18 *l.*, 894 p., 24 *l.*   illus.

1896. ———. Oriatrike or, Physick refined.
The common errors therein refuted, and the
whole art reformed & rectified ... now faithfully rendered into English ... by J.C. ...
London: for L. Loyd, 1662.
    23 *l.*, 1161 p., 11 *l.*   illus.

———. Praecipiolum: or the immature-
mineral-electrum. *In* Collectanea chymica
... 1684.

1897. ———. A ternary of paradoxes. The
magnetick cure of wounds, nativity of tartar
in wine, image of God in man ... Translated,
illustrated, and ampliated by Walter Charleton ... London: J. Flesher for W. Lee, 1650.
    26 *l.*, 147 p.

1898. HELVETIUS, Adriaan. [A collection
of pamphlets describing specific remedies
and proprietary preparations.] [18th cent.]
    var. pag.
    First six pages in manuscript.
    No title page.

1899. ———. Traité des maladies les plus
fréquentes et des remèdes propres à les
guérir. Nouvelle édition. Paris: L. Mercier,
1746.
    2 v.

1900. ———. Traité des pertes de sang, de
quelque espece qu'elles soient, avec leur
remede specifique, nouvellement découvert.
Accompagné de sa lettre sur la nature & la
guerison du cancer. Paris: L. d'Houry, 1697.
    7 *l.*, 168 p.   illus.

1901. HELVETIUS, Johann Friedrich. Vitulus aureus, quem mundus adorat & orat, in
quo tractatur de rarissimo naturæ miraculo
transmutandi metalla ... Amstelodami: J.
Jansson à Waesberge & vidua E. Weyerstraet,
1667.
    72 p.   port.

1902. ———. The golden calf, which the
world adores and desires: in which is handled
the most rare and imcomparable wonder of
nature, in transmuting metals ... Written in
Latin ... and faithfully Englished. London:
for J. Starkey, 1670.
    129 p.

———. A briefe of the golden calf.
In Cooper, W., The philosophical epitaph
... 1673.

1903. ———. Vitulus aureus quem mundus
adorat et orat. Oder ein sehr curieuses
Tractätlein, in welchem das rare und wundersame Werck der Natur in verwandelung
derer Metallen historice ausgeführet wird
... Aus dem Lateinischen ins Hochteutsche
übersetzet ... Franckfurth: P.W. Stock,
1726.
4 *l*., 68 p.

1904. ———. Theatridium Herculis trium-
phantis, ofte Kleyn schouw-tooneel, vand
den triumpherenden Hercules ... Midtsgaders
grondighe weder-legginghe der schriften van
sijn excell. Digby, aengaende Poudre sympathie ... s'Graven-Hage: J. Tongerloo,
1663.
8 *l*., 199 p. port.

1905. HEMPEL, Johann Gottfried. Phar-
macevtisch-Chemische Abhandlung über die
Natur der Pflanzensäuren und die Modifi-
cationen denen sie unterworfen sind, nebst
einer chemischen Untersuchung der Winter-
und Sommereiche. Berlin: E. Felisch, 1794.
xiv p., 1 *l*., 176 p.

1906. HEMSTERHUIJS, Sibout. Messis
aurea triennalis, exhibens; anatomica:
novissima et vtilissima experimenta ...
Lugduni Batavorum: A. Wyngaerden, 1654.
8 *l*., 347 p., 5 *l*.

1907. HENKEL, Johann Friedrich. Mineralo-
gische, chemische und alchymistische Briefe
von reisenden und andern Gelehrten an den
ehemaligen Chursächsischen Bergrath. Dresden: Walther, 1794-1795.
3 v.

1908. ———. Pyritologia: or, A history of
the pyrites ... Translated from the German
... London: for A. Millar and A. Linde, 1757.
xv, 376 p., 3 *l*. illus.

1909. HENNINGER, Johann Sigismund,
praeses. Dispvtatio medica sistens millepedas ... svbmittit Johannes Philippvs Elvert
... Argentorati: J. Staedelius, 1711.
1 *l*., 30 p.

1910. ———, *praeses*. Theses medicæ de
medicamentis martialibus ... submittit Georgius Henricus Eisenmann. [Argentorati] J.
Welper, 1715.
1 *l*., 26 p.

1911. HENRY, Thomas. Experiments and
observations ... on the preparation, calcination and medicinal uses of magnesia alba
... London: for J. Johnson, 1773.
xv, 142 p.

1912. HENSHAW, Nathaniel. Aero-chalinos:
or, A register for the air; in five chapters ...
Dublin: for S. Dancer, 1664.
6 *l*., 98 p.

1913. ———. ———. The second edition ...
London: for B. Tooke, 1677.
12 *l*., 166 p., 1 *l*.

1914. HERBAL. A newe herball of Macer,
translated out of Laten in to Englysshe.
[London: R. Wyer, ca. 1530?]
60 *l*.
Lacking the fourth leaf.
The Britwell Court copy with the arms of
William Miller in gilt on front and back
covers.

1915. ———. A boke of the propertyes of
herbes the whiche is called an herbal. [Lon-
don: Elizabeth Redman, 1541?]
76 *l*.

1916. ———. A booke of the properties of
herbes, called an herball, whereunto is
added the tyme that herbes, floures and
seedes should bee gathered to bee kept the
whole yeare, wyth the vertue of the herbes
when they are stylled. Also a generall rule
of all maner of herbes, drawen out of an
auncient booke of physicke by W.C. [Lon-
don: for Antony Kytson, ca. 1550?]
80 *l*.
The Britwell Court copy with the arms of
William Miller stamped in gold on the front
and back covers.

HERE BEGYNNETH a good booke of
medicines called the treasure of poore men.
See The treasure of poor men.

1917. HERMBSTÄDT, Sigismund Friedrich.
Bibliothek der neuesten physisch-chemischen
metallurgischen, technologischen und phar-
maceutischen Literatur. Berlin: A. Mylius,
1788-1795.
4 v. in 2. port.

1918. ———. Catechismus der apothecars-
kunst, of de eerste grondbeginzelen der art-
senijmengkunde ... Amsteldam: J.B. Elwe, 179?
1 *l*., ii, 278 p.
The *Aanhangzel*, Amsterdam: 1800, is boun
at the end.

1919. ———. Systematischer Grundris der allgemeinen Experimentalchemie zum Gebrauch seiner Vorlesungen entworfen ... Berlin: H.A. Rottmann, 1791.
  3 pts. in 1 v.

HERMES, *Trismegistus*. De compositione. *In* Philosophiae chymicae ... 1605.

———. Gülden Tractälein. *In* Alchymistisch Sieben-Gestirn ... 1697.

———. Les sept chapites dorez, & la Table d'Esmeraude. *In* Joly, G., Trois anciens traictes ... 1626.

———. *See also* Patrizi, F., Magia philosophica ... 1593.

1920. The HERMETICAL TRIUMPH. The hermetical triumph: or, The victorious philosophical stone ... Translated from the French. To which is added, The ancient war of the knights. Translated from the German original. As also, some annotations upon the most material points, where the two translations differ. Done from a German edition. London: P. Hanet, 1723.
  xxvi p., 1 *l*., 147, 39 p.   illus.

1921. ———. ———. London: for T. Harris [1725?].
  xxvi p., 1 *l*., 147, 39 p.   illus.

1922. ———. Le triomphe hermetique, ou La pierre philosophale victorieuse. Traitté plus complet & plus intelligible, qu'il en ait eu jusques ici, touchant le magistère hermetique. Amsterdam: H. Wetstein, 1689.
  7 *l*., 153 p.

1923. ———. ———. Amsterdam: H. Wetstein, 1699.
  7 *l*., 153 p.   illus.

1924. ———. Der Hermetische Triumph oder Der siegende philosophische Stein ... Hiebevor in Französischer Sprache gedruckt, zu Amsterdam bey Heinrich Wetstein, Anno 1689. Nunmehro gegenwärtig ins Deutsche versetzt. Franckfurt: J.P. Krauss, 1765.
  224 p.   illus.

1925. ———. Uhr-alter Ritter-Krieg, das ist, Ein alchymistisch kürtzliches Gesprach unsers Steins, des Goldes und des Mercurij ... von einem alten wohlerfahrnen Philosopho beschrieben. Hamburg: G. Wolff, 1680.
  16 p.

———. Le tres-ancien duel des chevaliers. *In* Divers traitez ... 1672.

A HERMETICALL BANQUET. *See* Vaughan, Thomas.

Das HERMETISCHE TRIUMPH. *See* The Hermetical Triumph.

1926. HERMETISCHER ROSENKRANTZ, das ist: Vier schöne, auserlesene chymische Tractätlein ... aus dem Lateinischen ins Teutsche übersetzt, und nun zum zweytenmal in Druck gegeben. Franckfurt am Mayn: J.F. Fleischer, 1747.
  112 p.

1927. HERMOGENES, *pseud*. Apocalypsis spagyrica et philosophica oder Wahrhaffter und untrüglicher Weg zu der höchsten Medicin, sowol auf menschliche als metallische Cörper zu gelangen ... Leipzig: J.S. Heinsius, 1739.
  224 p.

1928. HERRENSCHWAND, Johann Friedrich von. Traité des principales et des plus fréquentes maladies externes et internes ... Berne: F. Seizer, 1788.
  7 *l*., 540, xi, cliv p., 3 *l*.   port.

1929. HESSE, Heinrich. Neue Garten-Lust, das ist: Gründliche Vorstellung wie ein Lust-Küchen- und Baum-Garten ... anzurichten ... Damit es ein recht vollkommenes Garten-Buch ... auch mit dem gantzen vierdten Theile als beschreibung eines Artzney-Gartens ... versehen durch Theodorvm Phytologvm. Leipzig: J.L. Gleditsch und M.G. Weidmann, 1714.
  3 *l*., 389 p., 25 *l*.   illus.

1930. HEWSON, William. Experimental inquiries ... London: for T. Cadell, 1772-1774.
  2 v.   illus.

1931. HEYDON, John. The English physitians guide, or a holy-guide; leading the way to know all things, past, present & to come ... London: T.M. for [S. Ferris, 1662].
  6 pts. in 1 v.   port., illus.
  The 6 parts are each separately paginated and have special title-pages in variant forms.

1932. ———. לוראיר יבדדיחר להוזעם יהוה מין A new method of rosie crucian physick; wherein is shewed the cause; and therewith their experienced medicines for

the cure of all diseases, θεοπαράδοτα ...
London: for T. Lock, 1658.
4 *l*., 62 p.

1933. ———. The wise-mans crown: or,
The glory of the rosie-cross ... London: for
the author, 1664.
21 *l*., 54 p.; 2 *l*., 44 p. port.
Gathering A misbound before page 1.

1934. HEYL, Christopher. Hoc in volvmine
haec continentvr. Artificialis medicatio, constans paraphrasi in Galeni librum De artis
medicae constitutione ... Methodi cognoscendorum tam particularium, quam vniuersal-
ium morborum ... autore Bertrutio Bononiensi.
De idoneo auxiliorū usu, quaedam ex Ioanne
de Sancto Amando. Index in Mesuæi &
Nicolai Antidotaria. Mogvnt: [I. Schoeffer]
1534.
2 *l*., 90, 288 p., 6 *l*.
With Virdung, J., Nova medicinae methodus ... 1532.

1935. HEYLSAME HAUSS-APOTECKEN bestehend in allerhand sicheren guten und be-
währten auch von hochgelehrten Herren
Medicis gutgeheissenen Artzney-Mitteln ...
Ynsprugg: J.C. Wagner, 1714.
3 *l*., 190 p., 6 *l*.

1936. HIARNE, Urban. Actorum chemicorum
Holmiensium ... hoc est, Parasceve sive
præparatio ad tentamina, in Reg. Laboratorio
Holmiensi peracta ... cum annotationibus
Joh. Gotschalk Wallerii ... Stockholmiæ: L.
Salvius, 1753.
2 v. in 1. illus.

HIDEEN, Jacob. Ambrosiaca. *See*
Linné, C. von, *praeses.* Entry 2418.

1937. HIEBNER VON SCHNEEBERG, Israel.
Mysterivm sigillorvm, herbarvm & lapidvm
oder: Vollkommenes Geheimniss derer Sigil-
len, Kräuter und Steine in der Cur und Heilung
aller Kranckheiten, Schäden ... Franckfurt:
C. Weinmann, 1735.
4 *l*., 178 p., 15 *l*. illus.

1938. HIGGINS, Bryan. Experiments and
observations made with the view of improving the art of composing and applying cal-
careous cements and of preparing quick-lime
... London: for T. Cadell, 1780.
xi, 233 p.

1939. ———. Experiments and observations
relating to acetous acid, fixable air, dense
inflammable air, oils and fuel ... and other

subjects of chemical philosophy ... London:
for T. Cadell, 1786.
xvi, 353 p., 1 *l*.

1940. ———. Syllabus of Doctor Higgins's
course of philosophical, pharmaceutical,
and technical chemistry. [London: 1775?]
112 p.

1941. ———. ———. Another copy interleaved
with a manuscript in English consisting of
notes on chemistry, possibly lecture notes.

1942. HIGGINS, William. An essay on the
theory and practice of bleaching wherein
the sulphuret of lime is recommended as a
substitute for pot-ash ... London: for the
author, sold by Vernor and Hood, 1799.
xxxii, 71 p.

1943. HIGHMORE, Nathaniel. Corporis
hvmani disqvisitio anatomica; in qva sangvinis circvlationem in quavis corporis
particula plurimis typis novis, ac aenyg-
matum medicorum succincta dilucidatione
ornatam prosequutus est ... Hagae-Comitis:
S. Broun, 1651.
7 *l*., 262 p., 4 *l*.

1944. HILL, John. The British herbal: an
history of plants and trees, natives of
Britain ... London: for T. Osborne ... 1756.
2 *l*., 533 p., 1 *l*. illus.

1945. ———. The family practice of physic:
or, A plain, intelligible, and easy method of
curing diseases with the plants of our own
country ... London: for the author, 1769.
98 p. illus.

1946. ———. A general natural history: or,
New and accurate descriptions of the animals,
vegetables, and minerals, of the ... world;
with their virtues and uses ... in medicine and
mechanics ... London: T. Osborne, 1748-1752.
3 v. illus., charts.

1947. ———. A history of the materia medica.
Containing descriptions of all the substances
used in medicine ... London: T. Longman ...,
1751.
2 *l*., iv, 895 p., 4 *l*.

1948. ———. The old man's guide to health
and longer life: with rules for diet, exercise,
and physick ... The second edition. London:
for M. Cooper and J. Jolliffe [n.d.].
54 p.

1949. ———. A review of the works of the

Royal Society of London ... under the heads of arts, antiquities, medicine, miracles, zoophytes, animals, vegetables, minerals ... London: for R. Griffiths, 1751.

viii, 265 p., 1 *l*.

With his Thoughts concerning God ... 1755.

1950. ——. Spatogenesia. The origin and nature of spar; its qualities and uses: with a description and history of eighty-nine species ... London: for P. Elmsly, 1782.

1 *l*., 63 p.   charts.

1951. ——. Virtues of British herbs, with the history, description, and figures of the several kinds ... No. I.—To be continued occasionally, as new virtues are discovered in plants ... London: for R. Baldwin ..., 1770.

54 p.   illus.

No more published?

1952. ——. The virtues of honey in preventing many of the worst disorders; and in the certain cure of several others ... London: for J. Davis and M. Cooper, 1759.

54 p.

1953. HILL, Thomas.   The gardeners labyrinth: containing a discourse of the gardeners life ... Also the phisicke benefite of eche herbe, plant, and floure, with the vertues of the distilled waters of euery of them ... Gathered out of the best approved writers ... by Dydymus Mountaine. London: I. Wolfe, 1586.

4 *l*., 80 p., 4 *l*.; 180 p., 6 *l*.   illus.

1954. ——. A pleasant history: declaring the whole art of phisiognomy, orderly vttering all the speciall parts of man, from the head to the foot. [London] W. Iaggard, 1613.

2 *l*., 129 [i.e. 229] numb. *l*., 1 *l*.   illus.

1955. ——. The profitable arte of gardening, now the thirde time set forth: to which is added much necessaire matter, and a number of secrets, with the phisicke helpes belonging to eche herbe ... To this is annexed tvvo proper treatises, the one entitled, The maruellous gouerment ... of the bees ... And the other: The yearely coniectures ... Wherevnto is newly added a treatise of the arte of grafting ... London: H. Bynneman, 1574.

6 *l*., 134 p., 1 *l*.   illus.

Lacking pages 89-104.

1956. ——. ——. London: E. Allde, 1593.

4 *l*., 164 p.; 4 *l*., 92 p.

1957. HILLARY, William.   An inquiry into the contents and medicinal virtues of Lincomb Spaw water, near Bath ... London: for J. Leake, and sold by C. Hitch, 1742.

viii, 72 p.   illus.

1958. ——. An inquiry into the means of improving medical knowledge, by examining all those methods which have hindered or increased its improvement in all past ages. To which is added, an explanation of the motion and action of fire, in and upon the human body ... London: for C. Hitch and L. Hawes, 1761.

1 *l*., xvi, 461 p., 5 *l*.

HIORTZBERG, Lars.   De methodo investigandi vires medicamentorum chemica. *See* Linné, C. von, *praeses*.   Entry 2438.

1959. HIPPOCRATES.   Aphorismi Hippocratis, Nicolao Leoniceno interprete, lib. VII. Eivsdem Praesagia, Guilielmo Copo interprete, lib. III. Eivsdem De ratione victus in morbis acutis, lib. IIII. Eivsdem De natvra humana, Andrea Brentio interprete. Galeni Ars medicinalis interprete Nicol. Leoniceno. [Venetiis: in aedibus H. Pencii, sumptibus H. Paulucii, 1530.]

175 *l*.

1959a. ——. Aphorismorvm sectiones septē, recens è graeco in latinum sermonē cōuersae ... adiectis annotationibus, in quibus quotquot sunt in Galeni Commentarijs loci difficiles, ad unquem explicantur per Leonhartvm Fvchsivm ... Parisiis: O. Paruus, 1545.

8 *l*., 559 p., 22 *l*.

——. The presages. *In* Lowe, P., A discourse of the whole art of chyrurgerie ... 1634.

1960. ——. Coacae praenotiones ... Interprete & enarratore Lvdovico Dvreto ... Parisiis: B. Dv-Pvys, 1588.

6 *l*., 578 p., 28 *l*.

1961. ——. Epidemion liber sextvs, a Leonardo Fvchsio medico latinitate donatus, & luculentissima enarratione illustratus ... Basileae: I. Bebelivs et M. Isingrinius, 1537.

6 *l*., 188 numb. *l*., 6 *l*.

1962. ——. Liber de somniis. Cvm Ivlii Caesaris Scaligeri commentariis. Lvgdvni: S. Gryphivs, 1539.

4 *l*., 96 p., 2 *l*.

With Aretaeus, Libri septem ... 1552.

1963. ———. Opera qvae ad nos extant
omnia, per Ianvm Cornarium ... latina lingua
conscripta, & recognita. Cvm accessione
Hippocratis De hominis strvctvra libri ...
per Ioan. Culmā. nunc primū editis ...
Basileae: Froben, 1558.
804 p., 58 *l.*

1964. ———. Opera qvae extant graece et
latine ... à Hieron. Mercvriali. Venetiis:
Ivntarvs, 1588.
2 v.

1965. ———. ... Opera omnia qvae extant,
in VIII sectiones ex Erotiani mente distributa. Nvnc recens latina interpretatione, &
annotationibus illustrata, Anvtio Foesio ...
avthore ... Francofurti: A. Wecheli heredes
..., 1595.
2 v.

1966. ———. Opera omnia. Graece & latine
edita, et ad omnes alias editiones accommodata. Industriā & diligentiā Joan. Antonidae
vander Linden. Lugduni Batavorum: D., A. &
A. à Gaasbeeck, 1665.
2 v.

1967. ———. Opera omnia ex Jani Cornarii
versione una cum Jo. Marinelli commentariis
ac Petri Matthæi Pini indice ... Venetiis:
ex typographia Radiciana, apud C. Zane,
1737-1739.
3 v. port.

1968. HJÄRNE, Urban. Actorum chemicorum
Holmiensium, tomus primus [-secundus]. Hoc
est, Parasceve, sive præparatio ad tentamina, in reg. laboratorio Holmiensi peracta
... Cum annotationibus Joh. Gotschalk
Wallerii ... Stockholmiæ: L. Salvius, 1753.
2 v. in 1. illus.

1969. HODGES, Nathaniel. Loimologia:
or, An historical account of the plague in
London in 1665 ... To which is added, an
essay on the different causes of pestilential
diseases, and how they become contagious
... By John Quincy. London: for E. Bell and
F. Osborn, 1720.
vi, 288 p. chart.

1970. HOECHSTETTER, Philipp. Raravm
observationvm medicinalivm decades tres,
continentes, historias medicas, theorica &
practica varia, iocunda, vtilia, necessaria
tum ei qui ad praxim acccedit, tum qui eam
operatur. Avgvstae Vindelicorvm: A. Apergeri,
1624-1627.
2 pts. in 1 v. illus.

1971. HÖFER, Wolfgang. Hercules medicus,
sive Locorum commumium liber ... Noribergae:
M. & J.F. Endterorus, 1675.
20 *l.*, 613 p., 21 *l.* illus.

HOFFMAN, Anton. De potu choco-
latae. *See* Linné, C. von, *praeses.* Entry 2460.

1972. HOFFMANN, Christoph Ludwig. Von
der Empfindlichkeit und Reizbarkeit der Theile
... Münster: P.H. Perrenon, 1779.
6 *l.*, 270 p.

1973. HOFFMANN, Friedrich, ?-1675.
Clavis pharmacevtica Schroederiana ... cum
thesauro pharmacevtico qvorundam medicorum
nostri seculi. Editio secunda ... Halæ Saxonum: vidua et hæredes Myliani, 1681.
21 *l.*, 706 p., 18 *l.*; 4 *l.*, 117 p., 5 *l.*
port.

———. *See also* Schröder, Johann.

1974. HOFFMANN, Friedrich, 1660-1742.
Disquisitio physico-medica ou L'analyse
parfaite des eaux de la fontaine du Bas Selter ... Traduit de l'Allemand en François par
Mr.*****. Anvers: J.B. Jouret, 1739.
19 p.

1975. ———. Exercitatio medico-chymica
de cinnabari antimonii, ejusque eximiis
viribus ... Lugduni Batavorum: P. vander Aa,
1685.
157 p., 1 *l.*

1976. ———. New experiments and observations upon mineral waters ... The second
edition. To which is added ... An enquiry
into the contents, virtues, and uses of the
Scarborough spaw-waters ... By Peter Shaw
... London: for T. Longman, 1743.
2 pts. in 1 v.

1977. ———. Observationvm physico-
chymicarvm selectiorvm libri III ... Halæ:
Regner, 1722.
14 *l.*, 378 p., 11 *l.*

———. On those distempers which
arise from particular climates. *In* Ramazzini,
B., Health preserved ... 1750.

1978. ———. Opera omnia physico-medica
denuò revisa, correcta & aucta, in sex tomos
distributa ... Genevae: fratres de Tournes,
1740.
6 v. in 3.

1979. ———. Opvscvla pathologico-practica

sev Dissertationes selectiores antea diversis
temporibvs editae nvnc revisae et avctiores
... Halae: Renger, 1738.
    11 *l.*, 541 p., 8 *l.*

1980. ———. Sammlung auserlesener Ca-
suum von denen vornehmsten Krankheiten ...
Aus dem Lateinischen ins Deutsche ueber-
setzt von Samuel Schaarschmidt, nebst einem
vollstaendigen Register. Halle: Renger, 1735.
    8 *l.*, 822 p., 20 *l.*

1981. ———. A treatise of the extraordinary
virtues and effects of asses milk, in the
cure of various diseases ... Translated from
the Latin ... London: for J. Whiston & B.
White, 1754.
    viii, 50 p.

1982. ———, *praeses.* Caroli Hofmanni
Diatriba chymico-medica de acido vitrioli
vinoso ... Norimbergæ: W.M. Endter haeredes,
1733.
    1 *l.*, 44 p.

1983. ———, *praeses.* Disputatio solennis medica de hydrope pericardii rarissimo
... submittit Johannes Henricus Graetz.
[Halle] C.A. Zeitler [1697].
    32 p.

1984. ———, *praeses.* Dissertatio inavgvralis medica de salubritate febrium ... Proponet Fridericus Camel. Halae Magdeb.: C.
Salfeldi [1702].
    40 p.

1985. HOFFMANN, Georg Franz. Descriptio et adumbratio plantarum e classe
cryptogamica Linnaei quae lichenes dicuntur.
Lipsiae: S.L. Crusius, 1790-1801.
    3 v. in 1. illus.

1986. HOFFMANN, Maurice. Synopsis
institt. medicinae ex sanguinis natura vitam
longiorem artem breviorem promittentis
methodo nova perfacilique in Universitate
Altdorffina Norimbergensium disputata ...
Altdorffi: G. Hagen, 1663.
    32 *l.*

HOFMANN, Carl. Diatriba chymico-
medica de acido vitrioli vinoso. *See* Hoffmann, Friedrich, 1660-1742, *praeses.*

1987. HOFMANN, Caspar. Institvtionvm
medicarvm. Libri sex ... Lvgdvni: J.A. Hvgvetan, 1645.
    16 *l.*, 779 p., 44 *l.*

1988. HOGHELANDE, Theobaldus van. De
alchemiæ difficvltatibvs ... in qvo docetvr
qvid scire, quidque vitare debeat veræ
chemiæ studiosus ad perfectionem aspirans
... Coloniæ Agrippinæ: H. Falckenburg,
1594.
    14 *l.*, 165 p.

HOLLANDUS, Isaac. *See* Johannes
Isaaci, Hollandus.

HOLLBERG, Esaias. Norra Americanska Färgeörter. *See* Kalm, P., *praeses.*

1989. HOME, Francis. Clinical experiments,
histories, and dissections. Second edition,
corrected. London: for J. Murray, 1682 [i.e.
1782].
    xii, 499 p.

1990. ———. An essay on the contents and
virtues of Dunse-Spaw. In a letter to my
Lord ——— ... Edinburgh: R. Fleming for A.
Kincaid & A. Donaldson, 1751.
    216 p.

1991. ———. Experiments on bleaching ...
Edinburgh: Sands ..., 1756.
    vi, 330 p.

1992. ———. Methodus materiae medicae.
Editio altera. Edinburgi: J. Bell & G. Creech,
1781.
    xvi, 90 p.

1993. HOOKE, Robert. Micrographia: or
Some physiological descriptions of minute
bodies made by magnifying glasses. With
observations and inquiries thereupon. London: J. Martyn and F. Allestry, 1665.
    18 *l.*, 246 p., 5 *l.* illus.

1994. ———. ———. London: for J. Martyn,
1667.
    18 *l.*, 246 p., 5 *l.* illus.

HÖPFNER, Heinrich Ferdinand. De
alchemia medicinae. *See* Schroeder, Friedrich
Josef Wilhelm, *praeses.*

1995. HORLACHER, Conrad. Vestgegründeter
Beweiss das die eingeführten Meinungen von
denen Catarrhis ... nicht bessern Grund als
alte Weiber-Mährlein haben ... Nürnberg: Verlegung des Authoris, zu finden bey W.M. Endter, 1691.
    4 *l.*, 110 p.
    With Manget, J.J., Bibliotheca chemico-
curiosa ... 1707.

1996. HORN, Christopher. De avro medico philosophorvm ... dialogvs scholasticvs ... Francofurti: W. Richter, 1615.
  6 l., 88 p.

HORNBORG, Johan. Planta cimicifuga. *See* Linné, C. von, *praeses*. Entry 2488.

1997. HORNOT, Antoine. Traité des odeurs, suite du traité de la distillation. Paris: Bailly, 1777.
  x p., 1 l., 492 p.

1998. ——. Traité raisonné de la distillation; ou La distillation réduite en principes; avec un traité des odeurs. Paris: Nyon & Guillyn, 1753.
  x p., 1 l., 484 p., 4 l.

1999. ——. ——. Quatrieme édition, revue, corrigée & beaucoup augmentée par l'auteur ... Paris: Bailly, 1777.
  xvi, 461 p.

2000. HORST, Gregor. De natvra hvmana libri duo ... Francof. ad Moenvm: typis E. Kempferi, sumptibus C. Bergeri, 1612.
  8 l., 510 p., 7 l. illus.

2001. ——. Operum medicorum ... Cura Gregorii Horstii, junioris ... Norimbergæ: J.A. & W. Endter, 1660.
  3 v. in 1.

2002. HORTOLANUS, *junior, pseud.* The golden age: or, The reign of Saturn review'd. Tending to set forth a true and natural way, to prepare and fix common mercury into silver and gold ... Preserved and published by R.G. ... London: J. Mayos for R. Harrison, 1698.
  11 l., 215 p.

HORTULANUS. *See* Joannes de Garlandia.

2003. HOULLIER, Jacques. De morbis internis, lib. II. Illustrati doctissimis eiusdem authoris scholiis & obseruationibus non antea excussis: deinde Lvdovici Dvreti ... in eundem aduersariis & Anthonij Valetij ... exercitationibus luculentis. Eivsdem Hollerij De febribus. De peste. De rhemediis in Galeni libros. De materia chirurgica. Quae omnia Ant. Valet. opera auctiora & castigatiora in lucem prodeunt. Parisiis: C. Macaeus, 1577.
  4 pts. in 1 v.

2004. ——. Omnia opera practica. Doctissimis eivsdem scholiis & obseruationibus illustrata: deinde Lvd. Dvreti ... in evndem enarrationibvs, annotationibus, & Antonij Valetij exercitationibus luculentis. Accessit etiam ... Therapia puerperarum I. Le Bon ... Genevae: J. Stoer, 1623.
  8 l., 584, 317 p., 9 l.

2005. HOUPREGHT, John Frederick. Aurifontina chymica: or, A collection of fourteen small treatises concerning the first matter of philosophers, for the discovery of their ... mercury ... London: for W. Cooper, 1680.
  272 p., 1 l.
  Lacking 11 leaves preceding text and one leaf at end.

HUEBER, János Sámuel. Dissertatio inauguralis medica de ipecacuanha Americana. *See* Schulze, J.H., *praeses*.

2006. HUET DE LA MARTINIERE. Dissertation sur l'examen analytique des eaux minérales des environs de l'Aigle. Geneve: Glaçon, 1776.
  1 l., 56 p., 1 l.
  With Terrede, Examen analytique des eaux minérales ... 1776.

2007. HUFELAND, Christoph Wilhelm. Ueber die Natur, Erkenntnissmittel und Heilart der Skrofelkrankheit ... Zweite mit Anmerkungen vermehrte Auflage. Jena: 1797.
  xiv, 398 p.

2008. HUGHES, William. The American physitian; or, A treatise of the roots, plants, trees, shrubs, fruit, herbs, &c. growing in the English plantations in America ... London: J.C. for W. Crook, 1672.
  11 l., 159 p., 3 l.

2009. HUGINUS À BARMA. Le règne de Saturne, changé en siècle d'or, S.M.I.S.P. ou Le magistere des sages ... Le tout traduit du latin d'Huginus à Barmâ, par Mr. Pi. Th. An. ... Paris: P. Derieu, 1780.
  192 p.

——. Saturnisch Reich. *In* Taeda trifida chimica ... 1674.

2010. HULLIN, Jean Baptiste Louis. Tentamen chemico-physiologicum de actione aëris in respiratione & in combustione, nec-non de utriusque analogiâ ... Monspelii: J.F. Picot, 1787.
  16 p.

2011. HULSIUS, Anton, *praeses*. Disputatio medica inauguralis de somno & somnifero opio ... publico examini subjicit
Johannes Broen ... Lugduni Batavorum: A.
Elezevier, 1683.
   8 *l.*

2012. HUMBOLDT, Alexander, *freiherr* von.
Versuche über die chemische Zerlegung des
Luftkreises und über einige andere Gegen-
stände der Naturlehre. Braunschweig: F.
Vieweg, 1799.
   2 *l.*, 258 p.   illus., charts.

2013. ——. Versuche über die gereizte
Muskel-und Nervenfaser nebst vermuthungen
über den chemischen Process des Lebens in
der Thier-und Pflanzenwelt. Posen: Decker
..., 1797.
   2 v.

2014. HUMMEL, Johann. Topiarii hermetico-chemici partem alteram præstat
Olympvs astralis ... Francofurti ad Moenum:
J.F. Fleischer, 1739.
   38 p.

2015. ——. Topiarii hermetico-chemici
partem tertiam exhibet πᾶν τῶν πάντων
ὑποτιθέμενον. Hoc est: Mirabile â Deo ...
substitutum per cuncta dominivm ... Francofurti ad Moenum: J.F. Fleischer, 1739.
   112 p.
   With his Topiarii ... partem alteram ...
1739.

2016. HUNTER, Alexander. A treatise on
the nature and virtues of Buxton waters ...
London: for the author, 1768.
   3 *l.*, 66 p.

2017. HUNTER, John. The natural history
of the human teeth ... London: for J. Johnson,
1771.
   4 *l.*, 128 p., 16 *l.*   illus.

2018. ——. Observations on certain parts
of the animal oeconomy ... Second edition.
London: G. Nicol and J. Johnson, 1792.
   2 *l.*, ii, 273 p., 2 *l.*   illus.

2019. ——. A treatise on the blood, inflammation, and gun-shot wounds ... To
which is prefixed, a short account of the
author's life, by his brother-in-law, Everard
Home. London: J. Richardson for G. Nicol,
1794.
   1 *l.*, lxvii, 575 p.   illus.

2020. ——. A treatise on the venereal
disease. London: 1786.
   6 *l.*, 398 p., 13 *l.*   illus.

2021. ——. ——. Second edition. London:
G. Nicol and J. Johnson, 1788.
   6 *l.*, 398 p., 13 *l.*   illus.

2022. HUNTER, William. Anatomia uteri
humani gravidi tabulis illustrata ... The
anatomy of the human gravid uterus ex-
hibited in figures. Birminghamiae: J. Basker-
ville, 1774.
   21 *l.*, 34 plates. folio.
   English and Latin text.

2023. ——. An anatomical description
of the human gravid uterus, and its contents.
London: for J. Johnson and G. Nicol, 1794.
   xii, 88 p.

2024. ——. Medical commentaries. Part
1. Containing a plain and direct answer to
Professor Monro, jun., interspersed with remarks on the structure, functions, and diseases of several parts of the human body.
London: printed by A. Hamilton, sold by A.
Millar, 1762.
   4 *l.*, 113 p.   illus.

2025. ——. ——. The second edition.
London: for S. Baker ..., 1777.
   vii, 113, 33 p.

2026. ——. Two introductory lectures,
delivered by Dr. William Hunter to his last
course of anatomical lectures, at his theatre
in Windmill Street ... To which are added
some papers relating to Dr. Hunter's intended
plan for establishing a museum in London for
the improvement of anatomy, surgery, and
physic. London: for J. Johnson, 1784.
   1 *l.*, 130 p.   illus.

2027. HUTTEN, Ulrich von. De morbo
Gallico. Londini: T. Berthelet, 1533.
   4 *l.*, 79 numb. *l.*

2028. ——. Of the wood called gvaiacvm,
that healeth the Frenche pockes and also
helpeth the goute in the feete, the stoone,
the palsey, lepree, dropsy, fallynge euyll,
and other dyseases. Londini: T. Berthelet,
1539.
   4 *l.*, 79 numb. *l.*

2029. HUTTON, James. A dissertation
upon the philosophy of light, heat, and fire.
In seven parts. Edinburgh: for Cadell &
Davies, 1794.
   2 *l.*, xxiv, 326 p.

2030.   HUXHAM, John.   An essay on fevers. To which is now added, A dissertation on the malignant, ulcerous sorethroat. The third edition. London: for J. Hinton, 1757.
     xvi, 336 p.

2031.   ———.   Medical and chemical observations upon antimony. London: for J. Hinton, 1756.
     2 *ℓ*., 78 p., 1 *ℓ*.

2032.   ———.   Observations on the air and epidemic diseases from the year MDCCXXVIII. to MDCCXXXVII. inclusive; together with a short dissertation on the Devonshire colic. Translated from the Latin original, and now published with the doctor's approbation. London: for J. Hinton and H. Whitfeld, 1759-1767.
     2 v.   illus.

2033.   ———.   Opera physico-medica. Cvrante Georgio Christiano Reichel. Lipsiae: I.P. Kravs, 1764.
     3 v. in 1.   illus.

I, J

IBN SINA. *See* Avicenna.

2034. IMISON, John. The school of arts; or, An introduction to useful knowledge: being a compilation of real experiments and improvements, in several pleasing branches of science ... The fourth edition, with very considerable additions. London: for J. Murray and S. Highley, 1796.
xv, 319 p.; 4 *l*., 176 p. illus.

2035. IN DISSERTATIONEM nuper editam de medicorum apud veteres Romanos degentium conditione animadversio brevis ... Londini: J. Noon, 1727.
42 p., 1 *l*.

IN HOC volumine de alchemia. *See* De alchemia ... 1541.

INDAGINE, Innocentius Liborius ab, *pseud. See* Jäger, Johann Ludolph.

2036. INGENHOUSZ, Jan. Experiments upon vegetables, discovering their great power of purifying the common air in the sun-shine ... To which is joined, A new method of examining the accurate degree of salubrity of the atmosphere. London: for P. Elmsly and H. Payne, 1779.
lxviii, 302 p., 9 *l*. illus.

2037. INSTRUCTION GENERALE pour la teinture des laines et manufactures de laine de toutes coleurs, & pour la culture des drogues ou ingrediens qu'on y employe. Paris: F. Muguet, 1671.
175 p., 8 *l*.

2038. L'IRROE; o, Lo purgativ refrescant ... Barcelona: C. Gibert y Tuto ... [177?].
19 p.

2039. IRVINE, Christopher. Medicina magnetica: or, The rare and wonderful art of curing by sympathy ... By C. de Iryngio ... [London] 1656.

7 *l*., 110 p.

2040. IRVING, Ralph. Experiments on the red and quill Peruvian bark: with observations on its history, mode of operation, and uses ... Edinburgh: for C. Elliot ..., 1785.
2 *l*., 181 p., 1 *l*.

IRYNGIO, C. de. *See* Irvine, Christopher.

2041. ISTRUZIONE dei modi da praticarsi per coltivare il kali maggiore, o sia salsola-soda ... [Vencie] Z.A. Pinelli, 1780.
xxi p.

2042. JĀBIR IBN HAIYĀN, al-Tarasūsī. Summa perfectionis magisterii in sua natura, ex Bibliothecæ Vaticanæ exemplari ... edita ... Librique inuestigationis magisterii, & testamentum eiusdem Geberis ... & Auicennæ ... Mineralium additione castigatissima ... [Romæ: M. Silber, 1520?]
196 *l*. illus.
Last leaf reproduced in photostat.

2043. ———. De alchimia libri tres. Eiusdem liber inuestigationis perfecti magisterij, artis alchimicæ. Iis additus liber trium verborum. Epistola item Alexandri imperatoris ... [Argentoragi: I. Grieninger, 1531.]
lx numb. *l*. illus.
With Ulsted, P., Coelvm philosophorvm ... 1525.

2044. ———. Svmma perfectionis magisterij in sua natura ex bibliothecæ Vaticanæ exemplari ... Librique inuestigationis magisterij, & testamenti eiusdem Geberis, ac Aurei trium uerborum libelli, et Auicennæ ... Mineralium additione castigatissima. [Venetijs: P. Schoeffer & I.B. Pederzanus, 1542.]
7 *l*., 126 numb. *l*., 2 *l*. illus.

2045. ———. De alchemia traditio summæ perfectionis in duos libros divisa. Item: Liber investigationis magisterij ... [Stras-

burg] L. Zetzner, 1598.
    8 *l*., 203 [i.e. 302] p.

2046. ——. Chimia sive Traditio summæ
perfectionis et investigatio magisterij in-
numeris locis emendata à Caspare Hornio
... Accessit ejusdem Medulla alchimiæ
Gebricæ. Omnia edita à Georgio Hornio.
Lugduni Batavorum: A. Doude, 1668.
    10 *l*., 179 [i.e. 279] p.

2047. ——. Summa perfectionis magisterii
in sua natura ... deniéue libri investigationis magisterii & testamenti ejusdem
Gebri, ac Aurei trium verborum libelli, &
Avicennæ ... mineralium additione castigatissima. Gedani: B.L. Tancke, 1682.
    8 *l*., 278 p.   illus.

2048. ——. Curieuse vollständige chym-
ische Schrifftē ... wie auch Das Testament,
Güldene Buch der dreyen Wörter Kallid
Rachaidibi, und andere chymische Tractät-
gen ... an Tag gegeben von Philaletha.
Franckfurth: H.P. Ritschl, 1710.
    8 *l*., 288 p.   illus.

2049. ——. The works of Geber ... Faithfully Englished by R.R. ... London: for N.E.
by T. James, 1678.
    8 *l*., 302 p., 1 *l*.

2050. ——. The works of Geber, the most
famous Arabian prince and philosopher, of
the investigation and perfection of the
philosophers-stone ... London: for W. Cooper,
1686.
    8 *l*., 302 p., 1 *l*.

    ——. *See also* Artis chemicae ...
1572.

    ——. *See also* De alchemia ... 1541.

    JACKSON, Joseph.   Enchiridion medi-
cum practicum. *In* Fuller, T., Pharmacopoeia
extemporanea ... 1790.

2051. JACKSON, Robert.   An outline of the
history and cure of fever, endemic and contagious ... To which is added, An explanation of the principles of military discipline
and economy; with a scheme of medical
arrangement for armies. Edinburgh: for Mundell & Son ..., 1798.
    xi, 396 p.

2052. ——. A treatise on the fevers of
Jamaica, with some observations on the inter-
mitting fever of America, and an appendix ...

Philadelphia: for R. Campbell, 1795.
    xi, 276, 19 p., 2 *l*.

2053. JACQUET, Bernard.   Discours, ou
Histoire abrégée de l'antimoine, et particu-
lierement de sa préparation ... Paris: S.
Jorry, 1765.
    48 p.

2054. JACQUIN, Joseph Franz, *freiherr* von.
Elements of chemistry ... Translated from the
German. London: J.W. Myers for W. Treppass
..., 1799.
    xi, 415 p.   illus.

2055. JÄGER, Johann Ludolph.   Bifolivm
chemico-physico-metallicvm, bestehend in
zwo besondern Abhandlungen ... Ausgefertiget
und zu weiterer Untersuchung ans Licht
gestellet, von I.L. ab Indagine ... Amsterdam und Leipzig: J. Schreuder, 1771.
    6 *l*., 227 p.

2056. JAMES, Robert.   A medicinal dictionary; including physic, surgery, anatomy,
chemistry, and botany, in all their branches
relative to medicine ... London: for T. Osborne, 1743-1745.
    3 v.   illus.

2057. ——. Pharmacopoeia universalis:
or, A new universal English dispensatory ...
London: for J. Hodges and J. Wood, 1747.
    xxxi, 836 p., 23 *l*.

2058. ——. ——. The second edition ...
London: for J. Hodges, 1752.
    viii, 758 p., 18 *l*.

2059. JANIN DE COMBE BLANCHE, Jean.
L'antiméphitique ou Moyens de détruire les
exhalaisons pernicieuses & mortelles des
fosses d'aisance, l'odeur infecte des egouts,
celle des hôpitaux ... &c., &c., avec l'emploi des vuidanges neutralisées, & leur
produit étonnant ... Paris: P.D. Pierres,
1782.
    xxxii, 70, 8 p.

2060. ——. Détail de ce qui s'est passé
dans les expériences faites par M. Janin,
les 18 & 23 Mars, en présence des commissaires réunis de l'Académie Royale des
Sciences & de la Société Royale de Médecine ... Paris: P.D. Pierres, 1782.
    1 *l*., 25 p.
With his L'antiméphitique ... 1782.
Lacking p. 19-22.

2061. JANUA PATEFACTA.   Ianva patefacta

thesavro, per qvam secretam ad scientiam
facilé ingredi possunt veri Hærmetis filii.
Amstelodami: E. Weyerstraten, 1678.

4 pts. in 1 v.

Contents: *Monte Snyders* , J., Commentatio de pharmaco catholico; *Basilius Valentinus*, Les dovze clefs de philosophie;
Sendivogius, *M.*, Novvm lvmen chemicvm,
accessit tractatus de svlphvre; *Artephius*,
De arte occvlta.

The tracts are not bound in the correct
order. In Novvm lvmen chemicvm, the supplement preceeds the main work.

2062. JARAVA, Juan de. I qvattro libri
della filosofia natvrale ... Tradotti di Spag-
nuolo in Italiano dal Sig. Alfonso Vlloa ...
Vinegia: A. Rauenoldo, 1565.

150 p.

2063. JASOLINO, Giulio. De' rimedii
natvrali che sono nell' isola di Pithecusa,
hoggi detta Ischia. Libri dve ... Et in questa
seconda impressione ricorretto, & accresciuto con alcune annotationi del ... Gio.
Pistoya. E nell' vltimo aggiunti li bagni
d'Ischia di Gio. Elisio ... con le note di Gio.
Francesco Lombardo ... Nap.: G. Cacchij per
F. Mollo, 1689.

20 *l*., 274 p., 19 *l*., 12 p. map.

JEAN DE MEUN. Les remonstrances
de nature à l'alchymist errant. *In* Metallique,
De la transfromation metallique ... 1561.

2064. ———. Der Spiegel der Alchymie ...
Aus dem Lateinisch-Französischen übersetzt.
Dem noch beygefüget worden Ben-Adams
Traum-Gesichte durch Floretum a Bethabor;
nebst Friedrich Galli Reise nach der Einöde
St. Michael. Ballenstadt und Bernburg:
Biesterfeld, 1771.

48 p.

———. Le miroir d'alqvimie. *See also*
Bacon, R., Le miroir d'alqvimie ... 1613.

JEHIOR ... or The day dawning. *In*
Cooper, W., The philosophical epitaph ...
1673.

2065. JENNER, Henry. An address to the
public on the advantages of vaccine inocu-
lation: with the objections to it refuted ...
London: W. Bulgin ... [1799].

19 p.

JOANNES XXI, *pope*. L'art transmuta-
toire. *In* Bacon, R., De l'admirable povvoir
... 1629.

———. L'elixir des philosophes. *In*
Bacon, R., Le miroir d'alquimie ... 1557.

2066. ———. The treasvri of helth con-
taynynge many profytable medicines, gathered out of Hipocratz, Galē & Auicen ... &
trāslated into Englysh by Hūfre Lloyd ...
[London: W. Coplande, ca. 1550.]

217 *l*.

2067. JOANNES ACTUARIUS. De vrinis ...
libri VII, Anbrosio Leone Nolano interprete
... Antonij Thylesij ... De coloribus liber
... Pauli Aeginetæ De crisi & diebus decretorijs ... Basileæ: A. Cratandrus [1529].

8 *l*., 447 p.

With Scribonius, L., De compositione
medicamentorum ... 1529.

2068. JOANNES DE CUBA. Kreutterbüch
von allem Erdtgewächs ... Jetz widerum new
corrigirt vnd ... gemehrt ... Distillierbüch
Hieronymi Braunschwig von aller Kreuter
aussgebrenten Wassern hiemit füglich in-
geleibt. D. Eucharius Rhodion ... Franckfurt
am Meyn: C. Egenolph [1533].

8 *l*., ccxii p., 4 *l*. illus.

2069. JOANNES DE GARLANDIA. Compendivm alchimae ... cum dictionario eiusdem
artis, atque de metallorum tinctura præpara-
tioneque eorundem libello, ante annos DXX.
eodem authore conscripto. Adiecimus eiusdem Compendij per Arnoldvm de Villa Nova
explicationem ... Basileae: 1560.

8 *l*., 174 p.

———. ———. *In* Ventura, L., De ra-
tione conficiendi lapidis Philosophici ... 1571.

JOANNES DE PADUA. Κατοπθοσοφία,
id est, Consummata sapientia. *In* Schauberdt,
J., Κατοπθοσοφια ... 1602.

———. Lilium inter spinas. *In* Neander, T., Heptas alchymica ... 1621.

2070. JOANNES DE RUPESCISSA. De consideratione quintæ essentiae rerum omnium
... Arnaldi de Villa Nova Epistola de sanguine
humano distillato. Raymundi Lillij Ars opera-
tiua: & alia quædam ... Nunc primùm in lucem data. Accessit Michaelis Savonarolæ
Libellus optimus de aqua vitæ ... Item Hieronymi Cardani Libellus de æthere ... Basileæ
[1561].

341 p.

2071. ———. ———. Basileæ: C. Waldkirch, 1597.

292 p.

————. Liber lucis. *In* Broekhuizen, D. van, Secreta alchimiæ magnalia ... 1598, 1602.

2072. JOANNES TICINENSIS. Johannis Ticinensis ... Anthonii de Abbatia ... und Edoardi Kellæi ... vortreffliche und auss- führliche chymische Bücher ... in Teutscher Sprach übergesetzet ... Hamburg: G. Liebe- zeit, 1691.
112 p.
Lacking the work by Keller.
With Leursen, J., Chymischen Schau- Platzes ... 1708.

2073. JOHANNES ISAACI, *Hollandus*. Opera mineralia, siue De lapide philosophico, omnia, duobus libris comprehensa. Nunquam antehac edita, ac nunc primùm ex optimis manuscriptis Teutonicis exemplaribus fidelis- simè in Latinum sermonem translata à P.M.G. Middelburgi: R. Schilders, 1600.
8 *l*., 431 p.   illus.

2074. ————. Opera mineralia, et vegeta- bilia, sive De lapide philosophico, quæ reperire potuimus omnia ... Arnhemii: J. Jans- son, 1616.
7 *l*., 431, 88 p.

2075. ————. Das dritte Theil des Mineral- Wercks ... mit fleiss aus dem Niedern- ins Hochdeutsche übersetzet, durch einen geübten Liebhaber der Hermetischen Philo- sophy. Franckfurt: T.M. Götzen, 1666.
171 p.
With his Tractat genant Die Hand der Philosophen ... [1667].

————. Opere vegetabili & animali. *In* Paracelsus, Centum quindecim curationes ... 1582.

2076. ————. Opus vegetabile. Worin er den treuhertzigen filiis doctrinæ, getreuwahr- haffter massen ümbständlichen unterricht gibt ... Auss Niederländischen manuscriptis ... hergegeben vom Sohn Sendivogii, genant J.F.H.S. Amsterdam: H. Betkius, 1659.
144 p.

2077. ————. ... Tractat ... genant Die Hand der Philosophen, mit ihren verborgenen Zeichen ... Item: Opera vegetabilia ... auss ... Niederländischen manuscriptis verhoch- deutschet ... von einem geübten Liebhaber der Hermetischen Philosophy ... Franckfurt: T.M. Götzen [1667].
384 p.   illus.

————. Tractat von den Saltzen und Oehlen der Metallen. *In* Stahl, G.E., Chymia rationalis ... 1729.

2078. ————. Tractatus de lapide philo- sophico oder Vom Stein der Weisen. Franck- furt: in Verlegung T.M. Götzen, gedruckt bey B. Ilssnern, 1669.
4 *l*., 175 p.   illus.
With his Tractat genant Die Hand der Philosophen ... [1667].

————. A work of Saturn. *In* Basilius Valentinus, Of natural and supernatural things ... 1671.

————. *See also* Fioravanti, L., Three exact pieces ... 1652, 1653.

2079. JOHNSON, Alexander.   A collection of authentic cases, proving the practicability of recovering persons visibly dead by drown- ing, suffocation, stifling, swooning, con- vulsions, and other accidents. [London: 1773.]
2 *l*., 138 p.

2080. JOHNSON, Robert.   Praxis medicinæ reformata: or, The practice of physick re- formed ... London: for B. Aylmer, 1700.
2 *l*., xxii, 317 p., 3 *l*.   port.

2081. JOHNSON, William.   Lexicon chymi- cum, cum obscuriorum verborum, et rerum Hermeticarum, tum phrasium Paracelsicarum, in scriptis ejus: et aliorum chymicorum ... planam explicationem continens ... Londini: G.D. for W. Nealand, 1652-1653.
2 v. in 1.

2082. ————. ————. Londini: G.D. for W. Nealand, 1660.
2 v. in 1.

2083. JOHNSTONE, James.   Some account of the Walton water, near Tewkesbury; with thoughts on the use and diseases of the lymphatic glands. In a letter to [   ] ... Worcester: J. Tymbs ... [1787].
vii, 48 p.

2084. JOLY, Gabriel, *ed.*   Trois anciens traictez de la philosophie natvrelle. 1. Les sept chapitres dorez ... & le table d'esmeraude d'Hermes Trismegiste. 2. La response de Messire Bernard ... Treuisane, à Thomas de Boulongne ... 3. La chrysopée de Iean Augurel ... Les deux premiers n'ont encore esté tra- duits en François, & le troisiesme est corrigé

des fautes suruenuës en la precedente impression ... Paris: C. Hulpeau, 1626.
   4 *l*., 89 p.; 1 *l*., 130 p.
   The tracts are bound in the wrong order.

2085.   JONES, John.   The mysteries of
opium reveal'd ... London: for R. Smith,
1701.
   4 *l*., 371 p.   chart.

2086.   JONES, Robert.   An inquiry into the
state of medicine, on the principles of in-
ductive philosophy. With an appendix: containing practical cases and observations.
Edinburgh: for T. Longman ..., 1781.
   1 *l*., xvi, 376 p.

2087.   JONSTONUS, Joannes.   Thavmato-
graphia natvralis, in decem classes distincta
... Amsterdami: G. Blaev, 1632.
   6 *l*., 501 p., 1 *l*.

2088.   ———.   An history of the wonderful
things of nature: set forth in ten severall
classes ... Rendred into English ... London:
J. Streater, 1657.
   8 *l*., 354 p., 1 *l*.

2089.   JÖPSER, Jacob Joseph.   Isagoge, seu
Manuductio ad vitam longiorem ... Noribergae:
M. & J.F. Endter, 1680.
   16 *l*., 688 p., 12 *l*.   illus.

2090.   JORDAN, Thomas.   De aqvis medi-
catis Morauia, commentariolvs ... Franco-
furdi: heredes A. Wechel, 1586.
   14 *l*., 119 p., 3 *l*.

2091.   JORDEN, Edward.   A discourse of
natural bathes, and mineral waters ... The
third edition, revised and enlarged ... To
which is added, An appendix concerning
Bathe ... By Thomas Guidott ... London,
1669.
   12 *l*., 167 p.; 6 *l*., 60 p., 1 *l*.   chart,
illus.
   Lacking p. 1-16 in first part.

   JORLIN, Engelbert.   Plantae tinctoriae.
See Linné, C. von, *praeses*. Entry 2489.

2092.   JOSSELYN, John.   New-Englands rarities discovered: in birds, beasts, fishes,
serpents, and plants of that country. Together with the physical and chyrurgical
remedies wherewith the natives constantly
use to cure their distempers, wounds, and
sores ... London: for G. Widdowes, 1672.
   2 *l*., 114 p., 2 *l*.   illus.

2093.   JUBERA, Alonso de.   Dechado y refor-
macion de todas las medicinas compuestas
vsuales ... Valladolid: D.F. de Cordoua,
1578.
   12 *l*., 5-336 numb. *l*.

2094.   JUGEL, Johann Gottfried.   Freyent-
deckte experimental-Chemie ... In zwey
Theile abgefasset ... Leipzig: J.P. Krausse,
1766.
   7 *l*., 368 p.   port.

2095.   ———.   Gründliche Nachricht von
dem wahren metallischen Saamen, oder prima
materia metallorvm, wie aus derselbe das
gantze mineralische Reich seinen Ursprung
hat ... Leipzig: J.J. Schöps, 1754.
   4 *l*., 184 p.

2096.   ———.   Philosophische Unterredung
zwischen dem fliegenden Mercurium und
einem gemeinem Schmeltzer ... Berlin: J.A.
Rüdiger, 1743.
   254 p.   illus.

2097.   ———.   Von der Scheidung der vier
Elementen aus dem ersten Chaos ... Berlin:
J.A. Rüdiger, 1744.
   7 *l*., 348 p.   illus.

2098.   JUNCKER, Johann.   Conspectvs
chemiae theoretico-practicae ... in forma
tabvlarvm repraesentatvs, in qvibvs physica
... et corporvm natvralivm principia ... e
dogmatibvs Becheri et Stahlii potissimvm
explicantvr ... Halae Magdeb.: Orphanotropheus, 1738-1744.
   2 v.   port.

2099.   ———.   Conspectvs formvlarvm medicarvm ... Halæ Magdebvrgicæ: Orphanotropheus, 1723.
   112 p.
   With Carl, J.S., Specimen historiæ medicæ
... 1719.

   ———.   ———. *In* Bate, G., Pharmacopoea
Bateana ... 1776.

2100.   ———.   Conspectvs therapiae generàlis,
cvm notis in materiam medicam tabvlis XX
methodo Stahliana conscriptvs. Halae Magdeburgicae: Orphanotropheus, 1725.
   4 *l*., 520 p., 11 *l*.

2101.   ———, *praeses*.   Dissertatio inavgvralis chemico-medica sistens disqvisitionem
analyticam arcani tartari ... Respondens Al-
bertvs Reichardvs Revss. Halæ Magdebvrgicæ:

I.C. Hilliger, 1743.
  48 p.

2102. JÜNGKEN, Johann Helfrich. Chymia
experimentalis curiosa, ex principiis mathe-
maticis demonstrata ... Francofvrti: H. à
Sande, 1681.
  11 ℓ., 898 p.   illus.

2103. ———. Chymia experimentalis cvriosa,
sive Medicus præsenti seculo accomodandus
per veram philosophiam spagiricam ... Editio
postrema ... & priori auctior. Francofurti: H.
à Sande [1684?].
  10 ℓ., 840 p., 2 ℓ.

2104. ———. Corpus pharmaceutico-
chymico-medicum sive Concordantia pharma-
ceuticorum compositorum discordans ...
Francofurti ad Moenum: F. Knochius, 1697.
  2 v.   illus.
  Volume one only.

2105. ———. ———. Editio tertia ... Francofurti ad Moenum: F.D. Knochius, 1732.
  3 ℓ., 1228 p., 22 ℓ.   illus.

2106. ———. Lexicon chymico-pharmaceuticum, in duas partes distinctum ... Editio altera ... Francofurti ad Moenum: J. Zieger,
1709.

  2 pts. in 1 v.

2107. ———. ———. Editio tertia ... Norimbergæ: J.F. Rüdigerus, 1729.
  2 pts. in 1 v.

2108. ———. Sonderbahre nutzliche auch
nöthige Anmerkungen. Eine sorgfältige Auffer-
ziehung der jungen Kinder und deren Gebrechen betreffend ... Nürnberg: J. Zieger,
1688.
  180 p., 2 ℓ.

2109. JUSTI, Johann Heinrich Gottlob von.
Gesammlete chymische Schriften ... Berlin:
Buchladen der Real-Schule, 1760-1761.
  2 v.

2110. ———. Die Kunst das Silber au affini-
ren oder das mit andern Metallen vermischte
Silber wieder fein zum machen. Königsberg
und Mietau: J.J. Kanter, 1765.
  36 p.

2111. ———. Le secret des nouvelles teintures de Saxe, avec quelques réflexions sur
la théorie, & sur les avantages de ces nouvelles teintures ... Traduit de l'Allemand sur
l'original imprimé à Vienne 1751. Paris:
Durand, Pissot, 1752.
  54 p.

K

KAAU BOERHAAVE, Abraham. Discours académique, des qualités qui constituent les médecins. *In* Mead, R., Avis et préceptes ... 1757.

———. Sermo academicus de iis. *In* Gaubius, H.D., Sermones II ... 1776.

2112. KAEMPFER, Engelbert. Amoenitatum exoticarum politico-physico-medicarum fasciculi V ... Iemgoviæ: H.W. Meyer, 1712.
9 ℓ., 912 p., 16 ℓ. illus., port., maps.

2113. KALDE, Jacob. Dispensatorium Hamburgense, juxta quod medicamenta, tam chymica quam Galenica ... Hamburgi: C. Neumann, 1716.
8 ℓ., 184 p. illus.

2114. KALM, Pehr, *praeses*. Norra Americanska Färge-örter ... Framstälde och til allmän granstning öfwerlämnade uf Esaias Hollberg ... Åbo: J.C. Frenckell, 1763.
2 ℓ., 8 p.

2115. KARSTEN, Wenceslaus Johann Gustav. Physisch-chymische Abhandlungen durch neuere Schriften von hermetischen Arbeiten und andre neuere Untersuchungen veranlasset ... Halle im Magdeburgschen: Renger, 1786-1787.
2 v. in 1.

2116. KASTELL, Christoph Wilhelm de. Adeptus realis, das ist Kürzliche Zuschrifft eines wahrhafften Adepti, an alle respectivè hochgeneigte Liebhaber der wahren und reellen Alchymie ... Leipzig: F. Grosehuff, 1715.
8 ℓ.
With Faust, J.M., Philaletha illustratus ... 1706.

2117. KEIL, Christoph Heinrich. Compendiöses doch vollkommenes philosophisches Hand-Büchlein, das ist: Philosophische Grund-Sätze zur Universal-Tinctur auf Menschen und Metallen ... übereinstimmen ... Leipzig: J.G. Vierling, 1736.
176 p. illus.

2118. KEILL, James. The anatomy of the humane body abridg'd: or, A short and full view of all the parts of the body. Together with their several uses, drawn from their compositions and structures ... The third edition, revis'd. London: J.B. for R. Smith and W. Keble, 1708.
6 ℓ., 335 p.

———. Medicina statica Britannica. *In* Santori, S., Medicina statica ... 1737.

2119. KEIR, P. An enquiry into the nature and virtues of the medicinal waters of Bristol, and their use in the cure of chronical distempers. London: for R. Willock ..., 1739.
iv, 167 p.

KELLER, Johann Christian. De elementis. *See* Limmer, C.P., *praeses*.

2120. KELLEY, Edward. Tractatus duo egregii, de lapide philosophorum, vna cvm Theatro astronomiæ terrestri ... Nunc primum in lucem editi, curante J.L.M.C. Hamburgi: G. Schultz, 1676.
125 p. illus.

2121. KELLNER, David. Ars separatoria curiosa ac perutilis, oder Sehr nütz- und erbauliche Scheide-Kunst ... Leipzig: J.F. Gleditsch, 1693.
8, 112 p.

2122. ———. Erneuert- verbessert- und vermehrte, sehr nütz- und erbauliche Scheide-Künst, worinnen enthalten die rechte Art und Weise, wie man die vermischte Metalla ... künstlich von einander scheiden und bringen soll ... Chemnitz: G. Stössel, 1727.
4 ℓ., 164 p., 2 ℓ.

2123. ———. Kurtze Vorstellung der zur
edlen Chymie gehörigen Wissenschafft
bestehend in CLIII. Aphorismis oder kurtzen
Sätzen ... vormahls in lateinischen Sprache
zu Amsterdā von einem Liebhaber dieser
Kunst sich Eremitan Suburbanum nennend,
heraus gegeben ietzo aber ... in dero Mutter-
Sprache übersetzt ... von D. David Kellnern.
Nordhausen: A.M. Hynitzsch [n.d.].
    24 ℓ.

2124. ———. Via regia naturæ simplicis-
simæ simplicissima ducens per simplicis-
simum laborem ad utilissimam metallorum
meliorationem ... Nordhausen: C.C. Neuen-
hahn, 1704.
    109 p.   illus.

2125. ———, supposed author.   Die durch
selsame Einbildung und Betriegerey Schaden
bringende Alchymisten-Gesellschafft ... in
einen nützlichen Lust-Spiele vorgestellet
von J.D.K.   Franckfurht: G.H. Ziehler, 1700.
    6 ℓ., 227 p.   illus.

2126.   KENDALL, George.   An appendix to
the unlearned alchimist, wherein is contained
the true receipt of that excellent diaphore-
tick and diuretick pill ... commonly known
by the name of Matthew's pill ... London:
for J. Leigh [1664].
    4 ℓ., 54 p.

        KENNEDY, James.   Practical obser-
vations on goat's whey. In The argument of
sulphur ... 1762.

2127.   KENTISH, Richard.   Experiments and
observations on a new species of bark,
shewing its great efficacy in very small
doses ... London: J. Johnson, 1784.
    xii, 123 p.

2128.   K'EOGH, John.   Botanalogia universalis Hibernica, or, A general Irish herbal
... To which are added, two short treatises,
one concerning the chalybeat waters ...
another of the prophylactic ... part of medicine ... Corke: G. Harrison, 1735.
    9 ℓ., 145 p., 16 ℓ.

2129.   KERCKRING, Theodor.   Opera omnia
anatomica. Continentia Specilegivm anatomicvm, Osteogeniam foetvvm, nec non Anthro-
pogeniae ichnographiam ... Editio secunda.
Lugduni Batavorum: vid. & fil. C. Boutesteyn,
1717.
    12 ℓ., 303 p.   illus.

        ———. See also Basilius Valentinus,

Commentarius in curren triumphalem ...
1685.

2130.   KERNER, Arnold.   Balsamus vegetabilis vel sulphuris compositus ... Hiehvor
zu Leipzig bey Herrn Philips Witteln in anno
1618. getruckt, nunmehr aber in Verlegung
Ernesti Hayens Apothekern ... wieder auffgelegt. Cassel: S. Schadewitz, 1651.
    93 p.

2131. ———. D.O.M.A. Tetras chymiatrica
proponens præstantiam et in medicina efficaciam, auri, mercurii, antimonii, & vitrioli,
& medicamentorum ex illis paratorum ...
Erphordiæ: J. Birckner, 1618.
    143 ℓ.
    With Crusius, D., Theatrum morborum ...
1615.

2132.   KERTZENMACHER, Petrus.   [Alchimia.
Wie man alle farben, wasser, olea, salia,
vnd alumina ... machen sol ...] [Straszburg:
M.J. Camerlander, 1539.]
    1 ℓ., xli numb. ℓ., 3 ℓ.   illus.
    Lacking title page and following three
leaves.

2133. ———. ———. [Augspurg: H. Steyner]
1546.
    8 ℓ., 60 numb. ℓ.   illus.

        ———. ———. In Gertz, P., Neu-eröff-
nete Kunst-Kammer ... 1720.

2134. ———. Alchimi vnd Bergwerck ...
Strassburg: J. Cammerlander, 1534.
    4 ℓ., xl numb. ℓ.   illus.

2135.   KESSLER, Thomas.   Dreyhundert
ausserlesene chymische Process und Stücklein ... Strassburg: J.P. Sartorius, 1630.
    2 pts. in 1 v.

2136. ———. Keslerus redivivus. Das ist,
Fünff hundert ausserlesene chymische Process
vnd Artzneyen ... An tag gegeben vnd zum
vierdten mal auffgelegt, an jetzo aber von
einem vornehmen Chymico auffs new vbersehen, vnd mit Hinzusetzung dess fünfften
hunderten in formalische Ordnung vnd gewisse Classes gesetzet ... Franckfurt am
Mayn: J. Beyer, 1641.
    7 ℓ., 536 p., 7 ℓ.

2137.   KESTNER, Christian Wilhelm.   Bibliotheca medica, optimorvm per singvlas medicinae partes avctorvm delectv circvmscripta
... Ienae: C.H. Cvnonis, 1746.
    4 ℓ., 728 p., 20 ℓ.

2138. KEUP, Johann Bernard, *ed.* Libellus
pharmaceuticus composita et praeparata
praecipua praeparandi modum et encheireses
exhibens. Cui accedunt Tabulae pro com-
positionum pharmaceuticarum prospectu
facilioro. Duisburgi ad Rhenum: 1789.
    1 *l.*, 204 p.

2139. KHONN, Alphons. Transmutatio
metallica curiosa & genuina. [Ulm?] 1713.
    8 p.

2140. KHUNRATH, Conrad. Medulla distillatoria & medica, das ist, Warhafftiger,
eigentlicher, gründlicher Bericht, wie man
den Spiritum Vini ... distilliren, nachmals
in quintam Essentiam ... bringen sol ... Mit
sonderm fleis ... colligiret, vnd in Druck
öffentlich verfertiget, durch C.C.L. Leipzig
[n.d.].
    3 *l.*, 146 numb. *l.*, 11 *l.*

        ——. Tractätlein vom Urin. *In* Dol-
hopff, G.A., Lapis animalis ... 1681.

2141. ——. Traite de l'esprit de sel philosophiqve. Dont fait mention le famevs medecin Conrad Kunraths dans son livre intitulé
Medulla Distillatoria, partie premiere page
59. Imprimé à Hambourg l'an 1638. Traduit
de Latin en François par maistre Antoine Le
Maire ... [Paris: 1684.]
    20 p.

2142. KHUNRATH, Heinrich. ... Amphi-
theatrvm sapientiæ æternæ, solivs veræ ...
[Hamburg?: 1595?]
    1 *l.*, 24 p., 1 *l.* illus., oblong folio.
    Illustrated by four full-page circular en-
gravings, hand-colored and illuminated in
gold and silver.

2143. ——. ——. Francofurti: T. Gunder-
mann, 1653.
    1 *l.*, 60, 222 p., 1 *l.* illus., charts.

2144. ——. Confessio ... de chao physico-
chemicorvm catholico; in qvo catholice
habitat azoth sive materia prima mvndi ...
Magdeburgi: 1596.
    2 *l.*, 56 p.

2145. ——. ——. Argentorati: J.A. Dolhoff,
1699.
    2 *l.*, 84 p.

2146. ——. De igne magorum philosopho-
rum´que secreto extremo & visibili: das ist:
Philisophische Erklährung von vnd vber dem
geheymen-eusserlichen, sichtbaren, Gludt
vnd Flammenfewer der vhralten Magorum
oder Weysen, vnd andern wahren Philosophen
... Strassburg: L. Zetzner, 1608.
    4 *l.*, 157 p.
    With his Warhafftiger Bericht ... 1603.

2147. ——. Magnesia catholica philosophorvm, oder Eine in der Alchymie höchst
nothwendige und augenscheinliche Anweisung, die verborgene catholische Magnesia
des geheimen Universalsteins der ächten
Philosophen zu erlangen ... Neue, von den
Sprach- und Druckfehlern gesäuberte Auflage.
Leipzig: A.F. Böhmen, 1784.
    1 *l.*, vi, 112 p.

2148. ——. Symbolvm physico-chymicvm
... De chao physico-chymicorvm catholico
... [Hamburgk: H. Binders Erben] 1598.
    22, 23 p., 1 *l.*
    Part 2 has title: *Naturgemes-alchymisch
Symbolvm, oder, gahr kurtze Bekentnus von
allgemeinem Chao* ...
    With his Von hylealischen Chaos ...
1597.

2149. ——. Von hylealischen, das ist,
pri-materialischen catholischen oder alge-
meinen natürlichen Chaos, der naturgemessen
alchymiæ vnd alchymisten ... [Magdeburg:
A. Genen Erben, 1597.]
    12 *l.*, 469 p., 1 *l.*

2150. ——. Warhafftiger Bericht vom philosophischen Athanore; auch Brauch vnnd Nutz
desselbigen ... Editio secunda ... [Magdeburg?]
Verlegung des Authrois, 1603.
    1 *l.*, 60 p. illus.

    KIERNANDER, Jonas. Radix senega.
See Linné, C. von, *praeses.* Entry 2491.

2151. KIESLING, Johann, *praeses.* Dissertatio academica de philosophia hermetica
vera et experimentali ... publicæ eruditorum
disquisitioni exposita a Johanne Nicolao
Martio ... Erffurti: D. Sumphius [1698].
    16 *l.*

2152. KINDER-BETT des Steins der Weisen,
durch einen unbekandten Chevalier in Frant-
zösischer Sprache beschieben, und nun aus
dem Frantzösischen ins Teutsche übersetzet,
durch J.L.M.C. ... Hamburg: G. Liebernickel,
1692.
    45 p.
    An extract from: *Nodus sophicus enodatus*
... Hamburg, 1692.

2153. KIRANUS, *King of Persia, pseud.*

Moderante auxilio redemptoris supremi,
Kirani Kiranides, et ad eas Rhyakini Koro-
nides ... [Leipzig?:1638.]
   9 *l*., 159 p., 11 *l*.

2154. ——. Mysteria physico-medica, ob
augustissimos suos natales, uberrimamque
rerum haud quotidianarum, quibus referta
sunt segetem, curioso obtutu quam-maximè
veneranda, multis abhinc seculis Syriacè,
Arabicè, & Græcè conscripta; iterata nunc
vice è membranis Latinis publicæ luci exposita. Francofurti: J.J., Erythropilus, 1681.
   201 p., 6 *l*.

2155. KIRCHER, Athanasius. Ars magna
sciendi, in XII libros digesta ... Amstelodami: J. Janssonius à Waesberge & vidua
E. Weyerstraet, 1669.
   8 *l*., 481 p., 5 *l*. illus., port, charts.

2156. ——. Mundus subterraneus, in XII
libros digestus ... Editio tertia ... Amstelodami: J. Janssonius à Waesberge, 1678.
   2 v. in 1. illus., maps, charts.

2157. ——. Physiologia Kircheriana experimentalis ... Amstelodami: Janssonius-
Waesberge, 1680.
   4 *l*., 248 p., 4 *l*. illus.

2158. KIRCHMEYER, Karl Valentin. Uralter
Kukus-Brunn, anjetzo neu-erweckter Grad-
litzer Brunn-Quell ... Prag: G. Labaun, 1696.
   6 *l*., 92 p. illus., chart.

2159. KIRCHWEGER, Anton Joseph. Micro-
scopivm Basilii Valentini, sive Commenta-
riolvm et cribrellum über den grossen Kreuz-
apfel der Welt ... ein Euphoriston der ganzen Medicin, ex Theoria et Praxi Grauinii
... Berlin: 1790.
   172 p.

2160. ——, *supposed author*. Annulus
Platonis oder Physikalisch-chymische Erklärung der Natur nach ihrer Entstehung, Er-
haltung und Zerstöhrung von einer Gesell-
schaft ächter Naturforscher, aufs neue verbessert und mit vielen wichtigen Anmerkungen
herausgegeben. Berlin: G.J. Decker, 1781.
   xxxii, 551 p. illus.

2161. ——, *supposed author*. Aurea
catena Homeri. Oder: Eine Beschreibung von
dem Ursprung der Natur und natürlichen
Dingen ... Franckfurt: J.G. Böhme, 1723.
   6 *l*., 404 p., 18 *l*. illus.

2162. ——. ——. Neue Auflage ... Leip-

zig: S.B. Walther, 1738.
   8 *l*., 406 p., 9 *l*. illus., chart.

2163. KIRSTEN, Georg. Adversaria et
animadversiones, in Johannis Argicolæ ...
Commentaria in Poppium, & Chirurgiam
parvam ... Alte Stettin: G. Götzke, 1648.
   26 *l*., 594 p., 5 *l*.

2164. KIRWAN, Richard. An essay on
phlogiston, and the constitution of acids.
London: J. Davis for P. Elmsly, 1787.
   2 *l*., 146 p., 2 *l*.

2165. ——. An essay on the analysis of
mineral waters ... London: J.W. Myers for
D. Bremner, 1799.
   vii, 279 p. charts.

2166. KITE, Charles. Essays and observations, physiological and medical, on the
submersion of animals and on the resin of
the *Acoroides resinifera*, or yellow resin
from Botany Bay. To which are added, select
histories of diseases; with remarks. London:
G. Woodfall for C. Dilly, 1795.
   vii, 434 p. illus.

2167. KLOBIUS, Justus Fidus. Ambræ
historiam ... Wittenbergæ: sumptibus hæred.
T. Mevii & E. Schumacheri, typis M. Henckelii
1666.
   4 *l*., 76 p. illus., map.

2168. KNOLL, Heinrich Christoph Friedrich.
Dir Zauberhöhle in Schottland. Eine wunder-
volle Anecdote aus der Goldmacher-Zeit des
Doctor Price. Weimar: C.L. Hoffmanns Wittbe
und Erben, 1783.
   96 p.
   With Ettner, J.C. von, Rosetum chymicum
... 1724.

2169. KNÖR, Ludwig Wilhelm von. Basilius
Valentinus redivivus seu Astrum rutilans
alchymicum, das ist: Der wieder auffgelebte
Basilius Valentinus oder hellgläntzendes
Gestirn der Alchymie ... Samt beygefügten
kurtzen und deutlichen alchym-physologischen
raisonement ... Leipzig: in Verlegung des
Autoris, zu finden bey J.F. Braun, 1716.
   8 *l*., 160 p.

2170. KOEFFERLE, Caspar Franciscus
Xaverius. Dissertatio medica inauguralis
de febre catharrali epidemice grassante ...
Basileæ: J.H. Decker [1733].
   2 *l*., 18 p.

2171. KOFFSKY, Vincentius. Ein aussführ-

licher schöner und aussbündiger Bericht,
von der ersten Tinctur-Wurtzel, und auch
Materia prima dess gebenedeyten uhralten
Steins der Weisen ... Dantzigk: in Verlegung
B.L. Tancken, gedruckt bey J.F. Gräfen,
1681.
   1 *l*., 13 p.

2172. KÖNIG, Emanuel. Regnum minerale,
generale et speciale ... Basileæ: E. König,
1703.
   11 *l*., 181 p., 1 *l*.; 428 p., 2 *l*. port.

2173. ——. Regnum vegetabile ... Accessit selectus remediorum e triplici regno
juxta normam & ductum pharmaciæ Ludovi-
cianæ. Cum appendice Compositionis arti-
ficiosæ ... Georg. Wolfg. Wedelium. Basileae
Rauracorum: E. & J.G. König, 1688-1696.
   2 pts. in 1 v.

2174. KÖNIGLICHE Hermetische Special-
Concordanz ... Alles auf Anleitung Herrn
Johann Kunckel von Löwensterns sel seines
A. 1716. durch ... Joh. Caspar Engelleder ...
herausgegebenen Laboratorii chymici ... Von
einem Liebhaber der reinen Wahrheit ...
durch öffentlichen Druck an den Tag gegeben.
Bresslau: M. Hubert, 1723.
   703 p.

2175. KORNDORFFER, Bartholomaeus. De
tinctvra gemmarum, das ist, Ein warhaftige
Beschreibung wie die Edelgesteine nicht
allein von ihren gifftigen influentien corrigirt, sondern auch wie sie nach geschehener
Correction zu Nutz vor vielerley Kranckheiten
dem Menschen adhibiret werden können ...
[n.p.] 1635.
   28 *l*.

2176. KORNMANN, Heinrich. De miracvlis
mortvorvm ... collecta habentur, quæstiones
naturales, physicæ, medicæ, theologicæ &
iuridicæ traduntur ... [Frankfurt] typis I.
Wolffii, sumptibus I.I. Porsii, 1610.
   176 *l*.
   With his Templum naturae historicum ...
1611.

2177. ——. De miracvlis vivorvm, sev De
varia natvra, variis singvlaritatibvs, proprietatibus, affectionibus, mirandisque virtutibus,
facultatibus & signis hominum viuorum ...
Francofurti: typis viduæ M. Beckeri, impensis I. Fischeri, 1614.
   20 *l*., 298 p.
   With his Templum naturae historicum ...
1611.

2178. ——. Templvm natvræ historicvm
... in qvo de natvra et miracvlis qvatvor
elementorum, ignis, aeris, aqvæ terræ, ita
disseritur ... Darmbstadii: I.I. Porssius,
1611.
   334 p.

2179. KOSEGARTEN, David August Josua
Friedrich. De camphora et partibvs qvae
eam constitvvnt ... Goettingae: Barmeier,
1785.
   4 *l*., 69 p., 1 *l*.

2180. KRAMER, Johann Georg Heinrich.
Dissertatio epistolica de differentiis qvibvs-
dam inter hominem natvm et nascendvm in-
tercedentibvs deqve vestigiis divini nvminis
inde collegendis viro. Norimbergae: P.C.
Monath, 1736.
   1 *l*., 118 p. illus.

2181. KRAUSE, J. Der medizinische Land-
pfarrer, oder kurzgefasste medizinische Abhandlung und Heilart derjenigen Krankheiten,
welche am meisten auf dem Lande vorkommen.
Landau: Silberling, 1792.
   8 *l*., 206 p., 1 *l*.

2182. KRAUSS, Johan Carl. Afbeeldingen
der artseny-gewassen met derzelver nederduitsche en latynsche beschryvingen. Amsterdam: J.C. Sepp, 1796-1800.
   6 v. illus.

   KRÄUTERMANN, Valentin, *pseud. See*
Hellwig, Christoph von.

2183. KRIEGSMANN, Wilhelm Christoph.
Taaut oder Ausslegung der chymischen Zeich-
en; damit die Metallen und andere Sachen
von Alters her bemerckt werden: auff Begehren
beschrieben. Franckfurt: T.M. Götze, 1665.
   75 p., 2 *l*. illus.

2184. KUMMER, Johannes Gabriel. Dissertationem de coeliaca passione, gratiossimæ
facultatis medicæ indultu in illustri Academia
Basiliensi ... Basileæ: Genath [1709].
   8 *l*.

2185. KUNCKEL, Johann, von Löwenstern.
Chymische Anmerckungen: darinn gehandelt
wird von denen Principiis chymicis, salibus
acidis und alkalibus, fixis und volatilibus
... wie auch vom Geruch und Farben, &c.
... Wittenberg: in Verlegung J.W. Fincelij
seel Erben, druckts C. Schrödter, 1677.
   8 *l*., 192 p.
   With Basilius Valentinus, *pseud.*, Tractat

von dem grossen Stein ... 1626.

2186. ———. Collegium physico-chymicum
experimentale, oder Laboratorium chymicum
... II. edition. Hamburg: S. Heyl, 1722.
    15 ℓ., 455 [i.e. 739] p., 18 ℓ.

2187. ———. V. curiose chymische Tractätlein ... Wobey zugleich angehänget wird:
Christoph Brummets Tractätlein vom Blut
der Natur. Nebst einer Vorrede: De doctis
& nobilibus empiricis D. Johannis Philippi
Burggravii ... Franckfurth: W.C. Multz, 1721.
    6 ℓ., 512 p., 24 ℓ.

2188. ———. Philosophia chemica experimentis confirmata in qua agitur de principiis
chymicis ... Accedit Perspicilium chymicum
contra non-entia chymica. Amstelaedami: J.
Wolters, 1694.
    7 ℓ., 333 p.   illus.

———. An experimental confirmation
of chymical philosophy. In Pyrotechnical
discourses ... 1705, etc.

2189. ———. Utiles observationes sive
Animadversiones de salibus fixis & volatilibus ... Primùm ab authore Germanicè conscripta, nunc verò Latinitate donata à Carolo
Aloisio Ramsaio. Londini: H. Wilson, 1678.
    11 ℓ., 122 p.; 12 ℓ., 160 p.

———. See also Neri, Antonio, Ars
vitraria ... 1679.

2190. KUNSTBÜCHLEIN, auff mancherley

weiss Dinten vnd aller handt Farben zu
bereyten ... Cöllen: P. von Brachel, 1616.
    43 p., 1 ℓ.

2191. KURELLA, Ernst Gottfried, ed. Fascicvlvs dissertationvm ad historiam medicam
speciatim anatomes spectantivm ... Berolini:
A. Havde et I.C. Spener, 1754.
    4 ℓ., 485 p.

2192. Eine KURTZE HANDLEITUNG zum
himmlischen Rubin vom philosophischen
Stein und seiner Heimlichkeit. Berlin: 1746.
    56 p.
    With Hanstein, P.H. von, Wasser und
Geist ... 1756.

2193. KURTZER doch gründlicher Bericht vom
Sauer-Wasser im Langen Schwalbach ...
Andere Auflage. Franckfurth am Mayn: P.W.
Steck, 1739.
    44 p., 1 ℓ.   illus.

2194. KURTZER in der Theorie und Praxi
gegründeter Bericht von Universal-Artzneyen
... durch E.C.D.M. [n.p.] 1709.
    52 p.
    With Siebenstern, C.F.S. von, Practica
... 1721.

2195. KURZE BESCHREIBUNG und Heilungs-
art der Krankheiten, welche am öftesten in
dem Feldlager beobachtet werden, samt beygefügten Recepten, welche vor die Königl.
Französische Armee vorgeschrieben werden.
Münster: 1759.
    8 ℓ., 160, 48 p.

L

2196. LA CHÂTRE, René de. Le prototype
ov tres-parfait et analogiqve exemplaire de
l'art chimicque a la phisiqve ov philosophie
de la science naturelle ... Paris: J.A. Joallin,
1620.
    11 ℓ., 136 p.

2197. LACINIO, Giano, *ed.* Pretiosa margarita novella de thesavro, ac pretiosissimo
philosophorvm lapide. Artis huius diuinæ
typus, & methodus: Collectanea ex Arnaldo,
Rhaymundo, Rhasi, Alberto, & Michaele
Scoto; per Ian Lacinium ... nunc primum ...
in lucem edita. Venetiis: Aldi filios, 1546.
    20 ℓ., 202 numb. ℓ. illus.

2198. ———, *ed.* Præciosa ac nobilissima
artis chymiæ collectanea de occvltissimo
ac præciosissimo philosophorum lapide ...
Norimbergæ: G. Hayn, 1554.
    8 ℓ., 124 numb. ℓ. illus.

2199. ———, *ed.* Margarita pretiosa
novella exhibens introdvctionem in artem
chemiæ integram: ante annos plus minus
ducentos septuaginta composita, autore M.
Petro Bono ... Argentorati: L. Zetzner, 1608.
    10 ℓ., 398 p., 6 ℓ.

    LADO, Christian. Motus polyshres-
tus. *See* Linné, C. von, *praeses.* Entry 2445.

2200. LAFITAU, Joseph Francois. Mémoire
presenté a ... le Duc D'Orleans ... concernant la précieuse plante du gin seng de
Tartarie ... Paris: J. Mongé, 1718.
    88 p., 4 ℓ. illus.

2201. LA FOLLIE, Louis Guillaume de.
Der Philosoph ohne Anspruch oder Der seltene
Mann, ein physikalisches, chymisches,
politisches und moralisches Werk ... aus
dem Französischen übersetzt. Frankfurt am
Main: Andred, 1781.
    7 ℓ., 367 p. illus.

2202. LA FONTAINE, Jean de. La fontaine

des amovrevx de science ... Reueuë ... par
maistre Antoine du Moulin Masconnois.
Lyon: J. de Tovrnes, 1571.
    63 p. illus.

    ———. ———. *In* Metallique, De la
transformation metallique ... 1561.

2203. LA FRAMBOISIERE, Nicolas Abraham
de. Les oevvres ... ov sont ... descrites
l'histoire du monde, la medecinè, la chirurgie
& la pharmacie ... Derniere edition ... Lyon:
I. Thioly, 1669.
    8 ℓ., 977 p., 41 ℓ.

2204. LA GARAYE, Claude Toussaint Marot,
comte de. Chymie hydraulique pour extraire les sels des vegetaux, animaux et
mineraux, par le moyen de l'eau pure. Paris:
J.B. Coignard, 1745.
    xi p., 2 ℓ., 390 p. illus.
    Lacking title page.

2205. ———. ———. Nouvelle édition, revue,
corrigée & augmentée de notes, par M. Par-
mentier ... Paris: Didot le jeune, 1775.
    xxi p., 1 ℓ., 512 p., 4 ℓ.

2206. LAGNEAU, David. Harmonia sev
consensvs philosophorvm chemicorum ...
Parisiis: C. Morelius, 1611.
    16 ℓ., 326 p., 42 ℓ.

2207. LAGRANGE, B. Vollständige Apothe-
kerwissenschaft. Erster Theil. Naturlehre.
Aus dem Französischen übersetzt. Leipzig:
F.G. Baumgärtner, 1796.
    xxiv, 351 p.
    Volume one only.

2208. LAMARCK, Jean Baptiste Pierre Antoine de Monet de. Recherches sur les
causes des principaux faits physiques ...
Paris: Maradan, 1794.
    2 v.

2209. ———. Réfutation de la théorie pneu-

matique, ou De la nouvelle doctrine des chimistes modernes, présentée ... dans une suite de réponses aux principes rassamblés et publiés par ... Fourcroy, dans sa Philosophie chimique ... Paris: l'auteur et Agasse, 1796.
    2 *l*., 484 p.

2210. LA MARTINIÈRE, Pierre Martin de. Tombeau de la folie, dans leqvel se void les plus fortes raisons que l'on puisse apporter pour faire connoître la realité & la possibilité de la pierre philosophale ... Paris: l'auteur [n.d.].
    6 *l*., 128 p.   port.

    LAMBYE, John Baptista. *See* Agnello, Giovanni Battista.

2211. LA MÉTHERIE, Jean Claude de. Essai analytique sur l'air pur, et les différentes espèces d'air. Paris: 1785.
    3 *l*., 474 p., 1 *l*.

2212. ——. ——. Seconde édition. Paris: Cuchet, 1788.
    2 v.

2213. LA METTRIE, Julien Offray de. Abregé de la théorie chymique. Tiré des propres ecrits de M. Boerhaave ... Auquel on a joint le Traité du vertige ... Paris: A.C. Briasson, 1741.
    4 *l*., 301 p., 1 *l*.

2214. ——. Man a machine ... Translated from the French ... The third edition. London: for G. Smith, 1750.
    1 *l*., 87 p.

2215. LAMPÉRIÈRE, Jean de. L'ombre de Necrophore vivant chartier de l'Hostel Dieu. Av Sievr Iovyse medecin deserteur de la peste ... Rouen: D. Ferrant, 1622.
    16 *l*., 295 p.

2216. LANCILOTTI, Carlo. Der brennende Salamander, oder Zerlegung, der zu der Chimie gehörigen Materien, so da ist ein Wegweiser oder Unterricht sich in allen Arbeiten der Scheid-Kunst zu üben ... erst aus dem Italiänischen ins Holländische: nun aber aus der Holländischen in die Hochteutsche Sprache übersetzet durch J.L.M.C. Franckfurt am Mayn: J. Haass, 1681.
    7 *l*., 305 p., 4 *l*.   illus.

2217. ——. Farmacevitca antimoniale overo Trionfo dell' antimonio ... Modona: eredi Soliani, 1683.

35, 287 p.   illus.

2218. ——. Farmacevtica mercvriale overo Trionfo del mercvrio ... Modona: eredi Soliani, 1683.
    8, 209 p.

2219. ——. Gvida alla chimica, che per suo mezo conduce gl'affezionati alle operazioni sopra ogni corpo misto animale, minerale, ò vegetabile ... Divisa in sei libri ... Venetia: N. Pezzana, 1674.
    5 *l*., 326 p., 9 *l*.

2220. LANCISI, Giovanni Maria. De motu cordis et aneurysmatibus opus postumum in duas partes divisum. Neapoli: F.C. Musca, 1738.
    2 *l*., xxviii, 219 p.   illus.

2221. ——. De svbitaneis mortibvs. Libri dvo. Romae: J.F. Gleditsch, 1709.
    10 *l*., 313 p., 16 *l*.

2222. ——. Dissertatio de nativis, deque adventitiis romani coeli qualitatibus, cvi accedit Historia epidemiae rheumaticae, quae per hyemen anni MDCCIX. vagata est. Romae: F. Gonzagas, 1711.
    8 *l*., 258 p., 10 *l*.

2223. ——. Opera varia in unum congesta, et in duos tomos distributa. Venetiis: S. Pecori, 1739.
    2 v. in 1.   illus., maps.

2224. LANDRIANI, Marsilio. Dissertazione chimica sopra il bleu di Prussia e l'alkali flogisticato. [Milan?: ca. 1780.]
    1 *l*., 45 p.   illus.

2225. LANFRANCO, *of Milan*. A most excellent and learned vvorke of chirurgerie, called Cirurgia parua Lanfranci ... reduced from dyuers translations to our vulgar, or vsuall frase, and now first published in the Englyshe prynte by Iohn Halle ... London: T. Marshe, 1565.
    var. pag.   illus., port.

2226. LANGE, Johann Joachim. Systematis physico-chemici theoretico-practici sciagraphia in vsvm collegii chemici dogmatici et experimentalis ad tabvlas Ivnckerianas habendi consignata ... [Halle: 1745.]
    4 *l*., 66 p., 3 *l*.

2227. LANGELOTT, Joel. Epistolá ad præcellentissimos naturæ curiosos. De quibusdam in chymia praetérmissis, quorum occasione

secreta haud exigui momenti proq́ue non-
Entibus hactenus habita, candidè detergun-
tur & demonstrantur. Hamburgi: G. Schultz;
Amsterdam: J. Jansson à Waesberge, 1672.
    32 p.   illus.

2228.   LANGHAM, William.   The garden of
health, conteyning the sundry rare and hidden vertues and properties of all kindes of
simples and plants, together with the maner
how they are to be vsed and applyed in
medicine ... London: [deputies of C. Barker]
1579 [i.e. 1597].
    4 ℓ., 702 p., 28 ℓ.

2229.   ——.   ——. The second edition corrected and amended. London: T. Harper,
1633.
    4 ℓ., 702 p., 33 ℓ.

2230.   LANGHANS, Daniel.   Les gouttes
glaciales Helvetiques, éprouvées dans
nombre de maladies, et traité sur l'usage
des gouttes mercurielles dans tous les
maux vénériens ... Traduit de l'Allemand.
Genève: J.M. Broyset, 1759.
    xvi p., 2 ℓ., 236 p.

2231.   LANGIUS, Johannes Lembergius.
Medicinalivm epistolarvm miscellanea ...
Basileae: I. Oporinus, 1554.
    4 ℓ., 383 p.

2232.   ——.   Seconda epistolarum medicinalium miscellanea ... Basileæ: [ex officina N. Brylingeri, expensis I. Oporini]
1560.
    4 ℓ., 247 p., 28 ℓ.   port.
    With his Medicinalium epistolarum ...
1554.

2233.   LANGRISH, Browne.   The Croonean
lectures on muscular motion, read before the
Royal Society in the year MDCCXLVII ...
London: for C. Davis, 1748.
    3 ℓ., 66 p.   illus.
    With Stuart, A., Dissertatio ... 1738.

2234.   LAPRADE, Jacques Julien Richard de.
Analyse et vertus des eaux minérales du
Forez et de quelques autres sources ... Lyon:
au dépens des Associés, 1778.
    147 p.

    LARGUS, Scribonius.   See Scribonius
Largus.

2235.   LA RIVE, Charles Gaspard de.   Tentamen physiologicum inaugurale, de calore
animali ... Edinburgi: G. Mudi, 1797.

    2 ℓ., 60 p.

2236.   LA ROCHE, Daniele.   Pharmacopoea
Genevensis ad usum nosocomiorum. Auctoribus Daniele de La Roche, Ludovico Odier,
Carolo-Guielmo Dunant. Genevæ: J.P. Bon-
nant, 1780.
    xii, 199 p., 9 ℓ.

2237.   LAROUVIERE, Jean.   Nouveau système
des eaux minerales de Forges ... avec plusieurs observations de personnes qui ont
été guéries par leur usage ... Paris: L. d'Houry,
1699.
    12 ℓ., 251 p.   illus.

    LASNIORO, Joannis de.   De lapide
philosophico. In Tractatus de secretissimo
... 1611.

2238.   LATANE, Petrus.   Oratio inauguralis
de officio medici ... Franeqveræ: J. Gyzelaar,
[1693].
    70 p.
    With Queitsch, A.P., Ιατρομαθηματογραφία
... 1737.

2239.   LA TOURETTE, Alexandre de.   Bref
discovrs des admirables vertvs de l'or-
potable ... Avec vne apologie de la tresvtile
science d'alchimie ... Lyon: P. Roussin,
1575.
    47 numb. ℓ.

2240.   LAURENT, Joseph Adam.   Mémoire
clinique sur le tétanos chez les blessés.
Strasbourg: F.G. Levrault, 1797.
    viii, 160 p., 1 ℓ.

    LAURIN, Carl Gustaf.   De menthae
usu. See Linné, C. von, praeses. Entry 2454.

2241.   LAURO, Vincenzo.   Primo giardino,
nel qvale si contiene secreti de grande
esperienza & virtù ... Pavia: A. Viani, 1591.
    4 ℓ.

2242.   ——.   Scielta di varii secreti ...
Milano: P. Malatesta, 1603.
    4 ℓ.

2243.   ——.   Il tesoro nel quale si contiene
molti secreti di grandissime virtu a beneficio
de corpi humani ... Modona [n.d.].
    4 ℓ.

2244.   LAUTHIER, Honoré Maria.   Histoire
naturelle des eaux chaudes d'Aix en Provence,
avec les avis & la methode necessaire de se
servir de ces eaux utilement ... Aix: C. &

J. David, 1705.
    4 *l.*, 111 p., 6 *l.*
    With Castelmont, Traité des bains ...
1600.

2245. LAVATER, Johann Caspar. Essays on
physiognomy ... Translated from the last
Paris edition by ... C. Moore ... London:
H.D. Symonds, 1797.
    4 v. illus.

2246. LAVATER, Johann Heinrich, *praeses.*
Σκιαγραφία φερμολογίας γενικῆς: seu,
Adumbratio aquarum thermalium in genere
consideratum: quam, sub præsidio Joh.
Henrici Lavateri, examinandam proponit,
Joh. Henricus Lavaterus, f. ... Ad diem
Octobris. Horîs & loco solitis. Tiguri: 1667.
    8 *l.*

2247. LAVEDAN, Antonio. Tratado de los
usos, abusos propiedades y virtudes del
tabaco, café, té y chocolate ... Madrid:
Real, 1796.
    5 *l.*, 237 p.

2248. LAVOISIEN, Jean François. Dictionnaire portatif de médecine, d'anatomie,
de chirurgie, de chymie, d'histoire naturelle,
de botanique et de physique ... Nouvelle
édition, corrigée & augmentée ... Paris: T.
Barrois, 1793.
    iv, 717 p.

2249. LAVOISIER, Antoine Laurent. L'art
de fabriquer le salin et la potasse ... Paris:
l'Imprimerie Royale, 1779.
    1 *l.*, viii, 89 p. illus., charts.

2250. ——. ——. Paris: Cuchet [1794].
    viii, 106 p. illus.

2251. ——. Essays physical and chemical ... Translated ... by Thomas Henry. London: for J. Johnson, 1776.
    xxxii p., 1 *l.*, 475 p. illus.

        ——. Mémoires [de l'action du feu].
In Ehrmann, F.L., Essai d'un art de fusion ...
1787.

2252. ——. Abhandlungen ueber die Wirkung des durch die Lebensluft verstärkten
Feuers, aus dem Französischen übersetzt ...
von F.L. Ehrmann ... Strassburg: J.G. Treuttel,
1787.
    viii, 159 p. illus.

2253. ——. Traité élémentaire de chimie
... Nouvelle édition, à laquelle on a joint la

nomenclature ancienne & moderne ... Paris:
Cuchet, 1789.
    2 v. charts.
    Lacking the plates.

2254. ——. Traité élémentaire de chimie
... Seconde édition. Paris: Cuchet, 1793.
    2 v. illus., charts.

2255. LEANDRO, Lorenzo. Tesoro di varij
secreti ... esperimentati con grandissima
fatica, e spesa di tempo, e di danari ...
Venetia: 1614.
    4 *l.* illus.

2256. LE BAILLIF, Roch. Le demosterion
... Auquel sont contenuz trois cens aphorisme:
Latins & François. Sommaire veritable de la
medecine Paracelsique ... Rennes: P. Le
Bret, 1578.
    8 *l.*, 190 p. charts.

2257. LE BÖE, Frans de. A new idea of
the practice of physic ... Translated faithfully by Richard Gower ... London: for B.
Aylmer, 1675.
    22 *l.*, 511 p. port.

2258. ——. Opera medica ... Amstelodami: D. Elsevirius et A. Wolfgang, 1679.
    4 *l.*, 934 p., 13 *l.* port.

2259. ——. ——. Accessit huic editioni
hactenus ineditum Collegivm nosocomicvm
ab authore habitum ... Genevae: S. de Tovrnes
1681.
    9 *l.*, 747 p., 20 *l.*

2260. ——. ——. Editio nova, cui accedunt casus medicinales annor. 1659, 60 &
61 quos ex ore C. Sylvii calamo excepit
Joachimus Meriam. Trajecti ad Rhenum: G.
van de Water; Amstelodami: A. Schelte,
1695.
    4 *l.*, 934 p., 13 *l.*, 85 p., 4 *l.*

2261. LE BRETON, Charles. Les clefs de
la philosophie spagyrique, qui donnent la
connoissance des principes & de véritables
opérations de cet art dans les mixtes des
trois genres ... Paris: C. Jombert, 1722.
    4 *l.*, 398 p., 1 *l.*

2262. LEBRUN, Pierre. Lettres qui decouv-
rent l'illusion des philosophes sur la baguette
et qui detruisent leurs systems. Paris: J.
Boudot, 1696.
    14 *l.*, 255 p. illus.
    With Vallemont, P. le L., La physique oc-
culte ... 1696.

2263. LE CLERC, Daniel. Bibliotheca
anatomica sive Recens in anatomia inven-
torvm thesaurus locupletissimus, in qvo
integra atque absolutissima totius corporis
humani descriptio ... Genevae: J.A. Chovët,
1685-1703.
 3 v. illus.

2264. ——. Histoire de la medecine ...
Amsterdam: G. Gallet, 1702.
 3 pts. in 1 v. illus.

2265. ——. ——. Nouvelle edition, revue,
corrigée, & augmentée par l'auteur ... pour
servir à la continuation de cette histoire
depuis la fin du siècle II jusques au milieu
du XVII. La Haye: I. van der Kloot, 1729.
 9 *l.*, 820 p., 10 *l.*

2266. LE CLERC, Sebastien. Discours
touchant le point de vue, dans lequel il est
prouvé que les choses qu'on voit distincte-
ment ne sont vues que d'un oeil. Paris: A.
Cailleau, 1719.
 6 *l.*, 86 p. illus.

2267. LE CLERCQZ, Gabriel. Discursus
succinctus phisicomedicus de morbis pauperum. Insulis: J.C. Malte, 1683.
 3 *l.*, 209 p.

2268. L'ECLUSE, Charles de. Aliqvot
notæ in Garciæ aromatum historiam ... Antverpiæ: C. Plantin, 1582.
 43 p. illus.
 With Orta, G. de, Aromatvm ... 1579.

 ——. Beschriivinghe van de Indiaensche oft wtlandtsche boomen, heesteren
ende cryden. *In* Dodoens, R., Crvydt-boeck
... 1644.

2269. ——. Exoticorvm libri decem ...
Item Petri Bellonii Observationes, eodem
Carolo Clusio interprete ... [Leyden] Plantin,
1605.
 8 *l.*, 378 p., 18 *l.*; 52 p.; 6 *l.*, 242 p.,
1 *l.* illus.

2270. ——. Rariorum aliquot stirpium per
Hispanias obseruatarum historia ... Antverpiæ:
C. Plantin, 1576.
 529 p., 6 *l.* illus.

2271. ——. Rariorvm plantarvm historia
... Antverpiæ: ex officina Plantiniana, apud
I. Moretum, 1601.
 6 *l.*, 364, cccxlviii p., 6 *l.* illus., port.

 LE CROM, Alexandre, *pseud. See*

Colonna, Francesco Maria Pompeo.

2272. LE DROU, Noël Théodore. Demon-
strations de l'utilité des eaux minérales
de Spa. Liege: F.A. Barchon, 1737.
 9 *l.*, 154 p., 1 *l.*

2273. ——. Principes contenus dans les
differentes sources des eaux minerales de
Spa. Liege: F.J. Desoer, 1752.
 v, 149 p.

2274. LEEUWENHOEK, Anthony van. Anatomia seu interiora rerum, cum animatarum
tum inanimatarum, ope & beneficio exquisi-
tissimorum microscopiorum detecta ...
Lugduni Batavorum: C. Boutesteyn, 1687.
 4 *l.*, 258 p. illus.

 ——. Observations faites avec le
microscope. *In* Recueil d'experiences ...
1679.

2275. ——. [Opera omnia. Delphis Batavorum: H. a Krooneveld ..., 1695-1719.]
 4 v. illus., port.
 Binder's title. Imprint varies.

2276. ——. The select works ... containing his miscroscopical discoveries ... Translated from the Dutch and Latin editions ...
by Samuel Hoole. London: H. Fry ..., 1798-
1807.
 2 v. in 1. port., illus.

2277. LE FÈVRE, Nicolas. Traicté de la
chymie ... Paris: T. Jolly, 1660.
 2 v. illus.

2278. ——. ——. Corrigé de plusieurs
fautes. Leyde: A. Doude, 1669.
 2 v. illus.

2279. ——. A compleat body of chymistry
... Rendred into English by P.D.C. ... London: T. Ratcliffe for O. Pulleyn junior, 1664.
 2 v. in 1. illus.

2280. ——. ——. With additions. London:
for O. Pulleyn junior and J. Wright, 1670.
 2 v. in 1. illus.

2281. ——. Chymischer Handleiter, und
guldnes Kleinod: Das ist: Richtige Anführung,
und deutliche Unterweisung, so wol, wie
man die chymische Schrifften, welche von
chymischer Wissenschafft ins gemein handeln,
recht verstehen, als, wie man, nach ihrer
Ordnung, solche chymische Kunst, durch
wirckliche Operation, leicht und glücklich

practiciren ... Nürnberg: C. Endter, 1676.
16 *l.*, 867 p., 27 *l.* illus.

2282. ——. Neuvermehrter chymischer
Handleiter, und guldnes Kleinod ... Anitzo
aber ... aufs neue durchaus in vielem noch
mehr erläutert, und mit häuffigen Secreten
und nützlichen Artzneystücken vermehrt,
und zum andern mal durch den Druck publiciret von Joh. Hiskia Cardilucio ... Nürnberg: J.A. Endters Söhne, 1685.
26 *l.*, 1149 p., 9 *l.* illus.
Lacking pages 135-138.

2283. LE GALLOIS, Pierre. Conversations
de l'academie de Monsievr l'abbé Bovrdelot,
contenant diverses recherches, observations,
experiences, & raisonnemens de physique,
medicine, chymie, & mathematique ... Paris:
T. Moette, 1675.
9 *l.*, 76, 350 p.

2284. LEGATI, Domenico. Giardino di
varii secreti, hauuti da diuersi signori ...
Nouamente dato in luce ... Milano: P.
Malatesta [n.d.].
8 *l.*

2285. ——. Tesoro di varii secreti ...
Opera molto gioueuole alla sanità de' corpi
humani. Venetia [n.d.].
8 *l.*

2286. LE GIVRE, Pierre. Arcanum acidu-
larum novissime proditum principiorum chymicorum disquisitionis auxilio ... Additæ
sunt epistolæ multorum illustrium medicorum cum ejusdem responsis ... Amstelodami: Jansson-Waesberg, 1682.
4 *l.*, 366 p., 3 *l.*

2287. LE GRAND, Antoine. Curiosus rerum
abditarum naturæque arcanorum perscrutator
... Norimberga: sumptibus J. Zigeri, typis C.
Gerhardi, 1681.
250 p., 11 *l.*

2288. ——. Historia naturæ, variis experimentis et ratiociniis elucidata ... Editio
secunda ... Londini: J. Martin, 1680.
6 *l.*, 431 p., 8 *l.* illus.

2289. ——. Institutio philosophiæ, secundum principia D. Renati Descartes: nova
methodo adornata, & explicata ... Editio
quarta ... Londini: typis M. Clark, impensis
J. Martyn, 1680.
3 *l.*, xvi p., 9 *l.*, 731 p. illus., port.

2290. LEHR, Georg Philipp. Dissertatio

botanico-medica de olea evropaea ... in
Academia Georgia Avgvsta ... Gottingæ: J.C.
Dieterich, 1779.
1 *l.*, 70 p., 3 *l.* illus.

2291. LE MAITRE, Alexandre Christian.
Der astralische Geist oder Der Balsam dess
Lebens, bewiesen in der magnetischen bal-
samischen Krafft dess antimonialischen
gereinigten Vitriols ... [n.p.] Verlegung des
Authoris, 1684.
6 *l.*, 174 p.

2292. LEMERY, Louis. Traité des aliments
... où l'on explique leur nature & leurs
usages, suivant les principes chymiques &
méchaniques. Paris: J.B. Cusson & P. Witte,
1702.
28 *l.*, 541 p., 1 *l.*

2293. ——. A treatise of all sorts of food,
both animal and vegetable: also of drink-
ables ... Translated by D. Hay ... The third
edition. London: for W. Innys ..., 1745.
xii, 372 p., 12 *l.*

2294. LEMERY, Nicolas. Cours de chymie,
contenant la maniere de faire les operations
qui sont en usage dans la medecine, par une
methode facile ... Seconde edition. Reveuë,
corrigée & augmentée par l'autheur. Paris:
l'autheur, 1677.
15 *l.*, 584 p., 8 *l.*

2295. ——. ——. Dixième edition. Reveuë,
corrigée & augmentée par l'auteur. Lyon: C.
Rey, 1703.
8 *l.*, 836 p., 1 *l.* illus., chart.

2296. ——. ——. Onzième edition. Revuë,
corrigée & augmentée par l'auteur. Lyon: L.
Desclaustres, 1713.
8 *l.*, 836 p., 2 *l.* illus., chart.

2297. ——. ——. Nouvelle édition, revue,
corrigée & augmentée d'un grand nombre de
notes, & de plusieurs préparations chymiques
qui sont aujourd'hui d'usage, & dont il n'est
fait aucune mention dans les edition de
l'auteur, par M. Baron ... Paris: J.T. Herissant,
1756.
3 *l.*, xxiii, 945 p. illus., charts.

2298. ——. A course of chymistry ...
Translated by Walter Harris ... London: for
W. Kettibly, 1677.
16 *l.*, 323 p., 10 *l.*

2299. ——. ——. The second edition very
much inlarged. Translated from the fifth edition

in French ... London: R.N. for W. Kettibly,
1686.
    14 *l*., 548 p., 8 *l*.

2300.   ——.   ——. The fourth edition.
Translated from the eleventh edition in
French ... London: for A. Bell ..., 1720.
    1 *l*., xvi, 543 p.   illus.

2301.   ——. An appendix to a course of
chymistry ... Translated by Walter Harris
... London: for W. Kettilby, 1680.
    8 *l*., 140 p., 5 *l*.

2302.   ——. Cours de chymie, oder: Der
vollkommene Chymist ... Aus der neunten
frantzöischen Edition des 1697sten Jahres
ins Teutsche übersetzer. Dresden: J.J.
Winckler, 1698.
    12 *l*., 652, 388 p., 48 *l*.

2303.   ——.   —— bey ietziger andern Auff-
lage auffs neue und correcteste revidiret.
Dresden: J.J. Winckler, 1705.
    34 *l*., 652, 386 p., 21 *l*.

2304.   ——.   —— bey dieser fünfften Auflage aufs neue durchgesehen, corrigirt und
mit Zusätzen vermehret von D. Johann
Christian Zimmermann ... Dresden: Walther,
1754.
    4 *l*., 978 p., 23 *l*.; 46 p.   illus., port,
charts.

        ——. Corso di chimica. *In* Prospec-
tus pharmaceuticus ... 1729.

2305.   ——. Curso chymico ... Tradvcido
del idioma frances en el castellano, & aña-
dido por Don Felix Palacios ... Madrid: por
J.G. Infaçon, a costa de F. Anison, 1703.
    22 *l*., 492 p., 18 *l*.   illus.

2306.   ——.   ——. Y nvevamente ilvstrado
con vn florilagio theorico-practico segvndo
cvrso chimico, por Don Ioseph Assin y
Palacios de Ongoz ... Zaragoça: por D. de
Larumbe, a costa de J. de Mendoza, 1710.
    23 *l*., 632 p., 20 *l*.   illus.

2307.   ——. Nouveau recueil de secrets
et curiositez, les plus rares & admirables de
tous les effects, que l'art de la nature sont
capables de produire ... Cinquième edition
... Par le Sr. d'Emery ... Amsterdam: P. Mortier, 1697.
    2 v.   illus.

2308.   ——. Modern curiosities of art &
nature. Extracted out of the cabinets of the

most eminent personages of the French court
... Made English from the original French.
London: for M. Gilliflower & J. Partridge,
1685.
    22 *l*., 355 p., 2 *l*.   illus.

2309.   ——. New curiosities in art and
nature: or, A collection of the most valuable
secrets in all arts and sciences ... Translated into English from the seventh edition
... To which is added a supplement by the
translator. London: for J. King and J. Morphew,
1711.
    8 *l*., 354 p., 7 *l*.   illus.

2310.   ——. Curiosa arcana: being curious
secrets, artificial and natural ... From the
last edition in French ... To which is added,
A supplement of divers curiosities by the
translator ... London: F.N. [1711?].
    8 *l*., 354 p., 7 *l*., 12 p.   illus.

2311.   ——. Pharmacopée universelle,
contenant toutes les compositions de pharmacie qui sont en usage dans la medecine
... Paris: L. d'Houry, 1698.
    8 *l*., 1050 p., 19 *l*.

2312.   ——.   ——. Avec un lexicon pharmaceutique ... Seconde edition ... Paris: L.
d'Houry, 1716.
    10 *l*., 1092 p., 22 *l*.

2313.   ——.   ——. Quatrieme edition ...
La Haye: P. Gosse et J. Neaulme, 1729.
    8 *l*., 780 p., 13 *l*.

2314.   ——.   ——. Troisiéme edition. Revûë,
corrigée & augmentée. Paris: L. d'Houry, 1734.
    8 *l*., 1092 p., 21 *l*.

2315.   ——.   ——. Cinquième edition ...
Paris: d'Houry, 1764.
    2 v.   port.

2316.   ——. Pharmacopoeia Lemeriana
contracta: Lemery's universal pharmacopoeia
abridg'd in a collection of recepe's and observations ... London: for W. Kettilby, 1700.
    6 *l*., 167 p.
    With Boerhaave, H., Praxis medica ...
1716.

2317.   ——. Traité universel des drogues
simples ... Seconde edition ... Paris: L.
d'Houry, 1714.
    9 *l*., 922 p., 34 *l*.   illus.

2318.   ——. Dictionnaire universel des
drogues simples ... Troisième edition ...

Paris: la veuve d'Houry, 1733.
2 *l*., xxiv, 1015 p. illus., port.

2319. ——. ——. Nouvelle édition. Paris:
L.C. d'Houry, 1759.
2 *l*., xxiv, 1015 p. illus.

2320. ——. Vollständiges Materialien-
Lexicon ... ubersetzt von C.F. Richtern ...
Leipzig: J.F. Braun, 1721.
8 *l*., 1224 numb. col., 19 *l*. illus.

2321. ——. Dizionario overe Trattato
universale delle droghe semplici ... tradotta
in Italiano. Venezia: G.G. Hertz, 1721.
6 *l*., 390 p., 25 *l*. illus.

2322. ——. ——. Venezia: Hertz, 1737.
6 *l*., 374 p., 23 *l*. illus.

2323. ——. Trattato dell' antimonio ...
Traduzione ... di Selvaggio Canturani.
Venezia: G.G. Ertz, 1717.
11 *l*., 454 p., 13 *l*.

2324. LEMNIUS, Levin. De habitv et constitvtione corporis ... libri II ... Francofvrti:
typis N. Hofmanni, sumtibus I. Rhodii, 1604.
8 *l*., 185 p., 4 *l*.
With his De miracvlis occvltis ... 1611.

2325. ——. De miracvlis occvltis natvrae,
libri IIII. Item de vita cvm animi et corporis
incolvmitate recte institvenda, liber vnvs
... Coloniae Agrippinae: T. Baumius, 1583.
8 *l*., 627 p., 22 *l*.

2326. ——. ——. Francofvrti: typis I.
Savrii, impensis I. Fischeri, 1611.
8 *l*., 582 p., 28 *l*.

2327. ——. The secret miracles of nature:
in four books ... London: J. Streater ..., 1658.
8 *l*., 398 p.

2328. ——. Les occvltes merveilles et
secretz de natvre ... esposées en deux liures
... Nouuellement traduit de Latin en François,
par I.G.P. ... Orleans: P. Trepperel, 1568.
18 *l*., 250 numb. *l*., 20 *l*.

2329. ——. Occulta naturæ miracula.
Wunderbarliche Geheimnisse der Natur in
des Menschen Leibe vnd Seel ... nicht allein
aus dem Latein in Deutsche Sprach gebracht,
sondern auch zum dritten Mal vermehret, vnd
eines grossen Theils von newes selbs geschrieben, durch Iacobvm Horstivm ... Leipzig: [M. Lantzenberger, in Verlegung V.
Vögelini] 1592.

5 *l*., 629 p., 15 *l*.

2330. ——. Similitvdinvm ac parabolarvm,
qvæ in Bibliis ex herbis atque arboribus
desumuntur ... explicatio ... Seorsvm accesservnt De gemnis aliqvot ... libri II. Auctore
Francisco Rveo ... Item Levini Lemnii De
astrologia liber I. Francofvrti: apud N. Hoff-
mannum, impensis I. Rhodii, 1608.
8 *l*., 288 p.
With his De miracvlis occvltis ... 1611.

2331. ——. The touchstone of complex-
ions, generallye appliable, expedient and
profitable for all such, as be desirous &
carefull of their bodylye health ... First
written in Latine ... and now englished by
Thomas Newton ... London: T. Marsh, 1576.
7 *l*., 157 numb. *l*., 12 *l*.

LE MOINE, Wilhelm. Opobalsamum.
See Linné, C. von, *praeses*. Entry 2487.

2332. LE MORT, Jacob. Chymiæ veræ
nobilitas & utilitas, in physica corpusculari,
theoria medica, ejusque materia et signis,
ad majorem perfectionem deducendis. Com-
prehendens opera ejus omnia, hucusque typis
commissa. Quibus seorsim excusa Collectanea, Maetsiana & Marcgraviana, biblio-
polæ subjunxerunt. Lugduni Batavorum: F.
Haaring, C. Boutesteyn, 1696.
var. pag.

2333. ——. Pharmacia & chymia medico-
physica, rationibus et experimentis instructa.
Lugduni Batavorum: Peter van der Aa, 1684.
2 pts. in 1 v. illus.

2334. ——. Pharmacia, rationibus et experimentis auctioribus instructa, methodo
galenico-chymica adornata ... Lugduni Batav.:
P. vander Aa, 1688.
7 *l*., 255 p., 17 *l*.

LENAEUS, Knut Aug. De meloe-vesicatorio. *See* Linné, C. von, *praeses*. Entry
2453.

2335. LENGLET-DUFRESNOY, Nicolas.
Histoire de la philosophie hermétique. Accompagnée d'un catalogue raisonné des ecri-
vains de cette science ... Paris: Nyon, 1744.
3 v.

2336. LEONARDI, Camillo. Specvlvm lapidvm
... Cvi accessit Sympathia septem metallorum
ac septem selectorum lapidum ad planetas D.
Petri Arlensis de Scudalupis ... Parisiis: C.
Sevestre ... 1610.

18 *l*., 499 p.   illus., port.

Full brown morocco binding, gold stamped
and tooled, with the arms of J.A. De Thou
(1553-1617) on each cover and his mono-
gram five times repeated on the spine.

2337. ———. Speculum lapidum et D. Petri
Arlensis de Scudalupis ... Sympathia septem
metallorum ac septem selectorum lapidum
ad planetas. Accedit Magia astrologica
Petri Constantii Albinii Villanovensis. Hamburgi: C. Liebezeit, 1717.

15 *l*., 390, 84 p., 18 *l*.   port.

2338. ———. The mirror of stones ... Ex-
tracted from the works of Aristotle, Pliny,
Isiodorus, Dionysius Alexandrinus, Albertus
Magnus, &c. ... Now first translated into
English. London: for J. Freeman, 1750.

240 [i.e. 160] p.

2339. LEONHARD VON ALTENBURG. Delar-
vatio tinctvræ philosophorvm, das ist:
Kurtze und einfältige Erklährung des Lapidis
Benedicti ... durch einen, der wahren Philosophie Liebhabern entdecket und erkläret,
der in der Wahrheit genuine Feuer-Arbeit
liebet, und da es wohl heissen mag, Aut hic,
aut nusquam. Oder- und Nieder-Wasserberg:
M. Schweffelmann, 1747.

8 *l*., 94 p., 5 *l*.

2340. LE PAULMIER, Pierre. Lapis philosophicvs dogmaticorvm ... Adiecta est Historia læprosæ mulieris persanatæ. Parisiis:
D. Doulceur, 1609.

16 *l*., 160 p., 15 *l*.

2341. LE PELLETIER, Jean, *ed*. L'alkaest
ou le dissolvant universel de Van-Helmont,
revelé dans plusieurs traitez qui en dé-
couvrent le secret ... Rouen: G. Behourt,
1704.

2 *l*., 256 p., 2 *l*.

2342. ———, *ed*. L'art ou la maniere de
volatiliser les alcalis, & d'en préparer des
remedes succedanées ou aprochans de ceux
que l'on peut préparer par l'alkaest, tirez
des ouvrages de Starkey ... Rouen: G. Behourt, 1706.

1 *l*., 200 p., 1 *l*.

With his L'alkaest ... 1704.

LE PILEUR D'APLIGNY, *jt. auth*. The
art of dying wool. *See* Hellot, Jean.

2343. LE POIS, Charles. Selectiorum observationum et consiliorum de praetervisis
morbis affectibusque praeter naturam, ab

aqua seu serosa colluvie et diluvie ortis,
liber singularis ... Cum praefatione Hermanni
Boerhaave ... Amstelodami: fratres de Tournes,
1768.

xxxii, 496 p., 10 *l*.

2344. LEROUGE, Antoine. Les passe-temps
agréables des eaux minérales de Bagnères
en Bigorre, et du Béarn, et leurs propriétés.
Paris: Lerouge, 1785.

2 v.

2345. LEROY, Alphonse Vincent Louis Antoine. Essai sur l'histoire naturelle de la
grossesse et l'accouchement. Geneve: Leclerc ..., 1787.

2 *l*., 159 p.

2346. ———. Recherches sur les habille-
mens des femmes et des enfans, ou Examen
de la maniere dont il faut vêtir l'un & l'autre
sèxe. Paris: Le Boucher, 1772.

4 *l*., 347 p., 2 *l*.

2347. ———. Réponse ... à un mémoire sur
une imputation d'impéritie. Paris: L. Cellot,
1787.

1 *l*., 71 p.

With his Essai sur l'histoire ... 1787.

2348. LE ROY, Charles. De aquarum mineralium naturâ et usu propositiones prælectionibus academicis accomodatæ. Editio
altera. Monspelii: A.F. Rochard, 1762.

2 *l*., 48 p., 1 *l*.

2349. ———. Mélanges de physique et de
médecine. Paris: P.G. Cavelier, 1771.

6 *l*., 400 p.

2350. LESAGE, Georges Louis. [Essai de
chymie mechanique.] [Geneva?: 1758?]

113 p.   illus.

Lacking the title page.

2351. LESCHEVIN. Mémoire qui a remporté
le prix de l'Académie Royale de Chirurgie de
Paris en 1763, sur les maladies de l'oreille;
avec un autre Mémoire sur la cure des abscès.
Amsterdam: 1764.

3 *l*., 108 p., 1 *l*., 144 p., 1 *l*.

2352. LESLIE, Peter Dugud. A philosophical
inquiry into the cause of animal heat: with incidental observations on several phisiological
and chymical questions connected with the
subject ... London: for S. Crowder ..., 1778.

viii, 362 p.

2353. LESSIUS, Leonardus. Le vray moyen

de vivre plus de cent ans dans une santé parfaite. Traduction nouvelle des traitez de Lessius & de Cornaro. Avec des notes, par M.D.L.B. et Les moyens faciles & assurez pour conserver la santé par le Sr. Domergue. Paris: L. Coignard, 1705.

6 *l*., 168, 86 p., 1 *l*.

2354. A LETTER from an apothecary in London, to his friend in the country; concerning the present practice of physick ... London: for M. Cooper, 1752.

56 p.

2355. LETTERE chimico-farmaceutiche concernenti l'odierna pratica di alcuni speziali. Seconda edizione ... Milano: G. Barelle, 1791.

2 v.

2356. LETTRES d'un medecin de Montpellier, a un medecin de Paris pour servir de réponse à la critique du Traité de chimie de M. Malouin. Seconde edition. Paris: G. Cavelier, 1735.

24 p.

With Malouin, P.J., Traité de chimie ... 1734.

2357. LETTRES envoyées à Mr. de Gerzan, sur le sujet de ses oeuures. [n.p.: n.d.]

56 p.

Caption title. Lacking the title page.

With Du Soucy, F., Le grand or-potable ... 1653.

2358. LETTSOM, John Coakley. History of the origin of medicine: an oration delivered at the anniversary meeting of the Medical Society of London, January 19, 1778, and printed at their request ... London: J. Phillips for E. & C. Dilly, 1778.

1 *l*., viii, 168 p. illus.

2359. LEURSEN, Johann Gerhard. Chymischen Schau-Platzes Vortrab, das ist: Gründliche Anleitung zu der wahren Chymie ... Franckfurt am Mayn: 1708.

5 *l*., 54 p.

2360. LEUTMANN, Johann Georg. Instrumenta meteorognosiæ inservientia ... accedunt hyetostathmica dvo et exatmoscopium noviter inventa ... Wittenbergæ: B.G. Zimmermani vid., 1725.

14 *l*., 175 p. illus., charts.

2360a. ——. Vvlcanvs famvlans oder Sonderbahre Feuer-Nutzung welche durch gute Einrichtung der Stuben-Ofen, Camine, Brau-

und Saltz-Pfannen, Schmeltz, Destillier, Treib- und anderer Ofen kan erlanget ... Andere Edition ... Wittenberg: G. Zimmermann, 1723.

4 *l*., 154 p., 3 *l*. illus.

2361. LE VACHER DE LA FEUTRIE, A.F. Thomas. Heelkunding woordenboek, bevattende eene ontleedkundige beschryving der deelen van s'menschen licham ... Uit bet Fransch vertaald ... door Johannes Hiddinga. s'Gravenhage: I. du Mee, 1768.

3 v.

LEVELING, Heinrich Palmaz. Anatomische Erklärung der original-Figuren von Andreas Vesal. *See* Vesalius, Andreas.

2362. LEVIS, Giovanni Agostino de. Sulla pirenta murisenghina nuove osservazioni ed esperienze ... Torino: Mairesse, 1794.

154 p., 1 *l*.

2363. LEVRET, André. Observations sur la cure radicale de plusieurs polypes de la matrice, de la gorge et du nez ... Paris: Delaguette, 1749.

499 p., 2 *l*. illus.

2364. LEWIS, William. Commercium philosophico-technicum; or, The philosophical commerce of arts: designed as an attempt to improve arts, trades, and manufactures ... London: H. Baldwin, for the author, 1763.

2 *l*., xviii, x, 646 p., 7 *l*. illus.

2365. ——. ——. London: for the author, sold by R. Willock, 1765.

2 *l*., xviii, x, 646 p., 7 *l*. illus.

2366. ——. Expériences physiques et chymiques sur plusieurs matieres relatives au commerce & aux arts: ouvrage traduit de l'Anglois ... par M. De Puisieux ... Paris: Desaint, 1768-1769.

3 v. illus.

2367. ——. A course of practical chemistry. In which are contained all the operations described in Wilson's Complete course of chemistry ... London: for J. Nourse, 1746.

10 *l*., 432 p., 17 *l*. illus.

2368. ——. The Edinburgh new dispensatory: containing, I. The elements of pharmaceutical chemistry. II. The materia medica ... III. The pharmaceutical preparations and medicinal compositions of the latest editions of the London and Edinburgh pharmacopoeias

... The third edition, with ... account of the new chemical doctrines published by Mr. Lavoisier. Edinburgh: for W. Creech ... 1791.
656 p.   illus.

2369.   ——.   ——.   A new edition ... Philadelphia: T. Dobson, 1791.
656 p.   illus.

2370.   ——.   ——.   The fourth edition ... Edinburgh: for W. Creech ..., 1794.
xxxi, 622 p.   illus.

2371.   ——.   ——.   The fourth edition ... Philadelphia: T. Dobson, 1796.
xxvii, 622 p., 1 *l*.   illus.

2372.   ——.   ——.   The fifth edition ... Edinburgh: W. Creech, 1797.
xxxi, 622 p.   illus.

2373.   ——.   De nieuwe Britsche apotheek. Behelzende I. De algemeene beginselen der kruidmengkunst. II. De materia medica ... III. De bereidingen en saamenmengselen van de nieuwe Londensche en Edinburgsche apotheeken ... uit het Engelsch vertaald door Theodorus van Brussel. Amsterdam: G. Bom, 1772-1773.
10 *l*., 260 p., 4 *l*., 261-678 p., 17 *l*.

2374.   ——.   An experimental history of the materia medica, or of the natural and artificial substances made use of in medicine ... London: H. Baldwin, 1761.
xxii p., 1 *l*., 591 p., 16 *l*.

2375.   ——.   ——.   The second edition ... London: for R. Baldwin and W. Johnston, 1768.
xxiv, 622 p., 17 *l*.

2376.   ——.   ——.   The third edition with numerous additions and corrections by John Aikin. London: for J. Johnson and R. Baldwin, 1784.
xxiii, 691 p., 15 *l*.

2377.   ——.   Materia medica, oder Beschreibung der einfachen Arzneymittel. Nach der zwoten vermehrt und verbesserten Ausgabe aus dem Englischen ubersetzt von Joh. Heinrich Ziegler. Zürich: Drell, Gessner, Füesslin, 1771.
xxviii, 635 p.

2378.   ——.   Experiments and observations on American potashes with an easy method of determining their respective qualities ... London: by order of the Society, 1767.

1 *l*., 34 p.

2379.   ——.   The new dispensatory ... Intended as a correction and improvement of Quincy. London: for J. Nourse, 1753.
xii, 32, 664 p.

2380.   ——.   ——.   The second edition corrected, with large additions. London: for J. Nourse, 1765.
viii p., 2 *l*., 692 p.

2381.   ——.   ——.   The fifth edition, carefully revised and improved. London: for C. Nourse, 1785.
x p., 3 *l*., 688 p.

2382.   ——.   ——.   The sixth edition ... London: for F. Wingate ..., 1799.
viii p., 4 *l*., 606 p., 21 *l*.

——.   Remarks on Mr. Robert Dossie's Insitutes of experimental chemistry. *See* Z., A.

2383.   LEX TALIONIS; sive Vindiciæ pharmacoporum: or A short reply to Dr. Merrett's book; and others, written against the apothecaries ... London: M. Pitt, 1670.
3 *l*., 32 p.

2384.   LEYDEN. Ryksuniversiteit. Anatomisch Kabinet.   Mvsevm anatomicvm Academiae Lvgdvno-Batavae. Descriptvm ab Edvardo Sandifort. Lvgdvni Batavorvm: S. et J. Lvchtmans, 1793.
4 v.   illus.
Lacking volumes 3 and 4.

2385.   LIBAVIUS, Andreas.   ... Alchemia ... e dispersis passim optimorvm avtorum ... exemplis potissimum, tum etiam præceptis quibusdam operosè collecta ... methodo accuratâ explicata, & in integrum corpus redacta. Accesserunt tractatus nonnulli physici chymici ... Francofurti: excudebat I. Saurius, impensis P. Kopffij, 1597.
9 *l*., 424 p., 10 *l*.

2386.   ——.   ... Alchymia ... recognita, emendata, et aucta, tum dogmatibus & experimentis nonnullis; tvm commentario medico physico chymico ... Francofvrti: excudebat J. Saurius, impensis P. Kopffii, 1506 [i.e. 1606].
10 *l*., 196 p., 6 *l*.; 5 *l*., 402 p.; 192 p., 5 *l*.   illus.

2387.   ——.   ... Alchymia trivmphans de inivsta in se collegii Galenici spvrii in

Academia Parisiensi censvra; et Ioannis
Riolani maniographia, falsi conuicta, &
funditus euersa ... Francofurti: ex officina
I. Saurii, impensis P. Kopffii, 1607.
926 p.

2388. ——. ... Commentationvm metalli-
carvm libri qvatvor de natvra metallorvm,
mercvrio philosophorvm, azotho, et lapide
sev tinctura physicorum conficienda ...
Francofurti ad Moenum: in officina I. Saurij,
impensis P. Kopffij, 1597.
4 *l*., 392 p.
With his Alchemia ... 1597.

2389. ——. Praxis alchymiæ, hoc est,
Doctrina de artificiosa præparatione præ-
cipvorvm medicamentorum chymicorum:
duobus libris explicata ... Nunc ex Germa-
ico idiomate in Latinum traductus. Annexvs
est libellvs Iacobi Bessoni de absoluta
ratione extrahendi olea & aquas ... Francofurti: excudebat I. Saurius, impensis P.
Kopffii, 1604.
680 p., 10 *l*. illus.

2390. ——. Rervm chymicarvm epistolica
forma ad philosophos et medicos qvosdam
in Germania excellentes descriptarum liber
primus [-tertius] ... Francofurti: excudebat
I. Saurius, impensis P. Kopffij, 1595-1599.
3 pts. in 1 v.

2391. ——. ... Singvlarivm ... pars prima
[-secunda] ... Francofurti: typis I. Saurii,
impensis P. Kopffij, 1599.
2 pts. in 1 v.

2392. ——. ... Syntagmatis selectorvm
vndiqvaqve et perspicve traditorvm alchymiæ
arcanorum ... Francofvrti: excudebat N. Hoff-
mannus, impensis P. Kopffii, 1615-1613.
2 v.

2393. LIBOIS, Et. L'encyclopédie des
dieux et des héros sortis des qualités des
quatre éléments et de leur quintessence,
suivant la science hermétique ... Paris: la
veuve Duchesne, Pissot, 1773.
2 v.

2394. LICETI, Fortunio. De lvcernis antiqvorvm reconditis libb. qvatvor ... Venetiis:
E. Deuch, 1621.
34 *l*., 415 p. illus.

2395. ——. De monstris. Ex recensione
Gerardi Blasii ... Editio novissima ... Amstelodami: A. Frisius, 1665.
9 *l*., 316 p., 13 *l*. illus.

2396. ——. Litheosphorvs, sive De lapide
Bononiensi lucem in se conceptam ab am-
biente claro mox in tenebris mire conseru-
ante liber ... Utini: N. Schiratti, 1640.
4 *l*., 280 p., 1 *l*.

2397. LIEBAULT, Jean. Qvatre livres des
secrets de medecine et de la philosophie
chimiqve ... Paris: J. Du-Puys, 1573.
8 *l*., 298 numb. *l*., 18 *l*. illus.

2398. ——. ——. Paris: J. Du-Puys, 1579.
8 *l*., 297 numb. *l*., 14 *l*. illus.

2399. ——. ——. Derniere edition. Rouen:
T. Reinsart, "M.VI.C." [1600?].
4 *l*., 352 p., 3 *l*. illus.

2400. ——. Secrets de medecine et de la
philosophie chimiqve. Rouen: N. l'Oyselet,
1643.
8 *l*., 297 p., 14 *l*. illus.

2401. LIEBERKÜHN, Johann Nathaneal.
Dissertationes quatuor ... Omnia nunc primum
in unum collecta & edita cura et studio
Joannis Sheldon. Londoni: T. Cadell ...,
1782.
1 *l*., x, 25, 36 p.
With Sheldon, J., The history of the absorbent system ... 1784.

2402. LIEUTAUD, Joseph. Essais anatomiques, contenant l'histoire exacte de
toutes les parties qui composent le corps
de l'homme, avec le maniere de dissequer.
Paris: P.M. Huart, 1742.
xxi p., 1 *l*., 724 p., 8 *l*. illus.

2403. ——. Historia anatomico-medica
... Recensuit & suas observationes numero
plures adjecit ... Antonius Portal ... Parisiis:
Vicent, 1767.
2 v.

2404. ——. Synopsis universae praxeos-
medicae, in binas partes divisa ... Amstelodami: de Tournes, 1765.
2 v.

2405. LIMMER, Conrad Philipp, *praeses*.
Dispvtatio physica de elementis quam an-
nuente & prosperante divini-numinis gratia
... Johannes Christianus Kellerus ... autor
& respondens. Servestæ: J.E. Bezelivs,
1690.
16 *l*.

LIMOJON DE SAINT DIDIER, Alexandre
Toussaint. *See* The Hermetical Triumph.

2406. LINAND, Barthélmy. Nouveau traité
des eaux minerales de Forges ... Paris: L.
d'Houry ..., 1697.
    4 *l.*, 135 p.   map.

2407. LIND, James.   An essay on diseases
incidental to Europeans in hot climates.
With the method of preventing their fatal
consequences ... To which is added, an
appendix concerning intermittent fevers ...
The second edition, enlarged and improved.
London: for T. Becket and P.A. De Hondt,
1771.
    xv, 375 p., 4 *l.*

2408. ———. Traité du scorbut, divisé en
trois parties, contenant des recherches sur
la nature, les causes & la curation de cette
maladie ... Traduit de l'Anglois ... Auquel
on a joint la traduction du Traité du scorbut
de Boerhaave, commenté par Van Swieten.
Nouvelle édition. Paris: Méquignon, 1783.
    2 v.

    LINDBERG, Fredric.   Nutrix noverca.
See Linné, C. von, *praeses.* Entry 2483.

2409. LINDEN, Diederich Wessel.   An experimental dissertation on the nature, contents, and virtues of the Hyde saline purging
water, commonly called the Hyde spaw, near
Cheltenham in Gloucestershire ... London:
J. Everingham & T. Reynolds ..., 1751.
    viii, 66 p., 3 *l.*   illus.

2410. ———. Gründliche chemische Anmerckungen über Herrn D. Schüttens Physi-
calische Nachricht vom Ursprunge der
mineralischen Wasser und den Bestand-
Theilen in dem Clevischen Sauer-Brunnen-
Wasser ... aus dem Englischen übersetzt
und erleutert ... Amsterdam: P. Mortier, 1746.
    8 *l.*, 260 p., 6 *l.*   illus.

2411. ———. Lettres sur la minéralogie et
la métallurgie pratiques. Traduit de l'Anglois
... Paris: Durand & Pissot, 1752.
    11 *l.*, 201 p.

2412. ———. A treatise on the origin, nature, and virtues of chalybeat waters, and
natural hot-baths ... To which is added a
description of selter water ... The second
edition. London: for D. Browne and J. Ward,
1755.
    1 *l.*, xx, 341 p., 3 *l.*   illus.

2413. ———. A treatise on the three medicinal mineral waters at Llandrindod in Rad-
norshire, South Wales, with some remarks

on mineral and fossil mixtures ... London:
J. Everingham & T. Reynolds for the author,
1756.
    2 *l.*, xliv, 336 p.   illus.

2414. LINDEN, Johannes Antonides van der.
De scriptis medicis libri duo. Quibus præmittitur ad D. Petrvm Tvlpivm manuductio ad
medicinam. Amstelredami: J. Blaev, 1637.
    26 *l.*, 559 p., 12 *l.*

2415. LINDEN, Maximilian Joseph von, *ed.*
Handschriften für Freunde geheimer Wissen-
schaften zum Druck befördert von M.I.F.v.L**.
... Erster Band ... Wien: A. Blumauer, 1794.
    8 *l.*, 532 p., 2 *l.*   illus.
    All published.

    LINDHULT, Johan.   Dissertatio de
materia medica in regno lapideo. *See* Linné,
C. von, *praeses.* Entry 2441.

    LINDWALL, Johan.   Observationes
in materiam medicam. *See* Linné, C. von,
praeses. Entry 2484.

2416. LINNÉ, Carl von.   Materia medica
per regna tria natvrae secvndvm genera dif-
ferentias synonyma loca dvrationes cvltvras
nomina simplicia præparata qvalitates medos
potentias vires vsvs composita digesta.
Editio altera avctior curante Jo. Christiano
Dan. Schrebero. Lipsiae et Erlangae: W.
Walther, 1772.
    23 *l.*, 266 p., 35 *l.*

2417. ———, *praeses.*   Aer habitabilis ...
Publice ventilandum sistit Johannes Vict.
Siefvert ... Upsaliæ [1759].
    25 p.

2418. ———, *praeses.*   Ambrosiaca ... Publico submittit examini ... Jacobus Hideen ...
Upsaliæ [1759].
    14 p.

2419. ———, *praeses.*   Amoenitates academicae seu Dissertationes variae physicae,
medicae botanicae ... Erlangae: J.J. Palm,
1785-1790.
    10 v.   illus.
    Volumes 1-2, third edition; volumes 3-7,
second edition; volumes 8-10, first edition.

2420. ———, *praeses.*   Animalia composita
... Submittit Albertus Bäck ... Upsaliæ [1759].
    2 *l.*, 9 p.

2421. ———, *praeses.*   Canones medici,
quos dissertatione medica ... Auctor Sveno

And. Hedin ... Upsaliæ: J. Edman [1775].
1 *l*., 12 p.

2422. ——, *praeses*. Censura medicamentorum simplicium vegetabilium ... Submittit Gustavus Jac. Carlbohm ... Holmiæ:
P.G. Nyström [1753].
2 *l*., 24 p.

2423. ——, *praeses*. Circa fervidorum et
gelidorum usum paraenesis ... Submittit
Carolus Ribe ... Upsaliæ [1765].
23 p.

2424. ——, *praeses*. Consectaria elec-
trico-medica ... Publico examini subjicit ...
Pretrus Zetzell ... Upsaliæ: L.M. Höjer
[1754].
8 p.

2425. ——, *praeses*. De raphania dissertatio medica ... Offert ... Georgius Rothman ... Upsaliæ [1763].
1 *l*., 21 p.   illus.

2426. ——, *praeses*. De suturis vulnerum
in genere ... Exhibet auctor Christian Ern.
Boecler ... Upsaliae: Edman [1772].
21 p.

2427. ——, *praeses*. Diæta acidularis ...
Submittit ... Ericus Vigelius ... Upsaliæ
[1761].
1 *l*., 12 p.

2428. ——, *praeses*. Disputatio medica
de morsura serpentum ... Publice ventilandam
exhibet ... Joh. Gustavus Acrell ... Upsaliæ
[1762].
2 *l*., 19 p.

2429. ——, *praeses*. Disputatio medica
inauguralis, de generatione calculi ... Offert
... Joh. Otto Hagström. Upsaliæ [1749].
2 *l*., 27 p.

2430. ——, *praeses*. Disputationem
botanico-medicam inauguralem, qua ficus,
ejusque historia naturalis & medica exhibetur
... Publice ventilandam sistit Cornelius
Hegardt ... Upsaliæ [1744].
2 *l*., 28 p.

2431. ——, *praeses*. Dissertatio academica de Lavandula ... Publico examini subjicit ... Johannes Daniel Lundmark ... Upsaliæ:
J. Edman [1780].
1 *l*., 22 p.   illus.

2432. ——, *praeses*. Dissertatio acade-

mica, sistens inebriantia ... Publico examini
defert Olavus Reinh. Alander ... Upsaliæ
[1761].
26 p.

2433. ——, *praeses*. Dissertatio botanica,
qua plantæ Martino-Burserianæ explicantur
... Submissa ... Rolando Martin ... Upsaliæ
[1745].
4 *l*., 31 p.

2434. ——, *praeses*. Dissertatio botanico-
medica de viola ipecacuanha ... Auctor Daniel
Wickman ... Upsaliæ: Edman [1774].
12 p.

2435. ——, *praeses*. Dissertatio botanico-
medica, in qua fungus melitensis ... Proponitur a Johanne Pfeiffer ... Upsaliæ: L.M. Höjer
[1755].
1 *l*., 16 p.   illus.

2436. ——, *praeses*. Dissertatio botanico-
medica, sistens lignum qvassiæ ... Submittit
... Carolus M. Blom ... Upsaliæ [1763].
1 *l*., 13 p.   illus.

2437. ——, *praeses*. Dissertatio botanico-
medica sistens rariora Norvegiæ ... Offert
Henricus Tonning ... Upsaliæ: J. Edman [1768].
3 *l*., 19 p.

2438. ——, *praeses*. Dissertatio chemico
medica de methodo investigandi vires medicamentorum chemica ... Submittit Laurentius
Hiortzberg ... Upsaliæ: L.M. Höjer [1754].
16 p.

2439. ——, *praeses*. Dissertatio de cortice Peruviano ... Offert Joh. Christ. Pet.
Petersen ... Upsaliæ: L.M. Höjer [1758].
1 *l*., 38 p.

2440. ——, *praeses*. Dissertatio de materia medica in regno animali ... Subjicit ...
Jonas Sidren ... Upsaliæ [1750].
20 p.

2441. ——, *praeses*. Dissertatio de materia medica in regno lapideo ... Publico
eruditorum examini modeste subjicit ... Johannes Lindhult ... Upsaliæ: L.M. Höjer [1752]
28 p.

2442. ——, *praeses*. Dissertatio de morbis ex hyeme ... Submittit Sveno Brodd ...
Upsaliæ: L.M. Höjer [1752].
1 *l*., 23 p.

2443. ——, *praeses*. Dissertatio diætetica

de diaeta per scalam aetatis humanae observanda ... Offert Daniel Johan Öhrqvist ...
Upsaliæ [1764].
  12 p.

2444. ——, *praeses*. Dissertatio diætetica, in qua spiritus frumenti ... Publico
examini modeste sistit Petrus Bergius ...
Upsaliæ [1764].
  20 p.

2445. ——, *praeses*. Dissertatio diætetica in quo motus polychrestus ... Publice
ventilandam modeste proponit Christianus
Lado ... Upsaliæ [1763].
  1 *l*., 20 p.

2446. ——, *praeses*. Dissertatio fundamenta valetudinis sistens ... Ad publicum
examen defert Petrus Engstrom. Upsaliæ:
L. M. Höjer [1756].
  2 *l*., 13 p.

2447. ——, *praeses*. Dissertatio inauguralis medica, de hæmorrhagiis ex plethora ... Publice ventilandam sistit auctor
Ernest. J. M. ab Heidenstam. Upsaliae: Edmann [1772].
  2 *l*., 32 p.

2448. ——, *praeses*. Dissertatio medica
de acetariis ... Publice ventilandam sistit
Hieronymus von der Burg ... Upsaliæ: L. M.
Höjer [1756].
  2 *l*., 16 p.

2449. ——, *praeses*. Dissertatio medica,
de effectu et cura vitiorum diæteticorum
generali ... Submittit Johan Gabriel Bergman
... Upsaliæ [1766].
  24 p.

2450. ——, *praeses*. Dissertatio medica
de hæmorrhagiis uteri sub statu graviditatis
... Subj. disquisit. Ericus Er. Elff ... Upsaliæ
[1749].
  23 p.

2451. ——, *praeses*. Dissertatio medica
de ledo palustri ... Auctor et respondens ...
Johannes Petr. Westring ... Upsaliæ: Edman
[1775].
  1 *l*., 18 p.

2452. ——, *praeses*. Dissertatio medica
de medico sui ipsius ... Submittit Johannes
Grysselius ... Upsaliæ: J. Edman [1768].
  13 p.

2453. ——, *praeses*. Dissertatio medica

de meloe-vesicatorio ... Submittit Canutus
Aug. Lenæus ... Upsaliæ [1762].
  1 *l*., 15 p.

2454. ——, *praeses*. Dissertatio medica
de menthæ usu ... Publicæ submittit censuræ Carolus Gustav Laurin ... Upsaliæ:
J. Edman [1767].
  2 *l*., 11 p.

2455. ——, *praeses*. Dissertatio medica
de pulsu intermittente ... Ad publicum examen
defert Andreas Wählin ... Upsaliæ: L. M. Höjer
[1756].
  2 *l*., 18 p.

2456. ——, *praeses*. Dissertatio medica,
de spigelia anthelmia ... Ad publicum examen
defert Joh. Georg. Colliander ... Upsaliæ:
L. M. Höjer [1758].
  16 p.

2457. ——, *praeses*. Dissertatio medica
de varia febrium intermittentium curatione
... Exhibet Petrus C. Tillaeus. Upsaliæ: Edmann [1771].
  56 p., 1 *l*.

2458. ——, *praeses*. Dissertatio medica,
in qua potus coffeæ, leviter adumbratur ...
Publico submittit examini Hinricus Sparschuch
... Upsaliæ [1761].
  1 *l*., 18 p.   illus.

2459. ——, *praeses*. Dissertatio medica
inauguralis de haemoptysi ... Publico submittit examini Johan Martin Gräberg ...
Upsaliae: J. Edman [1767].
  14 p.

2460. ——, *praeses*. Dissertatio medica
inauguralis de potu chocolatæ ... Subjicit
Antonius Hoffman ... Holmiæ: L. Salvius
[1765].
  1 *l*., 10 p.

2461. ——, *praeses*. Dissertatio medica
inauguralis, sistens saporem medicamentorum
... Publice ventilandam sistit, Jacob Rudberg
... Holmiæ: L. Salvius [1751].

2462. ——, *praeses*. Dissertatio medica
odores medicamentorum exhibens ... Submittit
Andreas Wählin ... Stockholmiæ: L. Salvius
[1752].
  2 *l*., 16 p.

2463. ——, *praeses*. Dissertatio medica
sistens metamorphosin humanam ... ad pub-
licam censuram modeste defert Johannes

Adolphus Wadström ... Upsaliæ: J. Edman [1767].
2 *l.*, 18 p.

2464. ——, *praeses.* Dissertatio medica sistens purgantia indigena ... Publico subjicit examini ... Petrus Strandman. Upsaliæ [1766].
2 *l.*, 17 p.

2465. ——, *praeses.* Dissertatio medico-botanica, exhibens plantas officinales ... Placidæ bonorum censuræ subjicit Nicolaus Gahn ... Upsaliæ: L.M. Höjer [1753].
2 *l.*, 31 p.

2466. ——, *praeses.* Dissertatio medico botanica, sistens rhabarbarum ... Publice ventilandam sistit Samuel Ziervogel ... Upsaliæ: L.M. Höjer [1752].
3 *l.*, 24 p.   illus.

2467. ——, *praeses.* Dissertatio medico-botanica, sistens specifica canadensium ... Publico examini submittit Johannes von Coelln ... Scarae [1756].
2 *l.*, 28 p.

2468. ——, *praeses.* Dissertatio medico chirurgica de hirudine ... Exhibet ... Daniel Weser ... Upsaliæ [1764].
2 *l.*, 15 p.

2469. ——, *praeses.* Dissertatio physiologica de perspiratione insensibili ... Auctor Nicolaus Avellan ... Upsaliæ: J. Edman [1775].
11 p.

2470. ——, *praeses.* Dissertationem inauguralem, de maro ... Offert auctor Joh. Adolph. Dahlgren ... Upsaliæ: Edman [1774].
18 p.

2471. ——, *praeses.* Dissertationem medicam de varietate ciborum ... Submittit ... Adolph Fried. Wedenberg ... Upsaliæ: J. Edman [1767].
19 p.

2472. ——, *praeses.* Dissertationem medicam, qua morbi artificum leviter adumbrantur ... Publico subjicit examini Nicolaus Skragge. Upsaliæ [1765].
12 p.

2473. ——, *praeses.* Dissertationem physiologicam de venis resorbentibus ... Offert ... Carolus Petr. Thunberg ... Upsaliæ: J. Edman [1767].

2 *l.*, 10 p.

2474. ——, *praeses.* Exanthemata viva ... Publico examini sistit ... Johannes Nyander ... Upsaliæ: L.M. Höjer [1757].
16 p.

2475. ——, *praeses.* Febris Upsaliensis ... Publice examinandam sistit Andreas Boström ... Upsaliæ: L.M. Höjer [1757].
1 *l.*, 12 p.

2476. ——, *praeses.* Genera morborum ... Publico submittit examini Johannes Schröder ... Upsaliæ [1759].
32 p.

2477. ——, *praeses.* Generatio ambigena ... Publice examinandam sistit Christian. Lud. Ramstrom ... Upsaliæ [1759].
1 *l.*, 17 p.

2478. ——, *praeses.* Hypericum, quod dissertatione botanico-medica ... Exhibet Carolus Nicol. Hellenius. Upsaliæ: Edman [1776].
2 *l.*, 14 p.

2479. ——, *praeses.* Lepra, quam dissertatione medica ... Submittit Isacus Uddman ... Upsaliæ [1765].
1 *l.*, 14 p.

2480. ——, *praeses.* Lignum colubrinum leviter delineatum ... Submittit ... Johan. Andr. Darelius ... Upsaliæ [1749].
22 p.

2481. ——, *praeses.* Medicamenta purgantia ... pro gradu doctoris, proponet Johannes Rotheram ... Upsaliæ: J. Edman [1775].
24 p.

2482. ——, *praeses.* Morbi expeditionis classicæ MDCCLVI ... Publico examini committit ... Petrus Bierchen ... Upsaliæ: L.M. Höjer [1757].
22 p.

2483. ——, *praeses.* Nutrix noverca ... Publice examinandam sistit Fredericus Lindberg ... Upsaliæ: L.M. Höjer [1752].
20 p., 1 *l.*

2484. ——, *praeses.* Observationes in materiam medicam ... Submittit Johannes Lindwall. Upsaliæ: Edmann [1772].
1 *l.*, 8 p.

2485. ——, *praeses.* Obstacula medicinæ

... Subiicit ... Johannes Georg Beyersten ...
Strengnesiæ [1752].
  20 p.

2486. ——, praeses. Opium, quod dissertatione medica ... Publice ventilandum
sistit Georgius Eberhardus Georgii ... Upsaliæ: Edman [1775].
  1 ℓ., 17 p.

2487. ——, praeses. Opobalsamum de-
claratum in dissertatione medica ... Submittit ... Wilhelmus Le Moine ... Upsaliæ
[1764].
  2 ℓ., 19 p.

2488. ——, praeses. Planta cimicifuga
... Proponet Johannes Hornborg. Upsaliæ: J.
Edman [1774].
  1 ℓ., 10 p.

2489. ——, praeses. Plantæ tinctoriæ,
de quibus specimen botanico-oeconomicum
... Submittit ... Engelbertus Jörlin ... Upsaliæ
[1759].
  30 p.

2490. ——, praeses. Potus theae, quem
dissertatione medica ... Publico submittit
examini Petrus C. Tillæus. Upsaliæ [1765].
  2 ℓ., 16 p. illus.

2491. ——, praeses. Radix senega ...
Submittit Jonas Kiernander ... Holmiæ: L.
Salvius [1749].
  32 p. illus.

2492. ——, praeses. Respiratio diaetetica
... Offert Jonas Ullholm. Upsaliae: Edmann
[1772].
  1 ℓ., 26 p.

2493. ——, praeses. Senium Salomoneum
... Publice examinandum sistit Johannes Pil-
gren ... Upsaliæ [1759].
  24 p.

2494. ——, praeses. Specimen academi-
cum de taenia ... Submittit Godofredus Dubois ... Upsaliæ [1748].
  2 ℓ., 36 p.

2495. ——, praeses. Specimen inaugurale
de scorbuto ... Auctor Ernestus D. Salomon
... Upsaliæ: J. Edman [1775].
  23 p.

2496. ——, praeses. Specimen inaugurale,
sistens medicamenta graveolentia ... Submittit Jonas Theodor. Fagraeus ... Upsaliæ:

L.M. Höjer [1758].
  3 ℓ., 24 p.

2497. ——, praeses. Theses medicæ ...
Publico submittet examini Jo. Christ. Dan.
Schreber ... Upsaliæ [1760].
  4 p.

2498. ——, praeses. Vires plantarum,
dissertatione academica ... Examini publico
subjectae a Friderico Hasselquist ... Upsaliæ [1747].
  37 p., 1 ℓ.

2499. LINTHAUT, Henri de, sieur de Mont-
Lion. Commentaire ... svr Le tresor des
tresors de Christofle de Gamon, reveu &
augmenté par l'auteur. Lyon: C. Morillon,
1610.
  4 ℓ., 177 p., 1 ℓ.

2500. LIPEN, Martin. Bibliotheca realis
medica, omnium materiarum, rerum, et titu-
lorum, in universa medicina occurrentivm ...
Francofvrti ad Moenvm: sumptibus J. Friderici,
prelo J.N. Hummii, 1679.
  10 ℓ., 492 p., 21 ℓ.

2501. LIS, Wouter van. Pharmacopoea
galeno-chemico-medica probatissimis auctoribus, ratione & experientia fundata ...
in't Latyn en Duitsch te zamengestelt door
Wouter van Lis. Rotterdam: P. & J. Losel,
1747.
  15 ℓ., 341 p., 17 ℓ. illus., chart.

2502. ——. ——. Twede druk ... Amsteldam: J. Morterre, 1764.
  17 ℓ., 436 p., 30 ℓ. illus., chart.

2503. LISCHWITZ, Johann Christoph, praeses.
Dissertatio inavgvralis botanico-medica,
de ordinandis rectivs virgis avreis genvinis
aeqve ac spvriis, vsvqve officinalivm medico
... pvblisce defendet Io. Gotheofr. Tettel-
backivs ... Lipsiae: I. Langenhemius, 1731.
  7 ℓ., 80 p., 2 ℓ.

2504. LISTER, Martin. Exercitatio anatomica.
In qua de cochleis, maxime terrestribus &
limacibus, agitur ... Londini: S. Smith & B.
Walford, 1694.
  2 ℓ., xi, 208 p. illus.

2505. ——. Exercitatio anatomica altera,
in qua maxime agitur de buccinis fluviatilibus
& marinis ... His accedit Exercitatio medicinalis de variolis. Londini: S. Smith & B.
Walford, 1695.
  8 ℓ., 267 p.; 1 ℓ., 128 p. illus.

2506. ——. A journey to Paris in the year 1698. The third edition. London: J. Tonson, 1699.
    9 *l*., 248 p. illus.

2507. ——. Novæ ac curiosæ exercitationes & descriptiones thermarum ac fontium medicatorum Angliæ ... Editio ultima auctior & emendatior. Londini: W. Kettilby, 1686.
    4 *l*., 156 p. illus.

——. Tractatus de quibusdam morbis chronicis. *In* Morton, R., Opera medica ... 1696.

——. Tractatus de variolis. *In* Morton, R., Opera medica ... 1696.

2508. LOBB, Theophilus. A practical treatise of painful distempers ... London: for J. Buckland, 1739.
    xxx p., 1 *l*., 320 p., 7 *l*.

2509. L'OBEL, Matthias de. Plantarvm sev stirpivm historia ... Cui annexum est adversariorvm volvmen ... Antverpiæ: C. Plantin, 1576.
    671 p. illus.

2510. ——. Nova stirpivm adversaria, perfacilis vestigatio, lvcvlentaqve accessio ad priscorum, præsertim Dioscoridis, & recentiorum, materiam medicam ... Additis Gvillielmi Rondelletii aliquot remediorum formulis ... Antverpiæ: C. Plantin, 1576.
    2 *l*., 471, 15, 24 p., 8 *l*. illus.

2511. ——. Stirpium illustrationes. Plurimas elaborantes inauditas plantes, subreptitiis Joh: Parkinsoni rapsodiis ... sparsim gravatæ. Ejusdem adjecta sunt ad calcem theatri botanici ... Accurante Guil: How. Londini: typis T. Warren, impensis J. Kirton, 1655.
    19 *l*., 170 p., 3 *l*.

2512. LOBERA DE AVILA, Luis. Ein nutzlich Regiment der gesundtheit, genant das Vanquete, oder Gastmal der Edlen diener von der Complexion, Eigenschafft, Schad und nutz allerley Speyss, Trancks uñ von allem darmit sich der mensch in gesundtheit enthelt, mit sampt einem kurtzen Regiment, wie man sich in der Pestilentz Pestilentzischê fieber und Schweyss halten sol ... Durch Michaelem Krautwadel ... verteütscht ... [Augspurg: H. Steyner, 1531.]
    6 *l*., 91 numb. *l*., 2 *l*. illus.
    With Virdung, J., Nova medicinae ... 1532.

2513. LOCATELLI, Lodovico. Theatro d'arcani ... nel qvale si tratta dell'arte chimica, & suoi arcani, con gli afforismi d'Ippocrate commentati da Paracelso ... Milano: G.P. Ramellati, 1644.
    28 *l*., 456 p. illus.

2514. ——. ——. Venetia: P. Baglioni, 1667.
    8 *l*., 392 p., 11 *l*. illus.

2515. LOCHER, Maximilan. Observationes practicae circa luem veneream, epilepsiam et maniam ... Viennae: J.T. Trattner, 1762.
    108 p.

2516. LOCQUES, Nicolas de. Elemens philosophiqves des arcanes et dv dissolvant general ... Livre sixième. Paris: G. Marcher, 1668.
    10 *l*., 87 [i.e. 89] p.
    With his Les rvdimens de la philosophie natvrelle ... 1665, as issued.

2517. ——. Les rvdimens de la philosophie natvrelle tovchant le system dv corps mixte. Covrs theoriqve ... Livre premier[-second]. Paris: G. Marcher, 1665.
    2 v. in 1. illus.

2518. ——. Les rvdimens de la philosophie natvrelle tovchant le systeme dv corps mixte. De la fermentation ... Avec le traitté du sang & les propositions de la chymie resolutive ... Traité second. Paris: G. Marcher, 1665.
    2 pts. in 1 v.
    Pt. 2 has separate pagination and titlepage: *Propositions tovchant la physiqve resolvtive* ...
    With his Les rvdimens ... Livre premier [-second] ... 1665, as issued.

2519. ——. Les vertvs magnetiqves dv sang, de son vsage interne & externe, pour la guarison des maladies ... Paris: J. Le Gentil, 1664.
    8 *l*., 54 p.
    With his Les rvdimens de la philosophie natvrelle ... 1665, as issued.

2520. LODER, Just Christian. Chirurgischmedicinische Beobachtungen mehrentheils in der Herzoglich Sachsen-Weimarschen Medicinisch-Chirurgischen Kranken-Anstalt zu Jena. Weimar: Industrie-Comptoirs, 1794.
    2 v. illus.
    Volume one only.

2521. ——. Tabvlae anatomicae qvas ad

illvstrandam hvmani corporis fabricam. Collegit et cvravit. Vinariae: Industrie-Comptoir, 1794-1803.
  var. pag.   folio.
  Lacking the atlas.

2522. LOECHES, Juan de. Tyrochinium pharmaceuticum, theorico-practicum, galenochymicvm. Gerundæ: N. Oliva et P. Morera, 1755.
  8 *l.*, 59, 487 p.

  LOEN, S.E. von, *supposed author*. *See* Das Geheimnuss der Verwesung und Verbrennung ... 1759, 1771.

  LOHEN, Christophoro à. Dissertatio medica de hemiplexia. *See* Beckher, D.C., *praeses*.

2523. LOMBARDO, Giovanni Francesco. Σύνοψις eorvm, qvae de balneis aliisqꞋue miraculis Puteolanis scripta sunt ... Adiectis balneis Aenariarum, necnon locis obscurioribus non inutilibus scholiis ... Venetiis: impensis A. Sanuiti, apud A. Baccolum, 1566.
  4 *l.*, 128 p., 8 *l.*

2524. LOMET, Antoine François. Mémoire sur les eaux minérales et les établissemens thermaux des Pyrénées ... Paris: R. Vatar [1795].
  xxvii, 154 p.   illus.

2525. LOMMIUS, Jodocus. Commentarii de sanitate tuenda in primum librum De re medica Aurel. Cornelli Celsi ... Lugduni Batavorum: J.A. Langerak, 1724.
  14 *l.*, 326 p., 15 *l.*

2526. ——. Opservationum medicinalium libri tres ... Amstelodami: J.F. Bernard, 1715.
  8 *l.*, 290 p., 4 *l.*

2527. LOMONOSOV, Mikhail Vasil'evich. Oratio de vtilitate chemiae ... habita A.C. MDCCLI. viii. Idus Septembres ... Ex Rossica autem in Latinam linguam conversa a Gregorio Kositzki. Petropoli: Academiae Scientiarum [1751].
  1 *l.*, 30 p.

2528. LONDON. St. Bartholomew's Hospital. Pharmacopoeia nosocomii regalis Sancti Bartholomei. Londini: J. Adlard, 1799.
  84 p.

2529. The LONDON and country brewer ... In three parts. To which is added a supplement ... The sixth edition. London: for T.

Astley, sold by R. Baldwin, 1750.
  4 *l.*, 332 p., 3 *l.*

  The LONDON practice of physic. *See* La médecine pratique de Londres.

2530. LONGINUS, Caesar, *ed.* Trinvm magicvm, siue Secretorvm natvralivm, coelestivm, infernalivm opus ... Continens I. Marci Antonii Zimarae, Conclusiones physicas ... II. Alexandri Aphrodisei Quaestiones & solutiones physico-mathematicas. III. Alberti Magni, Tractatus tres, de virtutibus herbarum, lapidum & animalium ... Accessere eiusdem Alberti Libelli de mirabilibus mundi ... Francofvrti: ex officina I. Spieffii, sumptibꞋus A. Hummii, 1609.
  328 p.

2531. ——, *ed.* Trinvm magicvm, siue Secretorvm magicorvm opvs ... Accessere nonnulla secreta secretorum & mirabilia mundi ... Francofurti: A. Humm, 1616.
  10 *l.*, 603 p.

2532. ——. ——. Et Tractatus de proprii cujus nati dæmonis inquisitione. Francofurti: J.G. Seyler, 1673.
  10 *l.*, 498 p.

2533. LOOS, Onésime Henri de. Le diadême des sages, ou Démonstration de la nature inférieure ... Par Phylantropos, citoyen du monde ... Paris: Mérigot & Lesclapart, 1781.
  xvi, 240 p., 1 *l.*

2534. ——. Der Schmuck der Weisen, oder Gründliche Darstellung der physischen Unterwelt ... Von Philantropos, einem Weltbürger, übersetzt von F.v.Z. Wien: R. Grässer, 1782.
  197 p.

2535. LORME, de, *chevalier de St. Louis*. Traité de chymie. Paris: la veuve Duchesne ..., 1773.
  2 *l.*, 528 p.   chart.

2536. LORRY, Anne-Charles. De melancholia et morbis melancholicis. Lutetiae Parisiorum: P.G. Cavelier, 1765.
  2 v.

2537. ——. Essai sur les alimens, pour servir de commentaire aux livres dietetiques d'Hippocrate. Paris: Vincent, 1754.
  xxiv, 440 p., 2 *l.*

2538. LÖSEKE, Johann Ludwig Leberecht. Materia medica oder Abhandlung von den auserlesenen Arzneymitteln ... Vierte Auflage,

durchgängig verbessert ... von D. Johann
Friedrich Zückert. Berlin: F. Nicolai, 1773.
    8 *l.*, 614 p., 9 *l.*

2539. LOUIS, Antoine. Oeuvres diverses
de chirurgie. [Paris: J. Dufour & P. Roux,
1788.]
    2 v.

2540. LOVELL, Robert. Παμβοτανολογία
sive, Enchiridion botanicum. Or, a compleat
herball ... the second edition ... Oxford:
W.H. for R. Davis, 1665.
    84, 675 p., 3 *l.*

2541. LOVELL, William. Approved receipts,
or, The queens representation to this our
English nation ... Discovering divers infirmities in mans body ... London: for C. Tyus,
1663.
    8 *l.*
    With Boules, R., The queens royal closet
... [n.d.].

2542. ———. The dukes desk newly broken
up wherein is discovered divers rare receits
of physick and surgery, good for men, women
and children ... London: printed for the author,
1660.
    1 *l.*, 14 p.

2543. LOW, D. Chiropodologia, or, A
scientific enquiry into the causes of corns,
warts, onions, and other painful or offensive
cutaneous excrescences ... London: J. Rosea
... [1785].
    140 p.

2544. LOWE, Peter. A discovrse of the
whole art of chyrvrgerie ... Whereunto is
added the rule of making remedies which
chyrurgions doe commonly use: with the
presages of divine Hippocrates. The third
edition; corrected, and much amended. London: T. Purfoot, 1634.
    12 *l.*, 447 p., 20 *l.* illus.

2545. LOWER, Richard. Diatribae Thomae
Willisii. De febribus vindicatio, adversus
Edmundum de Meara. Amstelodami: G. Schagen,
1666.
    129 p.

2546. ———. Dr. Lower's and several other
eminent physicians receipts: containing the
best and safest method for curing most diseases ... The second edition with additions.
London: for J. Nutt, 1701.
    6 *l.*, 117 p.

2547. ———. Tractatus de corde. Item de
motu & colore sanguinis et chyli in eum
transitu. Amstelodami: D. Elzevirius, 1669.
    8 *l.*, 232 p. illus.

2548. LOWNDES, Thomas. Brine-salt improved: or, The method of making salt from
brine, that shall be as good or better than
French bay-salt ... London: for S. Austen, 1746.
    38 p.

2549. LUBBOCK, Richard. Dissertatio
physico-chemica inauguralis de principio
sorbili, sive communi mutationum chemicarum causa, quaestionem, an phlogiston
sit substantia, an qualitas, agitans; et
alteram ignis theoriam complectens ...
Edinburgi: Balfour & Smellie, 1784.
    3 *l.*, 137 p.

2550. LUCHTMANS, Petrus. Oratio inauguralis de anatomicis seculi XVIII incre-
mentis ... Trajecti ad Rhenum: J. Broedelet,
1760.
    45 p.

2551. ———. Waarneeming van een byzon-
der zoort van eene zo genaamde atresia ani
of gesloten aars ... Utrecht [1793?].
    25 p. illus.

LUDOVICI, Jacobus. De arsenico.
See Meibomius, B., *praeses*.

2552. LUDWIG, Christian Gottlieb. Institvtiones chirvrgiae praelectionibvs
academicis accommodatae. Lipsiae: Gleditsch, 1764.
    viii, 462 p., 5 *l.*

2553. ———. Institvtiones medicinae
clinicae praelectionibvs academicis accommodatae. Lipsiae: J.F. Gleditsch, 1758.
    7 *l.*, 538 p., 4 *l.*

2554. ———. Institvtiones pathologiae
praelectionibvs academicis accommodatae.
Lipsiae: Gleditsch, 1754.
    2 *l.*, 172 p., 4 *l.*
    With his Institvtiones medicinae clinicae
... 1758.

2555. ———. Institvtiones physiologiae
cvm praemissa introdvctione in vniversam
medicinam praelectionibvs academicis accommodatae. Lipsiae: Gleditsch, 1752.
    5 *l.*, 350 p., 4 *l.* illus.
    With his Institvtiones medicinae clinicae
... 1758.

2556. ——. ——. Coloniae Allobrogum:
Piestre & Delamolliere, 1785.
    x, 350 p., 4 *l*.   illus.

2557. ——. Institvtiones therapiae generalis praelectionibvs academicis accommodatae. Lipsiae: Gleditsch, 1754.
    4 *l*., 162 p., 3 *l*.
    With his Institvtiones medicinae clinicae
... 1758.

2558. ——, *praeses*.   De corde rvpto ...
Pro gradv doctoris disserit Dietericvs
Mvmmssen. Lipsiae: Langenhem [1764].
    42 p., 1 *l*., xiv p.   illus.

2559. LUDWIG, Daniel.   De pharmacia
moderno seculo applicanda; dissertationes
III. Editio secunda ... Gothæ: C. Reyherus,
1685.
    3 *l*., 749 p., 35 *l*., 195 p.   illus., port.

——. Thesaurus Ludovicianus. *In*
Fuller, T., Pharmacopoeia extemporanea ...
1790.

    LULL, Ramón.   Apertorium. *In* Al-
chymistisch Sieben-Gestirn ... 1697.

——. Ars operativa. *In* Joannes de
Rupesciasa, De consideratione ... [1561].

——. Clavicula. *In* Broekhuizen, D.
van, Secreta alchimiæ magnalia ... 1598,
1602.

2560. ——. Clavis Raymundi Lullii, ohne
welchen andere seine Bücher nicht zu verstehen, aus dem Latein ins Teutsche versetzt ... Den filiis hermeticæ doctrinæ ...
Strassburg: J.A. Dolhopff, 1699.
    1 *l*., 25-45 p.

2561. ——. De alchimia opuscula ...
Apertorivm. Item, Magica natvralis. Item,
De secretis natvræ, seu De quinta essentia
liber unus ... Norimbergæ: J. Petreius, 1546.
    113 numb. *l*.

2562. ——. De secretis naturæ siue
Quinta essentia libri duo. His accesserunt
Alberti Magni ... De mineralibus & rebus
metallicis libri quinque. Quæ omnia ... pub-
licata sunt per M. Gualtherum H. Ryff ...
[Argentorati: B. Beck] 1541.
    4 *l*., 183 numb. *l*.   illus.

2563. ——. ——. Venetiis: P. Schoeffer,
1542.
    324 p., 4 *l*.   illus.

2564. ——. De' secreti di natura, ò della
quinta essentia, libri dve. Alberto Magno ...
De cose minerali, & metalliche, libri cinqve.
Il tutto tradotto da M. Pietro Lauro ... Vinegia: G. & M. Sessa, 1557.
    28 *l*., 152 numb. *l*.   illus.

——. Elucidarium. *In* Alchymistisch
Sieben-Gestirn ... 1697.

2565. ——. Libelli aliquot chemici: nunc
primùm, excepto Vade mecum, in lucem opera
Doctoris Toxitæ editi ... Basileæ: P. Perna,
1572.
    8 *l*., 480 p., 16 *l*.

2566. ——. Liber, qui Codicillus, seu
Vade macum inscribitur, in quo fontes alchimicæ artis & reconditioris philosophiæ
traduntur, ante hac nunquam impressus.
Coloniæ: hæredes A. Birckmanni, 1563.
    171 p.

2567. ——. Codicillvs sev Vade mecvm
... in qvo fontes alchimicæ artis ac philosophiæ reconditioris vberrimè traduntur.
Secunda editio in qua innumerabiles loci
multorum exemplarium collatione restituuntur,
& multa prius omissa supplentur. Coloniæ:
hæredes A. Brickmanni, 1572.
    248 p.

2568. ——. Le vade-mecvm, ov Abregé
de l'art chimiqve, tovchant la transmvtation
des metaux, & vraye pierre des philosophes
... Traduict fidelement du Latin en François
... Paris: C. Hulpeau, 1627.
    3 *l*., 22 p.

2569. ——. Testamentum, duobus libris
vniuersam artem chymicam complectens,
antehac nunquam excusum. Item eivsdem
Compendivm animæ transmvtationis artis
metallorum ... Coloniæ Agrippinæ: J. Byrck-
mann, 1566.
    4 *l*., 240 numb. *l*., 8 *l*.

2570. ——. ——. Item Testamentvm novis-
simvm ... Vltima editio ... castigata diligentiâ
D.M. Ravlt ... Rothomagi: D. Berthelin, 1663.
    355 p., 5 *l*.; 6 *l*., 393 p., 13 *l*.   illus.,
charts.

    LUNDMARK, Johannes Daniel.   De
Lavandula. *See* Linné, C. von, *praeses*.
Entry 2431.

——. Ficus, ejusque historia
naturalis & medica exhibetur. *See* Linné,
C. von, *praeses*. Entry 2430.

2571. LUPTON, Thomas. A thousand no-
table things of sundrie sorts ... Newly corrected ... London: E. Allde for E. White, 1612.
3 *l.*, 214 p., 10 *l.*

2572. LUSSAULD, Charles. Apologie
povr les medecins ... Paris: P. Rocolet,
D. Fovcavlt, 1633.
7 *l.*, 187 p., 2 *l.*

M

M., A., *ed.* A rich closet of physical secrets. *See* A rich closet.

2573. M., J.U., *ed.* Neu-eröffnete Schatz-Kammer verschiedener Natur- und Kunst-Wunder ... Neben denen vornehmsten Natur- und Artzney- Seh- Hör- Feur- Bergwerck-Stein- Wasser- und Mathematischen Künsten enthalten seyn ... Nürnberg: zu finden bey J. Hofmann, druckts J.C. Drechsler, 1689.
4 *l.*, 1018 p., 17 *l.* illus.
Lacking pages 1-176. Between the fourth preliminary leaf and p. 177 are inserted the first 192 text pages of a similar work entitled: Schatz-Kammer rarer und neuer Curiositäten ...

M., Damoiselle M., *pseud. See* Meurdrac, Marie.

M., W., *ed.* The queens closet opened. *See* The queens closet.

2574. MACBRIDE, David. Experimental essays ... London: for A. Millar, 1764.
xiii p., 2 *l.*, 267 p., 1 *l.* illus., charts.

2575. MACER FLORIDUS. De herbarvm virtutibus, cum Ioannis Atrociani cōmentarijs ... Adhaec Strabi Galli ... Hortulus uernantissimus. [Fribvrgi: J.F. Emmeus, 1530.]
4 *l.*, 108 numb. *l.*

——. A newe herball. *See* Herbal.

2576. MACKAILE, Matthew. The diversitie of salts and spirits mantained. Or, the imaginary volatility of some salts and non-entity of the alcali ... Aberdeen: I. Forbes, 1683.
8 *l.*, 145 p. chart.

2577. ——. Moffet-Well: or, A topographico-spagyricall description of the mineral wells, at Moffet, in Annandale of Scotland ... As also, The oyly-well: or, A topographico-spagyricall description of the oyly-well, at St. Catharines chappel in the paroch of Libberton. To these is subjoyned, A character of Mr. Culpeper and his writings ... Edinburgh: for R. Brown, 1664.
196 p.

2578. MACKENZIE, James. The history of health, and the art of preserving it: or, An account of all that has been recommended by physicians and philosophers ... The third edition ... Edinburgh: for W. Gordon, 1760.
xii, 464 p.

2579. MACQUART, Louis Charles Henri. Manuel sur les propriétés de l'eau, particulierement dans l'art de guérir ... Paris: Nyon, 1783.
1 *l.*, xxiv, 476 p. charts.

2580. MACQUER, Pierre Joseph. Dictionnaire de chymie ... avec l'explication détaillée de la vertu & de la maniere d'agir des médicamens chymiques ... Paris: Lacombe, 1766.
2 v.

2581. ——. ——. Yverdon: 1767.
3 v.

2582. ——. ——. Seconde édition, revue & considérablement augmentée ... Paris: P.F. Didot juene, 1777.
3 v.

2583. ——. ——. Nouvelle édition corrigée sur les précédentes, avec un supplément séparé ... Neuchatel: la Société Typographique, 1789.
5 v.

2584. ——. A dictionary of chemistry. Containing the theory and practice of that science ... The second edition. To which is added, as an appendix, A treatise on the various kinds of permanently elastic fluids,

or gases ... London: for T. Cadell & P. Elmsly, 1777.
   3 v. illus., chart.

2585. ——. Elémens de chymie-pratique ... Paris: J.T. Herissant, 1751.
   2 v.

2586. ——. ——. Second edition, revûe & corrigée ... Paris: J.T. Hérissant, 1756.
   2 v.

2587. ——. Elemens de chymie theorique ... Paris: J.T. Herissant, 1749.
   xxii, 336 p., 12 *l*. illus.

2588. ——. ——. Nouvelle édition. Paris: J.T. Hérissant, 1756.
   xxii p., 1 *l*., 368 p., 7 *l*. illus., chart.

2589. ——. Elements of the theory and practice of chymistry. Translated from the French ... London: for A. Millar & J. Nourse, 1758.
   2 v. illus.

2590. ——. ——. The fourth edition. London: for C. Nourse ..., 1787.
   2 v. illus.

2591. ——. Plan d'un cours de chymie expérimentale et raisonnée, avec un discours historique sur la chymie. Paris: J.T. Herissant, 1757.
   2 *l*., lxiii, 80 p.

      ——, *jt. auth*. The art of dying wool. *See* Hellot, Jean.

      MADEIRA ARRAES, Duarte. Arbor vitae; or A physical account of the tree of li´e. *In* Bacon, R., The cure of old age ... 1683.

      MAETS, Carel Lodowyk de, *supposed author*. Chemia rationalis ... *See* T., P.

2592. MAGELHAENS, João Jacinto de. Description of a glass apparatus, for making mineral waters ... together with the description of some new eudiometers ... in a letter to the Rev. Dr. Priestley ... The second edition ... London: for W. Parker ... 1779.
   viii, 52 p., 1 *l*. illus.
   With Falconer, W., Experiments and observations ... 1776.

2593. ——. ——. The third edition, revised, corrected, and enlarged by the author, with an examination of the strictures of Mr.

T. Cavello ... upon these eudiometers. London: for the author, 1783.
   viii, 80 p. illus.

2594. MAGIRUS, Johann. Physiologiæ peripateticæ libri sex ... Quibus accessit Caspari Bartholini ... Metaphysica major ... Accessit denique Johannis Magiri De memoria artificiosa ... Cantabrigiæ: R. Daniel, 1642.
   4 *l*., 412 p., 2 *l*.; 1 *l*., 53 p.; 26 p.

2595. MAGNEN, Jean Chrysostome. De manna liber singularis ... Editio ultima à multis mendis repurgata. Hagæ-Comitis: A. Vlacq, 1658.
   6 *l*., 116 p., 2 *l*.
   With his De tabaco ... 1658.

2596. ——. De tabaco exercitationes quatuordecim ... Editio ultima à multis mendis repurgata. Hagæ-Comitis: A. Vlacq, 1658.
   24, 264 p.

2597. ——. Democritvs reviviscens sive De atomis ... Papiæ: I.A. Magrius, 1646.
   8 *l*., 276 p., 3 *l*. illus.

2598. MAGNI PHILOSOPHORVM arcani revelator, quo Hermetis discipuli, magnique scrutatores operis omnia ad suum laborem necessaria, clarissimé explicata invenient ... Genevæ: S. de Tournes, 1688.
   1 *l*., 490 p., 5 *l*. illus.

2599. MAGNOL, Antonius, *praeses*. Dissertatio de ferri usu et abusu in medicina ... Monspelii: F. Rochard, 1736.
   2 *l*., 40 p.

2600. MAGNUM INTEREST totius reip. Hermeticæ. Sive Epistola II. buccinatoria, ad clarissimos viros, Joan. Otton. Helbigium ... Joan. de Monte Hermetis anonymum, ac cæteros magnates Hermeticos, data a duumviris Hermeticis federatis ... Gedani: sumptibus B.L. Tancken, typis D.F. Rhetii, 1681.
   30 p.

2601. MAIER, Michael. Arcana arcanissima hoc est Hieroglyphica Aegyptio-Græca, vulgo necdum cognita, ad demonstrandum falsorum apud antiquos deorum, dearum, heroum, animantium & institutorum pro sacris receptorum, originem ... sex libris exposita ... [Oppenheimii?: 1614?]
   6 *l*., 285 p., 7 *l*.

2602. ——. Atalanta fvgiens, hoc est,

Emblemata nova de secretis naturæ chymica ... Oppenheimii: ex typographia H. Galleri, sumptibus J.T. de Bry, 1617.
　211 p., 1 *l*.　illus.

2603.　——.　——.　Oppenheimii: ex typographia H. Galleri, sumptibus J.T. de Bry, 1618.
　211 p., 1 *l*.　illus.

2604.　——.　Cantilenæ intellectuales de phoenice redivivo; ou Chansons intellectuelles sur la resurrection du phenix ... Traduites en François sur l'original Latin par M.L.L.M. ... Paris: Debure, 1758.
　4 *l*., 129 p.

2605.　——.　De circulo physico, quadrato: hoc est, Auro, eivsqve virtvte medicinali, svb dvro cortice instar nvclei latente ... Oppenheimii: typis H. Galleri, sumptibus L. Jennis, 1616.
　79 p.

2606.　——.　Examen fvcorvm psevdochymicorvm detectorvm et in gratiam veritatis amantium succincte refutatorum ... Francofurti: typis N. Hoffmani, sumptibus T. de Brij, 1617.
　47 p.　illus.

2607.　——.　Jocvs severvs, hoc est, Tribvnal æqvvm, qvo noctva regina avivm phoenice arbitro post varias deceptationes et qverelas volucrum eam infestantium pronunciatur, & ob sapientiam singularem, Palladi sacrata agnoscitur ... Francofurti: typis N. Hoffmanni, sumptibus T. de Brij, 1617.
　76 p.

2608.　——.　Lusus serius: or, Serious passe-time. A philosophicall discourse concerning the superiority of creatures under man ... London: for H. Moseley & T. Heath, 1654.
　4 *l*., 139 p., 8 *l*.

2609.　——.　Secretioris naturæ secretorum scrutinium chymicum, per oculis et intellectui accuratē accomodata ... ingeniosissima emblemata ... Francofurti: impensis G. H. Oehrlingii, typo J.P. Andreae, 1687.
　4 *l*., 150 p.　illus.

2610.　——.　Chymisches Cabinet, derer grossen Geheimnussen der Natur, durch wohl ersonnene sinnreiche Kupferstiche und Emblemata ... dargestellet un ausgezieret ... vor jetzo aber zum ersten mahl in das

Hochteutsche übersetzet ist, von G.A.K. ... Franckfurt: G.H. Oehrling, 1708.
　2 *l*., 153 p.　illus.

2611.　——.　Symbola avreæ mensæ dvodecim nationvm ... Francofurti: typis A. Hummij, impensis L. Iennis, 1617.
　10 *l*., 621 p., 21 *l*.　illus., port.

2612.　——.　Themis aurea. The laws of the fraternity of the rosie crosse. Written in Latin ... and now in English ... Whereto is annexed an epistle to the fraternity in Latine, from some here in England. London: for N. Brooke, 1656.
　15 *l*., 136 p., 4 *l*.

2613.　——.　Tractatvs de volvcri arborea, absqve patre et matre, in insulis Orcadvm, forma anserculorum proueniente ... Francofurti: typis N. Hoffmanni, sumptibus L. Jennis, 1619.
　180 p.

2614.　——.　Tractatus posthumus, siue Ulysses ... Una cum annexis tractatibus de fraternitate Roseæ Crucis. Francofurti: L. Jennis, 1624.
　274 p.
　With Potier, M., Philosophia pura ... 1619.

2615.　——.　Viatorium, hoc est, De montibvs planetarvm septem seu metallorum ... Oppenheimii: ex typographia H. Galleri, sumptibus J.T. de Bry, 1618.
　136 p.　illus.

2616.　——.　——.　Rothomagi: J. Berthelin, 1651.
　224 p.　illus.

2617.　——, *ed.*　Tripvs avrevs, hoc est, Tres tractatvs chymici selectissimi, nempe I. Basilii Valentini ... Practica ... II. Thomæ Nortoni ... Crede mihi seu Ordinale ... III. Cremeri cvivsdam abbatis Westmonasteriensis Angli Testamentum ... Francofurti: ex chalçographia P. Iacobi, impensis L. Iennis, 1618.
　196 p.　illus., port.

2618.　MAJOR, Johannes Daniel.　Genius errans sive De ingeniorum in scientiis abusu dissertatio. Kiliæ Holsatorum: J. Reumann, 1677.
　176 *l*.　illus.

2619.　——, *praeses*.　Disputatio medica quam de aurea catena Jovis coelo demisa ... Respondente thesium autore, Johanne

Crusio ... Kiliæ Holsatorum: J. Reumann,
1685.
    5 ℓ., 94 p., 2 ℓ.
    Lacking pages 1-2.

2620.   MALACARNE, Michele Vincenzo Maria.
Trattato delle regie terme Aquesi. Torino:
G. Briolo, 1778.
    4 ℓ., 143 p.   illus.

2621.   MALBEC DE TRESFEL, Jean.   Abregé
de la theorie et des veritables principes de
l'art appellé chymie ... divisé en deux
parties ... Paris: chez l'autheur, 1671.
    84, 116 p.

2622.   MALDINY, Joannes Jacobus de.
Mirabilia mundi, sive De scientiarum artium-
qve omnium origine et progressu tractatus
... Editio prima. Brunsvigæ: authoris impensis, 1726.
    8 ℓ., 186 p., 3 ℓ.   illus.

2623.   MALOUIN, Paul Jacques.   Traité de
chimie, contenant la maniere de préparer
les remedes qui sont les plus en usage dans
la pratique de la medecine ... Paris: G.
Cavelier, 1734.
    xx, 326 p., 1 ℓ.

2624.   MALPIGHI, Marcello.   Consulta-
tionum medicinalium, centuria prima, quam
in gratiam clinicorum evulgat Hieronymus
Gaspari ... Patavii: 1713.
    10 ℓ., 13-179 p.

2625.   ———.   De structura glandularum
conglobatarum consimiliumque partium,
epistola ... Lugduni Batavorum: P. vander
Aa, 1690.
    16 p.
    With his Opera omnia ... 1687.

2626.   ———.   ———.   Londini: R. Chiswell,
1697.
    1 ℓ., 10 p.
    With his Opera posthuma ... 1697.

2627.   ———.   Dissertatio epistolica de
bombyce, Societati Regiæ, Londini ... dicata.
Londini: J. Martyn & J. Allestry, 1669.
    5 ℓ., 100 p.   illus.

2628.   ———.   Epistolae anatomicae, virorum
clarissimorum Marcelli Malpighii et Caroli
Fracassati ... Amstelodami: C. Commelinus,
1669.
    2 ℓ., 260 p.   illus.

2629.   ———.   Exercitatione de viscerum,

nominatim pulmonum, hepatis, cerebri cor-
ticis, renum, lienis, structura, cum Dissertatione de polypo cordis. Editio altera.
Jenae: J. Gollner, 1677.
    5 ℓ., 280 p., 23 ℓ.

2630.   ———.   Discours anatomiques sur la
structure des visceres, sçavoir du foye, du
cerveau, des reins, de la ratte, du polype
du coeur, et des poulmons. Mis en François
par M.*****. Paris: L. D'Houry, 1683.
    9 ℓ., 374 p., 1 ℓ.   illus.

2631.   ———.   Opera omnia ... Londini: R.
Littlebury, 1687-1686.
    2 v. in 1.   illus.

2632.   ———.   ———.   Editio novissima ...
Lugduni Batavorum: P. vander Aa, 1687.
    2 v. in 1.

2633.   ———.   Opera posthuma ... Quibus
præfixa est ejusdem vita à seipso scripta.
Londini: A. & J. Churchill, 1697.
    2 ℓ., 110, 187 p.   illus., port.

2634.   ———.   La strvctvre du ver a soye,
et de la formation du poulet dans l'oeuf ...
Addressées en forme de lettre à l'Academie
Royale d'Angleterre ... mises en François
... Paris: M. Villery, 1686.
    2 ℓ., 384 p., 6 ℓ.   illus.

2635.   MANDEVILLE, Bernard.   A treatise
of the hypochondriack and hysterick diseases.
In three dialogues. The second edition: corrected and enlarged by the author. London:
for J. Tonson, 1730.
    xxii p., 5 ℓ., 380 p.

2636.   MANGET, Jean Jacques.   Bibliotheca
chemica curiosa, seu Rerum ad alchemiam
pertinentium thesaurus instructissimus ...
Genevæ: Chouet ..., 1702.
    2 v.   illus., port.

2637.   ———.   Bibliotheca chemico-curiosa
... Das ist: Kern und Stern der vornehmsten
chymischphilosophischen Schrifften ... heraus
gegeben durch Conrad Horlachern ... Franckfurt: W. Michahelles und J. Adolph, 1707.
    20 ℓ., 422 p., 12 ℓ.

2638.   ———.   Bibliotheca chirurgica, sive
Rerum ad artem machaonicam quoquô modô
spectantium thesaurus absolutissimus ...
Genevæ: G. de Tournes, 1721.
    4 v.

2639.   ———.   Bibliotheca pharmaceutico-

medica, seu Rerum ad pharmaciam galenico-
chemicam spectantium thesaurus refertis-
simus ... Genevæ: Chouet ..., 1703.
2 v. illus.

2640. MANGOLD, Christoph Andreas.
Chymische Erfahrungen und Vortheile in Bereitung einiger sehr bewährter Arzeneymittel,
nebst verschiedenen physicalischen Anmerkungen ... Erfurt: J.H. Nonne, 1748.
3 *l.*, 34 p.

2641. MANLIIS, Joannes Jacobus de, de
Bosco. Liber perutilis: qui luminare maius
dicitur ... nouiter impressus. Cinthius vt
totum radijs illuminat orbem. Illuminat
latebras sic medicina tuas. [Lugduni: J.
Moylin alias Cambray, 1503.]
cxxiiii numb. *l.*, 8 *l.*, xlvi numb. *l.*, 3 *l.*

2642. ———. Luminare maius. Cinthius vt
totum radijs illuminat orbem. Illuminat latebras sic medicina tuas. Lumen apothecariorum. Thesaurus aromatariorum. [Venetus:
sumptibus heredum O. Scotus, per B. Locatel-
luz, 1506.]
77 numb. *l.*, 2 *l.*, 66 numb. *l.*, 1 *l.*

2643. ———. Luminare maius ... Lumen
apothecarioru admoduz vtilis. Item thesaurus
aromatariorum non minus vtilis ... Cinthius
vt totum radijs illuminat orbem. Illuminat
latebras sic medicina tuas. [Lugduni: J.
Moylin als de Cambray, 1525.]
cxix numb. *l.*, 1 *l.*, lv numb. *l.*

2644. ———. Lvminare maivs omnibvs cvm
medicis, tvm aromatariis pernecessarium ...
Appositi etiam sunt duo illi libri aromatariis
familiarissimi, Lvmen apothecariorvm, &
Aromatariorvm thesavrvs. Venetiis: I. Gryphivs, 1553.
8 *l.*, 155 numb. *l.*, 2 *l.*

2645. MANNE, Louis Francois. Observation de chirurgie, au sujet d'un polipe ex-
traordinaire ... Avignon: A. Giroud, 1747.
4 *l.*, 95 p. illus.

2646. MAPLET, John. Epistolarum medicarum specimen de thermarum Bathoniensium
effectis ... Edente Thoma Guidott. Londini:
typis F. Leach, impensis editoris, 1694.
3 *l.*, 39 p.

2647. MARABELLI, Franz. Chemische Untersuchung der neuerlich bekannt gewordenen
gelben Peruvianischen Rinde ... Aus dem
Italienischen übersetzet, und mit Anmerkungen herausgegeben von Salomo Constantin

Titius. Leipzig: H.G. Feind, 1797.
3 *l.*, 120 p.

2648. MARAT, Jean Paul. Recherches
physiques sur le feu. Paris: C.A. Jombert,
1780.
2 *l.*, 202 p., 1 *l.*

2649. MARBODE, *bp. of Rennes.* De gemmarum lapidumque pretiosorum formis,
naturis, atque uiribus ... Coloniæ: H. Alo-
pecius, 1539.
124 numb. *l.*, 2 *l.*

2650. MARCHETTI, Domenico de. Anatomia:
cui responsiones ad Riolanum ... in ipsius
animadversionibus contra Veslingium additæ
sunt. Editio altera Patavina correctior. Har-
devici: ex offininâ Societates Typographicæ,
1656.
8 *l.*, 289 p., 1 *l.*

2651. MARENGUS, Joannes Baptista.
Palladis chymicæ arcana detecta, siuè
Mineralogia naturalis & artificialis ... Auctoris nomen in hoc puro anagrammate delite-
scit Ianus Gobrat sapiens manes. Genvæ:
A.G. Franchelli, 1674.
285 p., 1 *l.*

2652. ———. ———. Secvnda editio. In multis praxeis aucta, in omnibus clarius explicata, & in duas partes diuisa ... Genvæ:
A.G. Franchelli, 1678.
2 pts. in 1 v.

2653. MARET, Hughes. Mémoire dans
lequel on cherche à déterminer quelle influence les moeurs des Francois ont sur
leur santé ... Amiens: la veuve Godard, 1772.
3 *l.*, 159 p.

2654. ———. Mémoire sur la maniere d'agir
des bains d'eau douce et d'eau de mer et
sur leur usage ... Paris: Ladoué et Racle,
1769.
2 *l.*, vii p., 2 *l.*, 127 p. charts.

2655. MARGGRAF, Andreas Sigismund.
Chymischer Schriften. Berlin: A. Wever, 1761-
1767.
2 v. illus., charts.

2656. ———. ———. Neue verbesserte Auflage.
Berlin: A. Wever, 1768-1767.
2 v. in 1. illus.

2657. MARGGRAV, Christian. Jacob. Le
Mort pseudochemici & rationatoris dupon-
diarii ignorantia circa chemiam & universam

scientiam naturalem detecta ... Lugduni
Batavorum: P. de Graaf, 1687.
    6 ℓ., 97 p.

2658. MARIMPOEY, Paul. Apperçu sur
quelques-uns des avantages que la medecine peut retirer de la chimie végétale.
Dissertation présentée à l'Ecole de Médecine de Montpellier ... Montpellier: Fon-
tenay-Picot [1798].
    37 p., 1 ℓ.

2659. MARINI, Giuseppe. Breve tesoro
alchimistico de più valorosi alchimisti
moderni d'Europa ... Venetia: C. Bortoli,
1664.
    89 p.

2660. MARINO, Giovanni Antonio. Delle
acque termali de Vinadio usate in bevanda,
bagno, doccia, stufa, fango, muffe, ec.
commentario ... Torino: Mairesse, 1775.
    1 ℓ., xii, 200 p.   charts.

2661. MÄRKER, G. Allgemeine Abbildung
der ganzen Schöpfung oder Genealogie der
dreifachen Welt ... von Philotheus de Limitibus. Aus dem Lateinischen übersezt und mit
Anmerkungen begleitet von J.J. Grienstein.
Erstes Werkchen. Philadelphia [i.e. Wien]:
1792.
    8 ℓ., 172 p.   illus.

2662. ——. Das Hermetische Triklinium
oder Drei Gespräche vom Stein der Weisen
von Philotheus de Limitibus. Aus dem Lateinischen übersezt und mit Anmerkung begleitet
von J.J. Grienstein. Zweites Werkchen.
Philadelphia [i.e. Wien]: 1792.
    8 ℓ., 172 p., 1 ℓ.   illus.
    With his Allgemeine Abbildung ... 1792,
as issued.

    MAROT, Claude Toussaint, comte de
La Garaye. See La Garaye, Claude Toussaint Marot, comte de.

2663. MARS, pseud. Philosophisches
Bedencken von dem kalten Feuer, oder wun-
derbahrlichen Alkahest, sive Menstruo
philosophorum atque universali azoth ...
Franckfurt am Mayn: G.H. Dehrling, 1708.
    28 p.
    With Siebenstern, C.F.S. von, Practica ...
1721.

2664. MARSCIANO, Franciscus Onuphrius
de. Lux Hermetica clarificata, seu Circulus
quadratus sapientum, opus Hermeticum de
vero, ac probato lapide philosophico ...

[Wien?] J.F. Kleinmayr, 1742.
    284 p., 2 ℓ.   illus.

2665. MARSIGNY, Jean Charles de. Traitté
des elemens chymiques, ov est donné aux
cvrievx de l'art, la connoissance des sels,
dissoluans, menstruës, fondans & precipi-
tans ... Rouen: L. Cabut, 1671.
    3 ℓ., 116 p.

2666. MARSONNAT, abbé de. Analyse des
eaux minérales de Charbonniere dites de
Laval. [n.p.: 1784?]
    28 ℓ.
    Lacking the title page. Caption title.

2667. MARTEAU, Pierre Antoine. Traité
de l'analyse des eaux minérales, ou Mémoire sur des deux questions, proposées
par l'Académie-Royale des Belles-Lettres,
Sciences & Arts de Bordeaux: Quelle-est
la meilleure manière d'analyser les eaux
minérales? et l'analyse suffit-elle seule
pour pouvoir en déterminer la vertu et les
propriétés? ... Bourdeaux: M. Racle, 1777.
    74 p.

2668. MARTELLI, Giandomenico. Delle
acque Caje ovvero de' bagni di Viterbo opera
fisico-medica ... Roma: M. Pagliarini, 1777.
    xii, 92 p.   illus.

2669. MARTIN, Benjamin. The description
and use of a new, portable, table air-pump
and condensing engine ... London: the author,
1766.
    1 ℓ., ii, 38 p.   illus.

    MARTIN, Roland. Plantæ Martino-
Burserianae explicantur. See Linné, C. von,
praeses. Entry 2433.

2670. MARTINE, George. Dissertations
sur la chaleur avec des observations nouvelles
sur la construction et comparaison des thermométres ... Traduites de l'Anglois ... Paris:
J.-T. Herissant, 1751.
    xvi, 381 p., 1 ℓ.

2671. ——. Essais sur la construction et
comparaison des thermometres, sur la communication de la chaleur & sur les différens
degrés de la chaleur des corps. Traduit de
l'Anglois ... Paris: Durand et Pissot, 1751.
    3 ℓ., 224 p.   chart.

2672. MARTÍNEZ, Martin. Anatomia compendiosa, y noches anatomicas ... Madrid:
L.A. de Bedmar, 1717.
    6 ℓ., 78, 95 p., 4 ℓ.

MARTIUS, Johann Nikolaus. Dissertatio academica de philosophia hermetica. *See* Kiesling, Johann, *praeses.*

2673. MASCAGNI, Paolo. Vasorum lymphaticorum corporis humani historia et ichnographia. Senis: P. Carli, 1787.
2 *l.*, 138 p., 41 *l.* illus., folio.

——, *jt. auth.* Geschichte und Beschreibung der Saugadern des menschlichen Körpers. *See* Cruikshank, William.

2674. MASSA, Niccolò. Liber de febre pestilentiali, ac de pestichiis, morbillis, variolis, & apostematibus pestilentialibus, nunc primum in lucem editus ... [Venetiis: F. Bindonus, & M. Pasinus] 1540.
76 *l.*

2675. MASSAC, Raymond de. Pvgeae, seu De lymphis pugeacis libri duo. Editio secvnda. Parisiis: T. du Bray [ca. 1600?].
48 p.

2676. MASSARIA, Alexander. Practica medica. In qua methodus accuratissima traditur, & cognoscendi, & rectissimè curandi omnes humani corporis morbos, ad verissimam Hippoc. & Galen. mentem admirabili arte instituta ... additus est liber Responsorvm, & consvltationvm medicinalium eiusdem auctoris ... Venetiis: I.A. Iulianus, 1622.
14 *l.*, 500 p., 2 *l.*, 51, 48 p.

2677. MASSIMI, Lorenzo. Dell' acqua salubre e bagni di Nocera. Roma: G. Zempel, 1774.
xii, 118 p.

2678. MATHEWS, Richard. The vnlearned alchymist his antidote. Or, A more full and ample explanation of the use, vertue and benefit of my pill ... London: for J. Leigh ..., 1660.
7 *l.*, 143 p.

2679. ——. ——. Together with A precious pearl in the midst of a dunghill, being a true and faithful receit of Mr. Richard Mathers's pill ... presented to the world by Mris. Anne Mathews ... London: for J. Leigh, 1663.
2 pts. in 1 v.

2680. MATHIEU, Charles Léopold. Nouveau système de l'univers, ou Abrégé philosophique de la physique et de la chymie ... Paris: Janet & Croulebois, 1796.
xvi, 202 p. illus., charts.

2681. MATTE-LA FAVEUR, Sebastien. Pratiqve de chymie, divisée en quatre parties ... Avec un avis sur les eaux minerales. Montpelier: D. Pech, 1671.
7 *l.*, 360, 10 p., 17 *l.* illus.

2682. MATTIOLI, Pietro Andrea. Apologia adversvs Amathvm Lvsitanvm, cvm censvra in eiusdem enarrationes. Et: Epistolarum medicinalium libri V. Item Dialogus de morbo gallico. Francofvrti: N. Bassaeus, 1598.
236 p., 3 *l.*

2683. ——. Commentarii, in libros sex Pedacii Dioscoridis Anazarbei, De medica materia ... Venetiis: in officina Erasmiana, apud V. Valgrisium, 1554.
24 *l.*, 707 p. illus.

2684. ——. ——. Venetiis: Valgrisius, 1565.
86 *l.*, 1459 p., 6 *l.* illus., port.

2685. ——. Les commentaires ... svr les six livres de la matiere medecinale de Pedacivs Dioscoride, Anazarbéen. Traduits de Latin en François, par M. Antoine Dv Pinet ... Derniere edition ... Lyon, I.-B. de Ville, 1680.
4 *l.*, xcv p., 7 *l.*, 636 p., 17 *l.* illus., port.

2686. ——. I discorsi di M. Pietro Andrea Matthioli ... nelli sei libri di Pedacio Dioscoride Anazarbeo della materia medicinale ... Venetia: heredi di V. Valgrisi, 1581.
90 *l.*, 971 p., 6 *l.* illus.
Pages 969-970 supplied in manuscript.

2687. ——. Compendivm de plantis omnibus, vnà cum earum iconibus, de quibus scripsit suis in commentariis in Dioscoridem editis ... Accessit ... Opusculum de itinere, quo è Verona in Baldum montem plantarum refertissimum itur ... Francisco Calceolario ... auctore ... Venetiis: Valgrisius, 1571.
8 *l.*, 921 p., 7 *l.* illus.

2688. ——. De plantis epitome vtilissima ... nunc primum diligenter aucta, & locupletata, à D. Ioachimo Camerario ... Accessit ... liber singularus de itinere ab vrbe Verona in Baldum montem plantarum ad rem medicam facientium feracissimum, auctore Francisco Calceolario ... Francofvrti ad Moenvm: 1586.
6 *l.*, 1003 p., 14 *l.* illus.

2689. ——. Del modo di distillare le acqve da tvtte le piante, et come vi si possino conservare i loro veri odori, & sapori. [Venetia:

B. degli Alberti, 1604.]
    6 *l.* illus.
    Separated from his De i discorsi di M.
Pietro Andrea Matthioli nelli sei libri di
Pedacio Dioscoride della materia medicinale
... 1604.

2690. ———. Epistolarum medicinalium
libri quinque. Pragæ: G. Melantrichius,
1561.
    12 *l.*, 395 p. illus., port.

2691. ———. Kreutterbuch ... jetzt widerumb mit viel schönen neuwen Figuren, auch
nützlichen Artzeneyen, und andern guten
stücken, zum andern mal auss sonderm
fleiss gemehret, und verfertigt durch Ioa-
chimum Camerarium ... Franckfort am Mayn:
[gedruckt bey J. Feyrabendt, in verlegung
P. Fischers und H. Dacken Erben] 1590.
    10 *l.*, 460 numb. *l.*, 37 *l.* illus.

2692. ———. New Kreuterbuch mit den
allerschönsten vnd artlichsten Figuren ...
Durch Georgium Handsch ... verdeutscht
... Prag: G. Melantrich vnd V. Valgriss, 1563.
    38 *l.*, 575 numb. *l.* illus., port.

2693. ———. Neu vollkommenes Kräuter-
Buch, von allerhand gewächsen der Bäumen,
Stauden vnd Kräutern ... zum vierten mal ...
aussgefertiget durch ... Ioachimvm Camera-
rivm. Jetzund aber als ein neues Werck ...
von Bernhard Verzascha ... Basel: J.J. Decker
..., 1678.
    4 *l.*, 792 p., 36 *l.* illus.

2694. ———. Opera quæ extant omnia ...
[Francofvrti: N. Bassaeus] 1598.
    59 *l.*, 1027 p., 11 *l.*; 236 p., 3 *l.*
illus., port.

2695. ———. ———. Editio altera. Basileae:
J. König, 1674.
    60 *l.*, 1027 p., 10 *l.*; 236 p., 3 *l.* illus.

2696. ———. Opusculum, de simplicium
medicamentorum facultatibus secundum
locos ... Venetiis: V. Valgrisius, 1569.
    328 p., 2 *l.*
    Lacking all before p. 88.
    With Dioscorides, De materia medica ...
1554.

2697. MATY, Matthew. Essai sur la carac-
tére du grand medecin ou Eloge critique de
Mr. Herman Boerhaave. Cologne: P. Mar-
teaux, 1747.
    xix, 155 p.

2698. MAUGIN DE RICHEBOURG, Jean, *ed.*
Bibliotheque des philosophes chimiques.
Nouvelle edition, revûë, corrigée & aug-
mentée de plusieurs philosophes ... Par Mr.
J.M.D.R. ... Paris: A. Cailleau, 1741-54.
    4 v. illus.

2699. MAUL, Johann Philipp. ‎זות זבת מכד ן‎
sive Medicina theologica chymico irenica
& Christiano-cabbalistica, vorgestellet in
der ersten continuatio curioser und erbau-
licher Gespräche vom Gold von Mitternacht,
oder von der höchsten Medicin ... Wesel:
J. von Wesel, 1713.
    1 v. in 3.

2700. MAUPERTUIS, Pierre Louis Moreau
de. Dissertation physique a l'occasion du
negre blanc ... Leyde: 1744.
    6 *l.*, 132 p.

2701. ———. Venus physique. Septieme
edition, revue & augmentée. Geneve: J.S.
Cailler, 1780.
    4, 171 p.

2702. MAURER, Caspar. Kurtz- und lus-
tiges Tractätlein lehr- und sinnreicher
Fragstücke von natürlichen und andren
nützlichen Sachen ... Nürnberg: M. und J.F.
Endter, 1665.
    1 *l.*, 140 p., 12 *l.*
    With Cardilucius, J., Heilsame artzney
... 1681.

2703. MAURICEAU, François. The disease
of women with child, and in child-bed; as
also, the best means of helping them in
natural and unnatural labours ... The eighth
edition ... translated by Hugh Chamberlen.
London: for T. Cox and J. Clarke, 1752.
    xlii, 375 p., 3 *l.* illus.

2704. MAY, Franz Anton. Stolpertus ein
junger Arzt am Krankenbette. Von einem
patriotischen Pfälzer ... Zweite Auflage.
Mannheim: E.F. Schwan, 1778-1798.
    3 v. in 1.

2705. MAYER, Johann Christoph Andreas.
Anatomische Kupfertafeln nebst dazu ge-
hörigen Erklärungen ... Berlin: G.J. Decker,
H.A. Rottmann, 1783-1794.
    2 v. illus.

2706. MAYER, Martin. Kurtze Beschreibung
dess Egerischen Schleder-Sauerbrunnens,
was vor Mineralien derselbe mit sich führe
... Welchen beygefüget ein besonder Tractätlein, von Natur, Krafft, Würckung und Gebrauch

dess Egerischen gebräuchlichen Säuerlings,
gestellet durch Paulum Macasium ... Nürnberg: C. Endter, 1667.
    4 *l*., 163 p., 1 *l*.; 3 *l*., 105 p., 1 *l*.

2707. MAYERNE, *Sir* Theodore Turquet de.
Apologia, in qva vidre est inuiolitis Hippocratis & Galeni legibus, remedia chymicè
preparata, tutò vsurpari posse. Ad cvivsdam
anonymi calumnias responsio. Rupellæ:
1603.
    117 p.
    With Duchesne, J., Liber de priscorum
philosophorum ... 1603.

2708. MAYNWARING, Everard. Historia et
mysterium luis venereæ ... Francofurti: J.
Naumann & G. Wolff, 1675.
    176 p.

2709. ———. Ignota febris. Fevers mis-
taken in notion & practice shewing the fre-
quent fatal consequents thereof ... London:
J. Dawks, 1698.
    2 *l*., 157 p.

2710. ———. Medicus absolutus, ἀδέσποτος.
The compleat physitian, qualified and dig-
nified. The rise and progress of physick,
historically, chronologically, and philosoph-
ically illustrated ... London: for the book-
sellers, 1668.
    11 *l*., 169 p., 2 *l*.   port.

2711. ———. The pharmacopoeian physician's repository. Accommodated with elaborate medicinal arcana's ... London: 1669.
    123 p., 2 *l*.
    With his Vita sana & longa ... 1669, as
issued.

2712. ———. Vita sana & longa. The preservation of health, and prolongation of life,
proposed and proved ... London: J.D., 1669.
    4 *l*., 160 p.

2713. MAYOW, John. Chemical experiments and opinions extracted from a work
published in the last century. Oxford: Clarendon press ..., 1790.
    xli, 18 p., 1 *l*., 63 p.   illus.
    Edited by Thomas Beddoes.

2714. ———. Opera omnia medico-physica,
tractatibus quinque comprehensa ... Editio
novissima ... Hagæ-Comitum: A. Leers, 1681.
    4 *l*., 416 p., 12 *l*.   illus., port.

———. Tractatus duo. *In* Thurston, M.,
De respirationis ... 1708.

2715. MAZZELLA, Scipione. Sito, et anti-
chita' della citta di Pozzvolo, e del svo
amenissimo distretto ... Napoli: Stigliola,
1595.
    8 *l*., 291, 37 p., 3 *l*.   illus.

2716. MEAD, Richard. Bibliotheca Meadiana;
sive Catalogus librorum Richardi Mead, M.D.
qui prostabunt venales sub hasta, apud
Samuelem Baker, in vico dicto York Street,
Covent Garden, Londini, die lunæ, 18 Novem-
bris, M.DCC.LIV iterumque die lunæ, 7
Aprilis, M.DCC.LV. ... [London: 1754.]
    2 pts. in 1 v.
    Priced auction catalog.

2717. ———. A mechanical account of poisons in several essays. London: J.R. for R.
South, 1702.
    8 *l*., 175 p.   illus.

2718. ———. ———. London: R.J. for R. Smith,
1702.
    8 *l*., 183 p.   illus.

2719. ———. ———. The third edition, with
large additions. London: for J. Brindley, 1745.
    xlviii, 319 p.   illus.

2720. ———. ———. The fourth edition corrected. London: J. Brindley, 1747.
    xlviii, 320 p.   illus.

2721. ———. Medica sacra; or, A commentary on the most remarkable diseases, mentioned in the holy scriptures. Translated
from the Latin under the author's inspection,
by Thomas Stack. To which are prefixed,
Memoirs of the life and writings of the learned
author. London: for J. Brindley, 1755.
    1 *l*., 49, xxii, 120 p.

2722. ———. Medical precepts and cautions
... Translated from the Latin, under the author's inspection, by Thomas Stack. London:
for J. Brindley, 1751.
    xvi, 311 p.

2723. ———. Avis et préceptes de medecine
... Avec un discours académique, sur les
qualités qui constituent & perfectionnent les
médecins. Par M. Kaau Boerhaage. Traduit par
M de Puisieux. Paris: d'Houry, 1757.
    xi, 406 p., 1 *l*.

2724. ———. Of the power and influence of
the sun and moon on humane bodies; and of
the diseases that rise from thence ... London:
for R. Wellington, 1712.
    xxiii, 88 p.

2725. ———. A short discourse concerning
pestilential contagion, and the methods to
be used to prevent it ... The sixth edition.
London: for S. Buckley and R. Smith, 1720.
    4 *l*., 59 p.

        ———. *See also* Pharmacopoeia
Meadiana.

2726. MEARA, Edmund de. Examen diatribae Thomae Willisii ... De febribus. Cui
accesserunt Historiae aliquot medicae
rariores. Amstelodami: G. Schagen, 1667.
    233 p.

2727. MECKEL, Johann Friedrich. Nova
experimenta et observationes de finibus
venarum ac vasorum lymphaticorum in ductus
visceraque excretoria corporis humani,
ejusdemque structurae utilitate. Berolini: F.
Nicolas, 1772.
    viii, 104 p.

2728. La MÉDECINE pratique de Londres.
Prédédée d'un discours sur la meilleure
méthode de poursuivre les recherches en
médecine, & suivie des Observations sur les
maladies épidémiques de M. James Sims; le
tout traduit de l'Anglois par Mm. J.F. de
Williers & Jaubert. Yverdon: 1779.
    3 v. illus.

        MEDICÆ ARTIS principes ... 1567.
See Estienne, H.

2728a. MEDICAL EXTRACTS: on the nature of
health, with practical observations: and the
laws of the nervous and fibrous systems ...
A new edition ... London: for J. Johnson ...,
1796-1797.
    4 v.

2729. MEDICAL MUSEUM; or, A repository
of cases, experiments, researches, and discoveries, collected at home and abroad. In
anatomy, medicine, pharmacy, botany, chemistry, surgery, physiology, &c. By gentlemen
of the faculty. London: W. Richardson and S.
Clark, 1763-1764.
    3 v. illus.

2730. MEDICES, Christian de, *Freyherr von
Scharfenstein, pseud.* Concursus philosophorum, das ist Gründlichwahrhafftig- und
einfältige Beschreibung und philosophische
'Zusammenstimmung, welcher gestalt die
lieben Alten das grosse Geheimnüss vom
Stein der Weisen zu Wercke gerichtet und
hinterlassen ... zum öffentlichen Druck befördert durch Lt. Johanne Friederico Brebis

... Jena: J. Bielcken, 1706.
    7 *l*., 768 p.

2731. MEDICINA FLAGELLATA: or, The doctor scarify'd ... With an essay on health, or
the power of a regimen ... The second edition. London: for W. Meadows, 1727.
    xiv, 214 p.

2732. Il MEDICINAL TESORO di poveri,
raccolti, & esperimentati da diuersi eccel-
lentissimi medici d'Italia. Bologna [n.d.].
    4 *l*.

2733. MEDICINISCH-chymisch- und al-
chemistisches Oraculum darinnen man nicht
nur alle Zeichen und Abkürzungen welche so
wohl in den Recepten und Büchern der Aerzte
und Apotheker als auch in den Schrifften der
Chemisten und Alchemisten vorkommen findet
sondern deme auch ein sehr rares chymisches
Manuscript eines gewissen Reichs*** beygefüget. Ulm: Gaum, 1755.
    3 *l*., 72 p.

2734. ———. Neue Auflage, nebst einem
Auszug aus einem Briefe eines grossen Al-
chemisten an einen Unglaubigen. Ulm:
Stettin, 1782.
    3 *l*., 74 p.

2735. MEIBOMIUS, Brandanus, *praeses.*
Dissertatio inavgvralis chymico-medica
de arsenico ... avctor Jacobvs Lvdovici ...
Helmstadii: P.D. Schnorr [1729].
    28 *l*.

2736. MEISNER, Leonhart Ferdinand. De
caffe, chocolatae, herbae thee ac nicotianae
natura, usu, et abusu anacrisis, medico-
historico-diaetetica. Norimbergae: J.F.
Rudiger, 1721.
    1 *l*., 124 p. illus.

        MELAMPUS. Traicté des marques
naturelles du corps. *In* Cardano, G., La
metoposcopie ... 1658.

2737. MELICH, Georg. Dispensatorivm
medicvm sive De recta medicamentorvm ...
Cvi adiectvm est Compendium medicinæ
practicæ Franciscimariæ de Tectoris.
Francofurti: typographeo Paltheniano, 1601.
    12 *l*., 647 p., 47 *l*.

2738. MELVILL, John. Observations on the
nature and properties of fixible air, and on the
salutary effects of the Aqua Salubris, in preserv
ing health ... London: for the author ... [178-].
    1 *l*., ii, 92 p.

2738a. MEMORIE sopra i muli di varii autori ... [Modena: G. Montanari, 1768.]
4 *l.*, lxiii p.

2739. MENGHI, Girolamo. Flagellvm dae-monvm, exorcismos terribiles, potentissimos, et efficaces ... Accessit postremò pars secunda, quæ Fustis dæmonum inscribitur ... Lvgdvni: P. Landry, 1604.
2 pts. in 1 v.

2740. MENNENS, Wilhelm. Avrei velleris sive Sacræ philosophiæ vatvm selectæ ac vnicæ mysteriorvmqve Dei, natvræ, & artis admirabilium, libri tres ... Antverpiæ: vidua & heredes J. Belleri, 1604.
10 *l.*, 178 p.

2741. MENSENRIET. Vrim & thvmim Moysis welches Aaron im Amts-Schildlein getragen Feuer-bleibendes Wasser der Maccabæorum aus dem allgewaltigen grossen Buch der Natur hervor gebracht, und Sonnen-klar an das Tage-Liecht gegeben, durch die ohnbe-kandten Ritter der streitbahren Insul Colchon ... Nürnberg: J.F. Rüdiger, 1737.
96 p.
With Siebenstern, C.F.S. von, Practica ... 1721.

MENZINI, Benedetto. De literatorum hominum invidia. *In* Major, J.D., Genius errans ... 1677.

2742. MERCATOR, Nicolaus. In hydram, hoc est, In prooemium physiologiæ Aristotelis ... Parisiis: J. Albus, 1578.
52 p.

MERCKELL, Johannes Matthaeus. Exercitatio medica sistens ideam praescri-bendarum formularum. *See* Ettmüller, M., *praeses.*

2743. MERCURIALE, Girolamo. De venenis, et morbis venenosis tractatvs locvpletissimi ... Opera Alberti Scheligij ... Venetijs: P. Meietus, 1584.
8 *l.*, 44 numb. *l.*

——. Repugnantia, qua pro Galeno strenuè pugnatur. *In* Guilandini, M., Papyrus ... 1672.

2744. MERCURII zweyfacher Schlangen-stab, das ist: I. Glücks-Ruthe zu Paracelsi chymischem Schatz. II. Menstruum seu sol-vens universale philosophicum, darinnen das Gold sine strepitu, wie Eyss in warmen Wasser zerschmiltzt: samt gantzen philo-

sophischen Process. Ulm: B. Kühn, 1678.
2 *l.*, 112 p.

MERRET, Christopher. An account of freezing. *In* Boyle, R., New experiments touching cold ... 1665, etc.

2745. ——. A short reply to the postscript, etc. of H.S. shewing his many falsities in matters of fact ... London: T.R. for J. Allestry, 1670.
1 *l.*, 43 p.

——. *See also* Neri, Antonio, De arte vitraria ... 1668, etc.

2746. MESUE, Joannes, Damascenus. Mesue cum expositione Mondini super canones vniuersales ac etiā cum expositiōe Christophori de Honestis in antidotarium eiusdem. Additiones Petri Apponi. Additiōes Francisci de Pedemontiū. Antidotarium Nicolai cum expositione Platearii. Tractatus quid pro quo. Tractatus de sinonimis. Libel-lus Bulcasis sive Seruitoris ... Cōpendiū aromatariorū Saladini. Joannes de Sancto Amando super antidotarium Nicolai. [Venetijs: J. & G. de Gregorius, 1497.]
360 numb. *l.*

2747. ——. ——. [Lugdunen: G. de Villiers, sumptibus V. de Portonariis de Tridino, 1519.]
cccxxvii numb. *l.*, 7 *l.*

2748. ——. Opera ... nō pauca artis medicæ ... complectētia ... [n.p.] 1541.
335 numb. *l.*

2749. ——. Opera ... libri duo ... Atque item Ioannis Costæi annotationes ... Venetiis: [Ivntas] 1589.
2 v. in 1. illus.

2750. ——. Opus quibuslibet aromatariis necessariū. Mesue in uulgare rescripto. [Venice?: 1500?]
34 *l.*

2751. METALLIQUE. De la transformation metalliqve, trois anciens tractez en rithme Françoise. Ascavoir, La fontaine des amoureux de science: autheur I. de la Fontaine. Les remonstrances de nature à l'alchymist errant ... par I. de Meung ... Le sommaire philo-sophique de N. Flamel ... Paris: G. Guillard & A. Warancore, 1561.
4 *l.*, 75 p.

METALLISCHER Baumgarten. *See* Sie-benstern, Christian Friedrich Sendimir von.

2752. METTERNICH, Wolf, *freiherr von.*
Glückliche Erober- und Demolirung des
durch den Schall einer thönernen Elias-
Posaune, auf Befehl eines chymischen Pabsts
angekündigten Fegefeuers der Scheidekunst,
sampt den übrigen auf der Insul Schmäheland
aufgerichteten Schantzen. Oder Kurtze Wie-
derlegung des von einem Anonymo ... herausgegebenen schmähsüchtigen Teutschen Fegefeuers der Scheidekunst, aufgesetzet
durch Alethophilum. Leipzig: C.C. Neuen-
hahn, 1705.
    142 p. illus.
    With Siebenstern, C.F.S. von, Practica
... 1721.

2753. MEUDER, Ernst Peter. Analysis
antimonii physico-chymico-rationalis, darinn
des Grund aller gewöhnlichen und bekandten
Processe dieses Mineralis deutlich gezeiget
wird. Deme auf Verlangen noch beygefüget
ist des Autoris ohnlängst-edirtes Tractätgen:
Von den antimonialischen Tincturen, hin und
wieder revidirt und vermehrt. Dressden: G.
C. Hilscher, 1738.
    239 p.

——. Analyse raisonée de l'anti-
moine. *In* Rothe, G., Introduction a la chymie
... 1741.

2754. MEURDRAC, Marie. La chymie
charitable et facile, en faveur des dames.
Par Damoiselle M.M. Seconde edition. Paris:
J. d'Houry, 1674.
    12 *l.*, 334 p.

2755. ——. ——. Troisième edition.
Réveüe & augmentée de plusieurs préparations nouvelles & curieuses. Paris: L.
d'Houry, 1687.
    6 *l.*, 404, 6 p. chart.
    Lacking pp. 315-16, 337-38, 345-48, 351-
52, 383-84.

2756. MEY, Johann de. Sacra physiologia,
sive Expositio locorum sacræ scripturæ, in
quibus agitur de rebus naturalibus ... Editio
tertia, prioribus auctior atque emendatior.
Medioburgi Zeland: J. Fierensius, 1661.
    7 *l.*, 528 p.; pp. 225-293, 8 *l.* port.

2757. MEYER, Friedrich Albrecht Anton.
Beyträge zur Geschichte der Angustura-Rinde
... Göttingen: J.C. Dieterich, 1793.
    71 p.

2758. MEYER, Johann Friedrich. Alchymistische Briefe ... Hannover: H.E.C. Schlüter,
1767.

61 p., 1 *l.*

2759. ——. Lettres alchymiques ... a M.
André ... Mises en François par le traducteur
des Essais de chymie sur la chaux vive, &c.
... Paris: C. Herissant, 1767.
    xxviii, 76 p., 2 *l.*

2760. MEYRICK, William. The new family
herbal; or, domestic physician: enumerating
... all the known vegetables which are any
way remarkable for medical efficacy; with
an account of their virtues in the several
diseases incident to the human frame ...
Birmingham: printed by T. Pearson, sold by
R. Baldwin, 1790.
    xxiv, 498 p. illus.

2761. MICHEL. Nouvelles observations
sur le pouls, par rapport aux crises ... Paris:
De Bure, 1757.
    xxxiv, 118 p., 1 *l.*
    With Durade, J.C., Traite physiologique
... 1767.

2762. MICHELSPACHER, Steffan, *supposed
author.* Cabala, speculum artis et natvræ,
in alchymia ... Nunc è Germanico, Latino
versa à strenuo sapientiæ culture ...
Aug.: typis C. Schmidt, sumptibus I. Weh,
1667.
    7 *l.* illus.

2763. ——, *supposed author.* Cabala,
Spiegel der Kunst vnnd Natur: in Alchymia ...
Durch einen vnbekandten, doch genandten,
wie ihm das Signet in diser ersten Figur
zeugknuss gibt. Augspurg: gedruckt bey J.
Schultes, in verlegung S. Müschelspachern,
1615.
    7 *l.* illus.
    Lacking folding plates 3 and 4.

2764. MICROCOSMISCHE VORSPIELE des
neuen Himmels und der neuen Erde ... von
einem Liebhaber göttlicher und natürlicher
Geheimnisse. Andere von dem Autore selbst
verbesserte Edition. Amsterdam: 1744.
    7 *l.*, 128 p. illus.

2765. MIDGLEY, Robert. A new treatise of
natural philosophy, free'd from the intracacies
of the schools ... London: R.E. for J. Hindmarsh, 1687.
    6 *l.*, 342 p., 2 *l.*

2766. MILIONI, Pietro. Vago fioretto di
secretini, da praticarsi da persone cvriose
... Roma: P. Nestli [n.d.].
    4 *l.*

2767. MILLAR, John. Observations on the prevailing diseases in Great Britain: together with a review of the history of those of former periods, and in other countries. London: for T. Cadell and T. Noteman, 1770.
vi, 385 p.

2768. MILLER, Joseph. Botanicum officinale; or A compendious herbal giving an account of all such plants as are now used in the practice of physick ... London: for E. Bell ..., 1722.
4 *l*., 466 p., 11 *l*.

2769. MINARDI, Ventura. De balneis Calderii, in Agro Veronensi ... eorumque antiquitate, ac multiplici virtute ... monopanton ... Addito etiam compendio eiusdam, vernacula lingua ... Venetiis: 1571.
136, 68 numb. *l*.

2770. ——. ——. Venetiis: typographis nova Rubeana, 1689.
18 *l*., 206 p., 2 *l*.; 4 *l*., 81 p.
The second part is misbound before the first.

2771. MINDERER, Raymund. Aloedarivm marocostinvm. Augustæ Vindelicorum: [C. Mangius] 1616.
13 *l*., 235 p., 3 *l*.

2772. ——. —— cum dispensatorio particulari, sev propriarvm compositionvm cvstode ... Augustæ Vindelicorum: typis J. Prætorii, sumptibus S. Mylii, 1626.
17 *l*., 308 p., 4 *l*.; 53 p.

2773. ——. De calcantho sev vitriolo, eivsqve qvalitate, virtvte, ac viribvs, nec non medicinis ex eo parandis, disqvisitio iatrochymica ... Augustæ Vindelicorum: S. Mangin vidua, 1617.
1 *l*., 22, 113 p., 2 *l*.

2774. ——. De pestilentia liber vnus vetervm et neotericorum obseruatione constans ... Cvrae secvndae. [Augsburg: A. Aperger] 1619.
8 *l*., 402 p., 15 *l*.; 47 *l*.

2775. ——. Pharmacopoliolum campestre et itinerarium, oder Feld- und Reise-Apothecklein, begreiffend das vor diesem von Hn. D. Minderer für die Soldaten gestelltes vortreffliches Kriegs-Artzney-Büchlein ... vermehret und abermal ausgefertiget ... von Johanne Hiskia Cardilucio ... Nürnberg: W. M. Endter und J.A. Endters Söhnen, 1679.
18 *l*., 467 p., 28 *l*.

2776. ——. Threnodia medica sev Planctvs medicinæ lugentis ... [Augustæ Vindelicorum: A. Aperger] 1619.
24 *l*., 597 p., 9 *l*.

2777. MIRABILIA PUTEOLORUM. Libellus de mirabilibus ciuitatis Putheolorum et locorum vicinorum: ac de nominibus virtutibusque balneorum ibidem existentium ... Neapolis: A. de Bruxella, 1475.
44 *l*.

2778. MIRIAM, *the prophetess*. Die murrende aussätzige Mirjam wider Mosen ... Franckfurth: 1708.
39 p. illus.

Le MIROIR des alchimistes. *See* Bombaste, *comte de*, Le trompette François ... 1609.

2779. MISCELLANEA CHYMIÆ et metallvrgiæ, oder: Hundert und fünf und funfzig wahre Experimenta, aus denen hinterlassenen Schriften eines berühmten Chymici ... Hof: J.G. Vierling, 1766.
2 *l*., 152 p. illus.
The *Vorrede* misbound between pages 148-149.

2780. MIZAULD, Antoine. Alexikepvs sev Avxiliaris et medicvs hortvs, rervm variarvm, et secretorum remediorum accessione locupletatus. Coloniae: I. Gymnicus, 1576.
12 *l*., 200 p.
With his Historia hortensivm ... 1577.

2781. ——. Artificiosa methodvs comparandorvm hortensivm frvctvvm, olervm, radicvm ... quæ corpus clementer purgent, & varijs morbis ... blandè succurrant. Coloniae Agrippinae: I. Gymnicus, 1577.
8 *l*., 76 p.
With his Historia hortensivm ... 1577.

2782. ——. Historia hortensivm qvatvor opvscvlis methodicis contexta ... Coloniae Agrippinae: I. Gymnicus, 1577.
8 *l*., 296 p.

2783. ——. Memorabilivm, sive arcanorvm omnis generis, per aphorismos digestorum, centuriæ IX. Et Democritvs Abderita, De rebus naturalibus, & mysticis. Cum Synesii et Pelagii commentarijs, interprete de lingua Græca, Dominico Pizimentio Vibonensi ... Coloniæ: J. Birckmann, 1574.
41 *l*., 245 numb. *l*.

2784. ——. Memorabilivm aliqvot natvræ

arcanorvm silvvla, rerum variarum sympathias, & antipathias, seu naturales concordias & discordias, libellis duobus complectens. Francofvrti: I. Wechelus & P. Fischerus, 1592.
88 p.

2785. MODEL, Johann Georg. Chymische Nebenstunden ... St. Petersburg: Kaiserl. Akademie der Wissenschaften [n.d.].
11 ℓ., 326 p.

2786. ———. Fortsetzung seiner Chymischen Neben-Stunden ... St. Petersburg: Kayserl. Academie der Wissenschaften, 1768.
7 ℓ., 96 p.
With his Chymische Nebenstunden ... [n.d.].

2787. ———. Versuche und Gedanken über ein natürliches oder gewachsenes Salmiak ... Leipzig: J.F. Gleditsch, 1758.
8 ℓ., 64 p.

2788. The MODERN PRACTICE of the London hospitals ... London: J. Coote and W. Nicoll, 1764.
1 ℓ., vi, 255 p.

2789 MODO FACILE da difendersi dal gran freddo, con niuna, ò pochissima spesa ... Milano: P. Malatesta [n.d.].
4 ℓ.

2790. MOEBIUS, Gottfried. Neu- angezündt- hell-brennendes Feuer, oder Mercurial-Liecht, so denen verzagten Alchymisten aufs neue widerum angezündet wird, von einem wohl-bekandten, doch ungenanten Freund ... Augspurg: J. Koppmayer, 1680.
6 ℓ., 33 p.

2791. ———. Synopses epitomes institutionum medicinæ in gratiam tironum concinnatæ. Jenæ: S. Krebs, 1662.
33 numb. ℓ.
With Queitsch, A.P., Ιατρομαθηματολραφία ... 1737.

MOETIG, Gottlieb Friedrich. De risus. See Alberti, M., praeses.

2792. MOFFETT, Thomas. De ivre et præstania chymicorvm medicamentorvm dialogus apologeticus. Accesservnt etiam Epistolæ quædam medicinales ad medicos aliquot conscriptæ. Francofvrti: hæredes A. Wecheli, 1584.
111 p.
With Wittestein, K., Disceptatio... [1583].

2793. ———. Health's improvement: or, Rules comprizing and discovering the nature, method, and manner of preparing all sorts of food used in this nation ... Corrected and enlarged by Christopher Bennet ... London: T. Newcomb for S. Thomson, 1655.
3 ℓ., 296 p.

MOHAMMED RHASIS. See Muhammad ibn Zakarīyā Abū Bakr, al-Rāzī.

2794. MÖHSEN, Johann Karl Wilhelm. Verzeichnis einer Samlung von Bildnissen, gröstentheils berühmter Aerzte ... zur Geschichte der Arzeneygelahrtheit als vornehmlich zur Geschichte der Künste gehören. Berlin: F.W. Birnstiel, 1771.
6 ℓ., 243 p.; 1 ℓ., 240 p.

2795. MOISES, Hugh. A treatise on the blood, or, General arrangement of many important facts relative to the vital fluid ... London: for T. Evans and J. Stead [n.d.].
4 ℓ., xx, 270 p.

2796. MOJON, Bendetto. Pharmacopoea manualis reformata ... Genuæ: Repettus, 1784.
xxxvi, 240 p., 1 ℓ.

2797. MOLWIZ, Fr. Pharmacopoea exquisita ad observationes recentiores accommodata et principiis simplicissimis superstructa. Formulis tabulisque adjectis. Stuttgardiæ: Erhard, 1798.
3 ℓ., 138 p.

2798. MONARDES, Nicolas. De simplicibvs medicamentis ex Occidentali India delatis, qvorvm in medicina vsvs est ... Interprete Carolo Clvsio. Antverpiæ: C. Plantin, 1574.
88 p., 4 ℓ. illus.
With Orta, Garcia de, Aromatvm ... 1574.

2799. ———. ———. Altera editio. Antverpiæ: C. Plantin, 1579.
84 p., 2 ℓ. illus.
With Orta, Garcia de, Aromatvm ... 1579.

2800. ———. Simplicivm medicamentorvm ex novo orbe delatorvm, qvorvm in medicina vsvs est, historia ... Latio deinde donata, & annotationibus ... à Carolo Clvsio ... Altera editio. Antverpiæ: C. Plantin, 1579-1582.
2 pts. in 1 v. illus.
With Orta, G. de, Aromatvm ... 1579.

2801. ———. ———. Tertia editio ... Antverpiæ: ex officina Plantiniana, apud viduam &

I. Moretum, 1593.
   2 pts. in 1 v.   illus.
   With Orta, G. de, Aromatvm ... 1593.

      ——. Della historia de i semplici,
aromati, et altre cose. *In* Orta, G. de, Due
libri dell'historia de i semplici ... 1576, etc.

2802.   ——. Della cose che vengono portate dall'Indie Occidentali pertinenti all'uso
della medicina ... Nouamente recata dalla
Spagnola ... Venetia: G. Ziletti, 1575.
   2 v. in 1.   illus.

      ——. ——. *In* Orta, G. de, Due
libri ... 1582.

2803.   ——. Dos libros. El vno trata de
todas las cosas q̄ traē de nr̄as Indias Occi-
dētales, que siruen al vso de medicina ...
El otro libro, trata de dos medicinas ... la
piedra bezaar, y la yerua escuerconera ...
Seuilla: S. Trugillo, 1565.
   131 *l.*

      ——. Histoire des simples medi-
camens apportés de l'Amerique. *In* Orta, G.
de, Histoire des drogues ... 1602, etc.

2804.   ——. Ioyfvll nevves ovt of the newe
founde worlde, wherein is declared the rare
and singuler vertues of diuerse and sundrie
herbes, trees, oyles, plantes, and stones,
with their aplications, as well for physicke
as chirurgerie ... Englished by Jhon Frampton
... London: W. Norton, 1577.
   109 numb. *l.*   illus.

2805.   ——. ——. Newly corrected as by
conference with the olde copies may appeare.
Whereunto are added three other bookes ...
London: W. Norton, 1580.
   181 numb. *l.*   illus.

2806.   ——. ——. London: E. Allde, by the
assigne of B. Norton, 1596.
   187 numb. *l.*   illus.

2807.   ——. Primera y segvnda y tercera
partes de la historia medicinal de las cosas
que se traen de nuestras Indias Occidentales
que siruen en medicina. Tratado de la piedra
bezaar ... Dialogo de las grandezas del hierro
... Tratado de la nieve ... Sevilla: A. Escriuano, 1574.
   6 *l.*, 206 numb. *l.*, 1 *l.*   illus.

2808.   ——. Segvnda parte del libro, de
las cosas qve se traen de nuestras Indias
Occidentales, que siruen al vso de medicina

... Va añedido vn libro de la nieue ... Seuilla:
A. Escriuano, 1571.
   131, 48 numb. *l.*   illus.

   MONDENSTEIN, F.C.P.H. *See* Hanstein, Philipp Heinrich, *baron* von.

2809. MONGINOT, François de. A new
mystery in physick discovered, by curing
of fevers & agues by quinquina or Jesuites
powder. Translated from the French, by Dr.
Belon, with additions. London: for W. Crook,
1681.
   30 *l.*, 99 p., 4 *l.*

2810. MONNET, Antoine Grimoald. Démonstration de la fausseté des principes des
nouveaux chymistes. Pour servir de supplément au Traité de la dissolution des métaux
... Paris: H.J. Jansen [1798].
   395 p.

2811. ——. Exposition des mines, ou
Description de la nature et de la qualité
des mines ... Londres: P.F. Didot le jeune
et Edme, 1772.
   xii, 396 p.

2812. ——. Nouvelle hydrologie, ou Nouvelle exposition de la nature et de la qualité
des eaux ... ou l'on joint une description
des sels naturels. Londres et Paris: P.F. Didot
le jeune et Edme, 1772.
   xi, 312 p.

2813. ——. Traité des eaux minerales
avec plusieurs mémoires de chymie relatifs
a cet objet ... Paris: P.F. Didot le jeune,
1768.
   xxxii, 359 p., 4 *l.*

2814. MONRO, Alexander, 1697-1767. The
anatomy of the human bones, nerves, and
lacteal sac and duct. Eighth edition. Edinburgh: for J. Balfour, 1768.
   ix, 410 p.

2815. ——. Traité d'osteologie, traduit de
l'Anglois ... Ou l'on a ajouté des planches
en taille-douce, qui représentent au naturel
tous les os de l'adulte & du foetus, avec leur
explications. Par M. Sue. Paris: G. Cavelier,
1759.
   1 *l.*, xxxii, 317 p.   illus., folio.

2816. ——. An essay on comparative anatomy. London: for J. Nourse, 1744.
   22, 138 p.

2817. ——. The works ... Published by his

son Alexander Monro ... To which is prefixed, the life of the author ... Edinburgh:
for C. Elliot and G. Robinson, 1781.
   2 *l*., xxiv, 791 p. illus., port.

2818. MONRO, Alexander, 1733-1817. A
description of all the bursae mucosae of the
human body; their structure explained, and
compared with that of the capsular ligaments
of the joints ... Edinburgh: 1788.
   60 p. illus., folio.

2819. ——. Observations, anatomical
and physiological, wherein Dr. Hunter's
claim to some discoveries is examined ...
Edinburgh: Hamilton ..., 1758.
   2 *l*., 80 p. illus.

2820. ——. The structure and physiology
of fishes explained, and compared with
those of man and other animals ... Edinburgh: for C. Elliot ..., 1785.
   128 p. illus.

2821. MONRO, Alexander, 1773-1859.
Three treatises on the brain, the eye, and
the ear ... Edinburgh: for Bell ..., 1797.
   viii, 17-263 p. illus.

2822. MONRO, Donald. An essay on the
dropsy and its different species. The third
edition. London: for A. Millar ..., 1765.
   xiv, 272 p.

2823. ——. A treatise on medical and
pharmaceutical chymistry, and the materia
medica: to which is added, an English translation of the new edition of the Pharmacopoeia of the Royal College of Physicians of
London, 1788. In three volumes. London: for
T. Cadell, 1788-1790.
   4 v.

2824. ——. A treatise on mineral waters
... London: D. Wilson ..., 1770.
   2 v.

2825. MONTAGNANA, Bartholomeaus.
Consilia ... Tractatus tres de balneis Pa-
tauinis. De cōpositione et dosi medicinarum.
Antidotarium eiusdem. [Venetiis: sumptib' O.
Scoti, per B. Locatellū, 1497.]
   8 *l*., 388 numb. *l*.

2826. ——. ——. Consilia domini Antonij
Cermisoni Patauini. Tractatus de animali
theria domini Francisci Caballi. [Venetiis:
S. de Luere, 1514.]
   6 *l*., 413 numb. *l*.

2827. MONTAGNANA, Marcus Antonius.
De herpete, phagedæna, gangreana, sphacelo,
& cancro; tum cognoscendis, tum curandis,
tractatio accuratissima. Venetiis: P. Meiettus,
1589.
   8 *l*., 107 numb. *l*.

MONTALBANI, Ovidio. Bibliotheca
botanica. *In* Séguier, J.F., Bibliotheca botanica
... 1760.

MONTANUS, Ludwig Conrad. Gründliche Anweisung. *See* Orvius, Ludwig Conrad.

2828. MONTE, Lodovico. La ghirlandetta
fiorita di varij secreti bellissimi da intendere
per ogni spirito gentile ... Napoli: G. Monti
& C. Zenero, 1634.
   4 *l*.

2829. MONTE HERMETIS, Johann de, *pseud*.
Explicatio centri in trigono centri per som-
nium, das ist: Erlëuterung dess Hermetischen
güldenen Fluss ... auss einem Cabalistischen
Rätzel erkläret und an Tag gegeben ... Ulm:
G.W. Kühn, 1680.
   21 *l*., 78, 83 p., 9 *l*. illus.

2830. MONTE RAPHAIM, Johann de, *pseud*.
Vorbothe der am philosophischen Himmel
hervor-brechenden Morgen-Rothe. Hamburg:
S. Heyl, 1716.
   44 p.

MONTE SYNDER, Johann de. Commentatio de pharmaco catholico. *In* Reconditorium ... 1666.

   ——. ——. *In* Janua patefacta thesauro ... 1678.

2831. ——. Gründliche Einleitung zu allgemeine grossen Medicin, wie selbige aus
allen dreyen Reichen der Natur zu verfertigen,
durch das vortreffliche Universal-Menstruum
... Aus einem zu London gedruckten Lateinischen Exemplar ... ins Teutsche übersetzet
... von einem Jndagatore Artis Benedictæ.
Dressden: G. Leschen, 1727.
   12 *l*., 140 p., 8 *l*.
   With Siebenstern, C.F.S. von, Practica ... 1721

2832. ——. Metamorphosis planetarum,
das ist: Eine wunderbahrliche Verenderung
der Planeten und metallischen Gestalten in
ihr erstes Wesen ... Anietzo wiederumb zum
Druck befördert durch A. Gottlob B. Franckfurt: T. Oehrling, 1684.
   139 p. illus.

2833. ——. ——. Franckfurt am Meyn:
verlegts G.H. Oehrling, druckts G.E. Winckler, 1700.
142 p. illus.

2834. ——. Tractatvs de medicina vniver-
sali, das ist Von der Vniversal Medicin ...
Franckfurt am Mayn: T.M. Götze, 1662.
124 p.

2835. MORE, Henry. Observations upon
Anthroposophia theomagica, and Anima
magica abscondita. By Alazonomastix Philalethes ... Parrhesia [i.e. London]: O. Pullen,
1650.
3 ℓ., 94 p., 2 ℓ.

2836. MOREALI, Giam-Battista. Delle
febbri maligne, e contagiose nuovo sistema
teorico-pratico scoperta fatta nella medicina. In questa nuova edizione aggiuntovi
una ritrattazione dell' autore, e molte altre
cose. Venezia: G. Corona, 1746.
4 ℓ., 360 p.

2837. MORELL, Karl Friedrich. Chemische
Untersuchung einiger der bekanntern und
besuchtern Gesundbrunnen und Bäder der
Schweiz, inbesonders des Cantons Bern ...
Bern: E. Haller, 1788.
11 ℓ., 385 p. illus., chart.

2838. MORESCHINI, Massimo. Analisi
dell' acqua minerale di Rofanello. Jesi:
Bonell, 1784.
vii, 88 p.

2839. MORESCOTTI, Alfonso. Compendivm
medicinæ totivs ... Additis Formulis remediorum Petri Gorræi ... Herbornæ Nassoviorum:
1604.
399 p., 4 ℓ.

2840. MORGAGNI, Giovanni Battista. Adversaria anatomica omnia ... Patavii: J.
Cominus, 1717-1719.
6 pts. in 1 v. illus.

2841. ——. De sedibus, et causis morborum per anatomen indagatis, libri quinque
... Neapoli: ex typographia Simoniana,
sumptibus D. Terres, 1762.
5 v. in 2. port.

2842. ——. The seats and causes of diseases investigated by anatomy ... Translated
from the Latin by Benjamin Alexander. London: for A. Millar ..., 1769.
3 v.

2843. ——. Epistolae anatomicae duae
novas observationes, & animadversiones
complectentes, quibus anatome augetur,
anatomicorum inventorum historia evolvitur
... Lugduni Batavorum: J. á Kerkhem, 1728.
10 ℓ., 308 p., 1 ℓ.

2844. ——. Epistolæ anatomicæ duode-
viginti ad scripta pertinentes celeberrimi
viri Antonii Mariæ Valsalvæ ... Bassani:
Remondini, 1764.
xii, 427 p.

2845. ——. Opera omnia in qvinqve tomos
divisa, quorum operum quae antea, et ubi,
et quae nunc sint edita, praefatio ostendet.
[Venetiis] Remondini, 1764-1765.
5 v. in 2. illus., port., folio.

2846. ——. ——. Lugduni Batavorum: C.
Haak, 1765.
5 v. in 2.

2847. MORGAN, John. Πυοποίεδις, sive
Tentamen medicum de puris confectione ...
Edinburgi: typis Academicis, 1763.
viii, 55 p.

2848. MORHOF, Daniel Georg. De metallorum transmutatione ad ... Joelem Langelottum
... epistola. Hamburgi: ex officina G. Schultzen, apud J. Janssonium à Waesberge, 1673.
168 p.

2849. MORIENUS. De transfuratione metallorvm et occvlta, svmmaqve antiqvorvm
philosophorum medicina, libellvs ... Accessit
huic nunc primum Χρυσορρήμων, siue De arte
chymica, dialogvs ... Hanoviæ ad Moenum:
G. Antonius, 1593.
79 p.

——. See also Caesar, T., Alchimy
Spiegel ... 1613.

2850. MORIN, Claude. La platine, l'or
blanc, ou Le huitieme métal ... Paris: Le
Breton ..., 1758.
xvi, 194 p., 3 ℓ. chart.
Lacking pages v-vi.

2851. MORIN, Jean. Abregé du mécanisme
universel, en discours et questions physique,
... Chartres: J. Roux, 1735.
23 ℓ., 584 p. illus.

2852. MORIN, Jean Baptiste. Nova mvndi svb-
lvnaris anatomia ... Parisiis: N. Du Fossé, 1619.
8 ℓ., 144 p.

2853. MORISON, Thomas. Liber novvs
de metallorvm cavsis et transsvbstantione
... Francofurti: J. Wechel, 1593.
130 p., 1 *l*.

2854. MORLEY, Christopher Love. Collectanea chymica Leydensia, id est, Maëtsiana,
Margraviana, Le Mortiana ... Lugduni Batavorum: apud H. Drummond, sumptibus J.A.
de la Font, 1684.
16 *l*., 506 p., 11 *l*.

2855. ———. ———. Nunc ... plurimis ...
experimentis instructa & aucta ... per
Theodorum Muykens ... Lugduni Batavorum:
C. Boutesteyn & F. Haaring, 1693.
24 *l*., 587 p., 18 *l*.

2856. MORTON, Richard. Opera medica
quibus additi fuere tractatus sequentes I.
Gualt. Harris De morbis acutis infantum.
II. Gul. Cole Novæ hypotheseos ... III. Ejusd.
De secretione animali. IV. Mart. Lister De
morbis chronicis. V. Ejusdem De variolis.
VI. Thomæ Sydenham Processus integri in
morbis fere omnibus curandis ... Genevæ:
Cramer & Perachon, 1696.
var. pag.   port., charts.

2857. ———. Πυρετολογία : seu Exercitationes de morbis universalibus acutis ...
Londini: S. Smith, 1692.
41 *l*., 430 p., 9 *l*. port., charts.

2858. ———. Phthisiologia: or, A treatise
of consumptions. Wherein the difference,
nature, causes, signs, and cure of all sorts
of consumptions are explained ... Translated
from the original. London: S. Smith and B.
Walford, 1694.
5 *l*., 360 p., 8 *l*. port.

2859. MOSCATI, Pietro, *conte*. Neue Beobachtungen und Versuche über das Blut und
über den Ursprung der thierischen Wärme.
Aus dem Italiänischen übersetzt von Carl
Heinrich Köstlin. Stutgart: J.B. Mezler,
1780.
4 *l*., 56 p.

2860. MOSCHENI, Domenico Luigi. De'
bagni di Lucca trattato ... [Lucca: G. Rocchi,
1792.]
xiv p., 1 *l*., 312 p. illus., chart.

2861. MOSCHEROSCH VON WISSELSHEIM,
Johann Anton. Wohlmeinende, treue, und
sehr nützliche Ermahnungen an die Anfänger
in dem tiefsinnigen Studio der hermetischen
Philosophie ... Zum Beschluss folgt eine

kurze Dissertation über die Grundursach der
Electricität ... Nürnberg: G. Bauer, 1765.
4 *l*., 40 p.

2862. MOTHERBY, George. A new medical dictionary; or, General repository of
physic ... The second edition, considerably
enlarged and improved ... London: for J.
Johnson ..., 1785.
[771 p.] illus.

2863. MOULLIN DE MARGUERY. Traité
des eaux minerales nouvellement découvertes au village de Passy, près Paris ...
Paris: F. Barois, 1723.
8 *l*., 415 p., 5 *l*.

2864. MOULTON, Thomas. This is the
myrrour or glasse of helth necessary and
nedefull for euery person to loke in, that
wil kepe their bodye from the syckenesse
of the pestilence ... [London?: ca. 1540?]
50 *l*.
Lacking leaf B₁.

2865. ———. ———. [London: R. Wyer, ca.
1540?]
36 *l*.

2866. MOULTRIE, John. Dissertatio medica
inauguralis, de febre maligna biliosa Amer-
icae ... Edinburgi: R. Flamin, 1749.
2 *l*., 23 p., 4 *l*. illus.

MOUNTAINE, Dydymus, *pseud. See*
Hill, Thomas.

2867. MUHAMMAD IBN ZAKARĪYĀ, Abū Bakr,
al-Rāzī. Almansoris liber nonum cum expositione Sillani. Venetiis: O. Scotus, 1490.
90 *l*.

2868. ———. Diuisiones ... Viaticum Cōstan-
tini monachi. [Lugduni: expēsis V. de Porto-
narijs, per G. de Villiers, 1510.]
lxxxviii numb. *l*., 4 *l*., cii numb. *l*., 2 *l*.

2869. ———. Ob vsvm experientiamque
mvltiplicem, et ob certissimas ex demon-
strationibus logicis indicationes, ad omnes
praeter naturam affectus, atque etiam propter
remediorum uberrimam materiam ... opera
exquisitiora ... Per Gerardvm ... Cremonensem,
Andream Vesalium ... Albanvm Torinum,
latinate donata ... Basileae: H. Petrus [1544].
24 *l*., 590 p.

2870. ———. Opvs medicinae practicae
salvberrimum, antehac nusquam impressum,
Galeatij de Sancta Sophia in nonū tractatum

libri Rhasis ad regem Almansorem, de curatione morborum particularium, huic seculo
accommodatissimum ... Quæ omnia perrara
... & publicanit Georgius Kraut. Haganoe:
V. Kobian, 1533.
   4 ℓ., 125 numb. ℓ.

2871. MÜLLER, Friedrich, von Löwenstein.
Lexicon medico-galeno-chymico-pharma-
ceuticum, oder: Gründliche Erklärung acht-
zehen tausend medicinischer Nahmen ...
Franckfurt am Mayn: 1661.
   4 ℓ., 312 p.

2872. MÜLLER, Gerhard Andreas. Entwurff
eines neuen Lehrgebäudes der natürlichen
Philosophie und der Artzneykunst ... Franckfurt am Mayn: J.G. Garbe, 1752.
   8 ℓ., 288 p.
   With Bernhardt, J.C., Chymische Versuche
... 1755.

2873. ——. Einleitung zu dem Entwurf
einer neuen Methode ... Franckfurt am Mayn:
J.G. Garbe, 1754.
   6 ℓ., 211 p.
   With Bernhardt, J.C., Chymische Versuche
... 1755.

2874. ——, praeses. Dissertatio medico-
chemica inavgvralis de oleis essentialibvs
sive aethereis vegetabilivm, absqve destil-
latione parandis ... Avctor responsvrvs, Ioh.
Cornelivs Fridericvs Schweizer. Gissæ:
Braun [1756].
   2 ℓ., 36 p.

2875. MÜLLER, Johann Elias. Christ-
licher und vernunfftmässiger Begriff, vom
wahren Uhrsprung der Goldhervorbringenden
Wunder-Materie, oder des sogenannten
Steins der Weisen ... Franckfurt am Mayn:
J.L. Gleditsch, 1707.
   8 ℓ., 112 p.

2876. ——. Christ-schuldige Erinnerung
de Medicina hominis oder Von der dem Menschen allein eigenen Medicin ... Hamburg:
C. König ..., 1732.
   80 p.
   With Philosophisches Licht und Schat-
tung ... 1738.

2877. MÜLLER, Johann Heinrich. Collegivm
experimentale ... Accessit ob cognationem
appendix orationis ac differtationis ... Norimbergæ: sumptibus W.M. Endteri, typis J.E.
Adelbulneri, 1721.
   4 ℓ., 302 p., 8 ℓ. illus.

2878. MÜLLER, Philipp. Miracvla chymica
et misteria medica ... [Wittenberg] ex typographia L. Seuberlichs, sumptibus C. Bergeri,
1611.
   12 ℓ., 189 p. illus.

2879. ——. ——. Rothomagi: J. Berthelin,
1651.
   12 ℓ., 191 p. illus.

2880. ——. ——. Ex recensione Gerardi
Blasii. Amstelodami: E.J. Valckenier, 1659.
   11 ℓ., 140 p. illus.

2881. ——. Miracula & mysteria chymico-
medica, libris quinque ... enucleata ... Editio
secunda ... Accesserunt his: 1. Tyrocynium
chymicum. 2. Novum lumen chymicum. [Fri-
burgi] C. Berger, 1614.
   11 ℓ., 493 p., 2 ℓ. illus.

2882. ——. ——. [Friburgi] C. Berger,
1616.
   11 ℓ., 493 p., 2 ℓ. illus.

2883. MÜLLER, Theophil. Commentationum
biga quarum prima de oleis, variisque, ea
extrahendi modis. Secunda de quibusdam alchymiæ ortum & progressum breviter agit.
Hamburgi: viduæ G. Schultze, 1688.
   48 p.

   MUMMSSEN, Dieter. De corde rupto.
See Ludwig, C.G., praeses.

   MUNDANUS, Theodorus. See Dickinson, Edmund, De quintessentia philosophorum
... 1699.

2884. MUNTING, Abraham. Aloidarium, sive
Aloës mucronato folio Americanæ majoris,
aliarumque ejusdem speciei historia ... [Ams-
terdam] 1680.
   33 p., 9 ℓ. illus.
   With his De vera antiquorum herba ...
1681.

2885. ——. De vera antiquorum herba britannica, ejusdemque efficacia contra stomacac-
cen, seu scelotyrben, frisiis & batavis de
scheurbuyck ... Amstelodami: H. Sweerts, 1681.
   14 ℓ., 231 p. illus., port.

2886. ——. Waare oeffening der planten ...
Leeuwarden: H. Rintjes, 1671.
   37 ℓ., 652 p., 19 ℓ. illus.

2887. MURILLO VELARDE Y JURADO, Tómaz.
Aprobacion de ingenios y curacion de hipo-

chondricos, con observaciones y remedios
mvy particvlares ... Zaragoça: D. de Ormer,
1672.
    12 *l*., 146 numb. *l*., 7 *l*.

2888. MUSÆUM HERMETICUM, omnes
sopho-spagyricæ artis discipulos fidelis-
sime erudiens, quo pacto summa illa veraque
medicina ... inueniri ac haberi queat. Continens tractatvs chymicos nouem ... Francofurti: L. Jennis, 1625.
    8 *l*., 445, 35 p. illus.

2889. —— reformatum et amplificatum ...
Francofurti: H. à Sande, 1677.
    6 *l*., 863 p. illus.

2890. ——. Francofurti et Lipsiae: 1749.
    6 *l*., 862 p., 1 *l*. illus.

    MUSGRAVE, William. De arthritide
anomala, sive interna, dissertatio. *In* Sydenham, T., Opera medica ... 1769.

    ——. De arthritide symptomatica
dissertatio. *In* Sydenham, T., Opera medica
... 1769.

2891. MUSITANUS, Carolus. Ad Had. à
Mynsicht ... Thesaurum et armamentarium
medico-chymicum mantissa ... Cui accessit Andreæ Battimelli Auctuarium, et Hieronymi Piperi Corollarium. Genevæ: sumptibus
societatis, 1701.
    67 p., 1 *l*.; 37 p., 1 *l*.; 1 *l*., 76 p., 1 *l*.
    With Mynsicht, A. von, Thesavrvs ...
1697.

2892. MUSSCHENBROEK, Petrus van. Tentamina experimentorum naturalium captorum
in Academia del Cimento ... Ex Italico in
Latinum sermonem conversa. Quibus com-
mentarios, nova experimenta, et orationem
de methodo instituendi experimenta physica
addidit Petrus van Musschenbroek. Lugduni
Batavorum: J. et H. Verbeek, 1731.
    8 *l*., xlviii p., 6 *l*., 193, 192 p., 7 *l*.
illus.

2893. ——. ——. Viennæ: J.T. Trattner,
1756.
    8 *l*., xlviii p., 6 *l*., 193, 192 p., 6 *l*.
illus.

2894. MUTUS LIBER, in quo tamen tota
philosophia hermetica, figuris hieroglyphicis
depingitur ... authore cujus nomen est Altus.
Rvpellæ: P. Savovret, 1677.
    1 *l*., 14 plates, 1 *l*. illus.

2895. MUYS, Wyerus Gulielmus. Oratio
inauguralis de theoriæ medicæ usu atque
recta illam excolendi ratione ... Franeqveræ:
F. Halma, 1714.
    2 *l*., 71 p.
    With Queitsch, A.P., Ιατρομαθηματογραφία
... 1737.

2896. MUZQUIZ, Miguel de. Tratado in-
structivo, y practico sobre el arte de la tin-
tura: reglas experimentadas y metodicas para
tintar sedas, lanas, hilos de todas clases, y
esparto en rama. Madrid: B. Roman, 1778.
    xxx, 250 p. illus.

2897. MYLIUS, Johann Daniel. Anatomia
avri, siue Tyrocinivm medico-chymicvm, continens in se partes quinque ... Francofurti:
L. Jennis, 1628.
    13 *l*., 304, 27 p. illus.

2898. ——. Antidotarivm medico-chymicvm
reformatvm ... Francofvrti: L. Iennis, 1620.
    6 *l*., 1044 p., 36 *l*. ports.

2899. ——. Opvs medico-chymicvm: continens tres tractatus siue basilicas: quorum
prior inscribitur Basilica medica, secundus
Basilica chymica, tertius Basilica philosophic
Francofurti: L. Jennis, 1618.
    3 pts. illus.
    Lacking part 2, books 5-7, and all of part
3.

2900. ——. Philosophia reformata continen:
libros binos ... Francofurti: L. Jennis, 1622.
    19 *l*., 703 p., 17 *l*. illus.

2901. ——. Tractatvs secvndi, sev Basilica
chymicæ, liber septimvs: De animalibus.
Francofvrti: L. Iennis, 1620.
    2 *l*., 154 p. illus.

2902. MYNSICHT, Adrian von. Thesavrvs
et armamentarivm medico-chymicvm ... adiunc
tum est Testamentvm Hadrianevm De aureo
philosophorum lapide. Lvgdvni: I.A. Hvgvetan.
1640.
    20 *l*., 490 p., 34 *l*.

2903. ——. ——. Rothomagi: I. Berthelin,
1651.
    20 *l*., 490 p., 34 *l*.

2904. ——. ——. Lubecæ: impensis A.J. Be-
eri, typis hæredum Schmalhertzianorum, 1662.
    7 *l*., 532 p., 26 *l*., 24 p. illus., port.

2905. ——. ——. Francofurti: B.C. Wust-

ius, 1675.
 6 *l*., 525 p., 27 *l*., 22 p.

2906. ——. ——. Editio novissima emendatior. Genevæ: fratres de Tournes, 1697.
 8 *l*., 525 p., 27 *l*., 22 p.

2907. ——. Thesaurus & armamentarium
medico-chvmicum: or A treasury of physick.
With the most secret way of preparing remedies against all diseases ... Faithfully
rendered into English by John Partridge ...
London: J.M. for A. Churchill, 1682.

 8 *l*., 377 p., 17 *l*. port.

2908. ——. Medicinisch-chymische
Schatz- und Rüst-Kammer ... Stuttgardt:
J.B. Metzler und C. Erhardt, 1725.
 8 *l*., 663 p., 42 *l*.

 MYREPSUS, Nicolaus. *See* Nicolaus
Myrepsus.

 MYSTAGOGUS, Cleidophorus. *See*
Conti, Luigi de'.

N

2909. La NATURE dévoilée, ou Théorie de la nature ... Paris: Edme, 1772.
2 v.

2910. NAUDÉ, Gabriel. Apologie povr tovs les grands personnages qui ont esté faussement soupçonnez de magie ... Paris: F. Targa, 1625.
12 ℓ., 615 p., 11 ℓ.

2911. ———. The history of magick by way of apology, for all the wise men who have unjustly been reputed magicians ... Englished by J. Davies. London: for J. Streater, 1657.
8 ℓ., 306 p., 1 ℓ.

2912. NAVIER, Pierre Toussaint. Contrepoisons de l'arsenic, du sublimé corrosif, du verd-de-gris et du plomb ... Paris: la veuve Méquignon & fils; Didot le jeune, 1777.
2 v.

2913. NAXAGORAS, Ehrd von, *pseud.* Alchymia denudata revisa et aucta, oder: Das biss anhero nie recht geglaubte ... Wunder der Natur, nebst angehängter ausführlichen Beschreibung der unweit Zwickau in Meissen zu Nieder-Hohendorff und anderer umliegenden Orthen gefundenen goldischen Sande ... von J.N.v.E.I. ... Breslau: J.G. Stecks Wittwe und Erben, 1716.
15 ℓ., 202 p.

2914. ———. Aureum vellus, oder Güldenes Vliess: Das ist, Ein Tractat, welcher darstellet den Grund und Ursprung des uhralten güldenen Vliesses ... Franckfurth am Mayn: Stockische Erbe und Schilling, 1731.
384, 320 p.

2915. ———. Chymischer oder alchymistischer Particular-Zeiger, das ist: Treuer Unterricht vom Gold- und Silber- machen ... Rostock: J. Russworm, 1706.
8 ℓ., 75 p.

With Söldner, J.A., Fegfeuer de chymisten ... 1702.

2916. ———. ———. Dritte Auflage. Rostock: J.H. Russworm, 1715.
8 ℓ., 79 p.
With Cassius, A., De extremo illo ... 1685.

2917. ———. Experientia Naxagoræ, secundum annulos Platonicos, et catenam auream Homeri. Worinnen der wahrhaffte Process, die Universal-Medicin zu elaboriren, so wohl vor den menschlichen Leib, als die Metalla zu verbessern; klar und aufrichtig vor Augen lieget. Franckfurt am Mayn: auf Kosten guter Freunde, und in Commission bey D. von Sand, 1723.
4 ℓ., 184 p.

2918. ———. Sancta veritas Hermetica, seu Concordantia philosophorum consistens in sale et sole vel mercurio et sulphure, das ist: Die ehemals excerpirte und darauf mit eigener Hand experimentirte Sonnen-klare Wahrheit der Philosophen Schrifften ... Breslau: J.G. Stecks Wittib, 1712.
16 ℓ., 902 p.

2919. ———. Die Unlängst vom Monath Januario über Hamburg in gantz Teutschland sich geschwungene und wie Pontius Pilatus im Credo denckwürdig gemachte Fama Hermetica in circulo conjunctionem Saturni & solis sistens, cum notis variorum ... [n.p.] 1714.
31 p.

2920. NAZARI, Giovanni Battista. Della tramvtatione metallica sogni tre ... Aggiontovi di nvovo la concordanza de filosofi & loro prattica ... Brescia: P.M. Marchetti, 1599.
8 ℓ., 231 p. illus.

2921. NEANDER, Theophilus. Heptas alchymica das ist: Auszerlesene philosophische

Tractätlein von dem Magisterio Lapidis ...
Hall: Henning, 1621.
   incomplete. illus.
A collection of tracts of which only the
first three are present, bound in an irregular
order.

2922. NEDEGANDER, *pseud.* Kurze jedoch
gründliche und einfältige Anleitung zu dem
grossen Naturgeheimniss des Lapidis Philosophici in einem Briefe an die wahren Besitzer nebst einem Probierstein der Materia
... Hamburg: Trausold, 1753.
   32 p.

   NEDHAM, Marchamont. An episto-
lary discourse. *In* Bolnest, E., Medicina instaurata ... 1665.

2923. ———. Medela medicinæ. A plea for
the free profession, and a renovation of the
art of physick ... London: for R. Lownds,
1665.
   12 *l.*, 516 p.

2924. NERI, Antonio. De arte vitraria libri
septem, & in eosdem Christoph. Merretti ...
observationes & notæ ... Amstelodami: A.
Frisius, 1668.
   14 *l.*, 455 p., 8 *l.* illus.

2925. ———. ———. Amstelædami: H. Wetsten, 1686.
   18 *l.*, 440 p., 8 *l.* illus.

2926. ———. The art of glass, wherein are
shown the wayes to make and colour glass
... translated into English, with some observations on the author. Whereunto is added
an account of the glass drops, made by the
Royal Society, metting at Gresham College.
London: A.W. for O. Pulleyn, 1662.
   12 *l.*, 362 p., 2 *l.*

2927. ———. Art de la verrerie, de Neri,
Merret et Kunckel. Auquel on a ajouté Le sol
sine veste d'Orschall; l'Helioscopium vi-
dendi sine veste solem chymicum; le Sol non
sine veste; le chapitre XI. du Flora Saturni-
zans de Henckel ... un mémoire sur la maniere de faire le saffre; le secret des vraies
porcelaines de la Chine & de Saxe ... Traduits de l'Allemand, par M.D.***. Paris:
Durand & Pissot, 1752.
   1v, 629 p., 1 *l.* illus.

2928. ———. Johannis Kunckelii ... Ars
vitraria experimentalis, oder Vollkommene
Glasmacher-Kunst, lehrende, als in einem,
aus unbetrüglicher Erfahrung herfliessendem

Commentario über die von dergleichen Arbeit
beschriebenen sieben Bücher P. Anthonii
Neri ... und denen darüber gethanen gelehrten
Anmerckungen Christophori Merretti ... Amsterdam: auff Kosten des Autoris, bey H.
Betkio, 1679.
   2 pts. in 1 v. illus.
Lacking portrait, 9 plates, p. 221-224,
and four leaves of the index.

2929. ———. ———. Franckfurt: C. Riegel, 1689.
   6 *l.*, 472 p., 10 *l.* illus., port.

   ———. L'arte vetraria. *In* Baumé, A.,
Chimica sperimentale ... 1781.

2930. NESSEL, Edmond. A treatise concerning the medicinal Spaw waters ... Translated out of French into English ... London:
J. Downing, 1715.
   viii, 56 p.
English and French parallel texts.

   Die NEU-AUFFGEHENDE chymische
Sonne. *See* Siebenstern, Christian Friedrich
Sendimir von.

2931. NEUE APOTHECKER Tax-Ordnung, oder
Der Werth und Preiss aller ... Artzeneyen,
welche in denen ... Stadt-Wiennerischen
Apothecken ... gebräuchig seynd ... Wienn:
G. Kurtzböck, 1744.
   6 *l.*, 72 p., 1 *l.*
With Dispensatorium pharmaceuticum Aus-
riaco-Viennense ... 1744.

2932. ———. Wien: J.T. Edlen von Trattner,
1771.
   7 *l.*, 72 p., 1 *l.*

2933. NEUERÖFNETES GEHEIMNISS der naphta
nitri, und der naphta vitrioli, nebst einer gründlichen Anleitung die Tinctur und das Oehl des
Vitriols zu verfertigen ... Aus dem Englischen
übersetzt. Kempten: C.G.B. Fritzsch, 1773.
   31 p.

2934. NEUE SAMMLUNG von einigen alten
und sehr rar gewordenen philosophisch und
alchymistischen Schriften ... als eine neue
Fortsetzung des bekannten deutschen Theatri
chymici ... Franckfurt: Krauss, 1769-1770.
   2 v. in 1.

2935. NEUKRANTZEN, Johann Theodor. Oratio
inavgvralis de necessitate artis chemicae eius-
demque productu summo magna hominvm et
metallorvm medicina lapis philosophorvm dicta
... Vitembergae: vidua Gerdesia, 1725.
   15 *l.*

2936. NEUMANN, Kaspar. The chemical works ... abridged and methodized with large additions ... by William Lewis. London: for W. Johnston ..., 1759.
8 *l.*, 586 p., 19 *l.*

2937. ——. ——. London: for J. & F. Rivington ..., 1773.
2 v.

2938. ——. Chymiæ medicæ dogmatico-experimentalis ... Züllichau: J.J. Dendeler, 1749-1755.
4 vol. in 10.
Volume one, part one lacking.

2939. ——. Lectiones publicæ von vier subjectis pharmaceutico-chemicis, nehmlich vom gemeinem Saltze, Weinstein, Salmiac und der Ameise ... Leipzig: G.B. Frommann, 1737.
4 *l.*, 379 p.

2940. ——. Prælectiones chemicæ seu Chemia medico-pharmacevtica experimentalis & rationalis, oder Gründlicher Unterricht der Chemie ... herausgegeben vom D. Johann Christian Zimmermann ... Berlin: J. A. Rüdiger, 1740.
15 *l.*, 1872 p., 32 *l.* port.

2941. NEVETT, Thomas. The rational oeconomy of humane bodies, wherein the nature of the chyle, blood, lymph, and other juices, is discover'd ... London: T. Parkhurst and F. Robinson, 1704.
168 p.

2942. A NEW METHOD for the improvement of the manufacture of drugs: in a treatise on the elixir proprietatis ... London: for C. Davis, 1747.
1 *l.*, ii, 80 p.

2943. NICANDER, *of Colophon.* ... Alexipharmaca, seu De venenis in potu cibove homini datis eorumque remediis carmen ... Ex libris scriptis emendavit animadversionibusque et paraphrasi Latina illustravit Jo. Gottlob Schneider. Halae: Orphanotropheus, 1792.
xx, 346 p.
Greek and Latin texts.

——. Les oeuvres. *In* Grevin, J., Devx livres des venins ... 1568.

2944. ——. Theriaca & Alexipharmaca in Latinos uersus redacta, per Evricvm Cordum

... Francofordiae: C. Egenolph [1532].
38 *l.*

2945. ——. ... Theriaca interprete Io. Gorræo ... Parisiis: G. Morelius, 1557.
3 pts. in 1 v.
Greek and Latin texts.
Includes: Nicandri Alexipharmaca, Io. Gorræo interprete ...; In Nicandri Theriaca scholia incerti ... In eivsdem Alexipharmaca diuersorum auctorum scholia.
The various parts are not bound in the correct order.

2946. ——. ... Theriaca et Alexipharmaca. Ioannes Gorrhævs Latinus versibvs reddidit Italicis vero qvi nvnc primvm in lvcem prodevnt Ant. Mar. Salvinios ... Edita curante Aug. Mar. Bandino. Florentiae: Movckianus, 1764.
3 *l.*, 376 p.

2947. NICHOLSON, William. A dictionary of chemistry, exhibiting the present state of the theory and practice of that science ... London: for G.G. and J. Robinson, 1795.
2 v. illus.

2948. ——. The first principles of chemistry. London: for G.G.J. & J. Robinson, 1790.
xxvii, 532 p., 2 *l.* illus.

2949. ——. ——. Third edition, revised by the author. London: for G.G. and J. Robinson, 1796.
xxi p., 1 *l.*, 564 p., 2 *l.* illus.

2950. NICOLAI, Ernst Anton. Methodvs concinnandi formvlas medicamentorvm exemplis ad medici qvondam illvstris Friderici Hoffmanni mentem accommodatis illvstrata. Halae Magdebvrgicae: Renger, 1747.
12 *l.*, 576 p.

2951. ——. Rezepte und Kurarten mit theoretischpraktischen Anmerkungen. Zweite verbesserte und vielvermehrte Ausgabe. Jena: Cröker, 1788.
5 v.
Lacking volume 4.

2952. ——. Systema materiae medicae ad praxin applicatae. Halae Magdebvrgicae: C. H. Hemmerde, 1751.
8 *l.*, 343 p., 1 *l.*

2953. NICOLAS, Pierre François. Cours de chymie théorico-pratique, a l'usage des étudians et des amateurs ... Nancy:

C.S. Lamort, 1787 [i.e. 1777].
  iv, 314 p., 8 *l*.

2954. NICOLAUS MYREPSUS. Medicamentorvm opvs ... à Leonharto Fvchsio ... publico, è græco in latinum recens conuersum,
luculentissimisque annotationibus illustratum ... Basileae: I. Oporinus, 1549.
  8 *l*., 586 numb. col., 4 *l*.

  NICOLAUS PRAEPOSITUS. Antidotarium cum expositione Platearii. *In* Mesue,
Joannes, Damascenus. Mesue cum expositione ... 1497.

2955. ——. Dispensarium ... ad aroma-
tarios. Lugduni: J. Buguetan [1505].
  cv numb. *l*.

2956. ——. ... Dispensarium ... ad aroma-
tarios nuper diligētissime recognitum ...
Platearius ... De simplici medicina, nouis
exornatus additionibus. [Lugduneñ: C. Fradin,
1512.]
  6 *l*., xciiii, xl numb. *l*.

2957. ——. —— recognitus, ac nouis
exornatus additionibus per ... Michaelē de
Capella ... Lugduñ: C. Tupin, 1536.
  cx numb. *l*., 4 *l*.

2958. NICOLS, Thomas. Arcula gemmea:
or, A cabinet of jewels. Discovering the
nature, vertue, value of pretious stones ...
London: for N. Brooke, 1653.
  5 *l*., 239 p. chart.

2959. ——. A lapidary: or, The history of
pretious stones ... Cambridge: T. Buck, 1652.
  5 *l*., 239 p. chart.

2960. NIEUWE Nederduitsche apotheek ...
Leiden: P. van der Eyk, 1753.
  5 *l*., 440 p., 19 *l*.

2961. ——. ——. Tweede druk ... Leyden:
P. van der Eyk, 1766.
  8 *l*., 490 p., 31 *l*.

2962. NIEWE beschryvinge der kleine wae-
relt of verhandelinge over de menschelyke
natuur ... s'Gravenhage: voor den autheur,
1728.
  10 *l*., 390 p., 9 *l*. illus.

2963. NIHELL. Traité des eaux minérales
de la ville de Rouen ... Rouen: E.V. Machuel,
1759.
  6 *l*., xxxviii, 189 p.

With Heister, L., La methode de tailler,
1751.

2964. NODUS sophicus enodatus. Das ist,
Erleuterung etlicher vornehmen philosophischen
Schrifften vnd tractaten vom Stein der Weisen
... Durch einen trewen Teutschen Philo-
sophum vnd Liebhabern der Naturgemesen
chymischen Kunst vnd verborgenen Weissheit Gottes. [n.p.] F. Gruners Erben, 1639.
  128 p.

2965. NOLLE, Heinrich. Discursus posthumus. Pro verâ philosophiâ & medicinâ
Hermetis. Ex autoris relictis schedis descriptus ac editus. Rostochii: J. Hallervord,
1636.
  24 p.

2966. ——. Hermetical physick: or, The
right way to preserve, and to restore health
... Englished by Henry Uaughan. London: for
H. Moseley, 1655.
  4 *l*., 130 p.

2967. ——. Natvræ sanctvarivm: quod est,
Phisica Hermetica. In stvdiosorvm sincerioris
philosophiæ gratiam, ad promouendam rerum
naturalium veritatem, methodo perspicua &
admirandorum secretorum in natvræ abysso
latentium philosophica explicatione decenter
in vndecim libris tractata ... Francofurti:
typis N. Hoffmanni, sumptibus I. Rosæ, 1619.
  838 p., 6 *l*.

2968. ——. Theoria philosophiæ Hermeticæ,
septem tractatibvs ... explicata ... Hanoviæ:
P. Anton, 1617.
  119 p.

2969. ——. Via sapientiæ trivna ... edita
ab Anastasio Philareto Cosmopolita ... [Lüne-
burg: 1620.]
  28 *l*.
  With his Discursus ... 1636.

2970. NOLLET, Jean Antoine, *abbé*. L'art
des expériences, ou Avis aux amateurs de
la physique, sur le choix, la construction et
l'usage des instruments; sur la préparation
et l'emploi des drogues qui servent aux expériences ... Paris: P.E.G. Durand, 1770.
  3 v. illus.

2971. NORTON, Samuel. Alchymiæ complementum, et perfectio sev Modus et processus argumentandi, sive multiplicandi omnes
lapides, & elixera in virtute ... olim à Samuele
Nortono ... inchoatus, nunc verò ab Edmundo

Deano ... editus. Cvi accessit Explanatio
intentionis philosophorum, cum de decimo
loquuntur numero ... Francofurti: typis C.
Rötelii, impensis G. Fitzeri, 1630.
17 p. illus.

2972. ——. Catholicon physicorum, sev
Modvs conficiendi tinctvram physicam &
alchymicam ... Olim a Samvele Nortono ...
inchoatus: nunc verò editus labore & industriâ Edmvndi Deani ... Cvi accessit
Ramvs triplex de compositione lactis vir-
ginis, seu aceti philosophorum ... Francofurti: typis C. Rötelii, impensis G. Fitzeri,
1630.
16 p. illus.
With his Alchymiæ complementum ...
1630.

2973. ——. Elixer, sev medicina vitæ,
seu Modvs conficiendi vervm avrvm, et
argentum potalibe cum vtriusáue virtutibus
... Olim à Samvele Nortonio ... inchoatus:
nunc verò editus industriâ, & operâ Edmvndi
Deani ... Cui etiam accessit modus redden-
dum vitrum ductile, & malleabile ... Francofurti: typis C. Rötelii, impensis G. Fitzeri,
1630.
14 p. illus.
With his Alchymiæ complementum ...
1630.

2974. ——. Mercvrivs redivivvs, sev
Modvs conficiendi lapidem philosophicum
tèm album, quàm rubeum è mercurio. Olim
à Samvele Nortono ... inchoatus: nunc verò
editus opera & studio Edmvndi Deani ... Cvi
accessit Modvs faciendi vtrumáue fermentum
tàm album è luna ... quàm rubeum è sole ...
Francofurti: typis C. Rötelii, impensis G.
Fitzeri, 1630.
20 p. illus.

2975. ——. Metamorphosis lapidum igno-
bilium in gemmas quasdam pretiosas, sev
Modus transformandi perlas parvas, et minu-
tulas, in magnas & nobiles ... Olim à Samvele Nortonio ... inchoatus: nunc verò editus
diligentia Edmundi Deani ... Cvi accessit
modvs compenendi electrvm artificiale ...
Francofurti: typis C. Rötelii, impensis G.
Fitzeri, 1630.
12 p. illus.
With his Alchymiæ complementum ...
1630.

2976. ——. Satvrnvs satvratvs dissolvtvs,
et coelo restitvtvs, seu Modus componendi
lapidem philosophicvm tam albvm, qvam
rvbevm è plumbo ... Olim a Samuele Nortono

... inchoatus. Nunc vero edende Edmnvdo
Deano ... auctus, illustratus, & perfectus.
Cui accessit Accuratio operis Saturni, vna
cum modo extrahendi arg. viuum è plumbo
... Francofurti: typis J.N. Stoltzenbergeri,
impensis G. Fitzeri, 1630.
24 p. illus.
With his Alchymiæ complementum ...
1630.

2977. ——. Tractatvlvs de antiqvorvm
scriptorvm considerationibvs in alchymia
... Olim à Samvele Nortono ... inchoatus:
nunc verò editus studio, labore & industriâ
Edmvndi Deani ... Francofurti: typis C.
Rötelii, impensis G. Fitzeri, 1630.
13 p.
With his Mercvrivs redivvs ... 1630

2978. ——. Venvs vitriolata, in elixer
conuersa ... siuè Modvs conficiendi lapidem
philosophicum tàm è Venere, siuè cupro,
quam à Marte, siuè chalybe. Olim à Samvele
Nortonio ... inchoatus: nunc verò editus
studiis, & diligentiâ Edmvndi Deani ...
Francofurti: typis C. Rötelii, impensis G.
Fitzeri, 1630.
16 p. illus.
With his Alchymiæ complementum ... 1630.

NORTON, Thomas.   The ordinall of
alchimy. *In* Ashmole, E., Theatrum chemicum
... 1652.

——. Crede mihi seu Ordinale. *In*
Maier, M., Tripus aureus ... 1618.

2979. NOSE, Carl Wilhelm.   Versuch einiger
Beyträge zur Chemie. Wien: J.A. Edlen von
Trattner, 1778.
6 l., 136 p., 1 l.

2980. NOTT, John.   Of the Hotwell waters
near Bristol ... Bristol: S. Bonner ..., 1793.
3 l., 94 p., 1 l.

2981. ——. A posologic companion to the
London Pharmacopoeia ... The second edition,
with additions. Londini: G. Woodfall for J.
Johnson, 1794.
2 l., 115 p.
With Pharmacopoeia Londinensis ... [1788?]

2982. NOUVEAU RECUEIL des plus beaux
secrets de medecine ... Avec un traité des
plus excellens preservatifs contre la peste
... Paris: T. Guillain, 1694.
2 v. in 1.

2983. Le NOUVEAU TEINTURIER parfait. Ou

traité de ce qu'il y a de plus essentiel dans
la teinture ... Paris: C.A. Jombert, 1769.
2 v. in 1.

NOVA pharmacopoeorum taxa. *See*
Neue Apothecker Tax-Ordnung.

2984. NUCK, Anton. Adenographia curiosa
et uteri foeminei anatome nova. Cum epistola ad amicum, de inventis novis. Lugduni
Batavorum, J. Luchtman, 1692.
8 *l*., 152 p., 3 *l*. illus.

2985. ——. Sialographia et ductuum
aquosorum anatome nova ... Accedit Defensio ductuum aquosorum, nec non Fons
salivalis novus, hactenus non descriptus.
Lugduni Batavorum: P. vander Aa, 1690.
8 *l*., 158 p., 8 *l*. illus.

2986. ——. ——. Ejusdem Adenographia
curiosa et uteri foeminei anatome nova.
Accedit ... De motu bilis circulari ejusque
morbis, olim publicè proposita à ... Maurito
van Reverhorst ... Editio tertia. Lugd. Batavorum: S. Luchtmans, 1723.
var. pag. illus.

2987. NUREMBERG (Germany). Laws, statutes, etc. Leges ac statvta ampliss. senatvs
Norimbergensis, ad medicos, pharmacopoeos,
& alios pertinentia ... Noribergæ: P. Kaufmann, 1598.
6 *l*.
With Cordus, V., Dispensatorium ... 1598.

2988. Ein NÜTZLICHES HANDTBÜCHLEIN,
darinnen allerhandt Artzneyen für den gemeinen Mann ... zu hilff kommen kan. Fleissig corrigiert ... Basel: J. Schröter, 1610.
1 *l*., 218 p., 1 *l*. illus.

2989. NUYSEMENT, Jacques. Poeme philosophic de la verité de la phisiqve mineralle
... Paris: J. Perier & A. Buisard, 1620.
80 p., 1 *l*.
With his Traittez de l'harmonie ... 1621.

2990. ——. ——. La Haye: T. Maire, 1639.

57 p.
With his Traittez de l'harmonie ... 1639,
as issued.

2991. ——. Sal, lumen, & spiritus mundi
philosophici: or, The dawning of the day,
discovered by the beams of light ... Written
originally in French, afterwards turned into
Latin, by ... Lodovicus Combachius ... And
now transplanted into Albyons garden, by
R.T. [London] J.C. for N. Ekins, 1657.
15 *l*., 220 p., 1 *l*.

2992. ——. Traittez de l'harmonie et
constitvtion generalle dv vray sel, secret
des philosophes, & de l'esprit vniuerselle
du monde, suiuant le troisieme principe du
Cosmopolite ... Paris: J. Perier & A. Buisard,
1621.
14 *l*., 332 p.

2993. ——. ——. La Haye: T. Maire, 1639.
12 *l*., 115 p.

2994. ——. Tractatvs de vero sale secrete
philosophorum, & de universali mundi spiritu.
Gallicè primò scriptus ... Nunc ... Latinè
versus à Ludovico Combachio ... Cassellis:
typis J. Gentschii, impensis S. Köhlers, 1651.
4 *l*., 212 p., 1 *l*.

2995. ——. ——. Lugduni Batavorum: A.
Doude, 1672.
8 *l*., 244 p.

——. Abhandlung vom wahren ge-
heimen Salze der Weisen. *In* Birkholz, A.M.,
Die ganze höhere Chemie ... 1787.

NYLANDER, Johan C. Exanthemata
viva. *See* Linné, C. von, *praeses*. Entry 2474.

2996. NYLANDT, Petrus. De Nederlandtse
herbarius of kruydt-boeck ... als mede de
uytlandtsen of vreemde droogens ... Amsterdam: M. Doornick, 1670.
4 *l*., 342 p., 12 *l*. illus.
With Munting, A., Waare oeffening der
planten ... 1671.

O

2997. OBERMAYR, Franz Anton. Dissertatio experimentalis chemica de sale sedativo
Hombergii ... Vindobonæ: J.T. Trattner, 1766.
74 p.

OCCO, Adolf. Pharmacopoeia. *See*
Pharmacopoea Augustana ... 1574.

ODIER, Louis, *jt. auth.* Pharmacopoea Genevensis. *See* La Roche, Daniele.

2998. OEHME, Johann August. Medicamenta selecta: oder Medicinische Fama vom
philosophischen Gold-Pulver und orientali-
schen Gesundheits-Balsam ... Vierdte Edition. Dresden: G.C. Hilscher, 1738.
82 p., 3 *l.*
With Philosophisches Licht und Schatten
... 1738.

2999. ———. Medicinische Fama, als in
deren II. Theil vom Scorbut und einer dar-
wieder ersonnenen Tinctur gehandelt wird ...
Dressden: G.C. Hilscher, 1738.
59 p.
With Philosophisches Licht und Schatten
... 1738.

ÖHRQVIST, Daniel Johan. De diaeta
per scalam aetatis humanae observanda. *See*
Linné, C. von, *praeses.* Entry 2443.

3000. OLIVER, William. A practical dissertation on Bath-waters ... To which is
added, A relation of a very extraordinary
sleeper near Bath ... The fourth edition. London: for J. Leake and Mr. Hitch, 1747.
xvi, 199 p.

3001. ONOFRI, Fedele. Centvria di secreti
medicinali, e natvrali, nella quale si contiene cento secreti ... Firenze: F. Honofri,
1619.
8 *l.*

3002. ———. ———. Roma: Il Righettini, 1637.
16 p.

3003. [OPERA NVOVA intitolata Dificio de
ricette, nelle quale si contengono tre utilis-
simi ricettari ...] Vinetia: Giovantonio et
fratelli di Sabio, 1529.
6 *l.*, 20 numb. *l.* illus.
Lacking the title-page, which has been
supplied in photostat.

3004. OPUSCULA quædam chemica. Georgii
Riplei ... Medvlla philosophiæ chemicæ.
Incerti avtoris Canones decem ... Heliæ ...
Speculum alchymiæ. Ioan. Avrelii Avgvrelli
Chrysopoiæ compendium paraphrasticum.
Artefii Clavis maioris sapientiæ. Ioan.
Pontani Epistola de lapide philosophorum.
Galli Etschenrevteri ... epistola ad Guilielmum
Gratarolum ... Francofurti: J. Bringer, 1614.
157 p.

3005. ORIBASIUS. Collectorvm medicinalivm
libri XVII. Qvi ex magno septvaginta librorum
uolumine ad nostram aetatem soli peruenerunt,
Ioanne Baptista Rasario ... interprete. Venetiis:
P. Manutius [ca. 1554].
4 *l.*, 252 [i.e. 750] p.

———. Collectiones medicinales. *In*
Cocchi, A., Graecorvm chirvrgici ... 1754.

———. Euporiston. *In* Aurelianus, C.,
Tardarum passionum ... 1529.

3006. ———. Opera, qvae extant omnia, tribus tomis digesta, Ioanne Baptista Rasario
interprete ... Basileae: M. Isingrinius,
1557.
3 v. in 1. illus.

3007. ORSCHALL, Johann Christian. Oeuvres
métallurgiques ... Traduit de l'Allemand ...
Paris: Hardy, 1760.
xxxii, 394 p., 1 *l.* illus.

3008. ———. Sol sine veste. Oder dreyssig
Experimenta dem Gold seinen Purpur aus-
zuziehen ... Amsterdam: 1684.
11 *l.*, 91 p.

——. ——. *In* Gertz, P., Neu-eröff-nete Kunst-Kammer ... 1720.

——. ——. *In* Neri, A., Art de la verrerie ... 1752.

——. ——. *In* Vanderbeeg, I.C., Manuductio hermetico-philosophica ... [n.d.].

3009. ——. Wunder drey, das ist: Be-schreibung dreyer dem Ansehen nach unan-nehmlicher der Practic nach aber wohl prac-ticabler Particularien, auss eigener Experi-enz von einem Liebhaber der Chymie. Cassel: J. Ingebrand; Marburg: J.H. Stock, 1685.
4 *l.*, 84 p.

3010. ——. Wunder-Dreyes Continuatio, welches sind fernere Experimenta, so in Elaboratione dieser drey Processen obser-virt, in Anno 1684. herausgegebenen Wun-derdrey, auss sonderer Lieb dess Nächsten herausgegeben von eben selbigem Authore. Cassel: J. Ingebrand; Marburg: J.H. Stock, 1686.
152 p.
With his Wunderdrey ... 1685.

3011. ORTA, Garcia de. Aromatvm, et sim-plicivm aliqvot medicamentorvm apvd Indos nascentivm historia ... nunc verò Latino sermone in epitomen contracta ... à Carolo Clvsio. Antverpiæ: C. Plantin, 1574.
227 p., 3 *l.* illus.

3012. ——. ——. Tertia editio. Antverpiæ: C. Plantin, 1579.
217 p., 3 *l.* illus.

3013. ——. ——. Qvarta editio ... Ant-verpiæ: ex officina Plantiniana, apud viduam & I. Moretum, 1593.
456 p., 3 *l.* illus.

3014. ——. Dell'historia de i semplici aromati, et altre cose ... con alcune breui annotationi di Carlo Clvsio. Et dve altri libri ... di Nicolo Monardes ... tradotti ... da M. Annibale Briganti ... Venetia: heredi di F. Ziletti, 1589.
14 *l.*, 347 p.; 2 *l.*; 131 p., 6 *l.*

3015. ——. ——. Venetia: heredi di G. Scotto, 1597.
16 *l.*, 525 p. illus.

3016. ——. ——. Venetia: G. Salis, 1616.
16 *l.*, 525 p. illus.

3017. ——. Dve libri dell'historia de i semplici, aromati, et altre cose, che vengono portate dall'Indie Orientali ... et dve altri libri parimente di qvelle che si portano dall' Indie Occidentali, di Nicolo Monardes ... tradotti ... da M. Annibale Briganti ... Venetia: [G. & A. Zenari] 1576.
8 *l.*, 92, 44 numb. *l.* illus.

3018-19. ——. ——. Venetia: F. Ziletti, 1582.
13 *l.*, 347 p.; 7 *l.*, 249 p., 6 *l.* illus., port.

3020. ——. Histoire des drogves expiceries, et de certains medicamens simples, qvi nais-sent és Indes ... diuisée en deux parties. La premiere composée de trois liures, lex deux premiers de M. Garcie du Iardin, & le trois-iesme de M. Christophle de la Coste. La seconde composée de deux liures de M. Nico-las Monard ... Le tout ... translaté ... sur la traduction Latine de Clusius, par Anthoine Colin ... Lyon: I Pillehotte, 1602.
8 *l.*, 720 p., 15 *l.* illus.

3021. ——. Histoire des drogves expis-ceries, et de certains medicamens simples, qvi naissent és Indes & en l'Amerique. Ceste matiere comprise en six liures ... cinq tirés du Latin de Charles de l'Ecscluse: & l'his-toire du baulme adioustee de nouueau ... translaté en François par Antoine Colin ... Seconde edition ... Lyon: I. Pillehotte, 1619.
4 pts. in 1 v. illus.

3022. ORVIUS, Ludwig Conrad. Luc. Conr. Montani Gründliche Anweisung, zu der wahren Hermetischen Wissenschaft, und zu dem Ge-heimniss der Alten des Steins der Weisen zu gelangen. Aus einem sehr alten raren Bam-burgischen Manuscript, ans Licht gestellet, von Johann Ludolph ab Indagine. Franckfurt: 1751.
16 *l.*, 94 p., 1 *l.*

3023. OSTEN, Hans von. Eine grosse Herz-stärkung für die Chymisten; nebst einer Dose voll gutes Niesepulver, für die unkundigen Widersprecher der Verwandlungskunst der Metalle, im Kloser zu Oderberg, seit Anno 1426. aufbehalten ... Berlin: J.F. Vieweg, 1771.
7 *l.*, 108 p. illus.

OTHO, *Cremonensis*. De electione meliorum simplicium. *In* Petrina, G., Tractatus confec. de hyacinto ... 1619.

3024. ОЦѢНКА лѣкарствамъ ... Apotheker-Taxe, anbey: Apotheker-Ordung. Hebammen-Ordnung. Taxe für Aerzte, Wundärzte, Hebam-men. Zweyte Ausgabe. Санктпетербургъ : 1790.
152 p.

P

3025. PAGE, John. Receipts for the preparing and compounding the principal medicines made use of by the late Mr. Ward ...
London: for H. Whitridge ..., 1763.
    1 *l*., 33 p.

3026. PAGÈS, Jean. L'oeconomie des
trois familles dv monde svblvnaire a sçavoir
animale, vegetale, et minerale: et particv-
lierement de la natvre de l'homme: contre
tovte favsse philosophie naturelle, alchymie, cabale, astrologie iudiciaire ...
Paris: 1625.
    8 *l*., 478 p., 27 *l*.

3027. PAGLIARIZZO, Gratiano. Secretti
nvovi e rari, et approvati per salute delli
corpori humani ... Milano: P. Malatesta
[n.d.].
    4 *l*.

3028. PALACIOS, Felix. Palestra pharmacevtica, chymico-galenica, en la qval se
trata de la eleccion de los simples, sus
preparaciones chymicas, y Galenicas, y de
las mas selectas composiciones antiguas,
y modernas, vsuales assi en España ...
Segunda impression nuevamenta corregida,
y emendada. Barcelona: R. Figuero, 1716.
    6 *l*., 480 p., 12 *l*. illus.

3029. ——. ——. Madrid: herederos de
la viuda de J.G. Infanzon, 1723.
    9 *l*., 708 p., 14 *l*. illus.

3030. ——. ——. Madrid: J. Ibarra, 1763.
    11 *l*., 736 p. illus.

3031. ——. —— última impresion ...
Madrid: viuda de J. Ibarra, 1792.
    6 *l*., 736 p. illus.

3032. ——. La pharmacopea trivnfante de
las calvmnias, y imposturas, que en el
Hipocrates Defendido ha publicado el Doctor Don Miguèl Boix ... Madrid: F.M. Abad
[1713].

2 pts. in 1 v.

PALAEMON, Quintus Remnius. De
ponderibus & mensuris liber. *In* Celsus, A.
C., De re medica ... 1528.

PALEOLOGO, Giovanni Battista Diana.
See Diana Paleologo, Giovanni Battista.

3033. PALFIJN, Jan. Ontleed-kundige
beschryving, van de vrouwelyke deelen, die
ter voort-teeling dienen ... Gendt: J. du
Vivie, 1724.
    7 *l*., 125 p. illus.

3034. PALISSY, Bernard. Discovrs admirables, de la natvre des eavx et fonteines
... des metaux, des sels & salines, des
pierres, des terres, du feu & des emaux ...
Paris: Martin le jeune, 1580.
    8 *l*., 361 p., 11 *l*.

3035. PALLADIUS. De febribus concisa
synopsis Græce et Latine cum notis Jo.
Steph. Bernard. Accedunt glossæ chemicæ
et excerpta ex poetis chemicis ex codice
ms. Biblioth. D. Marci. Lugduni Batavorum:
P. Bonk & N. Muntendam, 1745.
    8 *l*., 164 p., 6 *l*.

3036. PALM, Johann Jakob. Versuch einer
medicinischen Handbibliothek oder Sammlung
aller Bücher so von der Arzneygelahrheit,
Anatomie, Chirurgie, Botanik, Chemie, Apothekerkunst, Hebammenkunst ... Erlangen: J.J.
Palm, 1788.
    4 *l*., 488 p.

PALMARIUS, Petrus. *See* Le Paulmier,
Pierre.

3037. PANCIROLI, Guido. Rerum memorabilium libri duo. Quorum prior deperditarum:
posterior noviter inventarum est. Ex Italico
Latinè redditi ... ab Henrico Salmuth. Editio
secunda. Ambergæ: M. Forster, 1607.
    8 *l*., 751 p., 16 *l*.

3038. ——. ——. Francofurti: G. Tampach
[1629]-1631.
2 v. in 1.

3039. ——. ——. Francofurti: G. Schönwetter vidua et hared., 1660.
2 v. in 1.

3040. ——. The history of many memorable
things lost, which were in use among the
ancients ... done into English ... from Salmuth's large annotations; with several
additions throughout ... London: for J. Nicholson and J. Morphew, 1715.
7 ℓ., 452 p., 6 ℓ., 16 p.

3041. PANSA, Martino. Pharmacotheca
publica et privata. Das ist: Stadt Hoff und
Hauss Apothecke ... Leipzig: J. Glück, 1622.
3 pts. in 1 v.

PANTALEONE, pseud. See Gassmann,
Franz.

3042. PANTHEO, Giovanni Agostino. Ars
transmvtationis metallicae cvm Leonis X.
ponti. max. et conci. capi. decemvirvm
Venetorvm edicto. [Venetiis: J. Tacuinus,
1519.]
38 numb. ℓ. illus.

3043. ——. Ars et theoria transmvtationis
metallicæ cum voarchadúmia, proportionibus,
numeris, & iconibus rei accomodis illustrata
... [Parisiis] V. Gualtherot, 1550.
34 numb. ℓ. illus.

3044. ——. Voarchadvmia contra alchímiam:
ars distincta ab archimía, & sophia: cum additionibus: proportionibus: numeris: & figuris
opportunis ... Venetiis: 1530.
3 ℓ., 69 numb. ℓ. illus.

3045. ——. ——. Parisiis: V. Gualtherot,
1550.
55 numb. ℓ., 1 ℓ.
With his Ars et theoria transmvtationis
... 1550.

3046. PAPA, Guiseppe del. Della natvra
dell'vmido, e del secco, lettera all' ...
Francesco Redi ... Firenze: V. Vangelisti,
1681.
220 p. illus.

3047. PAPACINO D'ANTONI, Alessandro
Vittorio. Examen de la poudre. Traduit de
l'italien par M. le Vicomte de Flavigny.
Amsterdam: M.M. Rey ..., 1772.
4 ℓ., 240 p. illus.

3048. PAPIN, Nicolas. De pvlvere sym-
patheico dissertatio. Amplissimo & excel-
lentiss v. Gvido Antonio Albanesio dicata.
Patavii: M. Cadorini, 1654.
6 ℓ., 48 p.

PARACELSUS. Abrégé de la doctrine
de Paracelse. See Colonna, Francesco Maria
Pompeo.

3049. ——. Archidoxa ... von Beymligkeyten
der Natur, zehen Bücher. Item, I. De tincura
physicorum. II. De occulta philosophia.
Strassburg: T. Rihel, 1570.
242 ℓ.

3050. ——. Paracelsus his archidoxes ...
disclosing the genuine way of making quint-
essences ... etc. Together with his books
Of renovation & restauration. Of the tincture
of the philosophers. Of the manual of the
philosophical medicinal stone ... And finally
his seven books, Of the degrees and compositions of receipts, and natural things ...
Englished, and published by J.H. London:
for W.S. and S. Thomson, 1660.
4 ℓ., 158 p., 1 ℓ., 171 p.

3051. ——. ——. London: for W.S. and S.
Thomson, 1661.
4 ℓ., 158 p., 1 ℓ., 171 p.

3052. ——. Avrora thesavrvsqve philosophorvm ... Accessit Monarchia physica
per Gerardvm Dornevm ... Præterea Anatomia
uiua Paracelsi ... Basileæ: T. Guarinus,
1577.
191 p. illus.

3053. ——. Paracelsus his aurora, & treasure of the philosophers. As also the water-
stone of the wise men ... Faithfully Englished
and published by J.H. ... London: for G. Calvert, 1659.
4 ℓ., 229 p., 1 ℓ.

3054. ——. Das Buch Paragranvm ... Item,
Von Anderlassens, Schrepffens vnd Purgirens
rechtem Gebrauch. Alles new publicirt durch
Doctrem Adamum von Bodenstein ... Franckfort: C. Egenolffs Erben, 1565.
8 ℓ., 175 numb. ℓ.

3055. ——. Das Buch Paramirvm ... Item,
Vom Fundament vnd Weissheit der Künsten,
der Seelen vnd Leibs Kranckheiten. New in Truck
verfertiget durch Doctorem Adamum von Bodenstein ... Franckfurt: C. Egenolffs Erben, 1565.
16 ℓ., 2-124 numb. ℓ., 4 ℓ.
With his Das Buch Paragranvm ... 1565.

3056. ———. Centum quindecim curationes
experimētáque, è Germanico idiomate in
Latinū versa. Accesserunt qvædam præclara
atque vtilissima à B.G. à Portu Aquitano
annexa. Item abdita quædam Isaaci Hellan-
di de opere vegetabili & animali ... Adiuncta
est denuo Practica operis magni Philippi à
Rouillasco Pedemontano ... Lugduni: J. Ler-
tout, 1582.
   8 *l.*, 165 p.
   With his De summis naturæ mysteriis ...
1584.

———. One hundred and fourteen experiments and cures. *In* Fioravanti, L.,
Three exact pieces ... 1652, 1653.

3057. ———. Chymischer Psalter, oder
Philosophische Grundsätze vom Stein derer
Weisen Anno 1522. Aus dem höchst seltenen
lateinischen Grundtext übersetzt, von einem
Liebhaber natürlicher Geheimnisse 1771.
Berlin: J.F. Vieweg [1771?].
   8 *l.*, 36 p.
   With Osten, H.v., Eine grosse Herzstärk-
ung ... 1771.

3058. ———. De summis naturæ mysteriis
commentarij tres, a Gerardo Dorn conuersi
... Basileæ: ex officina Pernæa per C. Waldkirch, 1584.
   8 *l.*, 173 [i.e. 149] p., 5 *l.*   illus., port.

3059. ———. Of the supreme mysteries of
nature. Of the spirits of the planets. Occult
philosophy. The magical, sympathetical,
and antipathetical cure of wounds and diseases. The mysteries of the twelve signs of
the zodiack. Englished by R. Turner ... London: J.C. for N. Brook and J. Harison, 1656.
   8 *l.*, 158 p., 2 *l.*   illus.

3060. ———. Etliche Tractat ... I. Von
natürlichen Dingen. II. Beschreibung etlicher
Kreuter. III. Von Metallen. IIII. Von Mineralien. V. Von edlen Gesteinen. Itzt wider
von newem auss Theophrasti Handschrifft
mit Fleiss vbersehen vnd corrigirt ... Strassburg: C. Müllers Erben, 1582.
   6 *l.*, 499 p.
   With Reusner, H., Pandora ... 1582.

3061. ———. Der grossem Wundartzney das
erst[-ander] Buch ... Getruckt nach dem
ersten Exemplar, so D. Paracelsi handge-
schrifft gewesen ... Augspurg: H. Steyner,
1537.
   2 v. in 1.   illus.

3062. ———. Wunder Artzney vnnd verbor-

gine Geheimnisse Allergeheimnissen, etc.
in III Bücher verfasset ... Basel: S. Henricpetri [1586].
   32 *l.*, ccxxiiii p., 2 *l.*   illus.

3063. ———. Gröstes und höchstes Ge-
heimnüsz aller seiner Geheimnüsse ... Nebst
einem Anhang noch mehr andrer fast unglaub-
lichen raren Curiositäten ... [Franckfurt] 1686.
   2 *l.*, 80 p.   illus.

3064. ———. Labyrintvs vnd Irrgang der
vermeinten Artzet. Item, Siben Defensiones,
oder Schirmreden. Item, Von Vrsprung vnd
Vrsachen des Griess, Sands, vnd Steins ...
Durch D. Adam von Bodenstein ... an tag
geben ... Basel: S. Apiarius, im Verlag P.
Pernae, 1574.
   8 *l.*, 171 numb. *l.*

3065. ———. Metamorphosis ... Durch D.
Adamen von Bodenstein ... in druck gegeben.
Basel: S. Apiarius, im Verlag P. Pernae, 1574.
   19 *l.*, 292 p.
   With his Labyrintvs ... 1574.

3066. ———. Of the chymical transmutation,
genealogy and generation of metals and minerals. Also, Of the Urim and Thummim of the
Jews. With an appendix, of the vertues and
use of an excellent water made by Dr. Trigge.
The second part of the mumial treatise. Whereunto is added, Philosophical and chymical
experiments of ... Raymund Lully ... Translated into English by R. Turner ... London:
for R. Moon and H. Fletcher, 1657.
   4 *l.*, 166 p.

———. Of the nature of things, nine
books. *In* Sendivogius, M., A new light of
alchymie ... 1650, 1674.

3067. ———. Opera omnia medico-chemico-
chirvrgica ... Editio novissima et emendatis-
sima, ad Germanica & Latina exemplaria ac-
curatissimè collata ... Genevæ: I. Antonij &
S. de Tournes, 1658.
   3 v.   port.

3068. ———. Operum medico-chimicorum
sive paradoxorvm ... Francofurto: Collegio
Musarum Palthenianarum, 1603.
   4 v. in 2.
   The first four of eleven volumes.

3069. ———. Prognosticatio ... ad illvstris-
simvm ac potentissimum principem Ferdinan-
dum Roman. regem ... atque archiducem Aus-
triæ conscripta. Anno 1536. [n.p.: ca. 1560-158
   36 *l.*   illus.

3070. ———. Sechster Theil der Bücher und Schrifften ... jetzt auffs new auss den Originalien und Theophrasti engener Handt-schrifft ... an Tag geben durch Ioannem Hvservm ... Franckfort an Meyn: J. Wechels Erben, 1603.

6 *l.*, 242 p.
The sixth part only.

3071. ———. The secrets of physick and philosophy, divided into two bookes ... First written in the German tongue ... and now published in the English tongue, by Iohn Hester ... London: A.M. for W. Lugger, 1633.

11 *l.*, 196 p., 8 *l.*

———. Three books of philosophy written to the Athenians. *In* Croll, O., Philosophy reformed ... 1657.

3072. ———. Zween vnderschiedene Tractat ... Auss dem fünfften vnd siebendem Theyl seiner operum in quarto zu Basel getruckt ... in offentlichen Truck publicieret durch Benedictū Figulum Utenhoviatem ... Strassburg: L. Zetzner, 1608.

303 p.   chart.

———. *See also* Cardilucius, J.H., Magnalia medico-chymica ... 1676.

———. *See also* Dorn, Gerhard, Congeries Paracelsicae chemiae de transmutationibus metallorum ... 1581.

———. *See also* Gohory, J., Theophrasti Paracelsi Compendium ... 1567.

3073. PARA DU PHANJAS, François. Theórie des êtres sensibles, ou cours complet de physique ... Paris: C.A. Jombert, 1772.

4 v.

3074. ———. Théorie des nouvelles découvertes en genre de physique et de chymie ... Paris: Didot, 1786.

604 p.   illus.

3075. PARÉ, Ambroise.   De chirurgie, ende alle de opera ... nu eerst uyt de Francoysche ... overgeset: door D. Carolum Battum ... Noch is op het niuws hier by ghevoeght De beschrijvinge der deelen des menschelijcken lithaems ... D. Joh. Fernelium ... Amstelredam: J. Markus, 1610.

8 *l.*, 940 p., 6 *l.*; 42 p., 1 *l.*

3076. ———. An explanation of the fashion and vse of three and fifty instruments of

chirvrgery. Gathered out of Ambrosius Pareus ... by H.C.   London: for M. Sparke, 1631.

2 *l.*, 60 p., 2 *l.*   illus., folio.
With Crooke, H., Μικροκοσμογραφία ... 1631, as issued.

3077. ———. Opera ... Latinitate donata, Iacobi Gvillemeav ... Parisiis: I. Dv-Pvys, 1582.

5 *l.*, 884 p., 12 *l.*   illus.

3078. ———. The works ... translated out of Latin, and compared with the French, by Th. Johnson: together with three tractates concerning the veins, arteries, and nerves: exemplified with large anatomical figures. Translated out of Adrianus Spigelius. London: printed by M. Clark, sold by J. Clark, 1678.

10 *l.*, 713 p.; 2 *l.*, 44 p., 9 *l.*   illus.

3079. PARIS. Université. Faculté de médecine.   Rapport de Messieurs les commissaires nommés par la faculté de médecine de Paris, pour se transporter aux nouvelles eaux minérales de Passy ... [Paris] la veuve Quillau, 1759.

32 p.

3080. ———. Statuts de la Faculté de Medecine en l'Université de Paris ... fait & mis en ordre par Maistre Denis Puylon ... Paris: F. Muguet, 1672.

var. pag.

3081. PARISOT, Jean Patrocle.   La foy devoilée par la raison, dans la connoissance de Dieu, de ses mysteres et de la natvre ... Premiere edition. Paris: chez l'auteur, 1681.

18 *l.*, 171, 97-280 p., 4 *l.*
Bound in full red morocco with the arms, on both covers, of Marie-Anne-Christine-Victoire de Bavière, wife of Louis Dauphin.

3082. PARIZ, Ferencz Pápai.   Pax corporis, Az az: az emberi testnek belso nyavalyáinak okairól, feszkeirol, s'-azoknak orvoslásának módgyáról való tracta ... Locsén: B. Samuel, 1692.

8 *l.*, 339 p., 2 *l.*

3083. PARKINSON, John.   Paradisi in sole paradisus terrestris. Or A garden of all sorts of pleasant flowers ... with a kitchen garden of all manner of herbes ... [London: H. Lownes and R. Yovng, 1629.]

6 *l.*, 612 p., 8 *l.*   illus., port.

3084. ———. ———. The second impression much corrected and enlarged. London: R.N.,

sold by R. Thrale, 1656.
6 *l*., 612 p., 8 *l*.   illus.

3085. ————. Theatrum botanicvm: The
theater of plants. Or, An herball of a large
extent ... London: T. Cotes, 1640.
10 *l*., 1755 p., 1 *l*.   illus.

3086. PARSONS, James.   The Crounian
lectures on muscular motion. For the years
MDCCXLIV and MDCCXLV. Read before the
Royal Society ... London: for C. Davis, 1745.
viii, 86 p.
With Stuart, A., Dissertatio de structura
et motu musculari ... 1738.

3087. ————. Human physiognomy explained
in the Crounian lectures on muscular motion.
For the year MDCCXLVI. Read before the
Royal Society ... London: for C. Davis, 1747.
2 *l*., viii p., 4 *l*., 82 p., 3 *l*.   illus.
With Stuart, A., Dissertatio de structura
et motu musculari ... 1738.

3088. PARTLIZ, Simeon, *von Spitzberg.* A
new method of physick: or, A short view of
Paracelsus and Galen's practice; in 3. treatises ... Written in Latin ... Translated into
English by Nicholas Culpeper ... London:
P. Cole ..., 1654.
10 *l*., 548 [i.e. 348] p.

3089. PARTRIDGE, John.   The treasurie of
commodious conceits, and hidden secretes,
commonlie called The good huswiues closet
of prouision, for the health of her houshold
... London: R. Jones, 1591.
47 *l*.
With Boules, R., The queens royal closet
... [n.d.].

3090. ————. The treasurie of hidden secrets.
Commonlie called, The good-huswiues closet
of prouision, for the health of her houshold
... London: I.R. for E. White, 1600.
27 [of 36] *l*.

3091. ————. ————. London: J. Bell, 1653.
36 *l*.

3092. ————. The widowes treasvre, plenti-
fully furnished with sundrey precious & approved secrets in physick and chirurgery ...
London: for J.W., 1655.
48 *l*.
Lacking the last leaf.
With Boules, R., The queens royal closet
... [n.d.].

3093. PASCAL, Jacques.   Discovrs conte-

nant la conference de la pharmacie chymiqve,
ou spagirique, auec la Galenique, ou ordi-
naire ... Tholose: D. Bosc, 1616.
24 *l*., 330 p., 2 *l*.

3094. ————. Traité des eaux de Bourbon
l'Archambaud selon les principes de la
nouvelle physique ... Paris: L. d'Houry, 1699.
7 *l*., 373 p., 3 *l*.

3095. PASSERA, Felice.   Il nvovo tresoro
degl' arcani farmacologici galenici, &
chimici, ò spargirici ... Venetia: G. Parè,
1688-1689.
2 v. in 1.   illus.

3096. PASTON, William.   A catalogue of
the library of the Right Honourable the Earl
of Yarmouth ... by Olive Payne. [London:
1734.]
1 *l*., 50, 16 p.

3096a. PATIN, Charles.   Traité des tovrbes
combvstibles. Paris: I. dv Bray & P. Variqvet,
1663.
10 *l*., 122 p., 3 *l*.

3097. PATIN, Guy.   L'esprit de Guy Patin,
tiré de ses conversations, de son cabinet,
et ses lettres, & de ses autres ouvrages.
Avec son portrait historique. Amsterdam: H.
Schelten, 1709.
● 11 *l*., 380 p.

3098. ————. Lettres choisies. Dans les-
quelles sont contenuës, plusieurs particu-
larités historiques sur la vie & la mort des
sçavans de ce siécle, sur leurs ecrits &
plusieurs autres choses curieuses depuis
l'an 1645. jusqu'en 1672. Augmentées de plus
de 300. lettres dans cette derniére edition;
et divisées en trois volumes. Cologne: P. du
Laurens, 1691.
3 v.   illus.

3099. PATRIZI, Francesco.   Magia philosophica hoc est ... Svmmi philosophi Zoroaster, & eius 320. oracula chaldaica. Asclepii
dialogus, & philosophia magma Hermetis
Trismegisti. Poemander. Sermo sacer. Clavis.
Sermo ad filium. Sermo ad Asclepium. Minerva
mundi & alia miscellanea. Iam nunc primum
ex Biblioteca Ranzoviana è tenebris eruta &
latine reddita. Hambvrgi: 1593.
1 *l*., 254 numb. *l*., 2 *l*.

3100. ————. Nova de vniversis philosophia
... Qvibvs postremo svnt adiecta, Zoroastis
oracula ... Hermetis Trismegisti libelli, &
fragmenta ... Asclepij discipuli tres libelli ...

Venetijs: R. Meiettus, 1593.
  var. par.

3101. PAULLI, Simon. Commentarius de
abusu tabaci Americanorum veteri, et herbae
thée Asiaticorum in Europa novo ... Argentorati: S. Paulli, 1665.
  11 ℓ., 56 numb. ℓ., 2 ℓ.   illus., port.

3102. ——. A treatise on tobacco, tea,
coffee, and chocolate ... now translated by
Dr. James. London: for T. Osborne ..., 1746.
  2 ℓ., 171 p.   illus.

3103. ——. Quadripartitum botanicum de
simplicivm medicamentorvm facultatibus ...
Argentorati: S. Paulli, 1667-1668.
  2 pts. in 1 v.

3104. PAULLINI, Christian Franz. Neu
vermehrte heylsame Dreck-Apotheke ... nun
zum viertenmahl um ein merckliches verbessert und mit dem andern Theil vermehrt.
Franckfurth am Mayn: F. Knochen, 1699-1714.
  2 v. in 1.   illus.

3105. ——. Sacra herba, seu Nobilis sal-
via, juxta methodum et leges illustris academiæ naturæ curiosorum ... Augustæ Vinde-
locorum: L. Kroniger ... [1688].
  8 ℓ., 414 p., 5 ℓ.   illus.

     PAULUS *Aegineta*. De crisi & diebus
decretorijs. *In* Joannes Actuarius, De urinis
... 1529.

3106. ——. Opera, a Ioanne Gvinterio
Andernaco medico exercitatissimo summique
iudicij conuersa, & illustrata commentarijs.
Adiectæ sunt annotationes Iacobi Govpyli
... Lvgdvni: G. Rouillius, 1551.
  8 ℓ., 846 p., 32 ℓ.

3107. PAYER, Wenceslaus. De thermis
Carolinis tractatvs ... cui adjunctæ sunt
ejusdem argumenti clarissimorum quorundam
medicorum epistolæ à D. Michaele Revdenio
... publicatæ. Accessit ejusdem D. Reudenii
judicium de novo gummi purgante, ad D.
Iohan-Adamum Schvvartzium ... Lipsiæ: L.
Cober, 1614.
  226 p.

3108. PAZ RODRIGUEZ, José Maria de la.
Disertacion fisico-chimica del examen,
analisis y virtudes medicinales de las aguas
de la fuente mineral de la villa de Espinoso
del Rey ... Madrid: la viuda e hijo de Marin,
1798.
  7 ℓ., 64 p.

3109. PEARSON, John. Practical observations on cancerous complaints ... Also, critical remarks on some of the operations performed in cancerous cases ... London: for
the author and J. Johnson, 1793.
  2 ℓ., iv, xii, 122 p.

3110. PEARSON, Richard. Thesaurus medi-
caminum. A new collection of medical prescriptions ... The second edition, with an
appendix, and other additions. By a member
of the London College of Physicians. London:
R. Baldwin, 1794.
  xx, 412 p.   charts.

3111. PECHEY, John. The compleat herbal
of physical plants. Containing all such English and foreign herbs, shrubs and trees, as
are used in physick and surgery ... London:
for H. Bonwicke, 1694.
  4 ℓ., 349 p., 16 ℓ.

3112. PECHLIN, Johann Nicolas. De purgantium medicamentorvm facultatibus exercitatio nova. Lugd. Batav. & Amstelod.:
D., A., & A. à Gaasbeek, 1672.
  15 ℓ., 515 p.   illus., charts.

3113. PELLETIER, Bertrand. Instruction sur
l'art de séparer le cuivre du métal des cloches;
publiée par ordre du Comité de Salut Public.
Paris: l'imprimerie du comitè de salut public
[1794].
  32 p.   illus.

3114. ——. Memoires et observations de
chimie ... recueillis et mis en ordre, par
Charles Pelletier ... Paris: Croullebois ...,
1798.
  2 v.   port., illus.

3115. PEMBERTON, Henry. A scheme for a
course of chymistry ... [London: 1731.]
  15 p.

3116. PEMELL, Robert. Tractatvs de simplicium medicamentorum facultatibus. A
treatise on the nature and qualities of such
simples as are most frequently used in medicines ... London: M. Simmons for P. Stephens,
1652.
  8 ℓ., [319] p., 6 ℓ.

     PENA, Pierre, *joint author*. Nova
stirpium adversaria. *See* L'Obel, M. de.

3117. PENICHER, Louis. Traicté des embau-
memens, selon les anciens et les modernes.
Avec une description de quelques compositions balsamiques & odorantes ... Paris:

B. Girin, 1699.
    12 *l*., 315 p., 1 *l*.

3118.   PENOT, Bernard Georges.   De de-
nario medico, qvo decem medicaminibvs,
omnibus morbis internis medendi via docetur.
Cui plures tractatus additi sunt ... Bernæ
Helvetiorum: J. Le Preux, 1608.
    1 *l*., 203 p., 1 *l*.

3119.   ——.   Penotus παλίμβιθ, or The
alchymists enchiridion. In two parts ... The
whole written in Latin long since ... and
now faithfully Englished and claused by
B.P. Philalethes. London: for J. Wyat, 1692.
    4 *l*., 61 p., 4 *l*.

3120.   ——, *ed.*   Tractatvs varii, de vera
præparatione et vsv medicamentorvm chymicorum nunc primum editi ... Francofurti:
apud I. Feyrabend, impensis P. Fischeri,
1594.
    256 p.

    ——.   *See also* Fioravanti, L.,
Three exact pieces ... 1652, 1653.

    ——.   *See also* Paracelsus, Centum
quindecim curationes ... 1582.

3121.   PERCY, Pierre François.   Manuel
chirurgien-d'armée, ou Instruction de
chirurgie-militaire sur le traitement des
plaies, & spécialement de celles d'armes
à feu ... Paris: Méquignon, 1792.
    xvi, 272 p.   illus.

3122.   PEREZ, Vincente.   El promotor de la
salud de los hombres, sin dispendio el
menor de sus caudales ... Toledo: T. Piferrer,
1753.
    8 *l*., 68 p.

3123.   PEREZ DE VARGAS, Bernardo.   De re
metallica en el qval se tratan mvchos y
diversos secretos del conocimento de toda
suerte de minerales ... Madrid: P. Cosin,
1569.
    18 *l*., 206 numb. *l*., 1 *l*.   illus.

3124.   ——.   Traité singulier de métallique
... Traduit de l'original Espagnol imprimé à
Madrid en 1568 ... Par G.G. Paris: Prault,
1743.
    2 v.   illus.

3125.   PERNAUER, Georg Ferdinand.   Panacea
mirabilis, corrigendi potissimum vitiosi
sangvinis ... nunc autem denuo revisa sum-
moque studio elaborata a P.C. Lipsiæ: J.

C. Martinus, 1718.
    2 *l*., 59 p.
    Text in Latin and German.

3126.   PERNETY, Antoine Joseph.   Dictionnaire mytho-hermétique ... Paris: Bauche,
1758.
    2 *l*., xx, 546 p., 3 *l*.

3127.   ——.   Les fables égyptiennes et
grecques ... avec une explication des hiéro-
glyphes ... Paris: Delalain, 1786.
    2 v.

3128.   PERRINET D'ORVAL, Jean Charles.
Essay sur les feux d'artifice pour le spectacle et pour la guerre. Paris: Coustelier,
1745.
    xii p., 2 *l*., 224 p.   illus.

3129.   PERSON, David.   Varieties: or, A
svrveigh of rare and excellent matters ...
Wherein the principall heads of diverse
sciences are illustrated ... London: R. Badger
for T. Alchorn, 1635.
    34 *l*., 256 p., 1 *l*., 105 p.

3130.   PERTHUIS DE LAILLEVAULT, Leon de.
L'art de febriquer le salin et la potasse.
Suivi des expériences sur les moyens de
multiplier la fabrication de la potasse, par
le citoyen Pertuis, & par le citoyen B.G.
Sage ... Paris: Cuchet [1794].
    viii, 106 p.   illus., chart.

3131.   PETERMANN, Andreas.   Chimia, opus
posthumum editum a filio D. Benj. Bened.
Petermanno ... Lipsiæ: F. Lanckis, 1708.
    2 *l*., 130 p., 18 *l*.

    PETERSEN, Johan Christian Peter.
Dissertatio de cortice Peruviano. *See* Linné,
C. von, *praeses.* Entry 2439.

3132.   PETETIN, Jacques Henri Désiré.
Mémoire sur la découverte des phénomenes
que présentent la catalepsie et le somnam-
bulisme ... [Lyon] 1787.
    2 pts. in 1 v.

3133.   PETIT, Jean Louis.   Traité des maladies des os, dans lequel on a représenté les
appareils & les machines qui conviennent à
leur guérison. Nouvelle edition, revue &
augmentée d'un discours historique & critique
sur cet ouvrage, & de l'eloge de l'auteur.
Par M. Louis. Paris: Méquignon, 1784.
    2 v.   illus.

3134.   PETRARCA, Francesco.   De remediis

vtriusquᵉ fortunæ. Libri dvo ... [Bern] I. Le Preux, 1595.
686 p., 22 *l*.

3135. ——. Phisicke against fortune, as well prosperous, as aduerse, conteyned in two bookes ... And now first Englished by Thomas Twyne. London: R. Watkyns, 1579.
8 *l*., 342 numb. *l*., 3 *l*.

3136. ——. Opera ... de rimedi de l'vna et l'altra fortvna, ad azone, tradotta per Remigio Fiorentino ... Vinetia: G.G. di Ferrari, 1549.
416 numb. *l*., 3 *l*.

3137. PETRINA, Gaspar. Tractatvs confec. de hyacinto, et confect. alchermes, cum commentariis Io. Lvdovici Bertavdi ... editio IIII. Accesserunt De electione simpliciũ medicamentorum rythmi M. Othonis Cremonensis & Io. Derrames ... additur præterea examen pharmaceuticum tyronibus faciendum ex operibus dicti Bertaudi excerptum ... Tavrini: de Calveriis, 1619.
109 p.

3138. PETRUS ARLENSIS DE SCUDALUPIS. D. Petrus Arlensis de Scudalupis enucleatus, oder Kurtzer Auszug der alchymistischen Processe und anderer Curiositäten, so dieser Autor, als Presbyter Hierosolymitanus, in seinem vormahls anno 1610 zu Pariss gedruckten, anietzo aber sehr raran Tractat von der Sympathia der sieben Metallen ... herausgegeben; nunmehr aus dem Lateinischen ins Teutsche übersetzt ... Berlin: J.A. Rüdiger, 1715.
4 *l*., 104 p.

——. Sympathia septem metallorum. *In* Leonardi, C., Speculum lapidum ... 1610, etc.

PETRUS DE ALLIACO. *See* Ailly, Pierre d', *cardinal*.

PETRUS *Hispanus. See* Joannes XXI, *pope*.

3139. PETTUS, *Sir* John. Fleta minor. The laws of art and nature, in knowing, judging, assaying, fining, refining and inlarging the bodies of confin'd metals. In two parts. The first contains Assays of Lazarus Erckern ... The second contains Essays on metallick words ... by Sir John Pettus ... London: for the author by T. Dawks, 1683.
2 pts. in 1 v. illus., port.

3140. ——. ——. London: S. Bateman, 1686.
2 pts. in 1 v. illus., port.

3141. PEYER, Johann Konrad. Exercitatio anatomico-medica de glandulis intestinorum, earumque usu & affectionibus. Cui subjungitur anatome ventriculi Gallinacei. Scafhusae: impensis O. à Waldkirch, typis A. Riedingii, 1677.
14 *l*., 136 p. illus.

3142. ——. Parerga anatomica et medica ... reliqua sex ... Amstelædami: H. Wetstenius, 1682.
140 p., 6 *l*. illus.

PEYRILHE, Bernard. *See* Dujardin, E., Histoire de la chirurgie ... 1774-1780.

PFEIFFER, Johan. Fungus melitensis. *See* Linné, C. von, *praeses*. Entry 2435.

3143. PFINGSTEN, Johann Hermann. Bibliotheck ausländischer Chemisten, Mineralogen und mit Mineralien beschäftiger Fabrikanten nebst derley biographischen Nachrichten ... Nürnberg: J.A. Stein, 1781-1784.
4 v. ports.

3144. ——. Deutsches Dispensatorium oder allgemeines Apothekerbuch nach den neuesten und besten lateinischen Dispensatorien und Pharmacopöen ... nach alphabetischer Ordnung eingerichtet. Frankfurt: J.B. Mezler, 1783.
4 *l*., xx p., 1 *l*., 900 numb. col.

3145. PHAEDRO, George. The art of chymistry, written in Latin ... and done into English by Nicholas Culpepper ... The third edition. London: for S. Neale, 1674.
1 *l*., 133 p.

3146. PHARMACIA galenica & chymica, Dat is: De vermeerderde ende verbeterde apotheker en alchymiste licht ende distilleer-konst ... Antwerpen: R. Sleghers, 1667.
8 *l*., 466 p., 11 *l*., 70 p., 1 *l*.

In the following entries (3147-3249) of Pharmacepoeias, the terminal spelling of the word pharmacopoeia (that is, -poea or -poeia) is not considered in alphabetizing. Title entries, such as Pharmacopoeia Chirurgica, follow these official entries. For other Pharmacopoeias, see Antidotarium, Apoteck, Codex, Codice, Conspectus,

Dispensatorium, Farmacopoea, Formulae,
Prospectus, and Ricettario.

3147. PHARMACOPOEA AMSTELREDAMENSIS.
Pharmacopoea Amstelredamensis, in qua
medicamenta, quæ Amstelodami in usu sunt,
artificiose præparantur ut et oerum vires et
doses. Lugduni Batavorum: C. Boutestein,
1701.
    4 *l.*, 189 p., 9 *l.*

3148. ——. ——. Senatus auctoritate
munita & recognita. Amsteled.: H. Wetsten
[1701?].
    134 p., 5 *l.*

3149. ——. ——. Amstelodami: P.H. Dronsberg, 1792.
    xvi, 210 p., 1 *l.*

3150. ——. Vernieuwde Amsterdamsche
apotheek, in Nederduitsch overgebragt. Amsterdam: P. van der Berge, 1733.
    7 *l.*, 210 p., 13 *l.*

3151. ——. ——. Amsterdam: J. Morterrf,
1767.
    5 *l.*, 210 p., 13 *l.*

3152. ——. De nieuwe Amsterdamsche
apotheek. Uit het Latyn vertaald. Amsterdam:
P.H. Dronsberg, 1795.
    1 *l.*, xvi, 180 p.

3153. PHARMACOPOEA ANTVERPIA. Pharmacia Antverpiensis galeno-chymica. A
medicis iuratis, & collegii medici official-
ibus ... edita ... Antverpiæ: G. Willemsens,
1660.
    24 *l.*, 285 p., 16 *l.*

3154. PHARMACOPOEIA ARGENTORATENSIS.
Pharmacopoeia Argentoratensis, incl. senatvs
jvssv pvbl. a collegio medico adornata.
Argentorati: J.R. Dulssecker, 1725.
    7 *l.*, 260 p., 8 *l.*, 60 p., 1 *l.*

3155. ——. ——. Revisa et ad usum hodiernum accommodata a collegio medico. Argentorati: J.G. Bauer, 1757.
    9 *l.*, 204 p., 6 *l.*

3156. PHARMACOPOEA AUGUSTANA.
Pharmacopoeia, sev Medicamentarium pro
Rep. Augustana. Cvi accessere simplicia
omnia officinis nostris vsitata, & annota-
tiones in eadem & composita, ab Adolpho
Occone ... omnia nunc denuo recognita.
[Avgvstæ Vindelicorvm: svmptibvs G. Vvilleri,
apud M. Mangerum, 1574.]

1 *l.*, 702 p., 15 *l.*

3157. ——. Pharmacopoeia Avgvstana
avspicio amplissimi senatvs cvra octava
collegii medici recognita Hippocratica et
Hermetica mantissa locvpletata. Augusta:
[A. Apergerus] 1643.
    8 *l.*, 83, 795 p., 46 *l.*   charts.

3158. ——. ——. Augusta: [A. Apergerus]
1646.
    5 *l.*, 26, 351 p., 16 *l.*, 56 p., 3 *l.* charts.

3159. ——. Pharmacopoeia Augustana reformata, et eivs Mantissa. Cum Animadversionibus Joannis Zwelferi ... Annexa ejusdem
autoris Pharmacopoeia regia. Goudæ: W. Ver-
hoeven, 1653.
    7 *l.*, 917 p., 9 *l.*; 8 *l.*, 198 p., 5 *l.*

3160. ——. ——. Accessere etiam huic
editioni bini discursus apologetici contra
Otth. Tachen & Francisc. Verny. Dordrechti:
V. Caimax, 1672.
    3 *l.*, 472 p.

3161. ——. Animadversiones in Pharma-
copoeiam Augustanam et annexam ejus
Mantissam, sive Pharmacopoeia Augustana
reformata ... Nunc secundum in lucem edita,
cum annexa appendice, operâ & studio Joannis Zwelfer ... Noribergae: W. & J.A. Endter,
1657.
    3 pts. in 1 v.

3162. ——. ——. Nunc quintâ vice revisa
... Norimbergæ: B.J. Endter, 1714.
    12 *l.*, 640 p., 17 *l.*, 112 p., 2 *l.*

3163. ——. Pharmacopoeia Augustana
renovata ... Augustae Vindelicorum: J.C.
Wagner, 1710.
    8 *l.*, 324 p., 6 *l.*, 40 p.

3164. ——. ——. Augustae Vindelicorum:
J.J. Lotter, 1734.
    8 *l.*, 326 p., 6 *l.*, 39 p.

3165. PHARMACOPOEA AUSTRIACA. Pharmacopoea Austriaco-provincialis. Editio quarta
auctior ... Viennæ: I.T.N. de Trattner, 1780.
    4 *l.*, 312 p., 9 *l.*

3166. ——. —— emendata. Viennæ: C.F.
Wappler, 1794.
    viii, 195 p.

3167. ——. Pharmacopoea Austriaco-
castrensis. Viennae: A.A. Patzowsky, 1795.
    2 *l.*, 102 p.

3168. ——. Apotheek der oostenrijksche staaten ... opgesteld door de hooggeleerde en wijdberoemde heeren A. Baron von Störk, N.J. de Jacquin, en J.J. de Well. Naar den tweeden druk uit het Latijn vertaald. Rotterdam: R. Arrenberg, 1780.
4 *l.*, 309 p., 17 *l.*

3169. ——. Oesterreichische provinzial-pharmakopee. Wien: J.T.E. von Trattner, 1790.
4 *l.*, 420 p., 10 *l.*

——. *See also* Physisch-therapeutische Erläuterung ... 1796.

——. *See also* Dispensatorium Austriaco-Viennense.

3170. PHARMACOPOEA BORUSSICA. Pharmacopoea castrensis Borussica. Editio altera emendata. Berolini: F. Maurer, 1791.
70 p.

3171. ——. Pharmacopoea Borussica. Cum gratia et privilegio sacrae regiae majestatis. Vratislaviae: T.G. Korn, 1799.
vi p., 1 *l.*, 216 p.

——. *See also* Dispensatorium Borusso-Brandenburgicum.

3172. PHARMACOPOEA BREMENSIS. Pharmacopoea in usum officinarum Reipublicae Bremensis conscripta quam auctam & emendatam recudi coravit Thomas Volpi. Editio prima Italica ... Ticini: haered. P. Galeati, 1793.
xii, 181 p.

3173. PHARMACOPOEA BRUXELLENSIS. Pharmacopoeia Bruxellensis; jussu amplissimi senatus edita. Bruxellæ: J. Mommart, 1641.
16 *l.*, 224 p., 4 *l.*

3174. ——. ——. Editio altera. Bruxellis: A. Stryckwant & A. d'Ours, 1759.
6 *l.*, 186 p., 7 *l.*

3175. PHARMACOPOEA DANICA. Pharmacopoea Danica, regia autoritate a Collegio Medico Hauniensi conscripta. Hauniae: Heineck & Faber, 1772.
4 *l.*, 338, 70 p., 1 *l.*

3176. ——. ——. Francofurti: 1786.
364, 70 p., 1 *l.*

3177. PHARMACOPOEIA DUACENA. Pharma-

copoeia Duacena galeno-chymica nobilissimi et amplissimi senatus authoritate et jussu. Duaci: J.F. Willerval, 1732.
2 *l.*, 180 p., 4 *l.*

3178. PHARMACOPOEA EDINBURGENSIS. Pharmacopoeia Collegii Regii Medicorum Edinburgensis. Edinburgi: typis J. Mosman, impensis J. Paton ..., 1722.
1 *l.*, v p., 2 *l.*, 192 p., 10 *l.*

3179. ——. ——. Editio secunda, emendatior. Londini: J. Clarke, 1732.
xi, 192 p., 10 *l.*

3180. ——. ——. Secvndvm editionis Edinbvrgensis ... Gottingae: [n.d.].
ix p., 2 *l.*, 192 p., 9 *l.*
With Boerhaave, H., Tractatus de viribus ... 1742.

3181. ——. ——. Edinburgi: W. Sands ..., 1744.
xii, 188 p., 8 *l.*

3182. ——. ——. Edinburgi: Hamilton ..., 1756.
ix, 206 p., 8 *l.*

3183. ——. ——. Secvndvm editionis Edinbvrgensis ... Bremae: G.L. Foerster, 1766.
xii, 146 p., 9 *l.*

3184. ——. ——. Edinburgi: G. Drummond et J. Bell, 1774.
xviii p., 1 *l.*, 184 p., 8 *l.*

3185. ——. ——. reformata. Rotterodami: H. Beman ..., 1775.
xvi, 146 p., 7 *l.*

3186. ——. ——. Additamentis avcta ab Ern. Godofr. Baldinger. Bremae: G.L. Foerster, 1776.
8 *l.*, xvi, 292 p.

3187. ——. ——. Edinburgi: J. Bell, 1783.
xvi, 236 p., 10 *l.*

3188. ——. ——. Additamenta adiecit Ernestvs Godofredvs Baldinger. Editio in Germania altera. Bremae: G.L. Foerster, 1784.
12 *l.*, xiii, 2 *l.*, 423 p., 3 *l.*

3189. ——. ——. Edinburgi: W. Sands ..., 1794.
xii, 188 p., 8 *l.*

3190. ——. The dispensatory of the Royal College of Physicians in Edinburgh. Translated

from the Latin, and illustrated with notes by Peter Shaw. London: for W. & J. Innys, 1727.
xii, 281 p., 1 *l*.

3191. ——. Pharmacopoeia Edinburgensis: or, The dispensatory of the royal college of physicians in Edinburgh. Translated and improved from the third edition of the Latin ... by Peter Shaw. The fourth edition. London: for W. Innys, 1740.
6 *l*., 265 p., 1 *l*.

3192. ——. ——. The fifth edition with additions. London: for W. Innys, 1746.
6 *l*., 265 p., 1 *l*.

3193. ——. The pharmacopoeia of the Royal College of Physicians at Edinburgh. Faithfully translated from the fourth edition ... by W. Lewis. London: for J. Nourse, 1748.
8 *l*., 362 p., 19 *l*.

3194. ——. Apotheek van het Koninglyk Genootschap der Geneesheeren te Edinburg. Rotterdam: R. Arrenberg, 1774.
vi p., 3 *l*., 184 p., 23 *l*.

——. *See also* Brookes, R., The general dispensatory.

——. *See also* Lewis, W., The new dispensatory.

3195. PHARMACOPOEA GANDAVENSIS. Pharmacopoea Gandavensis nobilissimi senatus jussu renovata. Gandavi: J. Begyn, 1786.
5 *l*., 466 p.

3196. ——. —— adjunctæ sunt variæ adnotationes criticæ & omstrictovæ à P. van Baveghem. Gandavi: L. Le Maire, 1787.
5 *l*., 192 p.

3197. PHARMACOPOEA GRONINGANA. Pharmacopoea Groningana. Groningæ: G. Elamæ, 1729.
5 *l*., 120 p., 11 *l*.

3198. PHARMACOPOEA HAGIENSIS. Pharmacopoea Hagiensis communi collegii medici ejusdem loci opera adornata. Hagæ Comitvm: J. Tongerloo, 1659.
6 *l*., 122 p., 5 *l*.

3199. ——. Pharmacopoea Hagana ex auctoribtate magistratus poliatrorum opera instaurata et aucta. Hagæ-Comitum: F. Boucquet, 1738.

12 *l*., 196 p., 12 *l*. illus., charts.

3200. ——. Haegsche apotheek, op het gezag der magistraet door den arbeid der stads-doctoren ... Gravenhage: J. de Cros, 1762.
11 *l*., 272 p., 4 *l*. illus.

3201. PHARMACOPOEA HELVETICA. Pharmacopoea Helvetica in duas partes ... Accedunt Syllabus medicamentorum ... Basiliæ: J.R. Im-Hof, 1771.
23 *l*., 212, 384, 54 p. illus.

3202. PHARMACOPOEA INSTITUTI CLINICI HAMBURGENSIS. Pharmacopoea pauperum in usum Instituti Clinici Hamburgensis. Edita a Societate Medica. Editio secunda auctior & emendatior. Hamburgi: B.C. Herold viduae, 1785.
8 *l*., 48 p.
With Keup, J.B., Libellus pharmaceuticus ... 1789.

3203. PHARMACOPOEA INSULENSIS. Pharmacopoea jussu senatus Insulensis. Tertio edita. Insulis Flandrorum: J. Henry, 1772.
xx, 318 p.

3204. PHARMACOPOE LEOVARDIENSIS. De Leeuwarder apotheek, volgens de galenische en chimische wyze ... Naar den tweden Latynschen druk in't Nederduitsch vertaalt. De sesde druk. Amsterdam: N. de Wit, 1731.
9 *l*., 165 p., 8 *l*.

3205. PHARMACOPOEA LEIDENSIS. Pharmacopoea Leidensis, amplissimorum magistratuum auctoritate instaurata. Lugduni Batavorum: S. Luchtmans, 1718.
11 *l*., 155 p., 8 *l*. illus.

3206. ——. ——. Editio tertia ... Lugduni Batavorum: S. Luchtmans, 1751.
19 *l*., 176 p., 10 *l*. illus., charts.

3207. ——. ——. Editio quarta. Lugduni Batavorum: S. et J. Luchtmans, 1770.
18 *l*., 176 p., 10 *l*.

3208. PHARMACOPOEIA LONDINENSIS. Pharmacopoeia Londinensis ... Diligenter reuisa, denuo, recusa, emendatior, auctior. Tertia editio. Opera Medicorum Collegij Londinensis ... London: for J. Marriott, 1627.
19 *l*., 204 p., 3 *l*.

3209. ——. ——. Londini: typis G. Dugard, impensis S. Bowtell, 1650.
7 *l*., 212 p., 4 *l*.

3210. ——. ——. Editio novissima á
multis mendis typographicis ... purgata.
Londini: 1680.
    10 *l*., 454 p., 15 *l*.

3211. ——. ——. Editio quarta ... Londini:
F. Walthoe ..., 1711.
    2 *l*., 104, 101 p., 1 *l*.

3212. ——. ——. Londini: typis G. Bowyer,
impensis R. Knaplock ..., 1721.
    9 *l*., 154 p., 6 *l*.   illus.

3213. ——. ——. Dublini: P. Wilson et J.
Edsall, 1746.
    176 p., 1 *l*.

3214. ——. ——. Juxta postremam reno-
vationem edita. Londini: T. Longman ...,
1746.
    xvi, 174 p.   illus.

3215. ——. ——. Londini: T. Longman ...,
1747.
    xvi, 188 p.

3216. ——. ——. Juxta postremam reno-
vationem edita Londini M.DCC.XLVI. Francofvrti ad Moenvm: hæredes Stock & Schilling,
1751.
    2 *l*., xiv, 141 p.   illus.

3217. ——. ——. Una cum Meadiana.
Francofurti ad Moenum: hæredes Stock ...,
1761.
    7 *l*., 134 p.; 4 *l*., 37 p., 1 *l*.   illus.

3218. ——. ——. Una cum Meadiana.
Francof. et Lipsiæ: Fleischer, 1762.
    5 *l*., 134 p., 2 *l*.; 4 *l*., 37 p., 1 *l*.   illus.

3219. ——. ——. Londini: J. Nourse et T.
Longman, 1763.
    xvi, 188 p.

3220. ——. ——. Una cum Meadiana.
Francof. et Lipsiæ: Fleischer, 1785.
    5 *l*., 134 p.; 4 *l*., 37 p., 1 *l*.

3221. ——. ——. Londini: J. Johnson,
1788.
    xxiv, 156 p.

3222. ——. ——. Londini & Rotterodami:
J. Johnson & C.R. Hake, 1788.
    xxiv, 156 p.

3223. ——. ——. Londini: J. Johnson,
1788.
    xxiv, 182 p.

3224. ——. ——. Londini: J. Johnson
[1788?].
    xxviii, 219 p.

3225. ——. ——. Londini: J. Johnson
[1788?].
    xxiv, 166 p.

3226. ——. ——. Londini: G. Street et
T. Street [n.d.].
    2 *l*., 113 p., 1 *l*.

3227. ——. ——. Juxta postremam reno-
vationem edita Londini M.DCC.XLVI. Amstelædami: I. Tirion [n.d.].
    xvi, 174 p.   illus.

3228. ——. The new dispensatory of the
Royal College of Physicians in London.
With copious and accurate indexes. Faithfully translated from the Latin of the Pharma-
copoiea Londinensis ... London: W. Owen,
1746.
    136 [i.e. 148] p.

3229. ——. The dispensatory of the Royal
College of Physicians, London, translated
into English with remarks, &c. by H. Pemberton. The fourth edition. London: for J.
Nourse and T. Longman, 1760.
    x, 414 p.

3230. ——. ——. The fifth edition. London: for J. Nourse and T. Longman, 1773.
    x, 414 p.

3231. ——. Pharmacopée du Collége Royal
des Médecins de Londres, traduite de l'Anglois sur la seconde édition donnée avec
des remarques, par le docteur H. Pemberton.
Augmentée de plusieurs notes & observations
... Paris: Didot, 1771.
    2 v.

3232. ——. Pharmacopæa Londinensis,
of Londische apotheek ... Amsterdam: J.
Hoorn, 1696.
    6 *l*., 364 p., 6 *l*.

3233. ——. Londner Apothekerbuch. Nach
der neuesten Originalausgabe übersetzt und
mit einigen Zusäzten und Anmerkungen herausgegeben von Christian Gotthold Eschenbach.
Leipzig: S.L. Crusius, 1789.
    xxiv, 208 p.

——. *See also* Brookes, Richard;
Culpeper, Nicholas; Lewis, William; Monro,
Donald; Quincy, John; and Salmon, Wil-
liam.

3234. PHARMACOPOEIA MATRITENSIS.
Pharmacopoeia Matritensis regii, ac supremi
Hispaniarum protomedicatus auctoritate ...
Editio secunda ... Martiti: A. Perez de Soto,
1762.
16 *l.*, 556 p.

PHARMACOPOEA PARISIENSIS. *See*
Codex medicamentarius.

3235. PHARMACOPOEA PERSICA. Pharmacopoea Persica ex idiomate Persico in
Latinum conversa ... Opus missionariis,
mercatoribvs ... Lutetiæ Parisiorum: S.
Michallet, 1681.
3 *l.*, 370 p., 14 *l.*

3236. PHARMACOPOEA ROSSICA. Pharmacopoea Rossica. Petropoli: 1782.
156 p.

3237. ——. Pharmacopoea navalis Rossica
avt catalogvs omnivm necessariorvm medicamentorvm ... Revisa et approbata a Collegio Medico Imperiali edita ab Andrea
Bacheracht ... Petropoli: 1784.
60 p.
With Pharmacopoea Rossica ... 1782.

3238. PHARMACOPOEIA SANCTI BARTHOLO-
MEI. Pharmacopoeia nosocomii regalis
Sancti Bartholomei. Londini: J. Adlard, 1799.
84 p.

3239. PHARMACOPOEA SARDOA. Pharmacopoea Sardoa ex selectionribus codicibus,
optimisque scriptoribus collecta ... edita a
Iacobo Iosepho Palietti ... [Cagliari] ex regia
typographia Caralitana, 1773.
4 *l.*, 190 p., 1 *l.*

3240. PHARMACOPOEA SUECICA. Pharmacopoea Svecica. Editio altera emendata.
Homiæ: H. Fougt, 1779.
4 *l.*, 158 p.

3241. ——. ——. Ad exemplar Holmiense
a MDCCLXXX recusa. Lipsiæ: J.H.S. Hell-
mann, 1784.
130 p.

3242. PHARMACOPOEA TAURINENSIS. Pharmacopoea Taurinensis nunc primum edita
jussu Augustissimi Regis. Augustæ Taurinorum: J.B. Chais, 1736.
4 *l.*, 246 p., 8 *l.* illus.

3243. PHARMACOPOEA ULTRAJECTINA.
Pharmacopoea Ultrajectina nova. Trajecti ad
Rhenum: J. Poolsum, 1749.

4 *l.*, 240 p., 11 *l.* chart.

3244. PHARMACOPOEA WIRTENBERGICA.
Pharmacopoea Wirtenbergica in duas partes
divisa, quarum prior, materiam medicam ...
posterior, composita et præparata ... Accedit Taxa seu pretium medicamentorum. Stuttgardiæ: C. Erhard, 1741.
3 pts. in 1 v.

3245. ——. ——. Editio secunda ... Stutgardiæ: J.C. Erhard, 1750.
3 pts. in 1 v.

3246. ——. ——. Editio tertia, revisa et
emendata ... Stutgardiæ: J.C. Erhard, 1754.
3 pts. in 1 v.

3247. ——. ——. Editio nova revisa aucta
et emendata. Stutgardiæ: J.C. Erhard, 1760.
3 pts. in 1 v.

3248. ——. ——. Stutgardiæ: I. Erhard,
1771.
3 pts. in 1 v.

3249. ——. ——. Editio denuo-revisa
aucta et emendata. Stutgardiæ: hæredes
J.C. Erhard, 1786.
3 pts. in 1 v. illus.

3250. PHARMACOPOEIA CHIRURGICA; or,
Formulæ for the use of surgeons ... All the
principal formulæ of the different hospitals.
The fourth edition, corrected and enlarged.
London: G.C. and J. Robinson, 1799.
viii, 204 p.

3251. PHARMACOPOEIA MEADIANA. In
three parts. Faithfully gathered from original
prescriptions ... with an appendix containing
Prælectiones Meadianæ, or Medical lectures
... London: J. Hinton, 1758-1757.
2 v. in 1.

——. *See also* Pharmacopoeia
Londinensis ... 1761, etc.

3252. PHARMACOPOEIA PAUPERUM: or, The
hospital dispensatory. Containing the medicines used in the hospitals of London, by
the direction of Dr. Coatsworth, Dr. Mead,
Dr. Cade, Dr. Wadsworth, Dr. Hales ... London: T. Warner, 1718.
108 p.

3252a. PHARMACOPOEIA PAUPERUM, in usum
nosocomii regii Edinburgensis. Edinburgi:
Hamilton, Balfour, et. Neill, 1752.
2 *l.*, 76 p.

3252b. ———. Francof.: Fleischer, 1762.
vi, 76 p.

3253. PHARMACOPOEIA REFORMATA: or, an
essay for a reformation of the London Phar-
macoeia ... London: R. Willock, 1744.
3 *l*., 25, 292 p., 8 *l*.

3254. PHARMACOPOLÆ JUSTIFICATI: or,
Apothecaries vindicated from the imputation
of ignorance ... London: for J. Scott, 1756.
2 *l*., 31 p.

3255. PHARUS CHYMIÆ, oder Hell-leuch-
tender Wegweiser zur chymischen Wissenschafft ... von einen In Chymicis Experimentis Cooperante. Regensburg: E.A. Weiss,
1752.
3 *l*., 120 p.

PHAYER, Thomas. A treatise of the
pestilence. *In* Goeurot, J., The regiment of
life ... 1560, etc.

3256. PHELSUM, Murk van. Twee brieven
raakende de verhandeling van den heer
Tissot over de vallende ziekte. Amsterdam:
M. de Bruyn, 1776.
1 *l*., 58 p.
With Tissot, S.A.A.D., Van den aart ...
1772.

PHILALETHES, Alazanomastix, *pseud.*
See More, Henry.

PHILALETHES, Eirenaeus, *pseud.*
Abyssus alchymiae exploratus: oder Verwandelung der Metallen. *In* Quadratum alchymisticum ... 1705.

3257. ———. Enarratio methodica trium
Gebri medicinarum, in quibus continetur
lapidis philosophici vera confectio. Authore
anonymo sub nomine Aerenæei Philalethes
... Amstelodami: D. Elzevir, 1678.
222 p., 1 *l*.

———. Introitus apertus ad occlusum
regis palatium. *In* Faust, J.M., Philaletha
illustratus ... 1706.

———. Offenstehender Eingang. *In*
Cardilucius, J.H., Magnalia medico-chymica
... 1676.

3258. ———. Secrets reveal'd: or, An open
entrance to the shut-palace of the king ...
Composed by ... Anonymus, or Eyræneus
Philaletha Cosmopolita ... Published ... by
W.C. ... London: W. Godbid for W. Cooper,
1669.
15 *l*., 120 p., 3 *l*.
Profusely annotated in the hand of Sir
Isaac Newton.

3259. ———. Ripley reviv'd: or, An exposition upon Sir George Ripley's hermetico-
poetical works ... Written by Eirenæus
Philalethes an Englishman stiling himself
Citizen of the world. London: T. Ratcliff &
N. Thompson for W. Cooper, 1678.
5 pts. in 1 v.

3260. ———. Three tracts of the great medicine of philosophers for humane and metal-
line bodies ... All written in Latein by Eirenæus Philalethes Cosmopolita. Translated into
English for the benefit of the studious by a
lover of art and them. London: T. Sowle, 1694.
14 *l*., 186 p.

3261. ———. Tres tractatus de metallorum
transmutatione ... Incognito auctore ... Adjuncta est appendix medicamentorum anti-
podagricorum & calculifragi ... nunc primum
in lucem edi curavit Martinus Birrius ...
Amstelodami: J. Janssonius à Waesberge &
viduam E. Weyerstraet, 1668.
8 *l*., 110 p. port.
With Fehr, J.M., Hiera picra ... 1668.

———. *See also* Starkey, George.

PHILALETHES, Eugenius, *pseud. See*
Vaughan, Thomas.

PHILALETHES, Eugenius, F.R.S., *pseud.*
See Samber, Robert.

PHILALETHES, Eugenius, jun., *pseud.*
See Samber, Robert.

3262. PHILANDER, Joachim, *pseud.* Das
goldene Kalb, ein Götzenbild der Anbetung,
oder Physico-critico-patheologico-moralische
Untersuchung der Natur und Wirkung des
Goldes ... Nebst einer Nachricht von den
Wundern des psychoptischen Spiegels, der
neulich erfunden ist ... Aus dem Englischen
übersetzt. Hamburg: Hertel, 1745.
1 *l*., 318 p., 2 *l*.

PHILANTHROPOS, *pseud. See* Goodwin, James.

PHILANTROPOS, citoyen du monde,
pseud. See Loos, Onésime Henri de.

PHILARETES, Honorius, *pseud. See*
Rappolt, Thomas.

3263. PHILOCTETES, Eyreneus, *pseud.*
Philadelphia, or brotherly love to the studious in the Hermetick art. Wherein is discovered the principles of Hermetick philosophy ... [London] T. Sowle, 1694.
16 *l.*, 70 p.

3264. PHILOSOPHIÆ CHYMICÆ IV. vetvstis-
sima scripta. I. Senioris Zadith ... Tabula
chymica. II. Innominati philosophi Expositio tabulæ chymicæ. III. Hermetis Trismegisti Liber de compositione. IV. Anonymi
veteris philosophi Consilium coniugii ...
Omnia ex Arabico sermone Latina facta, &
nunc primum in lucem producta. Francofurti:
J. Saur, 1605.
321 p.
With Harvet, I., Animadversiones ... 1604.

3265. A PHILOSOPHICAL ENQUIRY into
some of the most considerable phenomena's
of nature. In two parts ... The whole con-
formable to the doctrine of fermentation.
London: for W. Mears and J. Brown, 1715.
6 *l.*, 189 p., 1 *l.*

3266. PHILOSOPHISCHES LICHT und Schatten oder Ausführlicher Unterricht de prima
materia lapidis philosophorum ... Leipzig
und Nordhausen: J.H. Gross, 1738.
3 pts. in 1 v.

3267. PHILOSOPHORUM NUDA sine veste
Diana sive Lapidis physici e philosophorum
libris aperta demonstratio unde lapis evolvitur omnibus discussis illius involucris.
Hagæ-Comitum: A. Moetjens, 1695.
64 p.   illus.

PHILOTHEUS DE LIMITIBUS, *pseud.*
See Märker, G.

3268. PHILOVITE, *pseud.* La verité sortant
du puits hermetique, ou La vraye quintessence solaire et lunaire, baume radical de
tout estre, & origine de toute vie. Confection de la medecine universelle. Londres et
Paris: Lamy, 1753.
154 p.

3269. PHOENIX ATROPICUS de morte redux
... Aus Arabisch- Chaldæisch- Frantzösich-
und Lateinischer, in Hoch Teutscher Zungen
beseelet und vorgestellet. [n.p.] 1681.
88 p.

3270. PHYSICK FOR FAMILIES, discovering
a safe way and ready means, whereby every
one ... may ... be in a capacity of curing
themselves ... London: printed by J. Winter,

sold by R. Horn, 1669.
3 *l.*, 118 p., 1 *l.*

3271. A PHYSICO-MECHANICAL ESSAY on
improving the corpuscular philosophy ...
Submitted to the Royal Society ... By an
anonymous author. London: for the author
..., 1732.
46 p.
With Persius Flaccus, A., The Satyrs ...
1732.

3272. PHYSIOLOGIA, of Natuurkundige ont-
leding van het menschelyke lichaam ...
Zynde getrokken uit de schriften van ...
Boerhave, Malpighius, Ruysch, Morgagne,
Haller, doch inzonderheit uit de werken en
jaarlyksche lessen van ... B.S. Albinus.
Amsterdam: K. van Tongerlo, 1758.
16, 636 p., 35 *l.*

3273. PHYSISCH-therapeutische Erläuterung
aller jener Arzneymittel, welche in der neuen
verbesserten Osterreichischen Provincial-
Pharmakopöe enthalten sind. Von drey aus-
übenden Aerzten. Wien: F.J. Kötzel, 1796.
3 pts. in 1 v.

3274. PICO DELLA MIRANDOLA, Giovanni
Francesco. De avro libri tres ... Cvm explicatione pervtili & periocunda complurium,
tam philosophię quàm facultatis medicæ
arcanorum. Venetiis: G.B. Somaschus, 1586.
4 *l.*, 131 p.
Lacking pages 121-124.

3275. ——. ——. Ferrariæ: V. Baldinus,
1587.
8 *l.*, 133 p., 1 *l.*

3276. PICTET, Marc Auguste. Versuch über
das Feuer ... Aus dem Französischen ...
Tübingen: J.G. Cotta, 1790.
viii, 199 p.   illus.

3277. PICTORIUS, Georgius. Sermonum
conuiualium libri x ... Quibus accedunt
Ebrietatis in exilium relegatæ threnodia ...
[Basileæ: H. Petrus, 1559.]
16 *l.*, 218 p., 17 *l.*

3278. PICUS, Victorius. Ampliss. medicorum
collegii candidati melethemata inauguralia.
Augustae Taurinorum: J.M. Briolus, 1788.
3 *l.*, 283 p.   illus.

3279. PIDERIT, Philipp Jacob. Pharmacia
rationalis. Editio tertia ... Cassellis: J.J.
Cramer, 1791.
8 *l.*, 406 p., 1 *l.*

3280. PIEPENBRING, Georg Heinrich. Pharmacia selecta principiis materiae medicae
pharmaciae et chymiae superstructa. Oder:
Auswahl der besten wirksamsten Arzneymittel ... Erfurt: G. Keiser, 1792-1793.
    2 v.

3280a. ———. Ueber die Verbesserungen
des Spinnrades aus Rücksicht der Gesundheit des weiblichen Geschlechts. Leipzig:
F.G. Jacobäer, 1795.
    28 p.

3281. PILES, Roger de. Abregé d'anatomie,
accommodé aux arts de peinture et de sculpture ... Mis en lumiere par François Torte-
bat. Paris: N. Bonnart [ca. 1765].
    1 *l.*, 4 p., 7 *l.* illus.

    PILGREN, Johannes. Senium Salo-
moneum. *See* Linné, C. von, *praeses*. Entry
2493.

3282. PINCOT, Daniel. An essay on the
origin, nature, uses, and properties of artificial stone: together with some observations upon common natural stone, clays, and
burnt earths in general ... London: R. Hett
..., 1770.
    79 p.

3283. PINELLI, Flaminio. Lettera de'
bagni di Petriuolo ... Roma: A. de Rossi,
1716.
    4 *l.*, 132 p., 6 *l.*

3284. PINI, Ermenegildo. De venarum
metallicarum excoctione ... Mediolani: J.
Marelli, 1779-1780.
    2 v. illus.

    PIPER, Hieronymus. Corollarium. *In*
Musitanus, C., Ad Had. à Mynsicht ... 1701.

    PISANELLI, Baldassare. De esculen-
torum potulentorumque facultatibus. *In* Baricelli, G.C., Hortulus genialis ... 1620.

3285. ———. Trattato della natvra de' cibi
et del bere ... Venetia: G. Alberti, 1586.
    152 p.

3286. PISO, Willem. De Indiæ utriusque re
naturali et medica libri quatuordecim ...
Amstelædami: L. et D. Elzevirius, 1658.
    12 *l.*, 327 p., 2 *l.*; 39, 226 p., 1 *l.* illus.

3287. PISSINUS, Sebastianus. De cordis
palpitatione cognoscenda, & curanda. Libri
dvo. Francofvrti: C. Marnius & heredes

I. Aubrii, 1609.
    193 p., 11 *l.*

3288. PISTOI, Candido. Del meccanismo
col quale l'aria, e il fuoco elementare si
fissano nei misti, e diventano principj
constitvi di quei corpi, nei quali si trovano
dissertazione ... Siena: V.P. Carli, 1775.
    viii, cxxvii p. illus.

    PITCAIRNE, Archibald. Methodus
præscribendi formulas secundum. *In* Boerhaave, H., Praxis medica ... 1716.

3289. ———. Opera omnia medica ... Editio
novissima, cum indice locupletissimo. Lugduni Batavorum: J.A. Langerak, 1737.
    20 *l.*, 410, 31 p., 8 *l.*

3290. ———. Opuscula medica: quorum
multa nunc primum prodeunt. Editio tertia ...
Roterodami: Fritsch et Böhm, 1714.
    2 *l.*, 238 p., 1 *l.*

3291. ———. The works ... Wherein are
discovered the true foundation and principles
of the art of physic, with cases and observations upon most distempers and medicines.
Done from the Latin original. With some account of the author's life, prefixed. There is
also added his method of curing the small-
pox ... London: for E. Curll ..., 1715.
    15 *l.*, 275 p.

3292. PITSCHKI, Georg. Mercurius co-
agulatus oder Eigentliche Beschreibung, wass
das gehärtete Quecksilber für eine sonderliche geheime Medicin sey ... zum zweyten
Mahl vorgestellet ... [Hamburg?] 1678.
    12 *l.*

3293. PITT, Robert. The antidote: or, The
preservative of health and life ... London:
for J. Nutt, 1704.
    25 *l.*, 270 p.

3294. ———. The craft and frauds of physick
expos'd ... Second edition ... London: for T.
Childe, 1703.
    12 *l.*, 203 p., 4 *l.*

3295. PITTIS, William. Dr. Radcliffe's life,
and letters. With a true copy of his last will
and testament. The third edition. London: for
E. Curll, 1716.
    4 *l.*, 100 p. port.

3296. ———. ———. The fourth edition. London: for A. Bettesworth ..., 1736.
    3 *l.*, 102 p.

PLACOTOMUS, Johannes. *See* Bretschneider, Johann.

3297. PLANIS CAMPY, David de. Les
oevvres ... Contenant les plus beaux traictez
de la medecine chymique que les anciens
autheurs ont enseigné ... Reueues corrigées
... & augmentez de plusieurs traictez non
imprimez. Paris: D. Moreav, 1646.
7 *l.*, 752 p.

3298. PLAT, *Sir* Hugh. Delightes for
ladies, to adorne their persons, tables,
closets, and distillatories: with beavties,
banqvets, perfumes & waters ... London: H.
Lownes, 1609.
85 *l.*

3299. ——. The jewell house of art and
nature. Containing diuers rare and profitable
inuentions, together with sundry new ex-
perimentes in the art of husbandry, distillation, and moulding ... London: P. Short, 1594.
8 *l.*, 96, 60, 76 p.

3300. ——. ——. Whereunto is added, A
rare and excellent discourse of minerals,
stones, gums, and resins; with the vertues
and use thereof. By D.B. ... London: B. Alsop, 1653.
4 *l.*, 232 p. illus.

——. Sundry new, and artificial
remedies against famine. *In* Collectanea
chymica ... 1684.

PLATEARIUS, Matthaeus. De simplici medicina. *In* Nicolaus Praepositus,
Dispensarium ... 1512.

——. Circa instans. *In* Yūhannā
ibn Sarābiyūn, Practica ... 1497.

3301. PLATNER, Johann Zacharias. Ars
medendi singvlis morbis accommodata. Lipsiae: C. Fritsch, 1765.
8 *l.*, 530 p., 21 *l.*

3302. ——. Istitvtiones chirvrgiae rationalis tvm medicae tvm manvalis in vsvs
discentivm ... Editio altera cum appendice
nonnvllorvm medicamentorvm compositorvm.
Lipsiae: Fritsch,/1758.
8 *l.*, 944 p., 8 *l.* illus.

3303. PLATTER, Felix. Obseruationum, in
hominis affectibus plerisque corpori & animo,
functionum laesione, dolore, aliáve molestiâ
& vitio incommodantibus, libri tres ...
Basileae: impensis L. König, typis C. Wald-

kirchii, 1614.
24 *l.*, 845 p.

3304. ——. Praxeos medicae opus, quinque libris adornatum & in tres tomos distinctum ... Tertia hac editione ... Huic accessit eju'dem Quæstionum medicarum
paradoxarum & endoxarum, centuria posthuma,
opera primum Thomae Plateri. Basileæ: impensis E. König, typis viduæ J.J. Genathii,
1656.
3 v. in 1.

3305. ——. Praxeos seu de cognoscendis,
praedicendis, praecauendis, curandisque,
affectibus homini incommodantibus, tractatvs
secvndvs. De doloribus, libro vno ... Basileae:
C. Waldkirch, 1609.
8 *l.*, 972 p., 10 *l.*

3306. PLATTES, Gabriel. A discovery of
subterraneall treasure, viz. Of all manner of
mines and mineralls, from the gold to the
coale; with plaine directions and rules for
the finding of them in all kingdomes and
countries ... London: I. Okes for J. Emery,
1639.
4 *l.*, 60 p.

——. ——. *In* Barba, A., A collection
of treatises ... 1738.

3307. PLEIER, Cornelius. Medicus criticus-
astrologus, ex veteribus jatromathematicis
productus. Noribergæ: S. Halbmayer, 1627.
237 p. illus.

3308. PLENK, Joseph Jacob. Elementa
pharmaco-catagraphologiæ seu Doctrinæ de
præscriptione formularum medicinalium.
Viennæ: F. Wappler, 1799.
190 p.

3309. ——. Farmacologia chirurgica, ó
Ciencia de medicamentos externos é internos
precisos para curar las enfermedades de
cirugia ... Madrid: la Imprenta Real, 1798.
5 *l.*, 593 p., 2 *l.*

3310. PLUSIUS, Eduard, *pseud.* Spiegel der
heutigen Alchimie, das ist, Wohlgegündeter
Bericht, was von der so beruffenen Goldmacher-
Kunst zu halten ... aus dem Lateinischen ...
ins Deutsche übersetzt. Budissin: D. Richter,
1725.
80 p.

3311. POLEMANN, Joachim. Nouvelle lumiere de medecine, du' mistere du souffre
des philosophes ... Traduction du Latin. Rouen:

G. Behourt, 1721.
 4 *l*., 186 p., 1 *l*.
 With Sendivogius, M., Cosmopolite ...
1723.

 POLEMO, Antonius. La fisonomia
naturale. *In* Porta, G.B. della, La fisonomia
... 1652.

3312. POLI, Martino. Il trionfo degli
acidi vendicati dalle calunnie di molti
moderni; opera filosofica, e medica ... con-
tro il sistema, e prattica delli moderni
Democritici, & Epicurei riformati, divisa in
quattro libri ... Roma: G. Placho, 1706.
 12 *l*., 463 p. port.

 POLYBUS. De salubri victus ratione
privatorum. *In* Galenus, Liber de plenitudine
... 1528.

 ——. ——. *In* Scribonius, L., De
compositione medicamentorum ... 1529.

3313. ——. Opuscula aliquot nunc primum
è Græco in Latinum conuersa ... Albano
Torino ... interprete ... Basileæ: J. Oporinus,
1544.
 5 *l*., 208 p.

3314. POMET, Pierre. Histoire generale
des drogues ... Paris: J.B. Loyson ..., 1694.
 2 v. in 1. illus., port.

3315. ——. Le marchand sincere ou Traite
general des drogues ... Paris: l'auteur, 1695.
 2 v. in 1. illus., port.

3316. ——. Histoire generale des drogues
... Nouvelle edition, corrigée & augmentée
... par le Sieur Pomet fils ... Paris: E. & L.E.
Ganeau, 1735.
 2 v. illus.

3317. ——. A compleat history of druggs
... to which is added what is further observ-
able on the same subject from Messrs.
Lemery and Tournefort ... Done into English
from the originals ... London: R. Bonwicke
..., 1712.
 2 v. in 1. illus.

3318. ——. ——. The third edition. London: for J. & J. Bonwicke ..., 1737.
 12 *l*., 419 p., 4 *l*. illus.

3319. POMME, Pierre. Traité des affections vaporeuses des deux sexes; où l'on a
taché de joindre à une théorie solide une
pratique sure, fondée sur des observations.

Troisieme édition revue, corrigée et augmentée. Lyon, B. Duplain, 1767.
 569 p., 1 *l*.

3320. POMMEREAU, Etienne. Traité des
eaux minerales ou La nouvelle fontaine de
Saint Gondon, avec une pathologie chimique
des fiévres, & un discours raisonné sur la
maladie du tems ... Orleans: la veuve F.
Boyer & J. Boyer, 1676.
 9 *l*., 269 p., 2 *l*.

3321. PONCELET, Polycarpe. Chymie du
gout et de l'odorat, ou Principes pour composer facilement ... les liqueurs à boire, &
les eaux de senteurs ... Paris: Pissot, 1766.
 390 p., 1 *l*. illus.

3322. ——. Nouvelle chymie du goût et
de l'odorat, ou L'art de composer facilement
... les liqueurs à boire & les eaux de senteurs. Nouvelle édition, entièrement changée,
considérablement augmentée ... Paris: Pissot,
1774.
 2 v. in 1. illus.

3323. ——. La nature dans la formation
du tonnerre, et la reproduction des êtres
vivans, pour servir d'introduction aux vrais
principes de l'agriculture ... Paris: P.G. Le
Mercier & C. Saillant, 1766.
 2 v. in 1. illus.

 PONS, Pierre. Dissertatio de ferri.
See Magnol, Antonius, *praeses*.

 PONTANUS, Joannes. Epistola de
lapide philosophorum. *In* Opuscula quaedam
chemica ... 1614.

 ——. The epistle (mentioned in the
preface to the reader of Artephius his secret
booke). *In* Flamel, N., Nicholas Flammel, his
exposition ... 1624.

 ——. Ein Sendbrief. *In* Alchymistisch
Sieben-Gestirn ... 1697.

 ——. Upon the mineral fire. *In* Thor,
G., Cheiragogia Heliana ... 1659, etc.

3324. PONTE, Aniello da. Cento secreti
medicinali cauati dalli piu illustri & celebri
autori della medicina ... [n.p.] 1606.
 4 *l*.

3325. PONTEDERA, Guilio. Anthologia, sive
De floris natura libri tres ... Accedunt ejusdem Dissertationes XI ex iis, quas habiut in
horto publico Patavino anno 1719, quibus res

botanica, & subinde etiam medica illustratur.
Patavii: typis seminarii, apud J. Manfrè,
1720.
12 ℓ., 303 p.; 6 ℓ., 296 p., 28 ℓ. illus.

3326. POOLE, Robert. The chymical vade
mecum: or, A compendium of chymistry. Extracted from the best authors, but principally
from the late celebrated Boerhaave ... London: for E. Duncomb, 1748.
1 ℓ., viii, lx, 410 p.

3327. POPPIUS, Hamerus. Basilica antimonii, in qva antimonii natvra exponitvr et
nobilissimæ remediorum formulæ, quæ
pyrotechnica arte ex eo elaborantur, quam
accurate traduntur ... Francofurti: A. Hum-
mius, 1618.
50 p.

——. ——. In Hartmann, J., Praxis
chymiatrica ... 1647, etc.

3328. PÖRNER, Karl Wilhelm. Anmerkungen
über Herrn Baumé Abhandlung vom Thon ...
Leipzig: M.G. Weidmanns Erben, 1771.
8 ℓ., 226 p., 6 ℓ.

3329. PORTA, Giovanni Battista della. De
aeris transmvtationibvs libri IV ... Romae: B.
Zannettus, 1610.
4 ℓ., 211 p., 2 ℓ. illus., maps, charts.

3330. ——. De distillatione lib. IX ...
Romae: ex typographia R. Cameræ Apostolicæ,
1608.
10 ℓ., 154 p., 3 ℓ. illus., port.

3331. ——. Della fisonomia dell'hvomo
... Tradotti da latino ... per Giovanni di
Rosa ... Napoli: T. Longo, 1598.
10 ℓ., 243 p. illus., port.

3332. ——. La fisonomia dell'Hvomo et
la celeste ... Tradotti di Latino ... Con la
Fisonomia naturale di Monsignor Giouanni
Ingegneri di Polemone, & Adamantio. Venetia:
li eredi di G.B. Combi, 1652.
16 ℓ., 598 p.; 8 ℓ., 190, 134 p. illus.,
port.

3333. ——. Magiæ natvralis libri viginti
... Hanoviae: typis Aubrianis, sumptibus J.
Pressii, 1644.
16 ℓ., 622 p. illus.

3334. ——. ——. Lugd. Batavorum: P.
Leffen, 1651.
8 ℓ., 670 p. illus.

3335. ——. Natural magick ... Wherein
are set forth all the riches and delights of
the natural sciences. London: for T. Young
and S. Speed, 1658.
4 ℓ., 409 p., 3 ℓ.

3336. ——. Phytognomonica ... octo libris
contenta ... Francofvrti: I. Wechelus & P.
Fischerus, 1591.
8 ℓ., 552 p. illus., port.

3337. PORTAL, Antoine. Histoire de l'anatomie et de la chirurgie ... Paris: P.F. Didot,
1770-1773.
6 v. in 7.

3338. POTIER, Michael. Apologia contra al-
chymistam impostorem, qvi philosophvm hvnc
in arte lapidis philosophorum verum ac indubi-
tatum, imposturæ suspectum facere conatus
est, fidem ut sibi apud rerum incautos pararet
... Francofurti: sumptibus auctoris [1631].
6 ℓ., 131 p.

3339. ——. Fons chymicvs id est: Vera
avri et argenti conficiendi, ex naturalis
philosophiæ venis scaturiens ratio ... Colonia
C. Munich, 1637.
6 ℓ., 131 p.

3340. ——. Philosophia pura, qva non solvr
vera materia, vervsqve processvs lapidis
philosophici mvltò apertiùs, quàm hactenùs
... proponitur, sed etiam viva totius mysterij
revelatio filijs sapientiæ offertur ... Accessit svb calcem Jvdicivm de fratribus Roseæ
Crucis. Hæc omnia hac secvnda editione
diligintissimè recognita ... ab autore ipso ...
Francofurti: typis P. Jacobi, impensis L. Jennis, 1619.
214 p.

3341. POTIER, Pierre. Opera omnia medica,
et chymica. Lvgdvni: I.A. Hvgvetan, 1645.
6 ℓ., 792 p., 22 ℓ.

3342. ——. Opera omnia practica et chymic
cum annotationibus ... Friderici Hoffmanni ...
Accessit nova doctrina de febribus, ex principiis mechanicis solide deducta ... Venetiis:
ex typographia Balleoniana, 1741.
620 p.

3343. POTT, Johann Heinrich. Chymische
Untersuchungen welche fürnehmlich von der
Lithogeognosia ... Zweyte Auflage ... mit
einem neuen Anhange vermehret ... Berlin:
C.F. Voss, 1757.
3 pts. in 1 v. illus.

All three parts have separate title pages, bearing the respective dates 1757, 1751, 1754.

3344. ———. Lithogéognosie ou Examen chymique des pierres et des terres en général ... avec un dissertation sur le feu & sur la lumiere ... Ouvrages traduits de l'Allemand. Paris: J.T. Herissant, 1753.
     2 v. illus.

3345. ———. Exercitationes chymicæ ... sparsim hactenus editæ, jam vero collectæ restitutæ a mendis repurgatæ, variisque notis, experimentis et discussionibus ab autore adauctæ, illustratæ. Berolini: J.A. Rüdiger, 1738.
     4 *l*., 220 p.

3346. ———. Dissertations chymiques ... recueillies & traduites, tant du Latin que de l'Allemand, par M. Demachy ... Paris: J.T. Herissant, 1759.
     4 v.

3347. POTT, Percivall. An account of a particular kind of rupture, frequently attendant upon new-born children; and sometimes met with in adults ... London: for C. Hitch and L. Hawes, 1757.
     vi, 41 p.
     With his A treatise on ruptures ... 1756.

3348. ———. The chirurgical works ... London: for L. Hawes ..., 1771-1775.
     5 v. illus.

3349. ———. Farther remarks on the useless state of the lower limbs, in consequence of a curvature of the spine ... London: for J.Johnson, 1782.
     2 *l*., 64 p. illus.

3350. ———. Remarks on the disease, commonly called a fistula in ano. London: for L. Hawes ..., 1765.
     xi, 115 p., 1 *l*. illus.

3351. ———. A treatise on ruptures ... London: for C. Hitch and L. Hawes, 1756.
     xxx, 232 p., 2 *l*.

3352. POULLE, Alexandre. Positiones chemico-medicæ de aëre vitali, seu dephlogisticato, tanquam novo sanitatis præsidio ... Monspelii: J.F. Picot, 1784.
     64 p.

3353. POUSSE, François. Examen des principes des alchymistes sur la pierre philo-

sophale. Paris: D. Jollet & B. Girin, 1711.
     10 *l*., 254 p., 1 *l*.

3354. POWER, Henry. Experimental philosophy, in three books: containing new experiments microscopical, mercurial, magnetical ... London: T. Roycroft for J. Martin & J. Allestry, 1664.
     12 *l*., 193 p. illus.

     The PRACTICE of lights. *In* Collectanea chymica ... 1684.

     PRAEPOSITUS, Nicolaus. *See* Nicolaus Praepositus.

3355. PRAXIS medica et chirurgica nosocomiorum civitatis Londini. Cui additur index morborum & remediorum. Editio secunda, auctior et emendatior. Londini: S. Crowder ..., 1770.
     vi, 254 p., 3 *l*., xxvii p.

3356. PRESTWICH, John. Prestwich's dissertation on mineral, animal, & vegetable, poisons ... London: for F. Newbery ..., 1775.
     2 *l*., iv, 331 p. illus.

3357. PRETIUM MEDICAMENTORUM simplicium & compositorum ... Tax, oder Preiss-Ordnung aller Artzneyen, so in denen Apothecken zu Regenspurg zu finden seynd. Ratisbonae: J.C. Peezius, 1727.
     1 *l*., 42 p., 7 *l*.
     With Conspectus materia medicae ... 1727.

3358. PREVOST, Jean. Medicina pavpervm ... Qvibvs accessit De medicamentorum materia tractatus ... Lvgdvni: P. Ravavd, 1644.
     4 *l*., 718 p., 7 *l*.

3359. ———. Medicina pavpervm, sive De remediis facile parabilibus. Tractatus posthumus. Hvic pavpervm thesauro adiungitur eiusdem auctoris Libellus aurens de venenis. Editio quarta ... Venetiis: S. Curtius, 1679.
     6 *l*., 245 p.; 1 *l*., 53 p., 4 *l*.

3360. PRICE, James. An account of some experiments on mercury, silver and gold, made at Guildford in May, 1782 ... To which is prefixed an abridgment of Boyle's account of a degradation of gold ... Oxford: Clarendon press, 1782.
     vii, 28 p.

3361. PRIESTLEY, Joseph. Directions for impregnating water with fixed air; in order to communicate to it the peculiar spirit and virtues of Pyrmont water, and other mineral

waters ... London: for J. Johnson, 1772.
1 *l*., iii, 22 p., 2 *l*.   illus.

3362. ———. Experiments and observations
on different kinds of air ... London: for J.
Johnson, 1774-1777.
3 v.   illus.

3363. ———. Experiments and observations
relating to various branches of natural philosophy; with a continuation of the observations on air ... London: for J. Johnson, 1779-
1786.
3 v.   illus.

3364. ———. Experiments and observations
on different kinds of air, and other branches
of natural philosophy ... Being the former
six volumes abridged and methodized, with
many additions ... Birmingham: T. Pearson
[for] J. Johnson, 1790.
3 v.   illus.

3365. ———. Expériences et observations
sur différentes especes d'air, ouvrage traduit de l'Anglois ... par M. Gibelin ... Paris:
Nyon, 1777-1780.
5 v.   illus.

3366. ———. Expéreiences et observations
sur différentes branches de la physique,
avec une continuation des observations sur
l'air. Ouvrage traduit de l'Anglois ... par M.
Gibelin ... Paris: Nyon, 1782-1783.
3 v.   illus.

3367. ———. Hartley's theory of the human
mind, on the principle of the association of
ideas; with essays relating to the subject
of it ... London: for J. Johnson, 1775.
lxii, 372 p., 2 *l*.

3368. ———. Heads of lectures on a course
of experimental philosophy, particularly including chemistry, delivered at the new college in Hackney ... London: for J. Johnson,
1794.
xxviii, 180 p., 4 *l*.

———. Letter to Richard Kirwan. *In*
Scheele, K.W., Chemical observations ...
1780.

3369. ———. Observations on different
kinds of air. Printed for the Philosophical
Transactions, 1773, vol. lxii. London: W.
Bowyer and J. Nichols, 1772.
120 p.

3370. ———. Philosophical empiricism:

containing remarks on a charge of plagiarism
respecting Dr. H---s, interspersed with
various observations relating to different
kinds of air ... London: for J. Johnson, 1775.
2 *l*., 85 p., 3 *l*.
With his Experiments and observations
on different kinds of air. London, 1774-1777.

3371. PRIMEROSE, James. Ars pharmaceutica methodus brevissima de eligendis &
componendis medicinæ. Amsteledami: J.
Janssonius, 1651.
1 *l*., 272 p., 5 *l*.

3372. ———. De febribvs libri quatuor ...
Roterodami: A. Leers, 1658.
4 *l*., 459 p.
With Liceti, F., De monstris ... 1665.

3373. ———. De mulierum morbis et symp-
tomatis libri quinque ... Roterodami: A. Leers,
1655.
4 *l*., 390 p., 3 *l*.
With Liceti, F., De monstris ... 1665.

3374. ———. Popular errours. Or The errours
of the people in physick ... Translated into
English by Robert Wittie. London: W. Wilson
for N. Bournes, 1651.
12 *l*., 461 p., 6 *l*.

3375. PRINGLE, John.   A discourse on the
different kinds of air, delivered at the anniversary meeting of the Royal Society, November 30, 1773 ... London: for the Royal Society,
1774.
2 *l*., 31 p.

3376. ———. Observations on the diseases
of the army. The fourth edition enlarged. London: for A. Millar ..., 1764.
xxviii, 355, cxxviii p., 16 *l*.

3376a. PRIOR, Thomas.   An authentic narrative of the success of tar-water, in curing a
great number and variety of distempers ...
To which are subjoined, two letters from the
author of Siris ... A new edition, complete.
London: for W. Innys ..., 1746.
88 p.
With Berkeley, G., Siris ... 1744.

3377. PRISCIANUS, Theodorus.   Phaenomenon
euporiston, liber I. Logicus, liber II. Gynaecea
ad saluinam, liber III. Opus nunc primum aedi-
tum. Basileae: Froben, 1532.
150 p.

3378. PROBIR BÜCHLIN, Auff Goldt, Silber,
allerley Ertz vnd Metall. Mit vil kostbarlichen

alchimeijschen Künsten ... Strassburg: C.
Egenolph [1530].
48 numb. *l*. illus.
Lacking leaves 25 and 32.

3379. ———. Franckfort am Main: C. Egenolffs Erben ..., 1574.
78 numb. *l*. illus.

3380. PROSPECTUS d'élémens de chimie-
physique a l'usage des prytanées, presente
a l'administration. [Paris: Fuchs, n.d.]
31 p.

3381. PROSPECTVS PHARMACEVTICVS, svb
qvo antidotarivm Mediolanense spectandvm
proponitvr ... Qvibvs accessere tractatvs
De extractis, salibus, spiritibus, fucis ...
Mediolani: I.B. Ferrarius, 1668.
13 *l*., 438 p., 1 *l*.; 3 *l*., 102 p., 1 *l*.

3382. ———. Editio tertia ... Mediolani: C.
J. Galli, 1729.
3 pts. in 1 v. illus.

3383. PRUGGMAYR, Martin Maximilian.
Scrutinium philosophicum de vero elixere
vitæ, seu Genuino auro potabili philosophico,
qvo non solùm omnes humani corporis morbi
quondam sanabantur, verùm & immunda, ac
leprosa corpora metallorum curabantur ...
Salisburgi: J.B. Mayr, 1687.
15 *l*., 146 p., 3 *l*. illus.

3384. PRUSSIA. Laws, statutes, etc.
Königliche Preussische und Thrufürstliche
Brandenburgische medicinal Taxa ... von ...

Collegio Medico ... herausgegeben ... Berlin: C.A. Gäbert, 1749.
6 *l*., 166 p.

3385. PURMANN, Matthais Gottfried. A
treatise of salivation; shewing its true
methods ... Translated from the second
edition ... London: for T. Newborough,
1702.
4 *l*., 96 p.

3386. PUTEO, Zaccharias a. Clavis medica
rationalis, spagyrica, et chyrvrgica ... Cui
additur ... Consvltatio responsiva Hieronymi
Venerosii ... Venetiis: L. Aureatus, 1612.
14 *l*., 306 p., 42 *l*. illus.

3387. ———. Officina chymica fornacivm,
vasorvm, ac instrumentorum ad destillationem
pertinentium ... Venetiis: L. Auratus, 1611.
20 *l*. illus.
With his Clavis medica ... 1612.

3388. PYROTECHNICAL DISCOURSES. Being
I. An experimental confirmation of chymical
philosophy ... by John Kunkel ... II. A short
discourse on the original of metallick veins,
by George Ernest Stahl ... III. The grounds
of pyrotechnical metallurgy, and metallick
essaying, by John Christian Firtschius ...
All faithfully translated from the Latin ...
London: B. Bragg, 1705.
x, 1 *l*., 268 p.

3389. ———. The second edition. London:
for J. Darby ..., 1730.
x, 1 *l*., 268 p.

Q

3390. QUADRAMIO, Evangelista. La vera dichiaratione di tvtte le metafore, similitudini, & enimmi de gl' antichi filosofi alchimisti ... Con vn breve discorso della generatione de i metalli, & ... di tutti gl' alchimisti moderni. Roma: V. Accolti, 1587.
  12 ℓ., 230 p., 12 ℓ.

3391. QUADRATUM ALCHYMISTICUM: Das ist: Vier auserlesene rare Tractätgen vom Stein der Weisen, Speculum sapientiæ ... Centrum naturæ concentratum ... Discursus de universali ... Abyssus alchymiæ explorata ... herausgegeben von Einem Liebhaber vorborgener Künste. Hamburg: verlegts C. Liebezeit, druckts P.L. Stromer, 1705.
  3 pts. in 1 v. illus.

3392. QUADRIO, Giuseppe Maria. Uso, utilità, e storia delle acque termali di Trascorio ... Venezia: G. Tevernin, 1749.
  6 ℓ., 180 p. illus., port.

3393. QUARIN, Joseph. Animadversiones practicae in diversos morbos. Viennae: R. Graefferus, 1786.
  6 ℓ., 338 p.

3394. QUATTROCCHI, Alberto. Dispvtatio ... de officinæ pharmacevticæ veris & legitimis antiquorum ponderibvs ... Hvic qvoqve accedit epitome mensvrarvm Græcis, Romanis, et Arabibvs medicis olim familiarium ... Venetiis: A. Pinellus, 1617.
  86 p., 3 ℓ.

3395. The QUEENS CLOSET opened. Incomparable secrets in physick, chirurgery, preserving, candying, and cookery ... never before published ... [London] for N. Brook, 1655.
  5 ℓ., 296 p., 12 ℓ. port.
  The Britwell Court copy with the arms of William Miller in gold on the front and back cover.

3396. QUEITSCH, Anton Philipp. Ιατρομαθηματογραφία synoptica sive Totius corporis medicinæ archetypus ... Francofvrti ad Viadrvm: J.G. Conrad, 1737.
  36 ℓ.

QUERCETANUS, Josephus, pseud.
See Duchesne, Joseph.

3397. QUESNAY, François. L'art de guerir par la saignée ... Paris: G. Cavelier, 1736.
  12 ℓ., 375 p., 9 ℓ.

3398. ———. Histoire de l'origine et des progrès de la chirurgie en France. Paris: Huart & Moreau, 1749.
  2 v.

3399. ———. Traité de la suppuration. Paris: d'Houry, 1749.
  6 ℓ., 432 p.

3400. ———. Traité des fiévres continues, dans lequel on a rassemblé & examiné les principales connoissances que les anciens ont acquises sur les fiévres par l'observation & par la partique ... Paris: d'Houry, 1767.
  2 v.

3401. QUILLET, Claude. Callipaedia, &c. et Scaevolae sammarthani paedotrophia. Londini: J. Bowyer, 1709.
  2 v. in 1.

3402. ———. La callipédie, traduite du poeme Latin. Amsterdam: Durand & Pissot, 1749.
  1 ℓ., 203 p.

3403. QUIN, Charles William. A treatise on the dropsy of the brain, illustrated by a variety of cases, to which are added, observations on the use and effects of the digitalis purpurea in dropsies. London: for J. Murray and W. Jones, 1790.
  227 p.

3404. QUINCY, John. The dispensatory of

the Royal College of Physicians in London...
London: W. Bowyer for R. Knaplock ... 1721.
   8 *l*., 362 p., 12 *l*.   illus.

     ———. An essay on the different
causes of pestilential diseases. *In* Hodges,
N., Limonologia ... 1720.

3405. ———. Lexicon physico-medicum:
or, A new medicinal dictionary; explaining
the difficult terms used ... The third edition
... London: for J. Osborn and T. Longman,
1726.
   xvi, 480 p.   illus.

3406. ———. ———. The eleventh edition,
improved and corrected. London: for T. Longman, 1794.
   xii, 828 p.

     ———. Medico-physical essays. *In*
Santorio, S., Medicina statica ... 1737.

3407. ———. Pharmacopoeia officinalis &
extemporanea: or, A compleat English dispensatory, in four parts ... London: for A.
Bell ..., 1718.
   xv, 618 p., 27 *l*.

3408. ———. ———. The second edition,
very much improv'd. London: for A. Bell ...,
1719.
   xv, 618 p., 27 *l*.

3409. ———. ———. The third edition, with
large additions. London: for A. Bell ..., 1720.
   xiii, 621 p., 26 *l*.

3410. ———. ———. The fourth edition, much
enlarged ... London: for E. Bell ..., 1722.
   xv, 674 p., 29 *l*.

3411. ———. ———. The fifth edition ... London: for E. Bell ..., 1724.
   xvi, 674 p., 31 *l*.

3412. ———. ———. The sixth edition ...
London: for J. Osborn and T. Longman,
1726.
   xiv, 674 p., 31 *l*.

3413. ———. ———. The ninth edition, much

enlarged and corrected. London: for J. Osborn and T. Longman, 1733.
   xvi, 700, lx p.

3414. ———. ———. The eleventh edition ...
London: T. Longman, 1739.
   xvi, 700, lx p.

3415. ———. ———. The twelfth edition ...
London: for T. Longman, 1742.
   xvi, 700, lx p.

3416. ———. ———. The twelfth edition,
much enlarged and corrected. London: for T.
Longman, 1749.
   xxiv, 256, 504 p., 15 *l*.

3417. ———. ———. The thirteenth edition
... London: for T. Longman, 1761.
   xxiii, 1 *l*., 704 p., 32 *l*.

3418. ———. ———. The fifteenth edition ...
London: for T. Longman, 1782.
   x, 3 *l*., 656 p., 32 *l*.

3419. ———. Pharmacopée universelle
raisonnée ... Traduite de l'Anglois sur la
onzieme edition. Augmentée de beaucoup, &
corrigée par M. Clausier. Paris: D'Houry ...,
1749.
   3 *l*., xvii, 490, 516 p., 30 *l*.

3420. ———. Prælectiones pharmaceuticæ;
or, A course of lectures in pharmacy, chemical and galenical ... London: for E. Bell ...,
1723.
   2 *l*., 212 p.

     QUINTI, Joseph.   Les admirable
secrets. *See* Auda, Domenico.

3421. QUINTIIS, Camillus Eucherius de.
Inarmine seu De balneis pithecusarum libri
VI ... Neapoli: F. Mosca, 1726.
   20 *l*., 320 p., 12 *l*.

3422. QUINTON, John.   Practical observations in physick, but especially of the nature of mineral waters and metallick medicines ... The second edition ... London: J.
Morphew, 1711.
   4 *l*., 77 p.

R

R., A. Arcana microcosmi. *See* Ross, Alexander.

R., J.H. Philosophischer Phoenix. *See* Rist, Johann.

R., P.D. Le mercure Indien. *See* Rosnel, Pierre de.

R., W. Organon salutis. *See* Rumsey, Walter.

3423. RABIQUEAU, Charles. Le microscope moderne, pour débrouiller la nature par le filtre d'un nouvel alambic chymique ... Paris: Belin, 1785.
4 *l.*, 364 p. illus., map.

3424. ————. Le spectacle du feu elementaire, ou Cours d'electricité experimentale ... Paris: Jombert ... 1753.
2 *l.*, 296 p., 2 *l.*; 1 *l.*, 14, 34 p. illus.
Lettre electrique sur la mort de M. Richmann and *Relation curieuse et interessante pour le progres de la physique et de la medecine* follow the text of *Le spectacle du feu* ...

3425. RADIX CHIMIÆ, oder Würtzel des Universels, anweisend die ware Materiam universalis, dessen Præparation, Mittel, Anfang und Ende. Auffs klarund deutlichste angeweisen durch G.M.B.D.S. ... [n.p.]: 1680.
159 p.

3426. RAMAZZINI, Bernardino. Health preserved, in two treatises. I. On the diseases of artificers ... by Bern. Ramazini ... II. On those distempers which arise from particular climates, situations and methods of life ... by Frederick Hoffman ... Translated and enlarged with an appendix by R. James ... The second edition. London: for J. Whiston and J. Woodyer, 1750.
xv, 432 [i.e. 332] p.

RAMSTRÖM, Christian Ludwig. Generatio ambigena. *See* Linné, C. von, *praeses*. Entry 2477.

3427. RANCHIN, Francois. Oevvres pharmacevtiqves ... Assavoir, vn traicté general de la pharmacie ... Lyon: P. Ravavd, 1628.
12 *l.*, 876 p., 10 *l.*
Lacking pages 809-814, 845-848, 867-872.

3428. RAND, Isaac. Index plantarum officinalium, quas, ad materiæ medicæ scientiam promovendam, in horto Chelseiano, ali ac demonstrari curavit Societas Pharmaceutica Londinensis. Londini: J.W., 1730.
4 *l.*, 96 p.

3429. RANDOLPH, George. An enquiry into the medicinal virtues of Bath-water, and the indications of cure, which it answers ... London: for J. Nourse, 1752.
vi, 65 p.

3430. ————. An enquiry into the medicinal virtues of Bristol-water: and the indications of cure which it answers ... London: for R. Baldwin, 1750.
4 *l.*, 176 p.

3431. RAPHAEL, Pietro Paulo. Sepulchrum Hermetis reseratum sive De opere Hermetico libri tres authoris anonymi ... Venetiis: A. Poleti, 1715.
8 *l.*, 159 p.

3432. RAPPOLT, Thomas. Honori Philaretis Hermopolitani Jäger-Lust oder Philosophischer Nymphen-Fang, das ist: Gründliche und aussführliche Beschreibung des vhralten Steines der Weisen ... Hamburg: G. Wulff, 1679.
8 *l.*, 88 p.

RAUDORFF, Florian. A treatise of the stone. *In* Five treatises ... 1652.

3433. RAULIN, Joseph. Analyse des eaux minérales spathico-martiales de Provins, avec leurs propriétés dans les maladies ... Amsterdam & Paris: P.F. Didot le jeune, 1778.
    viii, 76 p.   port.

3434. RAY, John. Catalogus plantarum Angliæ, et insularum adjacentium ... cum observationibus & experimentis novis medicis & physicis. Londini: typis E.C. & A.C., impensis J. Martyn, 1670.
    11 *l.*, 358 p., 1 *l.*

    RAYNALDE, Thomas.   The birth of mankynde. *See* Röslin, Eucharius.

3435. REAUMUR, René Antoine Ferchault de. L'art de convertir le fer forgé en acier, et l'art d'adoucir le fer fondu, ou de faire des ouvrages de fer fondu aussi finis que de fer forgé. Paris: M. Brunet, 1722.
    10 *l.*, 566 p., 1 *l.*   illus.

3436. RECONDITORIUM ac reclusiorium opulentiæ sapientiæque numinis mundi magni, cui deditur in titulum Chymica vannus ... Amstelodami: J. Jansson à Waesberge & E. Weyerstraet, 1666.
    392 p.; 1 *l.*, 76 p., 1 *l.*   illus.

    ———. *See also* Chymiæ aurifondina ... 1696.

3437. RECORDE, Robert.   The vrinall of physicke ... London: T. Dawson, 1582.
    82 *l.*   illus.

3438. RECUEIL d'experiences et observations sur le combat, qui procede du mélange des corps. Sur les saveurs, sur les odeurs, sur le sang, sur le lait, etc ... [by N. Grew, R. Boyle and A. van Leeuwenhoek; translated by L. Le Vasseur]. Paris: E. Michallet, 1679.
    8 *l.*, 262 p., 1 *l.*

3439. RECUEIL de memories et d'observations sur la formation & sur la fabrication du salpêtre ... Paris: Lacombe, 1776.
    55, 622 p., 1 *l.*   illus.

3440. RECUEIL des mémoires les plus intéressants de chymie, et d'histoire naturelle, contenus dans les Actes de l'Académie d'Upsal, et dans les Mémoires de l'Académie Royale des Sciences de Stockolm; publiés depuis 1720 jusqu'en 1760. Traduits du Latin & de l'Allemand ... Paris: P.F. Didot le jeune, 1764.
    2 v.

3441. REDI, Francesco.   Esperienze intorno a diverse cose natvrali, e particolarmente a qvelle, che ci son portate dall'Indie ... Scritte in vna lettera al reverendissimo padre Atanasio Chircher ... Firenze: 1671.
    3 *l.*, 152 p.   illus.

3442. ———. Esperienze intorno alla generazione degl' insetti ... scritte in vna lettera all ... Carlo Dati. Napoli: G. Raillard, 1687.
    7 *l.*, 195 p., 28 *l.*   illus., port.

3443. ———. ———. Firenze: insegna della Stella, 1668.
    3 *l.*, 228 p.   illus.

3444. ———. Lettera intorno all'invenzione degli occhiali. Scritta ... all' ... Paolo Falconieri. Con aggiunta in questa nuova impressione. Firenze: P. Matini, 1690.
    15 p.

3445. ———. Opere ... Edizione Veneta seconda ricorretta. Venezia: eredi Hertz, 1742-1760.
    7 v. in 3.

3446. ———. Opvscvlorvm ... Accedit J. Frid. Lachmund De ave diomedea dissertatio. Amstelædami: H. Wetstenius, 1685-1686.
    2 v. in 1.

3447. ———. Osservazioni intorno agli animali viventi che si trovano negli animali viventi. Firenze: P. Matini, 1684.
    4 *l.*, 253 p., 23 *l.*   illus.

3448. ———. De animaculis vivis quæ in corporibus animalium vivorum reperiuntur, observationes. Ex Etruscis Latinas fecit Petrus Coste. Amstelædami: Wetstenius, 1708.
    12 *l.*, 342 p., 1 *l.*   illus.

3449. ———. Osservazioni intorno alle vipere ... E da lvi scritte in vna lettera all' illvstrissimo Signor Lorenzo Magalotti. Firenze: 1664.
    91 p., 2 *l.*

3450. REDMOND, William.   The principles and constituence of antimony ... London: printed by S. Chandler, sold by J. Curtis, 1762.
    1 *l.*, 49 p.

3451. REFORMATION Passawerischer Artzt vnd Apotecker Ordnung ... Mit angehencktem Teutschen Register wo, an welchem Blat vnd Capitel jedes zusuchen vnnd zufinden sey.

Auffgericht im Jar 1586. Passaw: M. Nen-
ninger [1586].
   10 ℓ., 44 numb. ℓ., 11 ℓ.
   With Pisanelli, B., Trattato della natura
... 1586.

3452.   REGIMEN SANITATIS SALERNITANUM.
Medicina Salernitana: id est, Conservandae
bonae valetvdinis praecepta ... Nova editio
... Francofvrti: M. Kempffer, 1628.
   16 ℓ., 478 p., 1 ℓ.

3453.   ——. Schola Salernitana, sive, De
conservandâ valetudine praecepta metrica
... Nova editio ... Roterodami: A. Leers,
1649.
   24 ℓ., 519 p., 5 ℓ.

3454.   ——. Regimen sanitatis Salerni.
This boke teachinge all people to gouerne
them in helthe, is translated out of the
Latyne tonge in to englyshe by Thomas
Paynel ... [Londini: T. Berthelet, 1541.]
   6 ℓ., 119 numb. ℓ.

3455.   ——. ——. [London: A. Vele, 1557.]
   19 ℓ., clxx numb. ℓ., 1 ℓ.

3456.   ——. The Englishmans doctor. Or,
The schoole of Salerne. Or, Physicall obseruations for the perfect preseruing of the
body of man in continuall health. London:
for I. Helme, 1609.
   22 ℓ.

3457.   ——. La scuola Salernitana per
acquistare, e custodire la sanita, tradotta
fedelmente dal verso Latino ... Con li Discorsi della vita sobria del Signor Lvigi
Cornaro. Parma: P. Monti, 1712.
   4 ℓ., 120 p.

      REGIUS, Henricus. *See* Roy, Henrick
de.

3458.   [REGLEMENT povr les maistres apo-
thicaires de Paris. Paris?: 1631?]
   var. pag.
   Caption title. Lacking the title page.

3459.   REGNAULT, Noel. L'origine ancienne de la physique nouvelle ... Amsterdam: la Compagnie, 1735.
   3 v.

3460.   REIBEHAND, Christoph. Filium
Ariadnes, das ist, Newer chymischer Discurs
von den grawsamen verführischen Irrwegen,
der Alchymisten, dadurch sie selbst vnd viel
Leute neben ihnen verleitet werden ... Durch

Heinrich von Batsdorff ... [n.p.]: F. Gruner,
1636.
   200 p.

3461.   ——. ——. Gotha: J. Mevius, 1718.
   8 ℓ., 136 p.

3462.   ——. Neun und siebenzig grosse
und sonderbahre Wunder, so bey einem
special angegebenem Svbiecto theils von
der Natur ... Leipzig: A. Boëtius, 1690.
   71 p.

3463.   REID, Thomas. An essay on the nature and cure of the phthisis pulmonalis.
London: for T. Cadell, 1782.
   xix, 155 p.

3464.   ——. ——. The third edition ... London: for T. Cadell and W. Davis, 1798.
   xv, 346 p.

3465.   REINESIUS, Thomas. Chemiatria,
hoc est, Medicina nobili et necessaria sui
parte, chemia, instrvcta et exornata ... Geræ
Ruthenicæ: A. Mamitzius, 1624.
   6 ℓ., 96 p.

3466.   ——. Epistolae. Lipsiæ: sumtibus
J. Scheibii, imprimebat J. Bauerus, 1660.
   6 ℓ., 681 p., 5 ℓ.   illus.

3467.   REINHART, Hans Christoff. Der
gülden Gesundbrunnen. Zu vnerschöpfflicher
Wolfart in Basilij Valentini Schrifften,
Schlüsseln vnd Capitteln ... Hall: gedruckt
durch E. Hynitzsch, in verlegung J. Krüsicken,
1611.
   32 ℓ.
   With Alchymia vera ... 1610?

3468.   ——. Liecht der Natur, das ist: Der
warhafftigen Kunst Alchimiæ höchstes Geheimniss ... Hall: gedruckt durch E. Hynitzsch,
in verlegung J. Krusecken, [n.d.].
   64 ℓ.
   With Alchymia vera ... 1610?

3469.   ——. Das Valete: Vber den Tractat
der Arcanorum Basilij Valentini zusammen
gesetzen Hauptschluss Puncten dess Liechts
der Natur ... Hall: gedruckt durch E. Hynitzsch,
in verlegung J. Krusecken, 1608.
   48 ℓ.
   With Alchymia vera ... 1610?

3470.   RÉMOND DE SAINTE ALBINE, Pierre.
Mémoire sur le laminage du plomb ... Troisieme edition. Paris: J. Guerin, 1746.
   xii, 78 p., 1 ℓ. ` illus.

RENATUS, Sincerus, *pseud.* *See* Richter, Samuel.

3471. RENAUDIN, Philibert. Quelques idées chymiques, physiologiques et médicinales sur l'air atmosphérique ... Montpellier: G. Izar & A. Ricard [1797].
  51 p.

3472. RENAUDOT, Eusèbe. L'antimoine ivstifie et l'antimoine triomphant ... Paris: J. Henault [1653].
  10 *l*., 396 p., 1 *l*.

3473. ———. A general collection of discourses of the virtuosi of France, upon questions of all sorts of philosophy, and other natural knowledg ... Render'd into English by G. Havers. London: for T. Dring and J. Starkey ..., 1664-1665.
  2 v.

RENNEWALD, Heinrich Konrad. De borace. *See* Alberti, M., *praeses.*

3474. RENOU, Jean de. Instititvtionvm pharmacevticarvm, libri qvinqve quibus accedunt De materia medica, libri tres. Omnibus succedit Officina pharmaceutica, siue Antidotarium ab eodem auctore commentariis illustratum ... Parisiis: vidua G. de la Nouë et D. de la Nouë, 1608.
  var. pag.   port.

3475. ———. Dispensatorivm Galeno chymicvm continens primo Ioannis Renodaei Institutionum pharmaceuticarum lib. V. De materia medica lib. III. Et antidotarium varium et absolutissimum. Secundo Iosephi Qvercetani Pharmacopoeam dogmaticorum restitutam per Petrvm Vffenbachivm ... Hanouiæ: D. Aubrius, 1631.
  22 *l*., 869 p., 27 *l*.

3476. ———. A medicinal dispensatory, containing the whole body of physick ... Together with a most perfect and absolute pharmacopoea ... now Englished and revised by Richard Tomlinson ... London: J. Streater ..., 1657.
  56 *l*., 738 p., 12 *l*.

3477. ———. Les oevvres pharmacevtiqves ... Augmentées d'un tiers en cette seconde edition par l'auteur ... mises en lumiere par M. Lovys de Serres ... Lyon: N. Gay, 1637.
  14 *l*., 762 p., 11 *l*.   illus.

3478. RESCH, Johann Ulrich. Osiandrische Experiment von Sole, Luna & Mercurio ...

Nürnberg: J.A. und W. Endter, 1659.
  4 *l*., 327 p.

3479. RESPOUR, P.M. de. Rares experiences svr l'esprit mineral, povr la preparation et transmvtation des corps metaliqves ... Par Monsieur D***. Tome premier. Paris: E. Langlois & C. Barbin, 1668.
  10 *l*., 72, 106, 100 p., 1 *l*.
  All published.

3480. RETZIUS, Anders Jahan. Primae lineae pharmaciae in vsvm praelectionvm svecico idiomate ... Iam Latine conversae. Gottingæ: J.C. Dieterich, 1771.
  2 *l*., 91 p.

3481. REUDEN, Michael. Bedencken ob vnd wie die Artzneyen, so durch die alchimistische Kunst bereitet werden, sonderlich vom Vitriol, Schwefel, Antimonio, Mercurio, vnd dergleichen fruchtbarlich zugebrauchen sein ... Mit einer kurtzen Vorrede von dem Vnterschied der Hermetischen vnd Galenischen Medicin Ioachimii Tanckij ... Leipzig: J. Rosen, 1605.
  12 *l*., 101 p.

———. *See also* Payer, W., De thermis Carolinis ... 1614.

3482. REUSNER, Hieronymus. Pandora, das ist, Die edelste Gab Gottes, oder der Werde vnnd Heisemme Stein der Weisen ... Basel: [S. Apiario] 1582.
  8 *l*., 309 p.   illus.

3483. ———. ———. Basel: S. Henricpetri, [1598].
  8 *l*., 317 p., 1 *l*.   illus.

REUSS, Albert Reichard. Disqvisitionem analyticam arcani tartari. *See* Juncker, J., *praeses.*

3484. REUSS, August Christian. Beschreibung eines neuen chemischen Ofens ... Leipzig: C.G. Hilscher, 1782.
  74 p., 1 *l*.   illus.

———. Dissertatio inauguralis chemicomedica de sale sedativo Hombergii. *See* Storr, G.C.C., *praeses*.

3485. REUSS, Christian Friedrich. Dictionarivm botanicvm oder Botanisches lateinisches und deutsches Handwörterbuch für Aerzte, Cameralisten, Apothecker ... nach dem Linneischen System. Leipzig: C.G.Hilscher, 1781.
  2 v.

3486. REUSS, Franz Ambros. Die Garten-
quelle zu Teplitz in Böhmen, in chemischer
und medizinischer Hinsicht untersucht ...
Prag: Walther, 1797.
39 p.

A REVELATION of the secret spirit.
See Apocalypsis Spiritus Secreti.

REVERHORST, Maurito van.   De motu
bilis circulari ejusque morbis. *In* Nuck, A.,
Sialographia ... 1723.

3487. REY, Jean.   Essays ... sur la recherche de la cause pour laquelle l'estain
& le plomb augmentent de poids quand on
les calcine. Nouvelle edition ... avec des
notes par M. Gobet. Paris: Ruault, 1777.
xxxii, 216 p.   illus.

3488. REYHER, Samuel.   Dissertatio de
nummis quibusdam ex chymico metallo
factis. Kiliæ Holsatorum: J. Reumann, 1692.
4 *l*., 141 p., 1 *l*.   illus., chart.

RHAZES. *See* Muhammad ibn Zakarīyā
Abū Bakr, al Rāzī.

3489. RHENANUS, Johann.   Opera chymiatrica, qvæ hactenvs in lvcem prodiervnt
omnia ... Francofurti: C. Eifrid, 1635.
16 *l*., 367 p.   illus., chart.

3490. ———. Solis e pvteo emergentis:
sive Dissertationis chymiotechnicæ libri
tres ... Cum præfatione chymiæ veritatem
asserente ... Francofurti: A. Humm, 1613.
3 pts. in 1 v.   illus., chart.

3491. RHODOKANAKIS, Constantine.
Alexicacus, spirit of salt of the world, which
vulgarly prepar'd is call'd the spirit of salt.
Or, The transcendent virtue of the true spirit
of salt long look'd for ... London: R.D., 1664.
4 *l*., 8 p.
With his Discourse ... 1664.

3492. ———. A discourse in the praise of
antimonie, and the vertues thereof ... [Lon-
don]: 1664.
1 *l*., 9 p.

3493. RHUMEL, Johann Pharamund.   Basilica
chymica, continens philosophicam descriptionem & usum remediorum chymicorum selectissimorum ... Tubingæ: E. Wild, 1630.
2 *l*., 48 p.
With his Opvscvla ... 1635.

3494. ———. Κάτοπτρον arcvlæ medico

pharmacevticæ svis medicamentis præcipvis
microcosmi affectibus debitis splendens cui
annexa est Balsamotechnia ... Tubingæ: E.
Wild, 1630.
2 *l*., 27 p.
With his Opvscvla ... 1635.

3495. ———. Medicina spagyrica oder
Spagyrische Artzneykunst ... Editio secunda.
Franckfurt: C. Hermsdorff, 1662.
30 *l*., 769 p., 11 *l*.

3496. ———. Opvscvla chymico-magico-
medica ... Item Panacea aurea, oder gründliche Beschreibung des auri potabilis ... Mit
angehengter Kriegs Artzney ... [Nurenberg]:
1635.
4 *l*., 458 p., 4 *l*.

RIBBEN, Carl.   Circa fervidorum et
gelidorum usum paraenesis. *See* Linné, C.
von, *praeses*.   Entry 2423.

3497. RICARDUS, *Anglicus*.   I. Correctorivm
alchymiae ... Das ist, Reformierte Alchimy
... II. Rainmvndi Lvlli Apertorium & accuratio
vegetabilium ... III. Des Königs Gebers auss
Hispanien Secretū ... Strassburg: B. Jobin,
1581.
8 *l*., 151 p.

3498. RICCI, Francesco.   Giardino di secretti rarissimi, vtili, & piaceuoli ... Bologna:
[n.d.].
12 *l*.   port.

3499. RICETTARIO FIORENTINO.   El ricettario dell'arte, et vniversita de medici, et
spetiali della citta di Firenze. Rivedvto dal
Collegio de Medici ... Fiorenza: L. Torren-
tino, 1550.
186 p., 10 *l*.

3500. ———. Ricettario Fiorentino di nvovo
illvstrato. [Fiorenza: G. Marescotti] 1597.
5 *l*., 296 p., 25 *l*.

3501. ———. ———. [Firenze: P. Ceccon-
celli] 1623.
5 *l*., 296 p., 23 *l*.

3502. Il RICETTARIO medicinale ... nel qvale
... si insegna tutto quello, che si puo de-
siderare intorno alla cognizione del prouedere,
eleggere, conseruare, preparare, & comporre
qual si voglia sorte di medicamento ... Seconda impressione. Fiorenza: Giunti, 1574.
14 *l*., 278 p., 16 *l*.   illus.

3503. RICETTARIO SANESE.   Ricettario Sanes

diviso in quattro parte ... Siena: L. e B.
Bindi, 1771.
    2 v. in 1.

3504. A RICH CLOSET of physical secrets,
collected by the elaborate paines of four
severall students in physick, and digested
together ... London: printed by G. Dawson,
sold by W. Nealand, 1652.
    4 *l.*, 71 p.; 3 *l.*, 146 p., 7 *l.*

———. *In* Fioravanti, L., An exact
collection ... 1653.

A RICH STOREHOUSE of treasurie for
the diseased. *See* T., A.

3505. RICHARDSON, W. ... The chemical
principles of the metallic arts; with an account of the principal diseases incident to
the different artificers; the means of prevention and cure; and a concise introduction
to the study of chemistry ... Birmingham:
printed by T. Pearson, sold by R. Baldwin,
1790.
    cii, 201 p., 2 *l.*   charts.

3506. RICHTER, August Gottlieb. Abhandlung von den Brüchen. Göttingen: J.C. Dieterich, 1778-1779.
    2 v. illus.

3507. ———. Medical and surgical observations. Translated from the German. Edinburgh: for T. Duncan ..., 1794.
    xix, 336 p.

3508. RICHTER, Christian Friederich.
Ausführlicher Bericht von der Essentia Dulci
... Halle: J. Montag, 1708.
    79 p.
    With Urbigerus, B., Besondere chymische
Schrifften ... 1705.

3509. ———. Kurtzer und deutlicher Unterricht von dem Leibe und naturlichen Leben
des Menschen ... [Leipzig: 1750?]
    8 *l.*, 544 p., 31 *l.*

3510. RICHTER, Friedrich Adolph. Lehrbuch der Chemie. Halle: Hemmerde und
Schwetschke, 1791.
    6 *l.*, 465 p., 10 *l.*

3511. RICHTER, Samuel. Theo-philosophia
theoretico-practica, oder Der wahre Grund
Göttlicher und natürlicher Erkänntniss, dadurch beyde Tincturen, die himlische und
irrdische, können erhalten werden ... Nebst
einer Erläuterung des Operis maximi und

Beyfügung versprochener Experimenten ...
von Sincero Renato. Bresslau: E. Fellgiebel
Erben, 1711.
    10 *l.*, 374 p.

RIEMER, Joanne Andrea. Pharmacopoea castrensis Borussica. *See* Pharmacopoea Borussica.

3512. RIGAUD, Etienne César. L'existence
de la pierre merveilleuse des philosophes,
prouvée par des faits incontestables. Dédié
aux adeptes par un amateur de la sagesse
... France: 1765.
    8 *l.*, 108 p.

3513. RIOLAN, Jean, 1538?—1605. Vni-
versae medicinae compendia. Editio tertia,
ab autore aucta & recognita. Parisiis: ex
officina Plantiniana, apud H. Perier, 1606.
    168 numb. *l.*, 4 *l.*

3514. RIOLAN, Jean, 1580-1657. Ad famo-
sam Tvrqveti apologiam responsio. Accessit
Censura scholæ Parisiensis. Parisiis: ex
officina Plantiniana, apud H. Perier, 1603.
    98 p., 1 *l.*

3515. ———. Anthropographia, et osteologia
... Parisiis: D. Moreav, 1626.
    39 *l.*, 938 p., 32 *l.*   illus., port.

3516. ———. Ioannis Antarveti ... Apologia,
pro iudicio Scholę Parisiensis de alchimia.
Ad Harveti & Baucyneti recoctam crambem.
Parisiis: ex officina Plantiniana, apud H.
Perier, 1604.
    88 p.

3517. ———. Censvra demonstrationvm
Harveti pro veritate alchymiæ ... Parisiis:
ex officina Plantiniana, apud H. Perier, 1606.
    84 p.

3518. ———. Cvrievses recherches svr les
escholes en medecine, de Paris, et de Montpelier ... Par vn docteur en medecine, de la
faculté de Paris. Paris: G. Meturas, 1651.
    7 *l.*, 291 p., 5 *l.*

3519. ———. Encheiridivm anatomicvm et
pathologicvm ... Editio quarta ... Parisiis:
C. Metvras, 1658.
    16 *l.*, 610 p., 33 *l.*

3520. ———. Opvscvla nova anatomica,
iudicium nouum de venis lacteis tam mesen-
tericis quàm thoracicis, aduersus Th. Bar-
tholinum. Lymphatica vasa Bartholini refu-
tata. Animaduersiones secundae ad anatomiam

reformatam Bartholini ... Parisiis: vidua M.
dv Pvis, 1653.
   var. pag.

      RIPLEY, George.   The bosome-book.
In Collectanea chymica ... 1684.

3521.   ———. Chymische Schrifften des ...
philosophi Georgii Riplæi ... Zuvor durch ...
Nicolaum Barnavdum ... zu Lateinischer
Sprache publiciret. Jetzo aber ... in Deutsche
gebracht ... Erffurt: J. Birckner, 1624.
   113 p.
A German translation of Barnaud's Quadriga aurifera.

3522.   ———. ———. Nach der Lateinisch-
und Englischen Edition Herrn William Salmon ... ins Teutsche übersetzet durch Benjamin Roth-Scholtzen ... Wienn: J.P. Krauss,
1756.
   2 *l*., 233 p., 1 *l*.   illus.

3523.   ———. The compovnd of alchymy.
Or The hidden art of archemie: conteining
the right & perfectest meanes to make the
philosophers stone ... Set foorth by Raph
Rabbards ... London: T. Orwin, 1591.
   52 *l*.   chart.

      ———. ———. *In* Ashmole, E., Thea-
trum chemicum ... 1652.

      ———. Medulla philosophiae chem-
icae. *In* Opuscula quædam chemica ... 1614.

3524.   ———. Opera omnia chemica, quotquot hactenus visa sunt, quorum aliqua jam
primùm in lucem prodeunt, aliqua MS. exemplarium collatione à mendis & lacunis repurgata, atque integritati restituta sunt ...
Cassellis: typis J. Gentschii, impensis S.
Köhlers, 1649.
   7 *l*., 439 p.
With Nolle, H., Discursus ... 1636.

      ———. Traité du mercure. *In* Arnauld,
P., Philosophie naturelle ... 1682.

3525.   RIST, Johann.   J.R.H. Philosophischer
Phoenix das ist: Kurtze jedoch gründliche
und Sonnenklare Entdeckunge der waaren und
eigentlichen Matery des alleredelsten Steins
der Weisen ... Nürnberg: W.E. Felssecker,
1668.
   4 *l*., 34 p.
   Extract from: Helvetius, J.H., ...*Guldenes
Kalb* ... Nürnberg, 1668, but with separate
title-page and pagination.

3526.   RISUGDASBIUS, Samuel, *pseud*.   Ein
schön Gesprech vnd Disputation von der
rechten materia lapidis philosophici ... ab
anonymo quodam vorlengst beschrieben ...
item, Vom Stein der Gesundheit vnd Reich-
thumbs Achatii Myconii ... Leipzig: T.
Schürer, 1608.
   37 p.
   With Paracelsus, Zween vnderschiedene
Tractat ... 1608.

3527.   RITTER, Johann Wilhelm.   Beweis,
dass ein beständiger Galvanismus den
Labensprocess in dem Thierreich begleite.
Nebst neuen Versuchen und Bemerkungen
über den Galvanismus ... Weimar: im Verlage
des Industrie-Comptoirs, 1798.
   xx p., 2 *l*., 174 p.   illus.

3528.   RITTER, Marcus Friedrich.   Astronomia
inferior, oder: Septem planetarum terrestrium
spagyrica recensio, das ist, Erzehlung vnd
Erwehlung der sieben irdischen Planeten ...
Durch Marcum Friederich Rosencreutzer ...
Nürnberg: W. Endter, 1646.
   11 *l*., 442 p., 16 *l*.   illus.

3529.   RIVIERA, Cesare della.   Il mondo
magico de gli heroi ... nel quale con inusitata
chiarezza si tratta qual sia la vera magia
natvrale: e come si possa fabricare la reale
pietra de' filosofi ... Hora di nouo ristampata
... Milano: P.M. Locarni, 1605.
   15 *l*., 222 p.   illus.

3530.   RIVIÈRE, Lazare.   Four books ... containing five hundred and thirteen observations, or histories, of famous and rare cures
... unto which is added ... Select medicinal
counsels of John Fernelius ... All Englished
by Nicholas Culpeper ... London: P. Cole,
1658.
   9 *l*., 417 p.   port.

3531.   ———. Institvtiones medicæ, in
qvinqve libros distinctæ, quibus totidem
medicinæ partes, physiologia, pathologia,
semeiotice, hygienine, & therapeutice dilu-
cide explicantur ... Lvgdvni: A. Cellier, 1656.
   8 *l*., 535 p., 1 *l*.   port., charts.

3532.   ———. The universal body of physick,
in five books; comprehending the several
treatises of nature, of diseases and their
causes, of symptomes, of the preservation
of health, and of cures ... Exactly translated
into English by William Carr ... London: for
H. Eversden, 1657.
   9 *l*., 417 p., 2 *l*.   charts.

3533. ———. Methodvs cvrandarvm febrivm. Lvgdvni: I.B. Devenet, 1649.
    3 *l.*, 201 p.
    With his Praxis medicae ... 1649.

3534. ———. Opera medica universa; quibus continentur, I. Institutionum medicarum
libri quinque. II. Praxeos medicae libri
septemdecim. III. Observationum medicarum
centuriae quatuor. Quibus accedunt observationes variae ab aliis communicatae ...
Editio novissima ... Genevae: fratres de
Tournes, 1737.
    2 *l.*, xvi p., 2 *l.*, 604 p., 20 *l.*, 92 p.

3535. ———. Praxis medicae. Editio quarta,
supra omnes alias adornata, & ab admissis
haud leuibus erratis diligenter emaculata.
Lvgdvni: I.B. Devenet, 1649.
    2 v.

3536. ———. The practice of physick in
seventeen several books ... By Nicholas
Culpeper ... Abdiah Cole ... and William
Rowland ... Being chiefly a translation of
the works of ... Lazarus Riverius ... To
which are added four books containing five
hundred and thirteen observations of famous
cures ... And a fifth book of Select medicinal
counsels, by John Fernelius ... London: for
G. Sawbridge, 1678.
    7 *l.*, 645 p.; 6 *l.*, 463 p., 16 *l.*   ports.

3537. ROBERTSON, Robert. An essay on
fevers ... London: for the author ..., 1790.
    4 *l.*, xv, 286 p.

3538. ———. Observations on the jail,
hospital, or ship fever. London: for J. Murray,
1783.
    x, 2 *l.*, 318 p.   illus.

3539. ROBERTSON, William, *praeses.*
Dissertatio inauguralis de aere fixo dicto,
aut mephitico ... Eruditorum examini subjicit Daniel Rutherford ... Edinburgi: Balfour
et Smellie, 1772.
    2 *l.*, 25 p.

3539a. ROBINSON, Bryan. A dissertation on
the food and discharges of human bodies.
Dublin: S. Powell for G. and A. Ewing and
W. Smith, 1747.
    vi, 120 p.

3540. ROCHAS, Henry de. La phisiqve
demonstative, divisee en trois livres ...
Paris: P. Lamy, 1643.
    208 p.; 4 *l.*, 183 p.; 3 *l.*, 363 p., 29 *l.*

3541. RODE, Johan. De ponderibus et
mensuris veterum medicorum inprimis Cor-
nelii Celsi dissertatio posthuma in lucem
protracta à Th. Bartholino. Accedit vita Celsi,
& judicia doctorum de acia Rhodiana. Hafniæ: literis M. Godicchenii, sumptibus P.
Hauboldi, 1672.
    71 p.
    With Angelocrator, D., Doctrina de pon-
deribus ... 1617.

———. In Castelli lexicon perutiles.
In Castelli, B., Amaltheum Castello-Brunonianum ... 1699.

———. Mantissa anatomica. *In* Bartholin, T., Historiarum anatomicarum ... 1661.

3542. RODRIGO Y ANDUEZA, Manuel. Libro
de los prodigiosos baños de Thyermas ...
Pamplona: J.J. Ezquerro, 1713.
    8 *l.*, 315 p., 2 *l.*

3543. ROEDERER, Johannes Georgius. Elementa artis obstetriciae in vsvm praelectionvm
academicarvm. Gottingae: 1753.
    8 *l.*, 352 p., 1 *l.*

3544. ROLFINCK, Werner. Chimia in artis
formam redacta, sex libris comprehensa.
Jenæ: S. Krebs, 1661.
    8 *l.*, 443 p., 5 *l.*   chart.

3545. ———. Dissertationes chimicæ sex
de tartaro, sulphure, margaritis, perfectis
metallis duobus auro et argento, antimonio,
et imperfectis metallis duris duobus ferro et
cupro. Jenæ: Krebs, 1679.
    var. pag.

3546. ———. Liber de purgantibus vegetabilibus, sectionibus XV absolutus. Jenæ:
impensis J.L. Neuenhahnii, typis J. Wertheri,
1667.
    12 *l.*, 454 p., 3 *l.*

3547. ———. Ordo et methodus generationi
dicatarum partium, per anatomen, cognoscendi fabricam, liber unus, ad normam veterum
& recentiorum scriptorum exaratus. Jenae: S.
Krebs, 1664.
    8 *l.*, 214 p., 7 *l.*

3548. ———. Ordo et methodus medicinae
specialis consultatoriae ὡς ἐν ἀτόμῳ, continens consilia medica, ad normam veterum
& novorum dogmatum adornata. Jenae: S.
Krebs, 1669.
    16 *l.*, 962 p., 11 *l.*

3549. ——, *praeses*. Scrutinium vitrioli erudito iatrogonistarum examini in
acroaterio medicorum Johann Georgius
Trumphius. Jenæ: S. Krebs, 1666.
    36 *l*.

    RONDELET, Guillaume.   Formulae
aliquot remediorum. *In* L'Obel, M. de, Nova
stirpium adversaria ... 1576.

3550. RONDELET, Martin.   Tentamen physiologicum de calore animali ... [Monspelii:
J.F. Picot, 1781.]
    8 p.
    Caption title.

3551. ROSACCIO, Gioseppe.   Della no-
bilita et grandezza dell'hvomo, della quale
si caua l'ordine, misura, & proportione di
quello, & si conosce per la fisonomia, qual
sia la complessione di tutti gl'huomini ...
Milano: G. Ferioli, 1596.
    8 *l*.

    ROSARIUM philosophorum. *In* De
alchimia opuscula complura veterum philosophorum ... 1550.

3552. ROSÉN VON ROSENSTEIN, Nils.
Traité des maladies des enfans, ouvrage
qui est le fruit d'une longue observation,
& appuyé sur les faits les plus authentiques.
Traduit du suédois ... par M. Le Fabvre de
Villebrune. Paris: P.G. Cavelier, 1778.
    xii, 582 p., 1 *l*.

    ROSENCREUTZER, Marcum Friederich,
pseud. *See* Ritter, Marcus Friedrich.

    ROSENSTENGEL, Johann Jacob.
Supplementa Beccheriana. *In* Becher, J.J.,
Oedipus chymicus ... 1716.

3553. RÖSLIN, Eucharius.   The birth of
mankynde, otherwyse named the womans
booke. Newly set forth, corrected, and augmented ... By Thomas Raynalde ... [London:
R. Jugge] 1565.
    14 *l*., cxxxi numb. *l*.   illus.

3554. ——. ——. Newly set foorth ...
[London]: R.I., 1565.
    14 *l*., cxxxi numb. *l*.   illus.
    This edition does not contain the 4 pages
of mounted anatomical cuts included in the
former.

3555. ROSNEL, Pierre de.   Le Mercvre Indien, ou Le tresor des Indes ... Par P.D.R.
Paris: [R. Chevillion] 1667.

    2 pts. in 1 v.

3556. ROSS, Alexander.   Arcana microcosmi:
or, The hid secrets of man's body discovered
... With a refutation of Doctor Brown's Vulgar
errors, the Lord Bacon's Natural History, and
Doctor Harvy's book De generatione, Comen-
ius, and others; whereto is annexed a letter
from Doctor Pr. to the author ... London:
printed by T. Newcomb, sold by J. Clark,
1652.
    8 *l*., 267 p., 4 *l*.
    Lacking pages 53-60, 97-98.

3557. ——. Medicus medicatus: or The
physicians religion cured, by a lenitive or
gentle potion: with some animadversions
upon Sir Kenelme Digbie's Observations on
Religio medici ... London: printed by J. Young,
sold by C. Green, 1645.
    7 *l*., 112 p.

3558. ——. The philosophicall touch-stone:
or Observations upon Sir Kenelm Digbie's
Discourses of the nature of bodies, and of
the reasonable soule ... London: for J. Young
and C. Green, 1645.
    8 *l*., 131 p.

3559. ROSSI, Francesco.   Nocturnae exer-
citationes in medicas historias ... Joannes
Garmers denuò edidit ... Hamburgi: typis
Pfeifferianis, sumptibus J. Naumanni, 1660.
    16 *l*., 489 p., 16 *l*.

3560. ROSSI, Girolamo.   De distillatione
liber ... Tertia hac editione ab avctore recognitus, ac multis locis locupletatus. Venetiis:
ex thypographia Guerræa, 1599.
    8 *l*., 181 p.   illus.

    ROTBART, Christofer. *See* Brotoffer,
Radtichs.

3561. ROTH, J.H.   Analyse historique des
eaux minérales de Niederbronn ... Strasbourg:
J.H. Heitz, 1783.
    2 *l*., 61 p., 1 *l*.

3562. ROTHE, Gottfried.   Anhang zu seiner
Chymie, handlend von denen metallischen
Saltzen und dem Schmertz- stillenden Schwefel
des Vitriols. Leipzig: C.J. Eyssell, 1727.
    96 p.
    With his Gründliche Anleitung zur Chymie
... 1727.

3563. ——. Gründliche Anleitung zur Chymie
... Dritte Auflage... Leipzig: C.J. Eysseln, 1727.
    6 *l*., 240 p., 2 *l*.

3564. ———. Introduction a la chymie, accompagnée de deux traitez ... avec une analyse raisonée de l'antimoine, & un traité sur les teintures antimoinales, par M. Meuder ... Traduit de l'Allemand par J. L. Clausier ... Paris: H.L. Guerin & J. Guerin, 1741.
   8 *l*., 503 p.

ROTHERAM, John. Medicamenta purgantia. *See* Linné, C. von, *praeses*. Entry 2481.

ROTHMAN, Göran. De raphania. *See* Linné, C. von, *praeses*. Entry 2425.

3565. ROTH-SCHOLTZ, Friedrich. Bibliotheca chemica. H.e. Collectio avctorvm fere omnivm, qui de natvrae arcanis, re metallica et minerali, item de melioratione corporvm artificiali etc. hermetica scripservnt ... editio secvnda. Norimbergae: haeredes J.D. Tavberi, 1735.
   238 [i.e. 328] p.   port.

3566. ———, *ed*. Deutsches theatrum chemicum, auf welchem der berühmtesten philosophen und alchymisten Schrifften, die von dem Stein der Weisen ... handeln ... vorgestellet werden ... Nürnberg: A.J. Felssecker, 1728-1732.
   3 v.   illus., port.

3567. ROUELLE, Guillaume François. Analyses d'une eau minérale faites par MM. Rouelle ... & Cadet ... [Paris, 1755.]
   29 p.

3568. ———. Tableau de l'analyse chimique; ou Procédés du cours de chimie. Paris: Vincent, 1774.
   xxxi, 182 p., 1 *l*.

ROUILLASCUS, Philippus. Practica. *In* Paracelsus, Centum quindecim curationes ... 1582.

3569. ROUSSEAU, *l'abbé*. Preservatifs et remedes universels, tirez des animaux, des vegetaux, & des mineraux ... Paris: C. Cellier, 1706.
   x, 176 p., 2 *l*.

3570. ———. Secrets et remedes éprouvez ... Derniere edition corrigée & augmentée des preservatifs & remedes universels ... ouvrage posthume ... Avec un remede specifique pour la guérison de toutes sortes de maladies veneriennes. Paris: C. Jombert, 1718.
   2 pts. in 1 v.

3571. ROY, Henrick de. Philosophia naturalis; in qua tota rerum universitas, per clara & facilia principia, explanatur. Amstelaedami: L. & D. Elzevirius, 1661.
   22 *l*., 523 p.   illus., port., maps.

ROYAL COLLEGE OF PHYSICIANS OF EDINBURGH. Pharmacopoea. *See* Pharmacopoea Edinburgensis.

ROYAL COLLEGE OF PHYSICIANS OF LONDON. Pharmacopoeia Londinensis. *See* Pharmacopoeia Londinensis.

3572. ROYAL SOCIETY OF LONDON. Musæum Regalis Societatis. Or a catalogue & description of the natural and artificial rarities belonging to the Royal Society and preserved at Gresham Colledge. Made by Nehemjah Grew ... Whereunto is subjoyned the comparative anatomy of stomachs and guts. By the same author. London: W. Rawlins for the author, 1681.
   6 *l*., 386 p., 1 *l*.; 1 *l*., 43 p.   illus., port.

3573. ROZIER, François. De la fermentation des vins, et de la meilleure maniere de faire l'eau-de-vie ... Lyon: freres Perisse, 1770.
   1 *l*., 266 p., 1 *l*.   illus.

RUBEUS, Francisco. *See* Rossi, Francesco.

RUBEUS, Hieronymus. *See* Rossi, Girolamo.

RUDBERG, Jakob. Saporem medicamentorum. *See* Linné, C. von, *praeses*. Entry 2461.

3574. RÜDIGER, Anton. Systematische Anleitung zur reinen und überhaupt applicirten oder allgemeinen Chymie ... Leipzig: J.G. Dyck, 1756.
   8 *l*., 784 p., 21 *l*.   illus.

3575. RUDIUS, Eustachius. De morbis occvltis, et venenatis, libri quinque ... Venetiis: T. Baglionus, 1610.
   5 *l*., 227 p.
   With Massaria, A., Practica medica ... 1622.

RUEO, Francisco. De gemmis aliquot. *In* Lemnius, L., Similitudinum ac parabolarum ... 1608.

3576. RUESENSTEIN, Alexius. Auserlesene

chymische universal und particular Processe,
welche Herr Baron von Ruesenstein auf
seinen zweyen Reisen mit sechs Adepten
... erlernet ... und wovon die Originalien
in seinem Schloss in einer Mauer gefunden
worden sind. Franckfurt: P.C. Monath, 1754.
    8 *l*., 284 p., 2 *l*.

    RUFUS, *of Ephesus*.   De corporis
humani. *In* Aretaeus, Libri septem ... 1552.

3577.   RUIZ LOPEZ, Hipólito.   Quinologia,
o Tratado del árbol de la quina ó cascarilla
... Madrid: Marin, 1792.
    7 *l*., 103 p., 2 *l*.

3578.   RULAND, Martin.   Alexicacvs chymiatricvs: pvris pvtis, mendaciis, atqve
calvmniis atrocissimis Ioannis Oberndorferi
... oppositus asserendæ veritatis & famæ
integritatis suæ iure ... Francofurti: Palthen,
1611.
    4 *l*., 111 p.

3579.   ——.   Lexicon alchemiæ sive Dictionarivm alchemisticvm, cum obscuriorum
verborum, & rerum Hermeticarum, tum Theo-
phrast-Paracelsicarum phrasium planam
explicationem continens ... Francofurti: Z.
Palthen, 1612.
    4 *l*., 471 p.   illus.

3580.   ——.   Progymnasmata alchemiæ,
siue Problemata chymica, nonaginta & vna
quæstionibus dilucidata: cvm Lapidis
philosophici vera conficiendi ratione ...
Francofurti: Collegio Musarum Paltheniano,
1607.
    3 pts. in 1 v.
    Part 3, with separate title-page and
pagination, lacks all after p. 160.

3581.   RUMSEY, Walter.   Organon salutis.
An instrument to cleanse the stomach, as
also divers new experiments of the virtue of
tobacco and coffee ... By W.R.   ... London:
R. Hodgkinsonne for D. Pakeman, 1657.
    12 *l*., 56 p.

3582.   RUSCELLI, Girolamo.   [De' secreti
... Nuouamente da lui medesimo migliorati
& aggiunti. Venice?: c. 1550?]
    277 numb. *l*., 3 *l*.
    Caption title. Lacking the title page.

3583.   ——.   De' secreti ... parti quattro.
Nvovamente ristampati ... Venetia: A. Bodio,
1674.
    554 p., 19 *l*.

3584.   ——.   De secretis libri sex ... ex
Italico in latinum sermonem nunc primum
translati per Ioannem Iacobum Weckerum ...
Antverpiæ: J. Steelsius, 1560.
    6 *l*., 316 p., 15 *l*.

3585.   ——.   ——.   Longe castigatiores &
ampliores quàm priore editione. Nam sex
prioribus septimus accessit ex eiusdem
authoris appendice factus ... Io. Iacobo
Weckero ... interprete. Basileæ: P. Perna,
1560.
    7 *l*., 354 p., 15 *l*.

3586.   ——.   ——.   Lugduni: G. Rouillius,
1561.
    344 p., 11 *l*.

3587.   ——.   [The secretes of ... Maister
Alexis of Piemont ... Translated oute of
Frenche into Englyshe by William Warde.
London: R. Hall for N. England, 1562.]
    Part 1 only of 3 parts.
    Imperfect.   The original title page has
been replaced by a title page to the second
part, adulterated by paste-over to read first
part.

3588.   ——.   ——.   Newely corrected and
amended ... London: H. Bynneman for J.
Wight, 1568.
    Parts 1 and 2 only of four parts.
    Lacking preliminary leaves 3–4 and spe-
cial title page to part 1.

3589.   ——.   —— somewhat inlarged in
certaine places ... London: P. Short for T.
Wight, 1595.
    6 *l*., 348 numb. *l*., 14 *l*.
    4 parts in 1 volume, paged continuously,
but with special title pages to each part.

3590.   ——.   ——.   London: W. Stansby for
R. Meighen and T. Jones, 1615.
    6 *l*., 348 p., 10 *l*.

3591.   ——.   The seconde parte of the secretes ... newely translated out of Frenche
into Englishe ... By Willyam Ward. London:
J. Kyngston for N. Englande, 1560.
    1 *l*., 79 numb. *l*., 7 *l*.
    With the The secretes ... 1562.

3592.   ——.   The thyrde and last parte
of the secretes ... Englished by Wylliam
Warde. London: H. Denham for J. Wyght
[1566?].
    1 *l*., 117 numb. *l*., 11 *l*.
    With his The secretes ... 1568.

3593. ――――. ――――. London: H. Denham for
J. Wyght [1566].
1 *l*., 75 numb. *l*., 9 *l*.
With his The secretes ... 1562.

3594. ――――. [The fourth and last part of
the secretes ... London: H. Denham, 1569.]
3 pts. in 1 v.
Lacking the title-page and 3 [?] following leaves; also pp. 7-8 of part 3.
With his The secretes ... 1568.

3595. ――――. Les secrets dv Seignevr Alexis
Piemontois ... Derniere edition. Roven: D.
Gevffroy, 1627.
911 p., 40 *l*. illus.

3596. ――――. ――――. Reueus & augmentez
d'une infinité de rares & admirables secrets.
Lyon: N. Gay, 1639.
675 p., 35 *l*.
Lacking pages 263-266, 451-454.

3597. ――――. ――――. Rouen: L. Maurry, 1662.
705 p., 35 *l*. illus.

3598. ――――. Artzney Buch ... Auss Wel-
scher und Latinischer sprach in Teutsch
gebracht, vnnd ordenlich zusammen verfasset durch Hans Jacob Wecker ... Basel:
P. Perna, 1575.
4 *l*., cccclxii p.

3599. RUSH, Benjamin. An account of the
bilious remitting yellow fever, as it appeared
in the city of Philadelphia in the year 1793.
Second edition. Philadelphia: T. Dobson,
1794.
x, 363 p.

3600. ――――. An eulogium in honor of the
late Dr. William Cullen ... delivered before
the College of Physicians of Philadelphia,
on the 9th of July ... Philadelphia: T. Dobson,
1790.
30 p., 1 *l*.

3601. ――――. An inquiry into the effects of
spirituous liquors on the human body. To
which is added a moral and physical ther-
mometer. Boston: Thomas and Andrews, 1790.
12 p.

3602. ――――. Medical inquiries and observations. Second American edition. Philadelphia: T. Dobson, 1794-1798.
5 v.

3603. ――――. An oration delivered before
the American Philosophical Society ... 27th

of February, 1786; containing an enquiry
into the influence of physical causes upon
the moral faculty ... Philadelphia: C. Cist,
1786.
4 *l*., 40 p.

3604. RUSSELL, Patrick. A treatise of the
plague: containing an historical journal and
medical account, of the plague, at Aleppo,
in the years 1760, 1761, and 1762 ... London: for G and J. Robinson, 1791.
12 *l*., 583, clix p., 4 *l*.

3605. RUSSELL, Richard. De tabe glandu-
lari, sive De usu aquae marinae in morbis
glandularum dissertatio. Oxon.: J. Fletcher,
1750.
3 *l*., 235 p.

RUTHERFORD, Daniel. Dissertatio
inauguralis de aero fixo dicto. *See* Robertson,
William, *praeses*.

3606. RUTTY, John. Aanhangsel tot de
nieuwe Britsche apotheek ... benevens
een bericht nopens de kragten van ver-
scheide onderwerpen der materia medica,
die in de Britische apotheek niet begreefen
zyn ... Uit het Engelsch vertaald door
Theodorus van Brussel. Amsterdam: G. Bom,
1778.
4 *l*., 64 p.
With Lewis, W., De nieuwe Britsche
apotheek ... 1772.

――――. The analysis of milk. *In* The
argument of sulphur ... 1762.

3607. ――――. A methodical synopsis of mineral waters ... in a method entirely new. Interspersed with tables ... and abstracts of
the principal authors who have treated of
mineral waters ... London: for W. Johnston,
1757.
xv, 660 p., 4 *l*. charts.

3608. RUYSCH, Frederik. Observationum
anatomico-chirurgicarum centuria. Accedit
Catalogus rariorum ... Amstelodami: Janssonio-
Waesbergios, 1737.
6 *l*., 188 p. illus.

3609. ――――. Opera omnia anatomico-medico-
chirurgica ... Amstelodami: Janssonio-Waesbergios, 1721-1729.
4 v. illus.

3610. ――――. ――――. Amstelodami: Janssonio-
Waesbergios, 1737 [i.e., 1724-1744].
3 v. illus., port.

3611. ———. Thesaurus anatomicus primus [secundus] ... Het eerste [twede] anatomisch cabinet ... Amstelædami: J. Wolters, 1701-1702.
2 pts. in 1 v.   illus.

3612. RYFF, Walther Hermann.   Der ander theyl der kleynern teütschen Apoteck, Confect oder Latwergen büchlins ... [Strassburg?: B. Beck?] 1542.
4 ℓ., clv numb. ℓ., 8 ℓ.
With his Rechter vnd nutzlicher gebrauch ... 1541.

3613. ———. Ein ausserlesen schön Artzney- und Kräuter Buch ... Erstlich durch ... Apollinarem ... zusammen getragen, jetzundt aber von newen ubersehen ... Erffurdt: T. Fritzsch, 1626.
3 pts. in 1 v.   illus.

3614. ———. Confect Büchlin vnd Hauss Apoteck. Kunstlich zu bereyten, einmachen, vnd recht gebrauchen, mancherhandt nutzbare Confect, Latwergen, Conserva ... Franckfort: C. Egenolff [1544].
32 ℓ., 159 numb. ℓ.   illus.

3615. ———. ———. Franckfurt am Mayn:

bey J. Saurn, in Verlegung V. Steinmeyer, 1610.
284 numb. ℓ., 9 ℓ.   illus.

3616. ———. New gross Distillier-Büch, wolgegründter künstlicher Distillation ... Franckfort: C. Egenolffs Erben [1556].
4 ℓ., cxcvii numb. ℓ.   illus.

3617. ———. Newe aussgerüste deutsch Apoteck ... verbessert ... durch Nicolaum Agerium ... Strassburg: L. Zetzner, 1602.
4 ℓ., 721 p., 12 ℓ.; 303 p., 4 ℓ.   illus.

3618. ———. Rechter vnd nutzlicher Gebrauch, ordenliche Vermischung vnd Zubereyttung aller Laxatiuen, purgierender oder treibender Artzney, eynfacher, gemeyner vnuermischter Stuck, auch vermischter vnd zusamen gesetzter, treibender Artzney, mancherley Compositzen von Latwergen ... [Straszburg: B. Beck] 1541.
4 ℓ., clxiii numb. ℓ., 4 ℓ.

3619. ———. Reformierte deutsche Apoteck darinnen eigentliche Contrafactur der fürnembsten vnd gebreüchlichsten Kreutter ... Strassburg: J. Rihel, 1573.
10 ℓ., 262 numb. ℓ., 14 ℓ., 128 numb. ℓ., 6 ℓ.   illus.

S

3620. S***, *graf von*. Experimentirte Kunst-Stücke oder Sammlung einiger rarer, curieuser und geheimer chymischer Processe und andere höchst-nützliche Arcana ... ans Licht gegeben worder von W.G.L.D. Braunschweig: Renger, 1731-1733.

3 v. in 1.

3621. S., G.A.P. Acerra medico-chymica in qua inveniuntur non solum variæ compositiones medicamentorum Hippocratico-Galenicorum, sed etiam plurima arcana, præsertim chymica, medicinæ tyroni itidem ac practico imprimis utilissima ... Lipsiæ: A. Martin, 1713.

8 *l*., 528 p., 6 *l*. illus.

SABOR, Chrysostomus Ferdinand von, *pseud. See* Siebenstern, Christian Friedrich Sendimir von.

3622. SACHS, Philipp Jacob. Αμπελογραφία sive Vitis viniferæ ejusǵve partium consideratio physico-philologico-historico-medico-chymica ... Lipsiæ: impensis viti J. Trescheri, typis C. Michaëlis, 1661.

22 *l*., 670, 70 p., 17 *l*. illus.

3623. SADLER, John. Enchiridion medicum: an enchiridion of the art of physick ... Written in Latine ... translated, revised, corrected and augmented by R.T. London: for R. Moone and H. Fletcher, 1657.

8 *l*., 208 p.

3624. SAGE, Balthazar Georges. Analyse chimique et concordance des trois règnes ... Paris: Imprimerie Royale, 1786.

3 v. illus., chart.

3625. ———. L'art d'essayer l'or et l'argent; tableau comparé de la coupellation des substances métalliques par le moyen du plomb ou du bismuth: procédés pour obtenir l'or plus pur que par la voie du départ ... Paris: imprimerie de Monsieur, 1780.

xii, 112 p. illus.

3626. ———. Description méthodique du cabinet de l'École Royale des Mines. Paris: l'Imprimerie Royale, 1784-1787.

2 pts. in 1 v.

3627. ———. Elémens de mineralogie docimastique. Paris: P. de Lormel, 1772.

xxiv, 276 p. chart.

3628. ———. ———. Seconde édition. Paris: l'Imprimerie Royale, 1777.

2 v. port., chart.

3629. ———. Examen chymique de différentes substances minérales ... traduction d'une lettre de Monsieur Lehmann, sur la mine de plomb rouge ... Paris: P. de Lormel, 1769.

xii, 151 [i.e., 251] p., 3 *l*.

3630. ———. Expériences propres à faire connoître que l'alkali volatil-fluor est le remède le plus efficace dans les asphyxies ... Paris: Imprimerie Royale, 1777.

1 *l*., vii, 62 p.

3631. ———. ———. Troisième édition augmentée. Paris: imprimerie de Monsieur, 1778.

2 *l*., xvi, 76 p.

3632. ———. Mémoires de chimie. Paris: Imprimerie Royale, 1773.

vii, 262, xxxviii p., 1 *l*. chart.

3633. SAIGNIER, Jean. Magni lapidis natvralis philosophia & vera ars ... Bremæ: J. Koehler, 1664.

3 *l*., 3-52 p.

3634. SAINT-HILAIRE. Les remedes des maladies du corps humain. Nouvelle edition, augmentée d'un grand nombre de remedes specifiques & experimentez ... Paris: J. Couterot & L. Guerin, 1685.

18 *l*., 504 p., 1 *l*. illus.

3635. SAINT ROMAIN, G.B. de. La science

naturelle, dégagée des chicanes de l'école:
ovvrage novveav, enrichi de plusieurs experiences curieuses tirées de la medecine
& de la chymie ... Paris: A. Cellier, 1679.
   5 ℓ., 391 p., 4 ℓ.

3636.   SALA, Angelo.   Chrysologia, sev
Examen auri chymicum ... Adjecti sunt in
fine ejusdem Aphorismi chymiatrici recogniti. Hamburgi: H. Carstens, 1622.
   72 ℓ., 103 p.

3637.   ———.   Descriptio brevis antidoti
pretiosi: quâ antiquissimæ ejus virtutes,
ususque multiplex variis in morbis, & humani corporis affectibus, recensentur ...
Marpurgi: P. Egenolph, 1620.
   63 p.

3638.   ———.   Hydrelæologia, darinnen, wie
man allerley Wasser, Oliteten, vnd brennende Spiritus der vegetabilischen Dingen,
durch gewisse chymische Regeln, vnd
manualia, in ihren besten Kräfften distillieren vnd rectificiren soll ... Rostock:
druckts J. Fuess, in verlegung J. Hallerfords,
1633.
   160 ℓ.

3639.   ———.   Opera medico-chymica qvæ
extant omnia ... Editio postrema auctior &
emendatior ... accessit tractatus peculiaris
Angeli Salæ De erroribus pseudochymicorum
& galenistarum ... Rothomagi: I. Berthelin,
1650.
   4 ℓ., 749 p., 6 ℓ.; 50 p., 1 ℓ.

3640.   ———.   Ternarius bezoardicorum &
hemetologia sev Trivmphvs vomitoriorvm ...
è Gallico sermone latinitate ... donati cum
Exegesi chymiatrica Andreæ Tentzelii ...
Erfurti: impensis J. Birckneri, typis haeredum
Mechlerianorum, 1618.
   2 pts. in 1 v.   illus.
   With Crusius, D., Theatrum morborum ...
1616.

3641.   SALADINUS Asculanus.   Compendium
aromatariorum. Ferrarie: A. Gallus, 1488.
   21 ℓ.

   ———.   ———.   In Mesue, Joannes,
Damascenus. Mesue cum expositione ...
1497.

3642.   SALMON, William.   Botanologia.
The English herbal: or, History of plants ...
London: I. Dawks for H. Rhodes ..., 1710.
   4 ℓ., 1296 p., 25 ℓ.   illus.

3643.   ———.   Collectanea medica, The
country physician: or, A choice collection
of physick ... London: J. Taylor, 1703.
   4 ℓ., 603 p., 2 ℓ.

3644.   ———.   Dictionaire hermetique, contenant l'explication des termes ... & manieres
de parler de vrais philosophes. Accompagné
de deux traitez singuliers & utiles aux curieux de l'art. Par un amateur de la science.
Paris: L. d'Houry, 1695.
   2 pts. in 1 v.

3645.   ———.   Doron medicum: or, A supplement to the new London dispensatory ...
The second edition ... London: for T. Dawks
..., 1688.
   7 ℓ., 776 p., 28 ℓ.

3646.   ———.   Medicina practica: or, Practical physick ... To which is added, the
philosophick works of Hermes Trismegistus,
Kalid Persieus, Geber Arabs, Artefius Longæ-
vus, Nicholas Flammel, Roger Bachon, and
George Ripley. All translated out of the best
Latin editions ... London: for T. Howkins, J.
Taylor, and J. Harris, 1692.
   15 ℓ., 696 p., 1 ℓ.   illus.

3647.   ———.   Παρατηρήματα or Select physical and chyrurgical observations: containing divers remarkable histories of cures ...
London: for T. Passinger and J. Richardson,
1687.
   8 ℓ., 523 p., 26 ℓ.   illus.

3648.   ———.   Pharmacopoeia Londinensis.
Or, The new London dispensatory ... The
second edition corrected and amended: whereto is added a table of diseases: & another
of the colledge's errors ... London: for T.
Dawks ..., 1682.
   8 ℓ., 877 p., 1 ℓ.

3649.   ———.   ———.   The third edition ...
London: for T. Dawks ..., 1685.
   8 ℓ., 877 p., 1 ℓ.

3650.   ———.   ———.   The fifth edition ... London: J. Dawks for T. Bassett ..., 1696.
   8 ℓ., 887 p., 1 ℓ.

3651.   ———.   ———.   The seventh edition ...
London: J. Dawks, 1707.
   8 ℓ., 896 p., 8 ℓ.

3652.   ———.   Polygraphice: or The arts of
drawing, engraving, etching, limning, painting, washing, varnishing, gilding, colouring,

dying, beautifying and perfuming ... To
which is added, I. The one hundred and
twelve chymical arcanums of Petrus Johannes Faber ... II. An abstract of choice chymical preparations ... The fifth edition ...
London: for T. Passinger and T. Sawbridge,
1685.
34 *l*., 767 p. illus., port.

3653. ——. Seplasivm. The compleat
English physician: or, The druggist's shop
opened ... London: for M. Gilliflower and G.
Sawbridge, 1693.
32 *l*., 1207 p.

3654. ——. Synopsis medicinae: or, A
compendium of the theory and practice of
physick. In seven books ... Third edition ...
London: I. Dawks, 1694.
17 *l*., 1064 p. port.

SALOMON, Ernst Didrik. De scor-
buto. *See* Linné, C. von, *praeses*. Entry
2495.

3655. SALTZMANN, Johann Rudolph. Kurtze
Beschreibung des heilsamen Bades vnd
Bronnens der Sahlbronnen, oder das Sehl-
bacher Bad genant ... Strassburg: L. Zetzner,
1632.
54 p.

——. ——. *In* Thurneisser zum
Thurn, L., Zehen Bücher ... 1612.

3656. SALUZZO, Giuseppe Angelo, *conte de
Menusiglio*. Lettre sur la conversion de
l'acide vitriolique en acide nitreux ... [Turin:
J.-M. Briolo, 1782?]
5 *l*.

3657. SAMBER, Robert. Long livers: A
curious history of such persons of both
sexes who have liv'd several ages, and grown
young again: with the rare secret of reju-
venescency of Arnoldus de Villa Nova ... By
Eugenius Philalethes ... London: for J. Holland and L. Stoke, 1722.
lxiv, 199, viii p.

3658. ——. Some reflections on a late
book, called, The golden age, &c ... By
Eugenius Philalethes Jun. London: for the
author and A. Baldwin, 1698.
30 p.

3659. SAMMLUNG der neuesten und merk-
würdigsten Begebenheiten, die sich mit unterschiedlichen Vermuthlich noch lebenden
Adepten und ihrer philosophischen Tinktur

zugetragen haben, nebst der ausführlichen
und sonderbaren Geschichte des grossen
Adepten Nicol. Flamelli. Hildesheim: Schröder,
1780.
148 p., 1 *l*.

3660. SAMOILOVICH, Danilo Samoilovich.
Memoire sur la peste, qui, en 1771, ravagea
l'Empire de Russie ... Paris: Leclerc ...,
1783.
xxiv, 286 p., 1 *l*.

SANCTORIUS, Sanctorius. *See* Santorio, Santorio.

3661. SANDIFORT, Eduard. Exercitationes
academicæ. Lugduni Batavorum: S. et J. Luchtman, P.v.d. Eyk et D. Vygh, 1783-1785.
2 v. in 1. illus.

——. Museum anatomicum Academiae
Lugduno-Batavae. *See* Leyden. Ryksuniversiteit. Anatomisch Kabinet.

3662. ——. Observationes anatomico-
pathologicae. Lugduni Batavorum: P.v.d. Eyk
et D. Vygh, 1777-1781.
4 v. in 2. illus.

3663. ——. Opuscula anatomica. Lugduni
Batavorum: S. et J. Luchtmans ..., 1784.
3 pts. in 1 v.

3664. ——. Tabulae intestini duodeni.
Lugduni Batavorum: P.v.d. Eyk et D. Vygh,
1780.
2 *l*., 50 p., 1 *l*. illus.

3665. ——. Tabulae uteri humani gravidi.
Lugduni Batavorum: sumtibus auctoris, 1778.
1 *l*., 12 p. illus.

3666. ——. Tabulae uteri puerperae. Lugduni Batavorum: sumtibus auctoris, 1781.
8 p. illus.
With his Tabulae uteri humani gravidi.
1778.

3667. SANKT JOACHIMSTHAL. Ordinances.
Bergkordnung des freyen koniglichen Bergkwercks Sanct Joachimsthal, sambt anderen
vmbligenden vnd eingeleibten Silberbergk-
wercken, auffs newe gebessert, Anno domini
M.D.XLVIII. [Zwickaw: W. Meyerpeck, 1548.]
81 *l*. illus.

3668. SANSEVERO, Raimondo di Sangro,
principe di. Lettres écrites par Moɪ:sieur
le Prince de S. Sevère de Naples, a Mons.
l'Abbé Nollet ... a Paris, contenant la relation

d'une découverte qu'il a fait par le moyen
de quelques expériences chimiques ...
Prémière partie. Naples: J. Raimond, 1753.
    5 *l*., xcii p.
    All published?

3669.   SANSOVINO, Francesco.   Della agri-
coltvra di M. Giovanni Tatti ... libri cinqve
... Venetia: F. Sansovino, 1560.
    4 *l*., 187 numb. *l*., 1 *l*.   illus.

3670.   SANTANELLI, Ferdinando.   Philosophiæ reconditæ sive Magicæ magneticæ
mumialis scientiæ explanatio ... Coloniæ:
1723.
    4 *l*., 108 p.
    With Maier, M., Secretioris naturæ secre-
torum ... 1687.

3671.   SANTEUL, Louis de.   Des proprietès
de la médecine, par rapport à la vie civile.
Paris: Briasson, 1739.
    2 *l*., xx, 105 p., 11 *l*.

3672.   ——.   Questions de medecine ou Il
s'agit de savoir, si le médecin est plus certain que le chirurgien. Paris: 1739.
    lvii p.
    Latin and French text.
    With his Des proprietés de la médecine
... 1739.

3673.   SANTORINI, Giovanni Domenico.
Septemdecim tabulae ... addit De structura
mammarum et de tunica testis vaginali
Michael Girardi ... Parmae: ex Regis Typographia, 1775.
    4 *l*., xxxv p., 1 *l*., 217 p.   illus., port.

3674.   SANTORIO, Santorio.   De medicina
statica aphorismi, commentaria, notasque
addidit A.C. Lorry. Neapoli: apud V. Ursinum,
expensis J. de Lieto, 1784.
    5 *l*., 279 [i.e. 379] p.   illus.

3675.   ——.   Medicina statica: being the
aphorisms of Sanctorius, translated into
English, with large explanations. To which
is added, Dr. Keil's Medicina statica Britannica ... As also Medico-physical essays ...
The fifth edition. By John Quincy ... London:
for T. Longman and J. Newton, 1737.
    1 *l*., viii, 463 p., 8 *l*.   illus.

3676.   SARTI, Cristofano.   Avviso al popolo
Toscano che puó servire di trattenimento
anche al filosofo intorno all'acidula della
selva ... Pisa: R. Prosperi, 1794.
    xxxi, 144 p.

3677.   ——.   Saggio di congetture su i
terremoti ... Lucca: F. Bonsignori, 1783.
    240 p.

3678.   SAUNDERS, Richard.   The astrologi-
cal judgment and practice of physick ...
London: for L.C. and T. Sawbridge, 1677.
    18 *l*., 208, 208 p.   illus., port., charts.
    Lacking pages 209-214.

3679.   SAUNIER DE BEAUMONT.   Lettres
philosophiques, serieuses, critiques, et
amusantes. Traitant de la pierre philosophale,
de l'incertitude de la médecine ... & autres
sujets interessans. Paris: Saugrain, 1733.
    6 *l*., 473 p., 5 *l*.

3680.   SAURI, *abbé*.   Cours de physique
expérimentale et théorique ... Paris: Froullé,
1777.
    4 v.   illus.

3681.   SAUVAGEON, Guillaume.   Traicté
chymiqve contenant les preparations, vsages,
facultez & doses des plus celebres medicamens chymiques. Reueu & augmenté en
cette derniere edition ... Paris: I. Bessin, 1643.
    6 *l*., 88 p.

    ——.   ——. *In* Bauderon, B., Pharma-
copée ... 1636, etc.

3682.   SAUVAGES DE LA CROIX, François
Boissier de.   Les chefs-d'oeuvres ... ou
Recueil de dissertations qui ont remporté
le prix dans différentes académies, auxquelles
on a joint la Nourrice maratre du Chevalier
Linné. Le tout corrigé, traduit ou commenté
par M.J.E.G.***. Lyon: V. Reguilliat, 1770.
    2 v.

3683.   ——.   Nosologie méthodique, ou dis-
tribution des maladies en classes, en genres
et en espéces, suivant l'esprit de Sydenham,
& la methode des botanistes ... Traduite sur
la denière édition latine, par M. Gouvion
... On a joint ... Linné ... Genera Morborum,
avec la traduction françoise à côte. Lyon:
J.M. Bruyset, 1772.
    10 v.

3684.   SAVONAROLA, Giovanni Michele.
De omnibvs mvndi balneis. Bononie: B. Hec-
toris, 1493.
    1 *l*., 39 numb. *l*.

3685.   ——.   ——. Venetiis: C. de Pensis
de Mandello [1496].
    35 [i.e. 32] numb. *l*.

———. Libellus de arte conficiendi aquam vitæ. *In* Joannes de Rupescissa, De consideratione ... [1561].

3686. ———. Practica medicinae, sive De aegritudinibus. Colle di Valdelsa: B. Gallus, 1479.
320 *l.*
Lacking leaves R₂ and R₃.

3687. ———. Practica Joānnis Michaelis Sauonarole. Venetiis: heredes O. Scoti, 1519.
6 *l.*, 276 numb. *l.*

3688. ———. Practica canonica de febribus ... Eiusdem De pulsibus, De vrinis, De egestionibus, De vermibus, & De balneis omnibus Italiæ ... Venetiis: Ivncta, 1563.
16 *l.*, 118, 26 numb. *l.*, 9 *l.*

SAWTRE, John. The booke concerning the philosophers stone. *In* Five treatises ... 1652.

3689. SCARDONA, Giovanni Francesco. Aphorismi de cognoscendis et curandis morbis ... Editio Itala tertia ... Patavii: typis Seminarii, apud J. Manfré, 1763-1762.
3 v. in 1.

3690. SCARIONI, Francesco. Centvria di secreti politici, chimichi, e natvrali ... Siena: N. Tebaldini, 1633.
8 *l.*

3691. ———. Centvria prima di secreti medicinali, politici, e naturali ... Perugia: B. Florimi [n.d.].
8 *l.*

3692. SCARMIGNANI, Iacomo. Tesoro di medicina ... Modona & Venetia: [n.d.]
4 *l.*

3693. SCATALONE, Gratiano. Il vero, et pretioso thesoro di sanita ... Milano: P. Malatesta [n.d.].
4 *l.*

3694. SCHÄFFER, Johann Gottlieb. Der Gebrauch und Nutzen des Tabackrauchclystiers nebst einer dazu bequemen Maschine. Regensburg: G. Neubauer, 1757.
4 *l.*, 71 p. illus.

3695. ———. Haus- und Reise-Apotheke. Zweyte Auflage. Regensburg: J.L. Montag, 1768.
12 *l.*, 56 p., 7 *l.*

3696. SCHAUBERDT, Johann, *ed.* Κατοπθοσοφία id est, Consummata sapientia seu philosophia sacra, praxis de lapide minerali des ... Johannis de Padua ... II. Epistola Iohannis Trithemii ... an Johan von Westeburgk geschrieben ... III. Epistola Iohannis Tevtzschescheni ... Magdeburg: 1602.
72 *l.*
With Vogel, H., Offenbarung der Geheymussen der Alchimy ... 1605.

3697. SCHEELE, Karl Wilhelm. The chemical essays ... Translated from the transactions of the Academy of Sciences at Stockholm. With additions. London: for J. Murray ..., 1786.
xiii, ii, 406 p.
Joseph Black's copy, annotated and corrected by him in manuscript throughout.

3698. ———. Opuscula chemica et physica. Latine vertit Godofredus Henric. Schaefer ... Edidit et praefatus est D. Ernestus Benaim Gottl. Hebenstreit ... Lipsiae: J.G. Müller, 1788-1789.
2 v. in 1.

3699. ———. Chemische Abhandlung von Luft und Feuer, nebst einem Vorberichte von Torbern Bergmann ... Zweyte verbesserte Ausgabe mit einer eigenen Abhandlung über die Luftgattungen, wie auch mit der Herren Kirwan und Priestley Bemerkungen und Herrn Sheelens Erfahrungen über die Menge der im Dunstkreise befindlichen reinsten Luft vermehrt ... von D. Johann Gottfried Leonhardi. Leipzig: S.L. Crusius, 1782.
32, 286 p. illus.

3700. ———. Chemical observations and experiments with fire ... With a prefatory introduction by Torbern Bergman; translated from the German by J.R. Forster ... To which are added notes by Richard Kirwan ... with a letter to him from Joseph Priestly ... London: for J. Johnson, 1780.
xl, 259 p. illus.

3701. ———. Traité chimique de l'air et du feu ... Avec une introduction de Torbern Bergmann ... Ouvrage traduit de l'Allemand par le Baron de Dietrich ... Paris: 1781.
268 p. illus.

3702. SCHENCK, Johann von Grafenberg. Observationum medicarvm rararvm, novarvm, admirabilivm et monstrosarvm. Liber primvs De capite hvmano, inqvo, qvae medici doctissimi & exercitatissimi, abdita, vulgo incognita, gravia, periculosaque in huius con-

formationibus, euisque morborum causis, signis, eventibus & curationibus accidere compererunt, exemplis ut plurimum, & historijs proposita exhibentur. Fribvrgi Brisgoiae: M. Beckler, 1599.
   23 *l*., 804 [i.e. 704] p.

3703. SCHERB, Jakob Christopher. Ueber die Linpropfung der Pocken. Zürich: J.C. Füessli und H. Steiner, 1779.
   188 p., 1 *l*.

3704. SCHERER, Johann Andreas. Beweis, dass Johann Mayow vor hundert Jahren den Grund zur antiphlogistischen Chemie und Physiologie gelegt hat ... Wien: C.F. Wappler, 1793.
   xxiv, 188 p., 1 *l*.   port.

3705. SCHERF, Johann Christian Friedrich. Dispensatorium lippiacum genio moderno accommodatum. Lemgoviae: Meyer, 1792–1794.
   2 v.

3706. SCHINZ, Salomon. Dissertatio physica, de aere, ejus speciebus præcipue, de aere fixo lapidis calcarii ... Turici: Gessner, 1778.
   1 *l*., 38 p.   illus.

3707. ———. Dissertatio physico-chemica de stanni et ejus miscelæ cum plumbo in re oeconomica usu ... Tiguri: Gessner, 1770.
   1 *l*., 23 p.

3708. ———. Dissertatio physico-medica inauguralis, de calce terrarum et lapidum calcariorum ... Lugduni Batavorum: J. Luzac, 1756.
   3 *l*., 49 p., 2 *l*.   illus.

3709. SCHLAPRITZ, Hieronymus. Kleine reiss- und hauss- apotheck ... Hamburg: Witwe von V. de Leeu, 1632.
   57 *l*.   illus., port.

3710. SCHLÜSSEL der wahren Weisheit, unter einem Gespräch eines wohlerfahrnen Sophisten mit der Weisheit in dreyen Theilen mit einem Supplement ... Leipzig: A.F. Böhme, 1787.
   viii, 440 p.

3711. SCHMID, Johann Georg. Der von Mose u. denen Propheten übel urtheilende Alchymist. wird fürgestellet in einer Schrifftgemässen Erweisung, das Moses und seine Propheten, wie auch David, Salomon, Hiob, Esra und dergleischen, keine Adepti Lapidis Philosophorum gewesen sind ... Chemnitz: C. Stössel, 1706.
   7 *l*., 144 p.   illus.

3712. SCHMID, Rudolph Johann Friedrich. Enchiridion alchymico-physicvm sive Disqvisitio de menstrvis universalibvs vel liqvoribvs alcahestinis philosophorvm illorvm æqve ac tintvræ et lapidis philosophorvm ... Jenæ: Buch, 1739.
   5 *l*., 155 p., 2 *l*.

3713. SCHMIDT, Johann Adam. Commentarius de nervis lumbalibus eorumque plexu anatomico-pathologicus, adjecta est duorum, qui in plexu brachiali majori continentur ... plexum minorum descriptio & adumbratio. Vindobonae: C.F. Wappler, 1794.
   5 *l*., 118 p.   illus.

SCHMIEDEKNECHT, P. Philosophische Traum und Beurtheilung. *In* Der Chymische Warsager ... 1748.

3714. SCHMIEDER, Sigismund. Aletophili Sinceri Via ad transmvtationem metallorvm fideliter aperta. Norimbergæ: Cremer, 1742.
   26 *l*., 304 p.

3715. SCHMUCK, Martin. Secretorum naturalium, chymicorum, & medicorum, thesauriolus, oder Schatzkästlein, darinnen 20. natürliche, 20. chymische, vnd 20. medicinische Secreta, vnd Kunst Stücklein zu befinden ... Schleusingen: P.S., 1637.
   80 p., 1 *l*.

3716. SCHNURR, Balthasar. Kunst- Hauss- und Wunder- Buch ... Auffs neue wiederumb verbessert ... mit noch zwölff nutzbaren Büchern vermehret ... Franckfurt am Mäyn: W. Serlin, 1664.
   8 *l*., 1376 p., 12 *l*.   illus., charts.

3717. SCHOEPF, Johann David. Materia medica Americana potissimvm regni vegetabilis. Erlangae: I.I. Palmius, 1787.
   xviii, 170 p.

3718. SCHOMBERG, Rudolf. Aphorismi practici sive Observationes medicae, quas tan ex veterum quam regentiorum scriptis ... Amstelaedami: J. Schreuderus & P. Mortier Junior, 1756.
   184 p.

3719. SCHOTT, Gaspar. Physica curiosa, sive Mirabilia naturæ et artis libris XII ... Editio tertia ... Herbipoli: excudit J. Hertz, sumptibus W.M. Endteri, 1697.
   20 *l*., 1389 p., 10 *l*.   illus.

3720. ——. Technica curiosa, sive Mirabilia artis, libris XII ... Norimbergæ: J.A.
Endter ..., 1664.
20 *l*., 1044 p., 8 *l*.   illus., port., charts.
Lacking plates 36 and 37 in part 1.

SCHREBER, Johann Christian Daniel
von. Theses medicae. *See* Linné, C. von,
praeses. Entry 2497.

3721. SCHRICK, Michael Puff von. Ain
guts nutzlichs büchlin von den aussgepren-
ten wassern. [Vlm: H. Zainer, 1498.]
14 *l*.   illus.

3722. ——. Von den aussgebranten Wassern. In welcher Mass man die nutzen vnd
prauchen sol, zu gesunthayt der Menschen.
[Augspurg: H. Froschauer, 1521.]
12 *l*.   illus.

3723. SCHRÖDER, Johann. Pharmacopoeia
medico-chymica, sive Thesaurus pharmacologicus ... Editione quinta ... Ulmæ Suevorum: impensis J. Görlini, typis J.W. Ross-
lini, 1662.
12 *l*., 516, 348 p., 30 *l*.

3724. ——. ——. Editione sexta ... Francofurti: sumptibus viduae J. Görlini, typis J.
Görlini, 1669.
34 *l*., 516, 348 p., 30 *l*., 24 p., 43 *l*.
illus., port.

3725. ——. Pharmacopoea Schrödero-
Hoffmanniana illustrata et aucta ... Com-
pilante Iohanne Iacobo Mangeto ... Coloniæ:
I. Martin, 1683.
28 *l*., 800 p., 48 *l*.   illus.

3726. ——. ——. Coloniæ: I. Martin,
1684.
28 *l*., 800 p., 48 *l*.   illus.

3727. ——. Pharmacopoeia medico-chym-
ica, sive Thesaurus pharmacologicus ...
Post editionem Horstio-Witzelianam, qua
appendix ... a Joanne Ludovico Witzelio ...
Studio ac opera Petri Rommelii ... Ulmæ
Suevorum: sumptibus D. Görlini, typis M.
Wagneri, 1685.
35 *l*., 916 p., 134 *l*.   illus.

3728. ——. The compleat chymical dispensatory, in five books ... Englished, by
William Rowland ... London: J. Darby ...,
1669.
3 *l*., 545 [i.e. 445] p., 6 *l*.

3729. ——. La pharmacopée raisonée de

Schroder, commentée par Michel Ettmuller.
Lyon: T. Amaulry, 1698.
2 v.

3730. ——. Vollständige und nutz-reiche
Apotheke. Oder: Trefflich versehener medicin-
chymischer höchstkostbarer Artzney-Schatz.
Nebst D. Friedrich Hoffmanns ... Anmerckungen ... Zweyten edition ... Franckfurt: J.
Hoffmann und E. Streck, 1709.
9 *l*., 1324, 120 p., 30 *l*.   illus., port.

3731. ——. Pharmacopoeia universalis,
das ist: Allgemeiner medicinisch-chimischer
Artzney-Schatz. Nebst D. Friedrich Hoffmanns ... Anmerckungen ... Nebst einem allgemeinen Apothecker-Tax ... Nürnberg: J.A.
Stein und G.N. Raspe, 1746-1747.
2 v.

——. *See also* Hoffmann, Friedrich,
?-1675.

SCHRÖDER, Johannes. Genera mor-
borum. *See* Linné, C. von, *praeses*. Entry
2476.

3732. SCHROEDER, Friedrich Josef Wilhelm,
praeses. De alchemia medicinæ necessaria
et medicamento chemicorum panchresto, dissertatio medica ... Pvblico examini svbmittit
Henricvs Ferdinandvs Hoepfner ... Marburgi
Cattorum: Müller, 1776.
1 *l*., 46 p.

3733. SCHULTZ, Gottfried. Dissertatio
pharmaceutico-therapeutica de natura tincturæ bezoardicæ D. Johannis Michaelis ...
Hall. Saxon.: sumptibus S.J. Hubneri, literis
C. Michaelis, 1678.
2 *l*., 197 p., 1 *l*.
With Maynwaring, E., Historia et mysterium
... 1675.

3734. ——. Scrutinium cinnabarinum seu
Triga cinnabriorum, qvæ sistit naturam cin-
nabaris antimonii nativæ & factitiæ vulgaris.
Nec non specifici cephalici ... D. Johann.
Michaelis, cum appendice de emplastro mag-
netico hernias scrotales curante ... Hall.
Saxon.: S.J. Hübner, 1680.
15 *l*., 192 p.   illus.

3735. SCHULTZE, Johann Dominik. Ueber
die grosse amerikanische Aloe richtiger Agabe
bey Gelgenheit der jetzt im Raths-Apotheker-
Garten blühenden. Hamburg: Herold, 1782.
64 p.

3736. SCHULZE, Johann Heinrich, *praeses*.

Dissertatio inavgvralis medica de ipecac-
vanha Americana ... Publice defendet auctor
Ioann. Samvel Hveber. Halæ Magdebvrgicæ:
J.C. Hilliger, 1744.
27 p., 2 ℓ.

3737. SCHÜRER, Friedrich Ludwig. Syn-
thesis oxygenii experimentis confirmata ...
Argentorati: J.H. Heitz, 1789.
2 ℓ., 66 p., 2 ℓ., 67–126 p., 2 ℓ.

SCHWARTZFUSS, Anonymus von.
Das Blut der Natur. In Drey curieuse chymische Tractätlein ... 1706.

——. ——. In Kunckel, J., V curiose
chymische Tractätlein ... 1721.

3738. ——. Sanguis naturæ, or, A mani-
fest declaration of the sanguine and solar
congealed liquor of nature. By Anonimus.
London: for A.R. and T. Sowle, 1696.
2 ℓ., 112 p.
Inserted is a 17th century manuscript
alchemical recipe, at the bottom of which
is a note in Newton's hand indicating purchase of the book.

3739. ——. Brunnen der Weisheit, und
Erkäntnüs der Natur ... Hamburg: G. König,
1706.
46 p. illus.
With Söldner, J.A., Fegfeuer der Chymisten ... 1702.

——. ——. In Drey curieuse chymische Tractätlein ... 1706.

3740. SCHWEIGHARDT, Theophilus. Prodromus rhodo-stavroticvs, parergi philosophici; das ist: Vortrab vnd Entdeckung, derer
hocherleuchten ... Brüderschafft vom Rosen
Creutz, philosophischen Parergi, sonsten
Lapis Philosophorvm genandt ... beschrieben
durch F.C.R.N.G.I.A. ... [n.p.]: 1620.
8 ℓ., 78 p. illus.

SCHWEIZER, Johann Cornelius Friedrich. Dissertatio medico-chemica inauguralis de oleis essentialibus. See Müller, G.A.,
praeses.

3741. SCOPOLI, Giovanni Antonio. Ele-
menti di chimica e di farmacia ... Pavia:
stamperia del R.I. Monast. di S. Salvat.,
1786.
380 p.

3742. ——. Fundamenta chemiæ prælectionibus publicis accommodata. Editio altera

aucta, & emendata. Papiæ: J. Bolzan [1778?]
4 ℓ., 238 p., 9 ℓ.

SCOTT, Michael. De secretis na-
tura. In Albertus Magnus, De secretis mulierum
... 1598.

3743. ——. Phisionomia ... [n.p.:n.d.]
32 ℓ.

3744. SCRIBONIUS, Wilhelm Adolph. Rervm
natvralivm doctrina methodica: post tertiam
editionem denuò copiosissimè adaucta ...
Basileae: ex officina Pernea, per C. Vvaldkirch, 1585.
19 ℓ., 167 p.

3745. SCRIBONIUS LARGUS. De compositione medicamentorū liber, iampridem Io.
Rvellii opera e tenebris erutus, & à situ
uindicatus. Antonij Beniuenij Libellus de
abditis nonnullis ... Polybus De salubri
uictus ratione priuatorum, Guinterio Ioanne
Andernaco interprete. [Basileae]: A. Cratandrus, 1529.
8 ℓ., 318 p., 1 ℓ.

——. ——. In Celsus, A.C., De re
medicae ... 1529.

3746. ——. Compositiones medicæ. Ioannes Rhodivs recensuit, notis illustrauit,
lexicon Scribonianvm adiecit. Patavii: P.
Frambottius, 1655.
11 ℓ., 144, 465 p., 21 ℓ. illus.

SCUDALUPIS, Petrus Arlensis de.
See Petrus Arlensis de Scudalupis.

3747. SCULTETUS, Johannes. Χειροπλοθήκη,
seu ... armamentarium chirurgicum XLIII tabvlis ... exornatum ... Ulmæ Suevorum: B. Kühn,
1655.
1 ℓ., 10, 131 p., 2 ℓ. illus.
Lacking plate XL.

3748. ——. L'arcenal de chirvrgie ... Mis
en François par Mre. François Deboze ...
Avec la description d'vn monstre humain
exposé à Lyon le 5 de Mars 1671. Lyon: A.
Galien, 1672.
10 ℓ., 385 p., 12 ℓ. illus.

3749. SECONDAT, Jean Baptiste de. Observations de physique et d'histoire naturelle
sur les eaux minerales de Dax, & de Barege
... Paris: Huart ..., 1750.
4 ℓ., 205 p., 1 ℓ.

3750. SECRETS concernant les arts et

metiers. Paris: C. Jombert, 1716.
26 *l*., 610 p., 1 *l*.

3751. SEDEY, Franciscus Nicolaus. Dissertatio chemico-medica, de sulphure, spiritu ejus volatili, et acido caustico. Vindobonæ: J.T. de Trattner, 1766.
63 p.

3752. SEEHL, Ephraim Reinhold. A new improvement in the art of making the true volatile spirit of sulphur ... London: for J. Robinson, 1744.
62 p.

3753. SÉGUIER, Jean François. Bibliotheca botanica, sive Catalogus auctorum et librorum, qui de re botanica, de medicamentis ex vegetabilibus paratis, de re rustica, & de horticultura tractant ... Accessit Bibliotheca botanica Jo. Ant. Bumaldi, seu Potius Ovidii Montalbani. Nec non Auctuarium in bibliothecam botanicam Cl. Seguierii, opera Laur. Theod. Gronovii. Lugduni Batavorum: C. Haak, 1760.
16 *l*., 450 p.

3754. SEIDEL, Bruno. Liber morborvm incvrabilivm cavsas ... explicans ... Francofurti: J. Wechel, 1593.
8 *l*., 146 p., 6 *l*.
With Morison, T., Liber novvs de metallorvm cavsis ... 1593.

3755. SEIGNETTE, Pierre. La nature, les effets et l'usage du sel alkali nitreux ... [Rochelle?:n.d.]
11 p.
Caption title.
With his Les principales utilitez ...

3756. ——. La nature, les effets et l'usage du sucre de Mars ... [Rochelle?: n.d.]
4 p.
Caption title.
With his Les principales utilitez ...

3757. ——. Les principales utilitez et l'usage le plus familier du veritable sel polychreste ... [Rochelle?: n.d.]
4 p.
Caption title.

3758. SEIP, Johann Philipp. A brief and distinct account of the mineral waters of Pyrmont ... Extracted from a treatise ... publish'd some time ago, in the German language ... Also, a like account of the waters of Spa, from the best authors, by George Turner. London: for A. Millar and J. Roberts, 1733.

4 *l*., 133 p., 1 *l*.

3759. SENAC, Jean Baptiste. Nouveau cours de chymie suivant les principes de Newton & de Sthall. Avec un discours historique sur l'origine & les progrez de la chymie ... Paris: J. Vincent, 1723.
1 v. in 2.

3760. ——. ——. Nouvelle edition revûe & corrigée ... Paris: J. Vincent, 1737.
2 v.

3761. ——. Traité de la structure du coeur, de son action, et de ses maladies. Paris: J. Vincent, 1749.
2 v. illus.

3762. ——. Traité des maladies du coeur. Seconde édition, revue & augmentée par l'auteur. Paris: J. Barbou, 1778.
2 v.

3763. SENDIVOGIUS, Michael. Chymische Schrifften ... Nebst einem kurtzen Vorbericht ans Liecht gestellet durch Friederich Roth-Scholtzen ... Nürnberg: J.D. Taubers Erben, 1718.
1 *l*., 250 [i.e. 350] p. illus.

3764. ——. Dialogvs Mercvrii alchymistæ et natvræ. Scriptvs in gratiam amici Coroades. Auctore eo, qui Divi Leschi Genvs Amat. Coloniæ: S. Erffens, 1607.
28 p.

——. Abhandlung vom Merkur. *In* Birkholz, A.M., Die ganze höhere Chemie ... 1787.

3765. ——. Fünf und funfzig Briefe, den Stein der Weisen betreffend. Aus dem Lateinischen übersetzt. Franckfurt: J.G. Fleischer, 1770.
152 p.

3766. ——. Novvm lvmen chymicvm ... Accessit Dialogus Mercurij, alchymistæ & naturæ. Parisiis: R. Ruell, 1608.
7 *l*., 135 p.
With Dee, A., Fascicvlvs chymicvs ... 1631.

3767. ——. De lapide philosophorvm tractatvs dvodecim ... Author sum, qui Divi Leschi Genvs Amo. Francofurti: typis I. Bringeri, sumptibus A. Hummi, 1611.
64 p.

3768. ——. Novvm lvmen chymicvm ... In

duas partes diuisum qvarvm prior XII. tractatibus de mercvrio agit. Posterior de svlphvre, altero naturæ principio. Author sum
qui Divi Leschi Genvs Amo. Genevæ: J. de
Tournes, 1628.
  202 p., 1 ℓ.

3769. ——. Novvm lvmen chymicvm ...
cvi accessit Tractatus de sulphure ...
Genevæ: J. de Tournes, 1639.
  229, 84 p.

3770. ——. ——. Venetiis: Combi, 1644.
  223 p.

3771. ——. ——. Genevæ: J.A. & S. de
Tournes, 1653.
  11 p., 1 ℓ., 175 p.

3772. ——. ——. Genevæ: I.A. & S. de
Tournes, 1673.
  11 p., 1 ℓ., 175 p.
  With Aubigné de la Fosse, N., Bibliotheca
chemica ... 1673, as issued.

3773. ——. ——. Amstelodami: E. Weyerstraten, 1678.
  65, 53 p.
  With Janua patefacta thesauro ... 1678,
as issued.

3774. ——. A new light of alchymie ... to
which is added a treatise of svlphvr ... Also
nine books of the nature of things, written
by Paracelsus ... Also a chymicall dictionary
... All which are faithfully translated out of
the Latin into the English tongue by J.F.
London: R. Cotes for T. Williams, 1650.
  8 ℓ., 147 p., 2 ℓ.; 4 ℓ., 145 p.; 25 ℓ.

3775. ——. ——. London: A. Clark for T.
Williams, 1674.
  8 ℓ., 351 p.

3776. ——. A philosophical account of
nature in general, and of the generation of
the three principles of nature ... Translated
from the French. By John Digby ... London:
for J. Hooke and T. Edlin, 1722.
  5 ℓ., 348 p.

3777. ——. Cosmopolite ov Novvelle
lvmiere de la phisique naturelle ... Traduit
nouuellement de Latin en François. Par le
sieur de Bosnay. Paris: C. Hulpeau, 1629.
  8 ℓ., 103 p.

3778. ——. ——. Paris: P. Billaine, 1629.
  8 ℓ., 103 p.

3779. ——. ——. La Haye: T. Maire,
1639.
  7 ℓ., 58 p.
  With Nuysement, J., Traittez de l'harmonie
... 1639, as issued.

3780. ——. Les oevvres dv Cosmopolite,
divisez en trois parties. [Paris: J. d'Houry,
1669.]
  3 pts. in 1 v.

3781. ——. Traitez du Cosmopolite nouvellement découverts... Paris: L. d'Houry,
1691.
  238 p.

3782. ——. Cosmopolite ou Nouvelle
lumiere chymique, pour servir d'éclaircisse-
ment aux trois principes de la nature, exactement décrits dans les trois traitez suivans.
Le Ier. De la nature en général ... Le II. Du
soufre. Le III. Du vray sel des philosophes.
Derniere edition, révûë & augmentée de la
lettre philosophique d'Antoine Duval ...
Paris: L. d'Houry, 1723.
  xii, 333 p.; 1 ℓ., 9 [i.e. 7] p.

3783. ——. Novum lumen chymicum novo
lumine auctum. Sive Zwölff geheime chymische Taffeln und Beischrifften über die XII.
Tractate Sendivogi nebenst kurtzen Commentario und angefügter Schluss Rede Orthelii.
Franckfurt: Verlegts J. Birckner, gedruckt bey
C.C. Kirsch, 1682.
  1 ℓ., 78, 232 p.   illus.

3784. ——. Traicté dv sovlphre, second
principe de natvre. Faict par le mesme
autheur, qui par cy deuant a mis en lumiere
le premier principe, intitulé le Cosmopolite.
Traduit de Latin en François par F. Gviravd
... Auec plusieurs autres opuscules du mesme
suject. Paris: A. Pacard, 1618.
  4 ℓ., 152 p., 1 ℓ.

3785. ——. ——. Paris: C. Hulpeau, 1629.
  4 ℓ., 152 p.
  With his Cosmopolite ... 1629, as issued.

3786. ——. ——. Paris: P. Billaine, 1629.
  4 ℓ., 152 p.
  With his Cosmopolite ... 1629, as issued.

3787. ——. ——. La Haye: T. Maire, 1639.
  4 ℓ., 49 p.
  With Nuysement, J., Traittez de l'harmonie
... 1639, as issued.

  ——. Abhandlung vom Schwefel. In

Birkholz, A.M., Die ganze höhere Chemie
... 1787.

SENEBIER, Jean. Considérations
sur la méthode suivie par Monsieur l'abbé
Spallanzani dans ses expériences sur la
digestion. *In* Spallanzani, L., Expériences
sur la digestion ... 1783.

3788. ——. Expériences sur l'action de
la lumière solaire dans la végétation.
Genève: Barde ..., 1788.
    xvi, 446 p., 1 *l*.

3789. ——. Mémoires physico-chymiques,
sur l'influence de la lumière solaire pour
modifier les êtres des trois règnes de la
nature, & sur-tout ceux du règne végétal
... Geneve: B. Chirol, 1782.
    3 v.   illus.

3790. ——. ——. Nouvelle édition.
Geneve: Barde ..., 1788.
    4 v.   illus.

3791. ——. Recherches analytiques sur
la nature de l'air inflammable ... Geneve:
B. Chirol, 1784.
    xxviii, 387 p.

3792. ——. Recherches sur l'influence
de la lumiere solaire pour métamorphoser
l'air fixe en air pur par la végétation ...
Geneve: B. Chirol, 1783.
    xxxii, 385 p.

3793. SENNERT, Daniel.   Aphorismi ex institutionibus medicis Sennerti, magna diligentia collecti, opera Joannis Ioachimi Becheri ... Francofurti: sumptibus J. Beyeri,
typis B.C. Wustii, 1663.
    11 *l*., 430 p., 14 *l*.

3794. ——. Auctarium epitomes physicæ
... Francofurti: C. Wächtlerus, 1650.
    1 *l*., 86 p.
    With his Epitome naturalis scientiae ...
1650.

3795. ——. De chymicorum cum Aristote-
licis et Galenicis consensu ac dissensu
liber ... Wittebergæ: Z. Schurerus, 1619.
    16 *l*., 709 p., 11 *l*.

3796. ——. Epitome institutionum medicinæ, et libr. de febribus. Amstelodami: J.
Jansonius, 1644.
    12 *l*., 710, 188 p.   illus.

3797. ——. Epitome natvralis scientiæ.

Francofurti: C. Wächtler, 1650.
    8 *l*., 706 p., 11 *l*.

3798. ——. Institutionum medicinae libri
V. Wittebergae: haered. T. Mevii, 1644.
    24 *l*., 1523 p., 26 *l*.   illus.

3799. ——. Opervm ... Editio nouissima,
cæteris omnibus auctior & correctior ...
Lvgdvni: I.A. Hvgvetan, & M.A. Ravavd,
1656.
    2 v.   port.

3800. ——. Physica hypomnemata. I. De
rerum naturalium principiis. II. De occultis
qualitatibus. III. De atomis & mistione. IV.
De generatione viuentium. V. De spontaneo
viuentium ortu ... Lvgdvni: P. Ravavd, 1637.
    16 *l*., 471 p., 11 *l*.

3801. ——. Thirteen books of natural philosophy ... unto which is added five books
more of natural philosophy in several discourses ... Written in Latin and English. By
Daniel Sennert ... Nicholas Culpepper ...
Abdiah Cole ... London: P. & E. Cole, 1661.
    9 *l*., 224 [i.e. 408] p.

3802. SERANE, Charles.   Lettre de Mr.
Chevrier ... a un de ses amis contenant un
traité du vert de gris par Mr. Maître Serane
... Avignon: J.C. Chastanie, 1714.
    1 *l*., 16 p.

SERAPION, Johannes.   *See* Yūhannā
ibn Sarābiyūn.

SERENUS SAMMONICUS, Quintus.
De omnium morburum cura. *In* Ulsen,
T., De pharmacandi comprobata ratione ...
1559.

——. Praecepta medica. *In* Celsus,
A.C., De re medica ... 1528.

3803. A SERIOUS ADDRESS to the public
concerning the abuses in the practice of
physic. London: W. Owen, 1752.
    56 p.

3804. SERMONDI, Gaspare.   De balneorvm
Bvrmiensivm præstantia ... Mediolani: P.
Pontius, 1590.
    2 *l*., 76 p., 4 *l*.

3805. SERVANT DE GRANGEAC, Vitalis.
Tentamen chemico-medicum de gas memphitici,
seu aeris fixi proprietatibus medicamentosis
... Monspelii: J. Martel, 1785.
    16 p.

3806. SERVI, Pietro. Dissertatio de vng-
vento armario sive De natvrae artisqve
miracvlis. Romae: D. Marciani, 1643.
  4 *l.*, 179 p., 2 *l.*

3807. SETTALA, Lodovico. Animadversionum, & cautionum medicarum libri novem,
denuò à J. Perio recogniti ... Quibus accessit ejusdem auctoris Liber de nævis ...
Dordrechti: V. Caimax, 1650.
  3 pts. in 1 v.

3808. SEVERIN, Petrus. Idea medicinæ
philosophicæ. Continens fundamenta totius
doctrinæ Paracelsicæ, Hippocraticæ, &
Galenicæ. Hagæ-Comitis: A. Vlacq, 1660.
  4 *l.*, 212 p., 1 *l.*

3809. SEVERINO, Marco Aurelio. De efficaci medicina libri III ... Francofvrti: J.
Beyer, 1646.
  8 *l.*, 297 p., 7 *l.*   illus.
  With Fabricius von Hilden, W., Opera
quæ extant omnia ... 1646.

3810. ——. De recondita abscessuum
natura, libri VIII ... [Editio secvnda]. Francofurti: I. Beyer, 1643.
  14 *l.*, 468 p., 23 *l.*   illus.

3810a. ——. Vipera pythia. Id est, De
viperæ natura, veneno, medicina, demonstrationes, & experimenta noua. Patavii: P.
Frambotto, 1651.
  7 *l.*, 522 p., 12 *l.*   illus., port.

3811. SEVERINO, Scipione. Glosa sopra
Raimvndo Lvllo, e sopra la turba filosofica,
per prodursi oro & argento, mediante la
natura e l'arte ... Venetia: 1684.
  2 *l.*, 66 p., 10 *l.*

      SEYMER, Richard. *See* Grete Herball
... 1526.

3812. SGOBBIS, Antonio de. Vniversale
theatro farmacevtico ... Venetia: P. Baglioni,
1682.
  6 *l.*, 820 p.   illus., port., charts.

3813. SHARP, Samuel. A cirtical enquiry
into the present state of surgery. The third
edition. London: for J. Tonson ..., 1754.
  4 *l.*, 314 p., 3 *l.*

3814. SHAW, Peter. Chemical lectures,
publickly read at London, in the years 1731,
and 1732; and since at Scarborough, in 1733;
for the improvement of arts, trades, and natural philosophy. London: for J. Shuckburgh &

T. Osborne [1734].
  xxiv, 439 p., 4 *l.*

3815. ——. ——. The second edition,
corrected. London: for T. and T. Longman
..., 1755.
  xxiv, 467 p., 5 *l.*

3816. ——. An enquiry into the contents,
virtues, and uses, of the Scarborough spaw-
waters: with the method of examining any
other mineral-water. London: for the author
..., 1734.
  viii, 166 p., 1 *l.*

      ——. ——. *In* Hoffmann, F., New
experiments ... 1743.

3817. ——. The juice of the grape: or,
Wine preferable to water. A treatise, wherein wine is shewn to be the grand preserver
of health, and restorer in most diseases ...
By a fellow of the college ... London: for
W. Lewis, 1724.
  2 *l.*, xii, 56 p.

3818. ——. Philosophical principles of
universal chemistry ... Design'd as a general introduction to the knowledge and practice of artificial philosophy: or, genuine
chemistry in all its branches. Drawn from
the Collegium Jenense of Dr. George Ernest
Stahl ... London: for J. Osborn & T. Longman,
1730.
  1 *l.*, xxviii, 424 p., 14 *l.*, 8 p.

3819. SHEBBEARE, John. A new analysis
of the Bristol waters: together with the cause
of the diabetes and hectic ... London: for T.
Cox, 1740.
  viii, 39 p.
  Lacking pages 19-20.

3820. SHELDON, John. The history of the
absorbent system, part the first. Containing
the chylography, or description of the human
lacteal vessels ... London: 1784.
  7 *l.*, vi, 52 p., 6 *l.*   illus.

3821. SHORT, Thomas. A comparative history of the increase and decrease of mankind
in England ... To which is added a syllabus
of the general states of health, air, seasons,
and food for the last three hundred years ...
London: for W. Nicoll and C. Etherington,
1767.
  viii, iv, 213 p.

3822. ——. A general chronological history
of the air, weather, seasons, meteors, etc. ...

together with some of their most remarkable
effects on animal (especially human) bodies,
and vegetables. London: for T. Longman &
A. Millar, 1749
  2 v.

3823. ——. Medicina Britannica: or A
treatise on such physical plants, as are
generally to be found in the fields or gardens in Great Britain ... The second edition.
To which is added an appendix ... London:
for R. Manby and H.S. Cox, 1747.
  1 ℓ., xxxi, 352, 40 p.

3824. ——. The natural, experimental,
and medicinal history of the mineral waters
of Derbyshire, Lincolnshire, and Yorkshire,
particularly those of Scarborough ... London:
for the author and F. Gyles, 1734.
  10 ℓ., xxii, 359 p., 1 ℓ.   illus.

3825. A SHORT ANSWER to a late book, entituled, Tentamen medicinale. With which
are reprinted several papers ... touching the
rise, growth, and usefulness of the dispen-
saries, erected by the College of Physicians
... London: for A. Roper, 1705.
  6 ℓ., 155 p.

3826. A SHORT DISCOURSE of the quintessence, or tincture of the philosophers ...
[n.p.:1709.]
  16 p.
  Caption title. Lacking title page.

3827. A SHORT ENQUIRY concerning the
Hermetick art ... By a lover of Philalethes.
To which is annexed A collection from Kab-
bala Denudata and translation of the chym-
ical-cabbalistical treatise, intituled, Aesch-
Mezareph; or, Purifying fire. London: 1714.
  2 ℓ., 92, 83, 71 p.

3828. SHULTZ, Benjamin. An inaugural
botanico-medical dissertation on the phyto-
lacca decandra of Linnæus. Philadelphia:
T. Dobson, 1795.
  5 ℓ., 55 p.   illus.

3829. SIBLY, Ebenezer. A key to physic,
and the occult sciences ... To which are
added, Lunar tables, calculated from sidereal
motion ... The whole forming an interesting
supplement to Culpeper's Family physician
... London: for the author and Champante and
Whitrow [n.d.].
  2 ℓ., 395, 75 p.   illus.

3830. SIBMACHER, Johann Ambrosius. Das
güldne Vliess, oder Das allerhöchste, edels-

te, kunstreichste Kleinod, und der urälteste
verborgene Schatz der Weisen ... beschrieben
und zusammen verfasset durch einen un-
gennanten, doch wohlbekannten &c. Ich
Sags Nicht ... Nürnberg: J.A. Schmidt, 1737.
  8 ℓ., 196 p., 2 ℓ., 197-208 p.   illus.,
chart.

3831. ——. Wasserstein der Weisen der
Chymische Tractätlein ... Dabey auch zwey
sehr nützliche andere Büchlein ... ange-
hängt: Nemlich, I. Johann von Mesung. II.
Via veritatis der einigen Warheit ... Bene-
benst eines anonymi sentiment, De materia
& praxi lapidis philosophorum. Franckfurt
am Mayn: J.M. von Sand, 1709.
  206 p.   illus.
  Lacking pages 15-16.

3832. SICHARDUS, Joannes, ed. Antidotvm
contra diversas omnivm fere secvlorvm
haereses ... Basileae: H. Petrus, 1528.
  17 ℓ., 275 numb. ℓ., 1 ℓ.

3833. The SICK-MAN'S magazine: or Lady's
mirror. A collection of remedies for most diseases ... Dvblin: 1738.
  36 p.

    SIDREN, Jonas. De materia medica
in regno animali. See Linné, C. von, praeses.
Entry 2440.

3834. SIEBENSTERN, Christian Friedrich
Sendimir von. Chrysostomi Ferdinandi von
Sabor, Practica naturæ vera, oder Sonnen-
klare Beschreibung derer Natur-Geheimnisse,
bestehend in wahrer præparation des lapidis
universalis; samt einem kurtzem Anhang vom
Antimonio und dessen sonderbaren Kräfften.
[n.p.]: auf Kosten der Rosencreutzer-Brüder-
schafft, 1721.
  3 ℓ., 39 p.   illus.

3835. ——, supposed author. Chymischer
Monden-Schein ... das wahre subjectum philosophiæ ... Franckfurt: Fleischer, 1760.
  55 p., 2 ℓ.   illus.
  With Leursen, J., Chymischen Shau-Platzes
... 1708.

3836. ——, supposed author. Metallischer
Baumgarten, in welchem das einzige wahre
Subjectum Philosophiæ oder Primum ens metallorum ... vor Augen gelegt, und beschrieben
worden ist ... Franckfurt: J.F. Fleischer, 1741.
  87 p.
  With his Practica ... 1721.

3837. ——, supposed author. Die neu-

auffgehende chymische Sonne, samt ihrem
Glantz und Schein, weiset alle Gott-erge-
bene Sucher, auf den rechten Pfad, subjectum ac primam materiam lapidis philosophorum & omnium rerum zu suchen, zu finden,
und zu elaboriren ... Von einem treu-meinen-
den Freunde zusammen getragen ... Franckfurt: J.F. Fleischer, 1750.
    127 p.

        SIEFVERT, Johan Victor.   Aer habita-
bilis. *See* Linné, C. von, *praeses*. Entry
2417.

3838.   SIGUAD-LAFOND, Joseph Aignan.
Description et usage d'un cabinet de physique experimentale ... Paris: P. F. Gueffier,
1775.
    2 v.   illus.

3839.   ———. Dictionnaire des merveilles
de la nature. Paris: 1781.
    2 v.

3840.   ———. Essai sur différentes especes
d'air, qu'on désigne sous le nom d'air fixe,
pour servir de suite & de supplément aux
Élémens de physique du même auteur ...
Paris: P.F. Gueffier, 1779.
    4 ℓ., xvi, 400 p.   illus.

3841.   ———. ———. Nouvelle édition, revue
et augmentée par M. Rouland ... Paris: P.F.
Gueffier, 1785.
    xxviii, 499 p.   illus.

3842.   ———. Leçons de physique experimentale ... Paris: La Doué, 1767.
    2 v.   illus.

3843.   SILVATICUS, Joannes Baptista.   De
compositione et vsv theriacae libri dvo.
[Heidelberg:] H. Commelinus, 1597.
    635 p.

3844. SILVATICUS, Matthaeus.   Liber
pādectarū medicine: omnia medicine simplicia cōtinens: quem ex omnibus antiquorum
libris aggregauit ... Vincentie: H. Lichten-
stein [1480].
    322 ℓ.

3845. SIMPSON, William.   Hydrologia
chymica: or, The chymical anatomy of the
Scarborough, and other spaws in York-shire
... London: W.G. for R. Chiswel, 1669.
    10 ℓ., 374 p.   illus.

3846.   ———. Hydrological essayes: or, A
vindication of Hydrologia chymica ... To

which is annexed an answer to Dr. Tunstal's
book, concerning the Scarborough spaw ...
London: J.D. for R. Chiswel, 1670.
    8 ℓ., 159 p.
    Lacking pages 1-2.

3847.   ———. Two small treatises: The first,
a further essay towards the history of this
present fever ... The second, a medico-phi-
losophical analogy betwixt vegetable and
animal juyces ... London: T.H. for E. Wyer,
1678.
    2 ℓ., 52 p.

3848.   ———. Zymologia physica, or A brief
philosophical discourse of fermentation,
from a new hypothesis of acidum and sulphur
... With an additional discourse of the sulphur-
bath at Knaresbrough ... London: T.R. & N.T.
for W. Cooper, 1675.
    8 ℓ., 149 p., 2 ℓ., 28 p.

        SIMS, James.   Observations sur les
maladies épidémiques. *In* Le médecin pratique
de Londres ... 1779.

        SINCERUS, Aletophilus, *pseud*. *See*
Schmieder, Sigismund.

3849.   SINGER, Franz.   Medicinisch-chem-
ische Abhandlung über ein sicheres Gegen-
gift auer Merkurialgifte ... Wien: 1786.
    8 ℓ., 221 p., 1 ℓ.

3850.   SINICKER, Emanuel.   Keiser Rudolff,
des andern dises namens spagyrische Hausz
vnd Reiss-Apothec ... verteutscht ... durch
Weylund H. Heinrich von Schennis. Zürich:
J.J. Bodmer, 1646.
    6 ℓ., 310 p., 7 ℓ.
    Lacking leaves 7 and 8 of the preliminaries.

        SKRAGGE, Nicolaus.   Morbi artificum
leviter adumbrantur. *See* Linné, C. von,
praeses. Entry 2472.

3851.   SLARE, Frederick.   Experiments and
observations upon oriental and other bezoar-
stones ... To which is annex'd, A vindication
of sugars against the charge of Dr. Willis ...
London: for T. Goodwin, 1715.
    2 ℓ., v, xviii, 4 ℓ., 47 p.; 5 ℓ., 64 p.,
5 ℓ.

3852.   SLEVOGT, Johann Adrian.   Prælvsio
inauguralis De lapide bezoar. Jenæ: Krebs
[1698].
    4 ℓ.
    With Wedel, G.W., *praeses*, De tinctvra
bezoardica ... 1698.

3853. SMITH, George. A compleat body
of distilling, explaining the mysteries of
that science ... In two parts. London: H.
Lintot, 1749.
    4 ℓ., 150 p., 1 ℓ.   illus.

3854. Smith, George, *18th cent.* The
laboratory, or School of arts ... translated
from the German. London: T. Cox, 1738.
    4 ℓ., 242 p., 3 ℓ.   illus.

3855. ——. ——. The second edition.
To which is added an appendix ... London:
for J. Hodges ..., 1740.
    4 ℓ., 236 p.; 1 ℓ., lxxx p., 2 ℓ.   illus.

3856. ——. ——. The third edition ...
London: J. Hodges and T. Astley, 1750.
    5 ℓ., 352 p., 4 ℓ.   illus.

3857. SMITH, Hugh. Formulae medicamentorum concinnatae: or, Elegant medical
prescriptions for various disorders. Translated from the Latin ... London: J.S. Barr,
1791.
    viii, 131 p.

3858. SMITH, John. The curiosities of
common water: or the advantages thereof,
in preventing and curing many distempers
... The sixth edition, with additions communicated by Mr. Ralph Thoresby ... and
others. London: for J. & B. Clark, 1724.
    80 p.
    With Hancocke, J., Febrifugum magnum
... 1723.

3859. SMYTH, James Carmichael. An account of the experiment made at the desire of
the Lords Commissioners of the Admiralty ...
to determine the effect of the nitrous acid in
destroying contagion, and the safety with
which it may be employed ... London: for J.
Johnson, 1796.
    75 p.   illus.

3860. SNAPE, Andrew. The anatomy of an
horse ... To which is added an appendix
containing two discourses: The one, of the
generation of animals; and the other, of the
motion of the chyle and the circulation of
the bloud ... London: M. Flesher for J. Hindmarsh, 1686.
    5 ℓ., 237, 45 p., 3 ℓ.   illus., port., folio.

3861. SOLANO DE LUQUE, Francisco.
Lapis sydos appollinis methodo segura, y la
mas vtil, assi para conocer, como para curar
las enfermedades agudas ... Madrid: J. Gon-
zalez, 1731.

90 ℓ., 400 [i.e. 300] p., 24 ℓ.

3862. SÖLDNER, Johann Anton. Fegfeuer
der Chymisten, worin für Augen gestellet,
die wahren Besitzer der Kunst ... Amsterdam:
1702.
    46 p.   ⸱

3863. ——. Keren Happuch, Posaunen
Eliæ des Künstlers, oder Teutsches Fegfeuer
der Scheide-Kunst ... Hamburg: G. Liber-
nickel, 1702.
    8 ℓ., 128 p.   illus.
    With his Fegfeuer der Chymisten ... 1702.

3864. SOLE, William. Menthæ Britannicæ:
being a new botanical arrangement of all the
British mints ... Bath: R. Cruttwell, 1798.
    viii, 55 p.   illus.

3865. SOMMER, Fabian. De inventione,
descriptione, temperie, viribvs, et in primis
vsv, thermatum D. Caroli IIII. imperatoris
libellvs brevis et vtilis. [Lipsiæ: Voegel
1571.]
    8 ℓ., 103 p.

3866. SÖMMERRING, Samuel Thomas von.
De basi encephali et originibus nervorum
cranio egredientium libri quinque. Goettingae:
A. Vandenhoeck vidua, 1778.
    4 ℓ., 184 p.   illus.

3867. ——. De concrementis biliariis
corporis humani. Traiecti ad Moenum: Varrentrapp et Wenner, 1795.
    68 p.
    With his De morbis vasorum ... 1795.

3868. ——. De morbis vasorum absorten-
tium corporis humani, sive Dissertationis
quae praemium retulit Societatis Rheno-
Traiectinae anno MDCCLXXXXIV ... Traiecti
ad Moenum: Varrentrapp et Wenner, 1795.
    xv, 223 p.

3869. ——. Tabula sceleti feminini iuncta
descriptione. Traiecti ad Moenum: Varrentrapp et Wenner, 1797.
    3 ℓ.   illus., folio.

3870. ——. Vom Baue des menschlichen
Körpers. Frankfurt am Main: Varrentrapp und
Wenner, 1791-1796.
    6 v. in 5.

3871. Die SONNE VON OSTEN oder Philosophische Auslegung der Kette des goldenen
Vliesses nebst dem Kreuze der Ritterorden
der Tempelherrn ... von Rosa Significet Hunnis

ea. 5783. [n.p.: 1783?]
    6 *l*., 278 p.   charts.

3872. SONNET, Thomas. Satyre contre les
charlatans, et psevdo-medecins empyriques
... Paris: I. Milot, 1610.
    16 *l*., 335 p.   port.

        SORANUS, of Epheus.   De signis
fracturarum. *In* Cocchi, A., Graecorvm chirvrgici ... 1754.

        SORANUS, of Epheus. *See* Aurelianus,
C.

3873. SORBAIT, Paul de.   Consilium medicum dialogus, oder Freundliches Gespräch
uber den ... Zustand der ... Wienn ... [Wien:
1679.]
    40 *l*.

3874. SOREL, Charles.   Des talismans, ov
figvres faites sovs certaines constellations
... Auec des obseruations contre le liure des
Cvriosites inovyes de M.I. Gaffarel. Et vn
traicté de l'vngvent des armes, ov vnguent
sympathetique & constellé ... Le tout tiré
de la seconde partie de la Sciences des
choses corporelles. Par le sieur de l'Isle.
Paris: A. de Sommaville, 1636.
    4 *l*., 417 [i.e. 281] p., 1 *l*.
    With Gaffarel, J., Cvriositez inovyes ...
1650.

        SORENSEN, Peder. *See* Severin,
Petrus.

3875. SPALLANZANI, Lazzaro.   Chimico
esame degli esperimenti del Sig. Gottling
... Modena: la Societa' Tipogrfica, 1796.
    2 *l*., 171 p.   chart.
    Pages 165-168 misbound after the title
page.

3876. ———.   Expériences sur la digestion
de l'homme et de différentes especes d'animaux ... Avec des considérations sur la
méthode de faire des expériences, & les
conséquences pratiques qu'on peut tirer en
médecine de ses découvertes, par Jean Senebier. Geneve: B. Chirol, 1783.
    1 *l*., cxlix, 320 p.

3877. ———.   Nouvelles recherches sur les
decouvertes microscopiques et la generation
des corps organises, ouvrage traduit de
l'Italien de M. l'abbé Spallanzani ... par M.
l'abbé Regley ... avec des notes des recherches physiques & métaphysiques sur la
nature & la religion, & une nouvelle théorie

de la terre, par M. de Needham ... London
& Paris: Lacombe, 1769.
    2 pts. in 1 v.   illus.

3878. ———.   Oeuvres. Pavie et Paris: P.J.
Duplain, 1787.
    3 v.   illus.
    Contents: Volumes 1-2, Opuscules de
physique animale et végétale; volume 3,
Expériences pour servir a l'histoire de la
génération des animaux et des plantes.

        SPARSCHUCH, Henrik.   Potus coffeæ
leviter adumbratur. *See* Linné, C. von,
praeses. Entry 2458.

3879. SPECTRVM spagiricvm, das ist: Der
guldene Irrwisch oder Spagirische Wauwau.
[Freyburg?]: 1721.
    56 p.

        SPECULUM Sapientiae. Das ist: Ein
Buch des Geheimnisses. *In* Quadratum alchymisticum ... 1705.

        SPIEGEL, Adriaan van de. Αγγειολογία:
or, A description of the vessels in the body
of man. *In* Paré, A., The works ... 1678.

3880. ———.   De formato foetv liber sin-
gularis, aeneis figvris exornatvs. Epistolae
dvae anatomicae. Tractatvs de arthritide.
Opera posthvma studio Liberalis Cremae ...
Francofvrti: impensis M. Meriani, typis C.
Rötelii, 1631.
    4 *l*., 105 p., 3 *l*.   illus.

3881. ———.   Opera quae extant, omnia.
Ex recensione Ioh. Antonidae vander Linden.
Amsterdami: I. Blaev, 1645.
    2 v. in 1.   illus., port., folio.

3882. SPIELMANN, Jacob Reinhold.   Anleitung zur Kenntniss der Arzneymittel in akadem-
ischen Vorlesungen eingerichtet. Aus dem
Lateinischen unter des Verfassers Aufsicht ins
Deutsche übersetzt. Strassburg: Bauer, 1775.
    4 *l*., 770 p., 48 *l*.

3883. ———.   Institutiones chemiæ prælectionibus academicis accommodatæ. Editio
altera ... Argentorati: J. Buaer, 1766.
    6 *l*., 350 p., 35 *l*.   table.

3884. ———.   Instituts de chymie. Traduits
du latin, sur la seconde edition, par M. Cadet.
Paris: Vincent, 1770.
    2 v.

3885. ———.   Pharmacopoea generalis ...

Argentorati: J.G. Treuttel, 1783.
2 pts. in 1 v.

3886. ——. ——. Editio prima Veneta.
Venetiis: J.A. Pezzana, 1785-1786.
3 v. in 1.   illus.

3887. ——, *praeses.* Examen acidi pinguis ... Solenni eruditorum disquisitioni
subjiciet Michael Fridericus Boehm. Argentorati: J.H. Heitz, 1769.
1 *l.*, 38 p.

3888.   SPINELLI, Giovanni Paolo de.   Lectiones avreæ, in omni qvod pertinet ad
artem pharmacopoeam lucubratæ ... Correctæ
in secunda impressione à Francisco Antonio
ex Spinellis ... Barii: denuò I. Gaidonum,
expensis I. Montini, 1633.
2 pts. in 1 v.

3889.   SPRAT, Thomas.   The history of the
Royal-Society of London, for the improving
of natural knowledge. London: T.R. for J.
Martyn and J. Allestry, 1667.
8 *l.*, 438 p., 1 *l.*   illus.

3890. ——. ——. The second edition
corrected. London: for R. Scot ..., 1702.
8 *l.*, 438 p.   illus.

3891. ——. ——. The third edition corrected. London: for J. Knapton ..., 1722.
8 *l.*, 438 p.   illus.

3892. ——. ——. The fourth edition. London: for J. Knapton ..., 1734.
8 *l.*, 438 p.   illus.

3893. ——. The plague of Athens, which
hapned in the second year of the Pelopon-
nesian War. First described in Greek by
Thucydides, then in Latin by Lucretius. Since
attempted in English by ... Thomas, Lord
Bishop of Rochester. London: for C. Brome,
1703.
3 *l.*, 34 p.

3894.   SPRENGEL, Kurt Polycarp Joachim.
Apologie des Hippokrates und seiner Grundsätze. Leipzig: Schwiekert, 1789-1792.
2 v.

3895.   SPURSTOW, William.   The spiritual
chymist: or, Six decads of divine meditations
on several subjects ... London: P. Chetwind,
1666.
12 *l.*, 182 p.

3896.   STAEHLING, Josephus Franciscus.

Dissertatio inauguralis chemico-medica
sistens methodum generalem explorandi
aquas medicatas ... Posonii: J.M. Landerer,
1772.
4 *l.*, 191 p.

3897.   STAHL, Georg Ernst.   Anweisung
zur Metallurgie, oder Der metallischen
Schmeltz- und Probier-Kunst. Nebst dessen
Einleitung zur Grund-Mixtion derer unterirr-
dischen mineralischen und metallischen
Cörper ... Leipzig: C.J. Eyssel, 1720.
8 *l.*, 144 p., 4 *l.*; 407 p., 8 *l.*

3898. ——. De motus haemorrhoidalis,
et fluxus haemorrhoidum, diversitate, benè
distinguenda ... Parisiis: F. Horth-hemels,
1730.
16 *l.*, 126 p.
With his Sileni alcibiadis ... 1730.

3899. ——. Experimenta, observationes,
animadversiones, CCC numero, chymicae
et physicae ... Berolini: A. Haude, 1731.
14 p., 7 *l.*, 420 p., 8 *l.*

3900. ——. Fundamenta chymiae dogma-
ticae & experimentalis ... Norimbergæ: W.
Mauritius, 1723.
4 *l.*, 255 p., 12 *l.*

3901. ——. Chymia rationalis et experimentalis; oder: Gründliche der Natur und
Vernunsst ... Nebst einer Zugabe von denen
Mercuriis Metallorum, Mercurio animato,
und Lapide Philosophorum. Zweyte Auflage
... mit Isaac Hollands Tractat von den Saltzen
und Oehlen der Metallen vermehret worden.
Leipzig: C.J. Eyssel, 1729.
8 *l.*, 560 p., 16 *l.*

——. Fundamenta chemico-pharma-
ceutica generalia. *In* Bate, G., Pharmacopoeia
Bateana ... 1776.

3902. ——. Gedancken von Verbesserung
der Metallen, und wie man einen mässigen
Gewinnst davon ziehen könne. Nürnberg: J.D.
Taubers Erben, 1720.
32 p.

3903. ——. Observationum chymico-
physico-medicarum curiosarum ... Francofurti: G. Müller, 1697-1698.
520 p.

3904. ——. Opusculum chymico-physico-
medicum ... Halæ Magdeburgicæ: typis
Orphanotrophei, 1715.
4 *l.*, 856 p., 19 *l.*   port.

———. A short discourse on the original of metallick veins. *In* Pyrotechnical discourses ... 1705, etc.

3905. ———. Sileni alcibiadis, i.e. Ars sanandi, cum expectatione, opposita arti curandi nuda expectatione: Satyra Harveana castigatæ ... Parisiis: F. Horth-hemels, 1730.
5 ℓ., 246 p.

———. Specimen Beccherianum. *In* Becher, J.J., Physica subterranea ... 1738.

3906. ———. Traité des sels, dans lequel on démontre qu'ils sont composés d'une terre subtile, intimement combinée avec de l'eau ... Traduit de l'Allemand. Paris: Vincent, 1771.
xxiv, 480 p.

3907. ———. Zymotechnia fundamentalis oder, Allgemeine grund-erkanntniss der Gährungs-Kunst ... aus dem lateinischen ins deutsche ubersetzet. Franckfurth: J.L. Montag [1734].
11 ℓ., 304 p.

———. *See also* Shaw, P., Philosopical principles ... 1730.

STAHL, Johann Ernest. De epilepsia. *See* Alberti, M., *praeses*.

3908. STAIR, James Dalrymple. Physiologia nova experimentalis in qua, generales notiones Aristotelis, Epicuri, & Cartesii supplentur ... Lugduni-Batavorum: C. Boutesteyn, 1686.
8 ℓ., 632 p. illus.

3909. STAPHORST, Nicholas. Officina chymica Londinensis, sive Exacta notitia medicamentorum spagyricorum ... Hamburgi: vidua G. Schultzen, 1686.
2 ℓ., 68 p.
With Müller, T., Commentationum biga ... 1688.

3910. STARIZ, Johann. Clavis, oder, Das zehende Buch der Archidoxen D. Philippi Theophrasti Paracelsi, Bombast von Hohenheim, etc. ... Magdeburg: J. Francken, 1624.
34 ℓ.

3911. ———. Neu-vermehrter Helden-Schatz, das ist, Naturkündliches Bedencken über und bey Vulcanischer ... [n.p.]: 1694.
6 ℓ., 532 p., 20 ℓ. illus.
Lacking pages 523-524.

STARKEY, George. The admirable efficacy of true oyl. *In* Collectanea chymica ... 1684.

3912. ———. George Starkey's pill vindicated from the unlearned alchymist and all other pretenders ... [n.p., n.d.]
16 p.
Bound at end of Collectanea chymica ... 1684.

3913. ———. Liquor alchahest, or a Discourse of that immortal dissolvent of Paracelsus & Helmont ... Published by J.A. Pyrophilus ... London: T.R. & N.T. for W. Cademan, 1675.
15 ℓ., 55 p.

3914. ———. The marrow of alchemy, being an experimental treatise, discovering the secret and most hidden mystery of the philosophers elixer. Divided into two parts ... By Eireneus Philoponus Philalethes. London: A.M. for E. Brewster, 1654.
5 ℓ., 70 p.
From Isaac Newton's library.

3915. ———. Kern der Alchymie, das ist, Ein durch Erfahrung bewährter Tractat welcher eröffnet das geheime und hochverborgene Geheimnüss des Elixirs der Weisen ... durch Irenæum Philoponum Philaletham. Aus dem Englischen übersetzt von Johann Langen. Leipzig: V. Adler, 1685.
4 ℓ., 206, 62 p.

3916. ———. Pyrotechny, asserted and illustrated, to be the surest and safest means for arts triumph over natures infirmities ... London: R. Daniel for S. Thomson, 1658.
9 ℓ., 172 p.

3917. ———. ———. London: W. Whistwood, 1696.
1 ℓ., xi, iv, 172 p.

3918. ———. Pyrotechnia ofte vuur-stookkunde, vast-gesteld en opgehelderd, ofte het sekerste en veiligste middel om de konst te doen triumpheren over de natuurlijke gebreken ... Met een opdragt des autheurs aan de heer R. Boyle ... Amsterdam: J. vande Velde, 1687.
16 ℓ., 192 p. illus.

———. The secret of the immortal liquor. *In* Collectanea chymica ... 1684.

3919. ———. A true light of alchymy. Containing, I. A correct edition of the Marrow of alchymy ... II. The errors of a late tract

called, A short discourse of the quintessence of philosophers ... III. The method and materials pointed at, composing the sophick mercury ... London: I. Dawks for the author, 1709.
3 *l*., 97 p.

——. *See also* Le Pelletier, Jean, *ed.*, L'alkaest ou le dissolvant universal de Van Helmont ... 1704.

——. *See also* Le Pelletier, Jean, *ed.*, L'art ou la maniere de volatiliser les alcalis ... 1706.

3920. STEEB, Johann Christoph. Coelum sephiroticum, hebræorum, per portas intelligentiæ, Moysi revelatas interiores naturalium rerum characteres abditosque recessus manifestans, ex vetustissima Hebraica veritate medicinæ, chymiæ, astronomiæ, astrologiæ, botanicæ, zoologiæ, anthropologiæ, aliarumque scientiarum nova principia ... Moguntiæ: sumptibus L. Bourgeat, typis C. Küchleri, 1679.
3 *l*., 140 p., 8 *l*. illus.

STEINBERGEN, Christian Friedrich von. *See* Siebenstern, Christian Friedrich Sendimir von.

3921. STENO, Nicolaus. Elementorvm myologiae specimen, sev Musculi descriptio geometrica ... Florentiae: ex typographia sub signo Stellae, 1667.
4 *l*., 123 p. illus.

3922. ——. ——. Amstelodami: J.J. à Waesberge & viduam E. Weyerstraet, 1669.
148 p., 2 *l*. illus.

STEPHANUS ANTIOCHENUS. De remedijs expertis. *See* Dioscorides, P., Alphabetum empiricum ... 1581.

3923. STERNHALS, Johann. Ritter-Krieg das ist: Philosophische-Gesicht, in Form eines gerichtlichen Processes ... Itzo wieder auffs neu übersehen und zum Druck herausgegeben. Hamburg: G. Wolff, 1680.
7 *l*., 96 p. illus.
With Uhr-alter Ritter-Krieg ... 1680, *as issued*.

3924. STILLER, Johann Martin. Chymischer Natur-Spiegel von denen drey Reichen der Welt bey dieser andern edition mit den zweyten Theile vermehret. Hannover: N. Förster, 1685.
2 pts. in 1 v. illus.

STIRIUS, Georg Friedrich. Dissertationem medicam de chirurgia infusoria. *See* Ettmuller, Michael, *praeses*.

3925. STOLCIUS, Daniel. Hortvlvs hermeticvs floscvlis philosophorvm cvpro incisis conformatvs ... Francofvrti: L. Jennis, 1627.
165 p. illus.

——. Hermetico-Spagyriches Lustgärtleine. *In* Grasshoff, J., Dyas chymica tripartita ... 1625.

3926. ——. Viridarium chymicum figuris cupro incisis adornatum ... Francofvrti: L. Jennis, 1624.
220 *l*. illus.

3927. STOLL, Maximilian. Aphorismi de cognoscendis et curandis febribus. Vindobonae: J.N. de Kurzbek, 1786.
8 *l*., 306 p., 1 *l*.

3928. ——. Aphorismes sur la connaissance et la curation des fièvres ... Traduits en français par J.N. Corvisart ... avec le texte latin. Paris: Régent ..., 1797.
xx, 581 p.

3929. ——. Dissertationes medicae in Universitate Vindobonensi habitae ad morbos chronicos pertinentes ... Edidit et praefatus est Joseph Eyerei. Viennae: C.F. Wappler, 1788-1792.
4 v.

3930. ——. Praelectiones in diversos morbos chronicos. Post ejus obitum edidit et praefatus est Josephus Eyerel. Vindobonae: C.F. Wappler, 1788.
vi, 425 p.

3931. ——. Rationis medendi in nosocomio practico Vindobonensi. Viennae: C.F. Wappler, 1780-1790.
7 v. illus.

3932. ——. Uber die Einrichtung der öffentlichen Krankenhäuser. Herausgegeben von Geor. Adalb. von Beeckhen. Wien: C.F. Wappler, 1788.
1 *l*., iv, 78 p.
With Weber, J.A., Anmerkungen über die Sammlungen ... 1780.

3933. STÖLLER, Friedrich Christian. Beobachtungen und Erfahrungen aus der innern und äussern Heilkunst, mit physiologischen, anatomischen und praktischen Anmerkungen

nebst Kupfern. Gotha: C.W. Ettinger, 1777.
8 ℓ., 159 p. illus.

3934. STÖRCK, Anton, *freiherr von.* Libellus, quo demonstratur: cicutam non solum usu interno tutissime exhiberi, sed et esse simul remedium valde utile in multis morbis, qui hucusque curatu impossibles dicebantur. Editio altera. Vindobonæ: J.T. Trattner, 1761.
8 ℓ., 110 p.

3935. ———. An essay on the medicinal nature of hemlock ... The third edition ... Dublin: for J. Exshaw, 1760.
80 p.

3936. ———. ———. To which is annexed a necessary supplement on the subject. Translated from the Latin ... Edinburgh: A. Donaldson and J. Reid, 1762.
1 ℓ., 279 p. illus.

3937. ———. Libellus secundus, quo confirmatur cicutam ... Vindobonæ: J.T. Trattner, 1763.
5 ℓ., 292 p.
With his Libellus, quo demonstratur: cicutam ... 1761.

3938. ———. A second essay on the medicinal virtues of hemlock ... together with corollaries and cautions. Translated from the original Latin, by a physician. London: for T. Becket & P.A. DeHondt, 1761.
4 ℓ., viii, 159 p.

3939. ———. Supplementum necessarium de cicuta ... Vindobonæ: J.T. Trattner, 1761.
67 p. illus.
With his Libellus, quo demonstratur: cicutam ... 1761.

3940. ———. A necessary supplement to the former essays on the medicinal virtues of hemlock ... With several corollaries and admonitions ... Translated from the original Latin, printed at Vienna, 1761, by a physician. London: for T. Becket & P.A. DeHondt, 1762.
iv, 47 p. illus.

3941. ———. Libellus, quo demonstratur: colchici autumnalis radicem ... Vindobonæ: J.T. Trattner, 1763.
96 p. illus.
With his Libellus, quo demonstratur: cicutam ... 1761.

3942. ———. Libellus, quo demonstratur:

stramonium, hysociamum, aconitum, non solum hominibus, verum et ea esse remedia in multis morbis maxime salutifera ... Vindobonae: J.T. Trattner, 1762.
2 ℓ., 118 p.

3943. STORR, Gottlieb Conrad Christian, *praeses.* Dissertatio inavgvralis chemico-medica de sale sedativo Hombergii ... Avctor respondens Avgvst Christian Revss. Tubingæ: Fues, 1778.
44 p.

STRABO, Walafrid. Hortulus vernantissimus. *In* Macer Floridus, De herbarum virtutibus ... [1530].

STRANDMAN, Pehr. Purgantia indigena. *See* Linné, C. von, *praeses.* Entry 2464.

3944. STRASBOURG. Catalogus et taxatio medicamentorum tam simplicium quam compositorum, quæ in officinis pharmaceuticis civitatis Argentinensis ... debent ... Register und Tax aller Artzeneyen, welche sich in den Apothecken zu Strassburg befinden ... Etat et taxe des medicaments simples & composés, qui se trouvent ... chez les apoticaires de la ville de Strasbourg ... Strassburg: S. Kürssner, 1759.
4 ℓ., 128 p., 15 ℓ.

3945. STROBELBERGER, Johann Stephan. Tractatus novus in quo de cocco baphica, & quæ indè paratur confectionis alchermes recto usu disseritur. Cui insertus est Laurentii Catelani genuinus ejusdem confectionis apparandæ modus, nunc primum in latinum sermonem è gallico breviter conversus ... Jenæ: J. Beithmann, 1620.
54 ℓ. chart.

3946. STROTHER, Edward. Dr. Radcliffe's practical dispensatory ... The fourth edition. London: for C. Rivington, 1721.
4 ℓ., 464 p., 5 ℓ.

3947. ———. An essay on sickness and health; wherein are contain'd all necessary cautions and directions for the regulation of diseas'd and healthy persons ... London: H.P. for C. Rivington, 1725.
lxviii, 463 p.

3948. STUART, Alexander. Dissertatio de structura et motu musculari ... Londini: S. Richardson, 1738.
xii, ix, 131 p. illus.

3949. STUBBE, Henry. Medice cura teip-

sum! or The apothecaries plea in some
short and modest animadversions, upon a
late tract entituled A short view of the
frauds and abuses of the apothecaries ...
By Christopher Merret ... From a well-wish-
er to both societies ... London: for W. Miller,
1671.
  1 ℓ., 50 p.

3950. STUPANI, Emmanuel.   Vere avreorvm
aphorismorum Hippocratis enarrationes &
commentaria aphoristica nova methodo
eiusmodi in ordinem digesta ... Basileae:
J. Schroeterus, 1615.
  13 ℓ., 530 p., 9 ℓ.   charts.

3951. STVPENDI et maravigliosi secreti,
mai più palesati da nessun'altro che da me,
Gio. Battista Figivolo del gran medico del
rè di Francia ... Milano: G. Lucino [n.d.].
  4 ℓ.

       SUARDUS, Paulus.   Thesaurus aroma-
tariorum. In Manliis, J.J. de, de Bosco,
Luminare maius ... 1506, etc.

       SUAVIUS, Leo, pseud. See Gohory,
Jacques.

       SUBURBANUS, Eremita, pseud. See
Helmont, Franciscus Mercurius van.

3952. SUCHTEN, Alexander von.   Of the
secrets of antimony: in two treatises. Translated out of High-Dutch by Dr. C. ... To
which is added B. Valentine's Salt of antimony, with its use. London: M. Pitt, 1670.
  4 ℓ., 122 p., 1 ℓ.

       ——. ——. In Basilius Valentinus,
Of natural and supernatural things ... 1671.

3953. ——. Tractatus de vera medicina
editus curâ Ioachimi Morsii. Hamburgi: H.
Carsten, 1621.
  24 ℓ.
  With Nolle, H., Discursus ... 1636.

3954. SUCKOW, Georg Adolph.   Anfangsgründe der ökonomischen und technischen
Chemie. Leipzig: Weidmann, 1784.
  xii, 645 p., 13 ℓ.   charts.

3955. SUE, Jean Joseph.   Anthropotomie:
ou L'art d'injecter, de disséquer, d'embaumer
et de conserver les parties du corps humain,
&c. Seconde edition, revue & considérablement augmentée. Paris: Cavellier, 1765.
  xx, 291 p.

3956. SÜE, Pierre.   Anecdotes historiques,
littéraires et critiques, sur la médecine, la
chirurgie & pharmacie ... Bruxelles: Dujardin, 1789.
  2 v.

3957. SUTHERLAND, Alexander.   Attempts
to revive antient medical doctrines ... London: A. Millar, 1763.
  2 v.

3958. ——. The nature and qualities of
Bristol-water: illustrated by experiments
and observations, with practical reflections
on Bath-waters ... Bristol: E. Farley ...,
1758.
  153 p.
  With Randolph, G., An enquiry ... 1750.

3959. SWAMMERDAM, Jan.   Tractatus
physico-anatomico-medicus de respiratione
usuque pulmonum ... Lugduni Batavorum: J.
vander Linden, 1679.
  8 ℓ., 121 p., 11 ℓ.   illus.

3960. ——. ——. Editio altera. Cui sub-
juncta est D. Alberti Haller ... De diaphrag-
matis musculis dissertatio anatomica.
Editio tertia. Lugduni Batavorum: C. Wishoff,
1738.
  8 ℓ., 95 p.   illus.

3961. SWIETEN, Gerard, freiherr von.
The commentaries upon the Aphorisms of
Dr. Herman Boerhaave ... concerning the
knowledge and cure of the several diseases
incident to human bodies. Translated into
English. London: for J. & P. Knapton, 1744-
1765.
  18 v.   illus.
  Lacking v. 15-18. Volumes 9-11 are second ed.; volumes 9-14 have imprint: London,
R. Horsfield and T. Longman, 1765.

3962. ——. Constitvtiones epidemicae et
morbi potissimvm Lvgdvni-Batvorvm obser-
vati ex evisdem adversariis. Edidit Maxi-
malianvs Stoll.   Vindobonae: R. Graeffervs,
1782.
  2 v.

3963. SYDENHAM, Thomas.   The entire
works; newly made English from the original
... To which are added, explanatory and practical notes, from the best medicinal writers.
The second edition, revised, corrected, and
enlarged with several additional notes. By
John Swan ... London: for E. Cave, 1749.
  1 ℓ., xi, xxii p., 2 ℓ., 685 p., 12 ℓ.

3964. ———. Opera medica; in tomos duos divisa. Editio novissima ... Genevae: fratres de Tournes, 1769.
  2 v.

3965. ———. Praxis medica experimentalis, sive Opvscvla vniversa ... nunc primùm in unum collecta volumen ... Lipsiae: T. Fritsch, 1711.
  32 *l*., 800 p., 22 *l*.   port.

3966. ———. Processus integri in morbis ferè omnibus curandi ... Nec non De phthisi tractatulo. Edinburgi: Hamilton, Balfour & Neill, 1750.
  xii, 122 p., 1 *l*.
  ˉ*With* Pharmacopoeia pauperum ... 1752.

  ———. ———. *In* Morton, R., Opera medica ... 1696.

3967. ———. The whole works ... Translated from the original Latin, by John Pechy. London: R. Wellington & E. Castle, 1696.
  12 *l*., 592 p.

3968. ———. ———. The fourth edition ... London: for R. Wellington, 1705.
  8 *l*., 453 p., 1 *l*.

3969. ———. ———. The eighth edition ... London: J. Darby for M. Poulson, 1722.
  xv, 447 p., 1 *l*.

  SYLVIUS, Franciscus de Le Boe. *See* Le Boë, Frans de.

  SYLVIUS, Joannes, *pseud. See* Dubois, Jacques.

  SYNESIUS. The true book. *In* Basilius Valentinus, Triumphant chariot ... 1678.

  ———. Le vray livre. *In* Arnauld, P., Trois Traitez ... 1612.

  ———. ———. *In* Arnauld, P., Philosophie naturelle ... 1682.

3970. A SYSTEM of anatomy and physiology, with the comparative anatomy of animals. Compiled from the latest and best authors, and arranged ... in the order of the lectures delivered in the University of Edinburgh ... A new edition, with additions, corrections, and notes ... Edinburgh: for W. Creech, 1795.
  3 v.   illus., port.

T

3971. T.   Lettre de M. de T*** a un de
ses amis, en réponse d'un mémoire de M.
Geoffroy, sur les sels essentiels de M. le
comte de la Garaye. On y a joint aussi une
dissertation de M. Grosse sur les même
sels ... Paris: D. Mouchet, 1743.
   2 *l*., 48 p., 1 *l*.

3972. T., A.   A rich storehovse of treasurie for the diseased ... First set foorth ...
by G.W. And now sixtly augmented and inlarged by A.T.   ... London: R. Blower, 1616.
   14 *l*., 176 [i.e. 146] numb. *l*.
   With Vicary, T., The English mans treasure ... 1613.

3973. T., P.   Chemia rationalis rationibus
philosophicis, observationibus medicis,
debitis dosibus, &c. illustrata ... Accedit
Praxis chymiatrica rationalis ... Auctore P.T.
... Lugd. Batav: J. Mocquee, 1687.
   2 *l*., 168 p., 4 *l*.; 1 *l*., 154 p., 10 *l*.

3974. ——. ——. Lugd. Batav: F. Haaring,
1690.
   2 *l*., 168 p., 4 *l*.; 1 *l*., 154 p., 10 *l*.

   TABERNAEMONTANUS, Jacob Theodore. *See* Theodorus, Jacobus.

3975. TACHENIUS, Otto.   Antiqvissimæ
Hippocraticæ medicinæ clavis manuali experientia in naturæ fontibus elaborata ...
Francofurti: J.P. Zubrod, 1669.
   286 p., 1 *l*.

3976. ——. ——. Venetiis: Combi & La
Nou, 1669.
   286 p., 1 *l*.
   With his Hippocrates chimicus ... 1668.

3977. ——. ——. Lutetiæ Parisiorum: J.
d'Houry, 1672.
   6 *l*., 273 p., 1 *l*.
   With his Hippocrates chimicus ... 1669.

3978. ——. Hippocrates chimicus, qui

novisimi viperini salis antiquissima fundamenta ostendit ... Brunsvigæ: sumpt. T.H.
Hauensteinii, typis J.H. Dunckeri, 1668.
   20 *l*., 271 p.

3979. ——. ——. Lvtetiæ Parisiorvm: I.
d'Hovry, 1669.
   18 *l*., 259 p., 2 *l*.

3980. ——. ——. Editio secvnda ... Accessit eiusdem authoris De morborvm principe
tractatvs ... Venetiis: Combi & LaNou, 1678.
   18 *l*., 473 p., 2 *l*.

3981. ——. Hippocrates chymicus discovering the ancient foundation of the late
viperine salt, with his Clavis thereunto
annexed. Translated by I.W.   London: N.
Crouch, 1677.
   11 *l*., 122 p., 5 *l*.; 7 *l*., 120 p., 7 *l*.

3982. ——. ——. London: W. Marshall,
1690.
   11 *l*., 122 p., 5 *l*.; 7 *l*., 120 p., 7 *l*.

3983. ——. La lumiere sortant par soi-
mesme des tenebres ... écrite en vers Ital-
iens, avec un commentaire; le tout traduit
en François par B.D.L. Seconde edition,
reveuë & augmentée de CLIII aphorismes
chymiques. Paris: L. d'Houry, 1693.
   11 *l*., 326, 33 p.

3984. ——. Das aus der Finsterniss von
sich selbst hervorbrechende Licht, in drey
Italienischen Gesängen nebst seiner Auslegung ... aus dem Französischen übersetzt
von C.F.K.   ... Langensalza: J.C. Martini,
1772.
   7 *l*., 250 p.

3985. TACKE, Johann.   De consanguinitate
auri, sacchari et spiritus vini, tractatus
brevis, perspicuus tamen ... Consciptus
autore Hoc viro sancta cos nidet. Gissæ:
C. Vulpius, 1659.
   56 p.

3986. ———. Triplex phasis sophicvs: Solis orbe expeditus, Humanæque fragilitati & Spei resurrectionis rerum consecratus. Francofurti: J.P. Zubrodt & haered J.B. Schöwetter, 1673.
3 pts. in 1 v.

3987. TÆDA trifida chimica, das its: Dreyfache chimische Facket ... nemlich Johannis Wolffgangi Dienheimii, Medicina universalis. Anonymi, Verbum dismissum. D. Hugini à Barma, Saturnia regna. Allesamt treulich verteutscht ... Nürnberg: J. Andreæ und W. Endters Erben, 1674.
16 *l.*, 303 p. illus.

3988. TAGAULT, Jean. De chirurgica institutione libri quinque ... His accessit sextus liber De materia chirurgica, authore Iacobo Hollerio Stempano ... Venetiis: ex officina Erasmiana, apud V. Vaugris, 1544.
32 *l.*, 417 numb. *l.*, 21 *l.* illus.

3989. ———. La chirvrgie. Diligemment reueuë & corrigée en cette derniere edition ... Roven: D. Lovdet, 1645.
25 *l.*, 845 p., 7 *l.* illus.

3990. TALPA, Petrus. Empiricvs, sive Indoctvs medicvs, dialogvs brevis et elegans ... Item, Exilium empiricorum ... Franekeræ: Aeg. Radæus, 1595.
83 p., 5 *l.*
With Dorn, G., Artificii chymistici ... 1594.

3991. TANCK, Joachim. Promptuarium alchemiæ, das ist: Vornehmer gelarten philosophen vnd alchimisten Schriffte vnd Tractat von dem Stein der Weisen ... Leipzig: H. Gross, 1610.
40 *l.*, 320 p., 8 *l.* illus.

3992. ———. Appendix primi tomi Promptvarii alchymiæ; das ist: Etliche alte ausserlesene philosophische Schrifften vnd Tractätlein von Stein der Weisen ... [Leipzig] 1610.
377 p. illus.
With his Promptuarium alchemiæ ... 1610.

3993. TARDY, Emmanuel. Dissertation sur le transport des eaux de Vichy, avec la maniére de se conduire avec succès dans leur usage. Moulins: J. Faure, 1655.
8 *l.*, 152 p.

3994. TASCHENBUCH für Alchemisten, Theosophen und Weisensteinsforscher, die es sind und werden wollen ... Leipzig: C.G.

Hilscher, 1790.
8 *l.*, 342 p.

TATTI, Giovanni, *pseud. See* Sansovino, Francesco.

3995. TAUVRY, Daniel. Traité des medicamens, et la maniere de s'en servir pour la guerison des maladies ... Paris: E. Michailet, 1691.
8 *l.*, 385 p., 1 *l.*

3996. ———. Treatise of medicines ... Written originally in French ... Translated from the last edition. London: for R. Wellington ..., 1700.
8 *l.*, 287, 291 p., 2 *l.*

3997. TAXA medicamentorum in pharmacopoea Austriaco-provinciali contentorum ... Wien: J.T. Edlen, 1785.
4 *l.*, 95 p.

TECTORIS, Franciscus Maria de. Compendium medicinae practicae. *In* Melich, G., Dispensatorium medicum ... 1601.

3998. TEICHMEYER, Hermann Friedrich. Elementa philosophiæ natvralis experimentalis ... Ienæ: J.F. Bielckius, 1717.
4 *l.*, 272 p., 24 *l.* illus.

TELESIO, Antonio. De coloribus liber. *In* Joannes Actuarius, De urinis ... 1529.

3999. TEMPLE, Richard. Practice of physic: wherein is attempted a concise exposition of the characters, symptoms, causes of diseases, and method of cure ... The second edition, with corrections and additions. London: for J. Johnson, 1798.
xv, 344 p.

4000. TENCKE, Jerome. Formules de medecine, tirees de la Galenique & de la chimie ... nouvellement traduites en François. Lyon: J. Certe, 1684.
10 *l.*, 498 p., 23 *l.*

4001. TENNETAR, Michel du. Élémens de chymie, rédigés d'après les decouvertes modernes; ou Précis de leçons publiques de la Société Royale ... Metz: P. Marchal, 1779.
1 *l.*, ii p., 2 *l.*, iv, 180 p.

4002. TENON, Jacobus Renatus. Mémoirs sur les hôpitaux de Paris: Paris: P.D. Pierres, 1788.
4 *l.*, lxxiv, 472 p. illus.

4003. TENTZEL, Andreas. Chymisch-
spagyrische Artzney-Kunst. Samt Georgi
Phaedronis raren chymisch-medicinischen
Arcanis und Geheimnüssen ... In das Deutsche übersetzt von P.C. ... Franckfurt und
Leipzig: 1736.
  4 *l.*, 370 p. illus.

———. Exegesis chymiatrica. *In*
Sala, A., Ternarius ... 1618.

4004. ———. Medicina diastatica, hoc est,
Singularis illa et admirabilis ad distans, &
beneficio mumialis transplantationis opera-
tionem & efficaciam habens ... Erfurti:
sumptibus J. Birckneri, excud. J.G. Hertz,
1666.
  8 *l.*, 188 p.

4005. ———. Medicinisch- philosophisch-
und sympathetische Schrifften ... Wie auch
darbey seine scripta gemina de amore &
odio. Nebst noch einem kurtzen Unterricht,
auf was Art die Thiere, Pflantzen und Ertze
zur natürlichen Magie zu brauchen und anzu-
wenden, zusammen heraus gegeben von P.C.
Leipzig: J.S. Strauss, 1725.
  8 *l.*, 286 p., 1 *l.* illus.
  With Faust, J.M., Philaletha illustratus
... 1706.

4006. TERREDE. Examen analytique des
eaux minérales des environs de l'Aigle en
Haute Normandie. Avec leurs propriétés dans
les maladies. Amsterdam et Paris: Vincent,
1776.
  iv, 103 p.

4007. ———. Reflexions sur une brochure
intitulée: Dissertation sur l'examen analytique des eaux minérales des environs de
Laigle, &c. [n.p.: 1776?]
  88 p.
  Half-title.
  With his Examen analytique des eaux
minérales ... 1776.

4008. TESORO de secreti raccolti da diuersi valent' huomini. A beneficio vniuersale.
Venetia: G. Simbeni [n.d.].
  4 *l.*

4009. TESSARI, Ludovico. Chymiæ elementa in aphorismos digesta ... Accedit
ejusdem Prodromus de phlogisto in coloranda
corporum superficie. Venetiis: N. Pezzana,
1772.
  xvi, 143 p.

TETTELBACH, Johann Gottfried. De
ordinandis rectius virgius aureis genuinis
aeque ac spuriis. *See* Lischwitz, J.C.,
praeses.

TETZEN, Johann von. *See* Joannes
Ticinensis.

TEUTZSCHENSCHEN, Johann. Epis-
tola de lapide philosophorum. *In* Schauberdt,
J., Κατοπθοσοφία ... 1602.

TEXTOR, Joannes Ravisius. *See* Tixier,
Jean.

THARSANDER, *pseud. See* Wegener,
Georg Wilhelm.

4010. THEATRUM CHEMICUM, præcipuos
selectorum auctorum tractatus de chemiæ
et lapidis philosophici antiquitate, veritate
... continens ... Argentoratii: L. Zetzner,
1613-1661.
  6 v.

4011. ———. ———. Argentorati: heredes E.
Zetzneri, 1659-1661.
  6 v.
  Volume 5 is dated 1622.

4012. THEATRUM SYMPATHETICUM, in quo
sympathiæ actiones variæ, singulares &
admirandæ tàm macro-quam microcosmicæ
exhibentur ... Editio altera, priori emendatior.
Amstelædami: T. Fontan, 1661.
  6 *l.*, 259 p.

4013. THEATRUM SYMPATHETICUM auctum,
exhibens varios authores ... Editio novissima ... Norimbergæ: J.A. Endter, 1662.
  4 *l.*, 722 p., 21 *l.* illus.

4014. THEOBALD, John. Medulla medicinæ universæ: or, A new compenduous
dispensatory ... The second edition ... London: 1748.
  4 *l.*, 108 p.

4015. ———. ———. The third edition ...
Dublin: for G. and A. Ewing, 1750.
  4 *l.*, 112 p.

4016. THEODORUS, Jacobus. Neu vollkommen Kräuter Buch ... Zum andern durch
Hieronymus Bauhinum ... vermehrt. Und nun
zum dritten mal ... übersehen ... Basel: J.L.
König und J. Brandmyller, 1687.
  6 *l.*, 1529 p., 48 *l.* illus.

4017. ———. Neuw Wasserschatz, das ist:
Von allen heylsamen metallischen minerischen

Bädern vnd Wassern ... Auch wie man diesel-
bigen vnnd alle metallische Wasser zu mancherley Kranckheiten vnd Leibs gebrechen
... Franckfurt am Mayn: [N. Basseus] 1584.
   8 ℓ., 649 p., 34 ℓ.

4018. THEOPHILUS, *pseud.* Mineralogia,
oder Chymischer Schlüssel ... Franckfurt:
J. Zieger, 1706.
   23 ℓ., 466 p.

4019. THEOPHRASTUS. De historia plantarum lib. ix. Et decimi principium duntaxat.
Eiusdem De causis plantarum lib. v. Theodoro Gaza interprete. [n.d.: n.p.]
   16 ℓ., 284 numb. ℓ.

4020. ———. De svffrvticibvs, herbisqve,
ac frvgibvs libri qvattuor, Theodoro Gaza
interprete. [Argentorati: H. Sybold, 1529.]
   86 ℓ.

4021. ———. ... History of stones. With an
English version, and critical and philosophical notes ... by John Hill. To which are added two letters: one ... on the colours of the
sapphire and turquoise, and the other ...
upon the effects of different menstruums on
copper ... London: for C. Davis, 1746.
   xxiii, 211 p.

4022. ———. ———. The second edition; enlarged by the addition of a Greek index of
all the words in Theophrastus. Also observations on the new Swedish acid ... by Sir John
Hill. London: for the author ..., 1774.
   viii, 342 p., 23 ℓ.

4023. ———. Traité des pierres ... traduit
du Grec; avec des notes physiques & critiques, traduites de l'Anglois de M. Hill ...
Paris: J.T. Herissant, 1754.
   xxiv, 287 p.

4024. ———. Libellvs de odoribvs, ab Adri-
ano Turnebo latinitate donatus, & scholiis
atque annotationibus illustratus. Lvtetiae:
M. Vascosanus, 1556.
   32, 10 numb. ℓ.

4025. THEORIA & practica arboris avreæ &
argenteæ. [n.p.] 1624.
   1 ℓ., 78 p.

4026. THEOSOPHIA physico-chymica, das
ist Gottesgelahrheit durch natürliche und
chymische Werke erkläret und bewiesen.
[n.p.] 1791.
   1 ℓ., 164 p., 1 ℓ. illus.

4027. THESAURUS medicus Edinburgensis
novus: sive, Dissertationum in Academia
Edinensi, ad rem medicaṁ pertinentium, ab
anno 1759 ad annum 1785 ... Edinburgi: C.
Elliot ..., 1785.
   4 v. illus.

4028. THESORO di varii secreti natvrali,
hauuti da diuersi signori. Milano: G. Ferioli,
1608.
   4 ℓ.

4029. THIBAUT, Pierre. Covrs de chymie.
Paris: T. Jolly, 1667.
   8 ℓ., 285 p., 8 ℓ.

4030. ———. ———. Derniere edition. Leyde:
A. Dovde, 1672.
   415 p., 14 ℓ. illus.

4031. ———. ——— augmenté de la composition du baume vert vulneraire, avec son
emplastre stiptique; du febrifuge de F. Del-
boe Sylvivs; d'vn excellent ermetique ...
Paris: J. d'Houry, 1674.
   8 ℓ., 285, 7, 16 p., 8 ℓ.

4032. ———. The art of chymistry: as it is
now practised ... translated into English ...
London: for J. Starkey, 1668.
   16 ℓ., 279 p., 3 ℓ.

4033. THIÉRY, François. Erfahrungen in
der Arzneywissenschaft. Aus dem Französischen übersetzt ... Leipzig: A.F. Böhme,
1778.
   4 ℓ., 180 p.

4034. ———. Médicine experimentale, ou
résultat de nouvelles observations pratiques
et anatomiques. Paris: Duchesne, 1755.
   341 p.

THÖLDE, Johann. *See* Basilius Valentinus.

THOMAS ACQUINAS, *Saint.* Secreta
alchimiæ magnalia. *In* Broekhuizen, D. van,
Secreta alchimiæ magnalia ... 1598, 1602.

———. Thesaurus alchimae secretis-
simus. *In* Broekhuizen, D. van, Secreta alchimiæ magnalia ... 1598, 1602.

4035. THOMSON, George. The anatomy of
the human bones, with an account of muscular
motion and the circulation of the blood, also
of digestion and nutrition with a description
of the four senses ... London: for R. Ware

..., 1734.
18 *l*., 299 p., 12 *l*.   illus.

4036.   THOR, George.   Cheiragogia Heliana.
A manducation to the philosopher's magical
gold ... To which is added: Ἄντρον Μίτραϛ;
Zoroaster's cave ... Together with the famous
catholic epistle of John Pontanus ...   London:
for H. Moseley, 1659.
6 *l*., 96 p.

4037.   ——.   An easie introduction to the
philosophers magical gold; to which is
added, Zoroasters cave; as also John Pontanus epistle upon the mineral fire ... London: for M. Smelt, 1667.
6 *l*., 96 p.

4038.   THOUVENEL, Pierre.   Mémoire chymique et médicinal sur les principes et les
vertus des eaux minérales de Contrexeville
en Lorraine. Nancy & Paris: Babin & Valade,
1774.
128 p.

4039.   ——.   Précis chimique sue les principes de la formation de l'acide nitreux ...
Copenhague: P.H. Höecke, 1784.
32 p.

4040.   THRUSTON, Malachi.   De respirationis usu primario diatriba. Accedunt Animadversiones a cl. viro in eandem conscriptae, una cum responsionibus auctoris. Ut et
Johannis Mayow ... Tractatus duo, quorum
prior agit De respiratione, alter De rachitide.
Lugd. Batavor.: T. Haak, 1708.
5 *l*., 165 p., 4 *l*.; 1 *l*., 57 p.   illus.

THUNBERG, Karl Peter.   De venis
resorbentibus. *See* Linné, C. von, *praeses*.
Entry 2473.

4041.   THURNEISSER ZUM THURN, Leonhard.
Historia unnd beschreibung influentischer
elementischer und natürlicher Wirckungen
... [Berlin: M. Hentzske, 1578.]
6 *l*., 156 p., 12 *l*.   illus., port.

4042.   ——.   Μεγαλη χψμία, vel magna alchymia. Das ist ein Lehr und Vnterweisung
von den offenbaren und verborgenlichen
Naturen ... Berlin: N. Voltz, 1583.
6 *l*., 144 p., 6 *l*.   illus., port.
With his Historia unnd beschreibung ...
1578.

4043.   ——.   [Quinta essentia, das ist, Die
höchste Subtilitet, Kraft und Wirkung, beider
der furtrefelichisten ... Könsten der Medicina

und Alchemia ... Leipzig: H. Steinman, 1574.]
ccx numb. *l*., 2 *l*.   illus., port.
Lacking the title page and leaf A₆.

4044.   ——.   אלבו καὶ Εκπλήρωσιϛ und
Impletio, oder Erfüllung der verheissung
Leonhardt Thurneissers zum Thurn ... welche
Zusagung von ihme zu Berlin Anno 1580 den
x tag Martii .. zu leisten beschehen ...
Durch den Authorem selbert zum andern
mal mit fleiss Corrigirt ... Nürmberg: [ge-
druckt zu L. Heussler, in verlag J. Lochners]
1581.
84 *l*.   illus., port., charts.

4045.   ——.   πγ°בל καὶ Ἑρμηνεία das ist
ein Onomasticvm und Interpretatio ... uber
etliche frembde uñ ... unbekante Nomina,
Verba, Prouerbia, Dicta, Sylben, Caracter,
und sonst Reden ... Das ander Theil ... Berlin: N. Voltze, 1583.
6 *l*., 188 p.
Lacks the eight tables.
With his Historia unnd beschreibung ...
1578.

4046.   ——.   Zehen Bücher von kälten,
warmen, minerischen und mettalischen Wassern. Samt deren Vergleichung mit den Plantis
oder Erdgewächsen ... Dem ein Kurtze Beschreibung des Selbacher Brummens oder
Badts ... durch Joannen Rudolphum Saltzman.
Strassburg: L. Zetzner, 1612.
3 *l*., 324 p., 26 *l*., 13 p.

TICINENSIS, Joannes.   *See* Joannes
Ticinensis.

4047.   TILEMANN, Johann.   Experimenta,
circa veras & irreducibiles auri solutiones,
ante triennium in Italia edita, & nunc in
gratiam philo-chymicorum denuo recusa.
Cum praefatione D. Joelis Langelotti ...
Hamburgi: G. Schultz, 1673.
9 *l*., 34 p.

4048.   TILING, Mathias.   Anchora salutis
sacra, seu De laudano opiato, medicamine
isto divino ac coelitus demisso ... Francofurti: W.H. Stockius, 1671.
12 *l*., 554 p., 3 *l*.

4049.   ——.   Prodromus praxeos chimiatricæ
... Rintelii: sumptibus T.H. Hauensteinii,
typis G.C. Wächter, 1674.
15 *l*., 1004 p., 26 *l*.   charts.

TILLAEUS, Pehr Cornelius.   De varia
febrium intermittentium curatione. *See* Linné,
C. von, *praeses*. Entry 2457.

————. Potus theae. *See* Linné, C. von, *praeses*. Entry 2490.

4050. TISSOT, Samuel Auguste André David. Avis au peuple sur sa santé ... Nouvelle édition conforme à la seconde originale à laquelle on a joint la traduction de la préface Allemande de M. Hirzel, & des notes par M***. Lyon: J.M. Bruyset, B. Duplain, 1764.
2 v.

4051. ————. Raadgeeving voor de gezondheid van den gemeenen man ... Derde druk ... Rotterdam: R. Arrenberg, 1772.
xxxii, 752 p.

4052. ————. ————. Naar den laatsten Franschen druk vermeerderd ... door L. Bicker. Utrecht: G. van den Brink, 1775.
xvi, 264 p., 2 *l.*
With his Onanismus ... 1775.

4053. ————. ————. Rotterdam: R. Arrenberg, 1779.
xxiv, 518 p., 1 *l.*

4054. ————. Anleitung für das Landvolk in Absicht auf seine Gesundheit. Zweyte vermehrte und verbesserte Auflage. Aus dem Französischen übersetzt durch H.C. Hirzel ... Zürich: Heidegger, 1763.
lxiv, 671 p.

4055. ————. ————. [Augsburg?: J. Wolff, 1766?]
13 *l.*, 652 p., 11 *l.*
Lacking the first two leaves, including the title page, and the final leaves of the index.

4056. ————. Essai sur les maladies des gens du monde. Seconde édition augmentée. Lausanne: F. Grasset, 1770.
xvi, 173 p., 1 *l.*

4057. ————. An essay on bilious fevers; or, The history of a bilious epidemic fever at Lausanne, in the year MDCCLV ... Translated into English. London: for D. Wilson and T. Durham, 1760.
12 *l.*, 228 p.

4058. ————. Onanismus of verhandeling over de ziekten, oorspronglyk uit de zelfbesmetting ... vertaald uit het Fransch ... met eenige aanmerkingen door P.M. Nielen. Utrecht: G.T. van Paddenburg, 1775.
20 *l.*, 231 p.

4059. ————. Traité de l'epilepsie. Faisant le tome troisieme du traité des nerfs & de leurs maladies. Paris: P.F. Didot, 1770.
4 *l.*, 419 p.

4060. ————. Verhandeling over de vallende ziekte ... Amsterdam & Harlingen: P. Conradi & F. van der Plaats, 1774.
vi, 304 p.
With his Van den aart ... 1772.

4061. ————. Van den aart en geneeswyze van verscheidene zwaare ziekten ... Waar by de vermaarde brief aan Graaf Roncalli, over de inenting kinderpokjes. Leiden & Harlingen: S. en J. Luchtmans & F. van der Plaats, 1772.
1 *l.*, 350 p.

4062. TIXIER, Jean, *seigneur de Ravisy.* Cornvcopiae Ioannis Ravisii Textoris epitome ... Lugduni: S. de Honoratis, 1560.
79 p.
With his Officiniae epitome ... 1560.

4063. ————. Officinae Ioannis Ravisii Textoris epitome ... Lugduni: S. de Honoratis, 1560.
2 v. in 1.

4064. TOELTIUS, Johann Georg. Coelvm reseratvm chymicvm, oder Philosophischer tractat ... Franckfurth: C.F. Jungnicols Wittwe, 1737.
8 *l.*, 337 p.

TOEPFER, Benedikt. *See* Figulus, Benedictus.

4065. TOFANI, Giuseppe. Idea di un repertorio per i risultati d'osservazioni, o esperienze relative alle materie combustibili ... Firenze: P. Allegrini, 1796.
viii, 92 p. chart.

TOLET, Pierre. *See* Bagellardo, P., Opusculum ... 1538.

4066. TOLLIUS, Jakob. Epistolae itinerariae ex auctoris schedis postumis recensitæ, suppletæ digestæ ... cura & studio Henrici Christiani Henninii. Amstelædami: F. Halmæ, 1700.
8 *l.*, 260 p., 7 *l.*

4067. ————. ————. Secunda editio. Amstelædami: J. Oosterwyk, 1714.
8 *l.*, 260 p., 7 *l.*

4068. ————. Fortuita, in quibus, præter critica

nonnulla, tota fabularis historia Græca, Phoenicia, Ægyptiaca, ad chemiam pertinere asseritur. Amstelædami: Janssonio-Waesbergios, 1687.
8 *l*., 375 p., 16 *l*.   illus., chart.

4069. ———. Insignia itinerarii Italici, quibus continentur antiquitates sacræ. Trajecti ad Rhenum: F. Halma & G. vande Water, 1696.
7 *l*., 199 p., 5 *l*.
With his Epistolae itinerariae ... 1714.

4070. ———. Manuductio ad cælum chemicum. Amstelædami: Janssonios-Waesbergios, 1688.
16 p.
With his Fortuita ... 1687.

4071. ———. Manuductio ad coelum chemicum, das ist: Handleitung zu dem chemischen Himmel ... Nebst einer Vorrede, in welcher das Leben Jacobi Tollii beschrieben wird. Jena: J.C. Cröker, 1752.
8 *l*., 62 p.
With Der Weisheit Morgenröthe ... 1762.

4072. ———. Sapientia insaniens, sive Promissa chemica ... Amstelædami: Janssonio-Waesbergios, 1689.
64 p.   chart.
With his Fortuita ... 1687.

4073. ———. Sapientia insaniens oder Tolle Weissheit ... ins Deutsche übersetzet, und mit einigen Anmerckungen erläutert ... von J.C.L. Jena: C.F. Gollner, 1753.
138 p., 11 *l*.
With Der Weisheit Morgenröthe ... 1762.

4074. TOMAI, Tommaso. Ideé dv iardin dv monde. Traduit d'Italien par Nicolas le Movl [inet]. Paris: E. Davbin, 1648.
1 *l*., 228 p.
The title page of Tomai's Abrege cvrievx ... 1648 has been tipped in preceding the title page of the present work.

The TOMB of Semiramis. *See* Tumba Semiramidis.

4075. TONDU DE NANGIS, Jacques. Analyse des eaux minérales de Merlange, près la ville de Montereau-Fautyonne ... Paris: la veuve Quillas, 1761.
46 p.

TONNING, Heinrich. Rariora Norvegiae. *See* Linné, C. von, *praeses*. Entry 2437.

4076. TORELLI, Gioan Battista. Novo giardino di secreti cvriosi, et esperimentati ... Bologna: Moscatelli, 1628.
4 *l*.

4077. TORRES, Alexos de. Los doctores a pie de la Evropa. Politico-medicos español, italiano, aleman, frances y saboyano ... Barcel.: M. Marti, 1735.
3 *l*., 58 p.

4078. TORRES Y VILLARROEL, Diego. Los desauciados del mundo, y de la gloria. Sueno mystico, moral, y phisico, util para quantos desean morir bien, y conocer las debilidades de la naturaleza ... Madrid [n.d.].
3 pts. in 1 v.

4079. ———. Libros en que estan reatados diferentes quadernos physicos, medicos, astrologicos, poeticos, morales, y mysticos ... Salamanca: V. Villargordo y P.O. Gomez, 1752.
24 *l*., 268 p.   ports.

4080. ———. [Obras.] Madrid: viuda de Ibarra, 1794-1799.
15 v. in 14.

4081. ———. Vida, ascendencia, nacimiento, crianza y aventuras del Doctor Don Diego de Torres Villarroel ... Madrid: B. Cano, 1789.
2 pts. in 1 v.

4082. ———. Vida nàtvral y catholica. Medicina segura para mantener menos enferma la organizacion del cuerpo ... Madrid: Castellana [n.d.].
50 *l*.

4083. TORTI, Francesco. Therapeutice specialis ad febres periodicas perniciosas. Editio tertia auctior, cui subnectuntur ejusdem auctoris responsiones Jastro-Apologetica ad clarissimum Ramazzinum. Venetiis: L. Basilius, 1732.
9 *l*., 526 p., 1 *l*.   illus., port.

4084. TOURNEFORT, Joseph Pitton de. Institutiones rei herbariæ. Editio tertia appendicibus aucta ab Antonio de Jussieu. Parisiis: typographia Regia, 1719.
3 v. in 2.   illus.

4085. ———. The compleat herbal: or, The botanical institutions ... Carefully translated from the original Latin. With large additions from Ray, Gerarde, Parkinson, and others ... With a short account of the life

and writings of the author. London: for R.
Bonwicke ..., 1719-1730.
2 v. illus.

4086. ———. Histoire des plantes qui
naissent aux environs de Paris, avec leur
usage dans la medecine. Paris: l'Imprimerie
Royale, 1698.
28 *l*., 543 p., 9 *l*.

4087. ———. ———. Seconde edition. Revue
& augmentée par M. Bernard de Jussieu ...
Paris: J. Musier, 1725.
2 v.

4088. ———. History of plants growing
about Paris, with their uses in physick; and
a mechanical account of the operations of
medicines. Translated into English, with
many additions. And accommodated to the
plants growing in Great-Britain. By John
Martyn. London: for C. Rivington, 1732.
2 v.

4089. ———. Materia medica; or, A description of simple medicines generally us'd in
physick ... Translated into English. The second edition corrected. London: W.H. for A.
Bell, 1716.
10 *l*., 406 p., 1 *l*.

TRACTATUS aliquot chemici singvlares summum philosophorum arcanum. *See*
Combach, L., *ed.*

4090. TRACTATUS chymicus antiqvissimvs
& vere aureus, in quo spectare licet fundamenta veræ chymiæ ... Augustæ Vind.: D.R.
Mertz & J.J. Mayer, 1721.
25 *l*. illus.

4091. TRACTATUS de secretissimo antiquorum philosophorum arcano. Quo non solum
omnes ægritudines totius corporis humani
mirabiliter sanantur: verùm & immunda ac
leprosa corpora metallorum in perfectum
lunificum & solificum transmutantur ... [Leip-
zig?: 1611.]
2 pts. in 1 v.
Lacking part 3. Part 2 has separate title
page: *Tractatus II. De lapide philosophico
Joannis Lasniori Bohœmi* ...
With Morienus, De transfiguratione ... 1593.

4092. Le TRAICTIE des eaues artificielles,
les vertus et proprietes dicelles. [Paris: A.
Caillaut, c. 1495.]
38 *l*.
Title page in facsimile.

4093. TRAITÉ de chymie, philosophique et
hermetique. Enrichi des opérations les plus
curieuses de l'Art. Paris: C.M. d'Houry,
1725.
2 *l*., 292 p., 2 *l*.

4094. TRAITÉ de la poudre de projection,
divisé en deux lettres ... Bruxelles: 1707.
68 p.
Signed: "D.L.B."

4095. TRAITÉ physique sur la lumiere,
source du feu philosophique principe de
toutes choses ouvrage ... La Haye: 1790.
4 *l*., 252 p., 1 *l*. illus.

4096. TRALLES, Balthasar Ludwig. Usus
opii salubris et moxius in morborum medela,
solidis et certis principiis superstructus.
Vratislaviæ: C. Meyer, 1757-1760.
3 v.

4097. TRAMULLAS Y FERRERA, José.
Promptuario y guia de artifices plateros,
en que se dan reglas para ligar, religar,
abonar, y reducir qualesquiera cantidad de
oro ... Madrid: herederos de F. del Hierro,
1734.
16 *l*., 215 p.

4098. ———. Promptuario y guia de plateros,
en que se dan reglas para ligar, religar, y
abonar qualesquier cantidad de oro ... Madrid:
J. de Oliveras, 1747.
4 *l*., 59 p.
With his Promptuario y guia de artifices
plateros ... 1734.

4099. THE TREASURE OF POOR MEN. Here
begynneth a good booke of medicines called
the treasure of poore men. [London: R. Lant,
1547.]
80 numb. *l*.
The Britwell Court copy, with the arms of
William Miller stamped in gold on the front
and back covers.

4100. ———. ———. [London: W. Powell,
1551].
80 numb. *l*.

4101. The TREASURY of hidden secrets, commonly called, The good-huswives closet of
provision, for the health of her houshold ...
Now newly inlarged ... London: J. Bell, 1653.
36 *l*.

A TREATISE concerning the plague and the
pox. *In* Fioravanti, L., An exact collection ... 1653.

4102. A TREATISE of the small-pox and measles. Wherein their cause, nature, kinds, diagnosticks ... By a physician. London: for B. Lintott, 1711.
    4 *l.*, 78 p., 1 *l.*

    TRES ancien duel des chevaliers. *See* The Hermetical Triumph.

4103. TREUTLER, Fridericus Augustus. Observationes pathologico-anatomicae auctarium ad helminthologiam humani corporis continentes. Lipsiae: I.G. Mueller, 1793.
    1 *l.*, iv p., 1 *l.*, 44 p.   illus.

4104. TRIGG, *Dr.* Dr. Trigg's secrets, arcana's and panacea's approved by his long admired experience and practice ... Now ... published as a legacy to his patients. By Eugenius Philanthropos. London: R.D. for D. Page, 1665.
    4 *l.*, 200 [i.e. 168] p.

4105. TRILLER, Daniel William. Dispensatorivm pharmaceviticvm vniversale sive Thesavrvs medicamentorvm tam simplicivm qvam compositorvm locvpletissimvs ex omnibvs dispensatoriis ... Francofvrti ad Moenvm: F. Varrentrapp, 1764.
    2 v. in 1.

4106. TRIOEN, Cornelius. Observationum medico chirurgicarum fasciculus. Lugduni Batavorum: P. van der Eyk et J. van der Kluis, 1743.
    10 *l.*, 143 p.   illus.

    Le TRIOMPHE hermetique. *See* The Hermetical Triumph.

    TRISMEGISTUS. *See* Hermes Trismegistus.

4107. TRISMOSIN, Salomon, *pseud.* Avrei velleris oder Der guldin Schatz- vn̄ Kunstkam̄er tractatus quartus. Philosophischer vn̄ spagyrischer Geschrifften, alter vnnd newer philosophorvm, medicorvm vnd spagyricorvm ... Basel: J. Exertier, 1604.
    3 *l.*, 303 p.
    Lacking pages 3-6.

4108. ———. La toyson d'or, ov La flevr des thresors, en laqvelle est svccinctement & methodiquement traicté de la pierre des philosophes ... Traduict d'Alemand en François, & commenté en forme de paraphrase sur chasque chapitre par L.I. Paris: C. Sevestre, 1613.
    9 *l.*, 219 p.   illus.

4109. TRISSINO, Aloisio. Problematū medicinalium, ex Galeni sententia, libri sex ... Basileae: I. Parcvs, 1547.
    107 unnumb. *l.*
    With Fuchs, I., Methodvs sev ratio ... 1541.

    TRITHEMIUS, Johannes. De lapide philosophorum. *In* Neander, T., Heptas alchymica ... 1621.

    ———. Epistola an Johan von Westeburgk. *In* Schauberdt, J., Κατοπθοσοφία ... 1602.

4110. TROIS traitez de la philosophie natvrelle, non encores imprimez; sçavoir, La tvrbe des philosophes ... Plvs, La parole delaissee de Bernard Trevisan. Et vn petit traicté ... intitulé, Les dovze portes d'alchymie, autres que celles de Ripla. Paris: J. Sara, 1618.
    3 pts. in 1 v.
    With Lull, R., Le vade-mecvm ... 1627.

4111. TROMMSDORFF, Johann Bartholomä. Chemische Receptirkunst oder Taschenbuch für praktische Aertze ... Zweite vermehrte und verbesserte Ausgabe. Erfurt: Beyer und Maring, 1799.
    350 p.

4112. ———. Kurzes Handbuch der Apothekerkunst zum Gebrauch für Lernende. Stettin: J.S. Kaffke, 1790.
    99 p.   charts.

4113. TRONCHIN, Théodore. De colica pectonum. Genevae: fratres Cramer, 1757.
    4 *l.*, 184 p.

    A TRUE light of alchymy. *See* Starkey, George.

    TRUMPH, Johann Georg. Scrutinium vitrioli. *See* Rolfinck, W., *praeses*.

4114. TRYON, Thomas. The good housewife made a doctor ... with some remarks on the practice of physick and chymistry ... The second edition ... London: for H.N. & T.S., 1692.
    6 *l.*, 285 p.

4115. ———. Letters, upon several occasions ... London: for G. Conyers and E. Harris, 1700.
    7 *l.*, 240 p.

4116. ———. A new art of brewing beer, ale, and other sorts of liquors; so as to render them more healthful to the body ... The second edition. To which is added, The art of making maults ... London: for T. Salusbury, 1691.

   3 *l*., 137 p.

4117. ——. A treatise of dreams & visions ... To which is added, A discourse of the causes, natures and cure of phrensie, madness or distraction. By Philotheos Physiologus. [London: 1689?]

   7 *l*., 299 p., 2 *l*.

4118. ——. Pythagoras his mystick philosophy reviv'd; or, The mystery of dreams unfolded ... To which is added, A discourse of the causes, natures, and cure of phrensie, madness or distraction. London: for T. Salusbury, 1691.

   7 *l*., 299 p., 2 *l*.

4119. ——. The way to health, long life and happiness: or, A discourse of temperance ... To which is added, A treatise of most sorts of English herbs ... The second edition, with amendments. London: H.C. for D. Newman, 1691.

   7 *l*., 500, 18 p.

4120. ——. ——. The third edition. To which is added a discourse of the philosophers stone ... London: T. Carruthers, 1697.

   8 *l*., 456, 24 p.

4121. TUBICINIUM convivale hermeticum, sive Epistola III buccinatoria ... Gedani: sumptibus B.L. Tancken, typis D.F. Rhetii, 1682.

   51 p.

4122. TULP, Nicolaas. Observationes medicae. Editio quinta. Cui brevis ipsius authoris vitae narratio est praefixa, ac textuum auctorum illustrationibus. Lugduni Batavorum: J. du Vivie ..., 1716.

   8 *l*., 392 p., 4 *l*.   illus., port.

4123. ——. ——. Editio sexta ... Lugduni Batavorum: G. Wishoff, 1739.

   4 *l*., 51 p., 2 *l*., 392 p., 4 *l*.   illus., port.

4124. ——. ——. Editio sexta, prioribus emendatior & auctior, cum oratione funebri Ludovici Walzogeni, tum dualbus elegiis Petri Francii, in decessum ... auctoris. Lugduni Batavorum: G. Wishoff, 1789.

   4 *l*., 392 p., 4 *l*.   illus., port.

4125. TUMBA SEMIRAMIDIS hermeticè

sigillata, quam si sapiens aperuerit, non Cyrus, ambitiosus, avarus, regum ille thesauros, divitiarum inexhaustos, quod sufficiat, inveniet. H.V.D. [n.p.] 1674.

   37 p.

   With Balduin, C.A., Aurum superius ... 1675.

   ——. *In* Gassman, F., Disceptatio de lapide physico ... 1678.

   TUMBA SEMIRAMIDIS. The tomb of Semiramis. *In* Collectanea chymica ... 1684.

   TURBA PHILOSOPHORUM. La turbe des philosophes. *In* Divers traitez ... 1672.

   ——. ——. *In* Trois traitez ... 1618.

4126. TURNER, Daniel. De morbis cutaneis. A treatise of diseases incident to the skin. In two parts, with a short appendix ... The second edition revised and very much enlarged. London: for R. Bonwicke ..., 1723.

   9 *l*., x, 524 p., 1 *l*.   port.

   TURNER, George. A brief account of the mineral waters of Spa. *In* Seip, J.P., A brief account of the waters of Pyrmont ... 1733.

4127. TURNER, William. A new boke of the natures and properties of all wines that are commonlye vsed here in England, with a confutation of an errour of some men, that holde, that Rhennish and other small white wines ought not be drunken of them that either haue, or are in daunger of the stone, the reuine, and diuers other diseases ... Whervnto is annexed the booke of the natures and vertues of triacles ... London: W. Seres, 1568.

   48 *l*.

4128. ——. A new booke of spirituall physik for dyuerse diseases of the nobilite and gentlemen of Englande ... [Rome: M.A. Constantius] 1555.

   7 *l*., 95 numb. *l*.

4129. ——. A new herball, wherin are conteyned the names of herbes in Greke, Latin, Englysh, Duch Frenche, and in the potecaries and herbaries Latin, with the properties degrees and naturall places of the same ... London: S. Mierdman, 1551.

   94 *l*.   illus.

4130. ——. The seconde part of Guilliam Turners herball ... Here unto is ioyned also

a booke of the bath of Baeth in Englande ...
Collen: A. Birckman, 1562.

   3 *l*., 171 numb. *l*., 2 *l*.; 4 *l*., 17 numb. *l*.
illus.

With his A new herball ... 1551.

4131. ———. The first and seconde partes
of the herbal ... lately ouersene corrected
and enlarged with the thirde parte ... Here
vnto is ioyned also a booke of the bath of
Baeth in England ... Collen: A. Birckman,
1568.

   3 pts. in 1 v.   illus.

     TURQUET DE MAYERNE, Theodore.
See Mayerne, Theodore Turquet de.

4132.   TYMME, Thomas.   A dialogve philosophicall. Wherein natvres secret closet is
opened ... London: T.S. for C. Knight, 1612.

   4 *l*., 72 p.

4133.   TYROCINIUM medicum, oder: Kurtze
Anleitung zu den medicinischen Terminis,
mit einigen höchst-nöthigen Cautelen zum
Nutzen der Anfänger. Aufgesetzet von J.S.B.
Breslau: E.C. Beachvogel, 1723.

   208 p.

4134.   TYTLER, James.   A treatise on the
plague and yellow fever ... Salem: J. Cush-
ing for P.B. Macanulty, 1799.

   2 *l*., 568 p.

U,V

UDDMAN, Isac. Lepra. *See* Linné, C. von, *praeses*. Entry 2479.

UHR–ALTER Ritter-Krieg. *See* The Hermetical Triumph.

ULLHOLM, Jonas. Respiratio diaetetica. *See* Linné, C. von, *praeses*. Entry 2492.

4135. ULSEN, Theodoricus. De pharmacandi comprobata ratione ... libri duo ... nunc primum D. Georgii Pictorij ... ex blattarum conflictu uindicati ... Quibus alius quoque liber accedit Q. Sereni Samonici ... De omnium morborum cura, à capite ad calcem descriptus: & eiusdem D. Pictorii commentarijs breuiter quoque explanatus ... Basileæ: [H. Petri, 1559.]
118 p., 5 *l*.
With Pictorius, G., Sermonum convivalium ... 1559.

4136. ULSTED, Philipp. Coelvm philosophorvm sev De secretis naturæ, liber. [Argentorati: J. Grienynger, 1528.]
lxiiii numb. *l*. illus.

4137. ——. ——. Denuo reuisus & castigatus. [Argentorati: J. Grüninger, 1530?]
lvii numb. *l*. illus.

4138. ——. —— ex variis authoribus ... collectus. Parisiis: V. Gaultherot, 1543.
8 *l*., 95 numb. *l*. illus.

4139. ——. ——. Parisiis: V. Gaultherot, 1544.
8 *l*., 95 numb. *l*. illus.

4140. ——. ——. Nvnc recèns adiecimus Ioan. Anto. Campesji Directorium summæ summarum medicinæ. Lvgdvni: G. Rouilius, 1553.
431 p., 7 *l*. illus.

4141. ——. ——. Nvnc avtem recens apposvimvs Rosarium philosophorum M. Arnaldi de Villanova ... Avgvstae Trebocorvm: C. Dietzel & hæredes C. ab Heyden, 1630.
6 *l*., 347 p., 6 *l*. illus.
With Vigani, G., Medulla chymiæ ... 1683.

4142. ——. Le ciel des philosophes, ov sont contenvs les secretz de nature ... de nouueau traduict de Latin en Francoys ... Paris: V. Gaultherot, 1547.
16 *l*., 96 numb. *l*. illus.

4143. —— Coelum philosophorum. Von heimlichkeit der Natur, das ist, wie man nicht allein auss Wein, sonder auch auss allen Metallen, Früchten, Fleisch ... unnd aus viel anderen dingen mehr sol distilliern Aquam vite ... Auss Raymundo Arnoldo de Villa Noua und Alberto Magno zusammen ins Latein geschrieben, aber jetzundt vonn newem Verteutsch ... Item Marsilii Vicini Regiment des Lebens ... Franckfurdt am Mayn: H. Güfferichen, 1551.
4 *l*., lxiiii numb. *l*. illus.

4144. UNDERWOOD, Michael. Surgical tracts, containing a treatise upon ulcers of the legs ... The second edition ... To which are now added, Observations on the more common disorders of the eye, and on gangrene ... London: J. Mathews, 1788.
xxiv, 151, 77 p., 1 *l*.

4145. The UNIVERSAL family physician, and surgeon ... With a system of family surgery, an universal herbal, and a complete dispensatory. Perth: R. Morison jr. for R. Morison, 1796.
768 p.

4146. UNTZER, Matthias. Anatomia mercurii spagirica, seu De hydrargyri naturã, proprietate, viribus atque usu, libri duo ... Hallæ-Saxonum: impensis M. Oelschlegelii, typis excudit P. Faber, 1620.
19 *l*., 264 p. chart.

With Lacinio, G., Præciosa ac nobilissima artis chymiæ collectanea ... 1554.

4147. ———. Physiologia salis, seu, De
salis natura ... Commentatio philosopho-
medica vario doctrinarum genere referta ...
[Halle] M. Oelschlegelius, 1525.
    10 *l*., 166 p.

4148. ———. Tractatus medico-chymici
septem, ut de sale, sulphure, mercurio,
nephritide seu renum calculo, duplices de
peste, & epilepsia ... multis in locis ab
ipso autore aucti ... Halæ Saxonum: M.
Oelschlegelius, 1634.
    8 *l*., 2511 numb. col., 24 *l*.

      URALTER Ritter-Krieg. *See* The Her-
metical Triumph.

4149. URBIGERUS, Baro, *pseud.* Aphorismi
Urbigerani, or Certain rules clearly demo-
strating the three infallible ways of preparing the grand elixir or circulatum majus
of the philosophers ... London: for H. Faithorne, 1690.
    5 *l*., 86 p.   illus.

4150. ———. Besondere chymische Schrifften, wie nemlich I. Die Medicina universalis
zu præpariren ... II. Viele Manieren wie ein
jedwedes Metall vor und an sich selbst Via
Particulari zu verbessern sey; III. Die Tugenden und Eigenschafften des Antimonij ...
IV. Allerhand rare Secreta für Medicos ...
V. 101 Gewisse Regeln oder kurtze Aphorismi
... herausgegeben von Baron Ubigero. Hamburg: B. Schiller, 1705.
    5 *l*., 109 p., 56 *l*.   illus.

4151. The USE and abuse of physic: or,
The danger and folly of taking even the best
medicines from unskilled hands ... London:
for J. Robinson [n.d.].
    32 p.

4152. The USEFUL family herbal: or, An
account of all those English plants, which
are remarkable for their virtues ... London:
for W. Johnston & W. Owen, 1754.
    liv, 404 p.   illus.

4153. USLAR, Johann Julius von. Chemico-
physiological observations on plants. Translated from the German, with additions, by G.
Schmeisser. Edinburgh: for W. Creech, 1795.
    xii, 171 p.

4154. V., J.R. Güldene Rose, d.i. Einfältige
Beschreibung des alergrössesten von dem

allmächtigsten Schöpffer Himmels und der
Erden Jehovah, in die Natur gelegten, und
dessen Freunden und Ausserwehlten zuge-
theilten Geheimnüsses, als Speigels der
Göttlichen und natürlichen Weisheit, ans
Licht gebracht ... Hamburg: G. König, 1705.
    28 *l*.   illus.
    With Grasshoff, J., Dyas chymica tri-
partita ... 1625.

      ———. ———. *In* Drey curieuse chym-
ische Tractätlein ... 1706.

4155. VACCA, Franciscus. Liber de inflam-
mationis morbosae quae in humano corpore
fit, natura causis, effectibus, et curatione.
Florentiae: C. Albizzini, 1765.
    viii, 93 p., 1 *l*.

4156. VACHER, Gilles. Dissertation sur
la cancer des mammelles ... Paris: Durand,
1743.
    7 *l*., 181 p., 14 *l*.

4157. VALENTINI, Michael Bernhard.
Amphitheatrum zootomicum tabulis æneis
quamplurimis exhibens historiam animalium
anatomicam ... Francofurti ad Moenum:
sumptibus hæredum Zunnerianorum, typis J.
Muller, 1720.
    10 *l*., 231, 231, 114 p., 2 *l*.   illus.

4158. ———. Medicina nov-antiqua, h.e.
Cvrsvs artis medicæ, e fontibus Hippocratis juxta principia naturæ mechanica
mentemque modernorum erutus & perpetuis
commentariis illustratus ... Francofvrti
ad Moenvm: apud J.D. Zunnerum, typ. H.
Mulleri, 1698.
    4 *l*., 372 p.   port.

4159. ———. Museum museorum, oder Vollständige Schau-Bühne aller Materialien und
Specereyen ... Franckfurt am Mayn: J.D. Zunner, 1704.
    3 v. in 2.   illus.

4160. ———. Praxeos medicinæ infallibilis
pars altera chirurgica ... Cum nosocomii
academici continuatione ... Francofurti ad
Moenum: D. à Sande, 1715.
    12 *l*., 952 p., 11 *l*.   illus., charts.

4161. VALERIIS, Valerius de. Avrevm sane
opvs, in quo ea omnia breviter explicantvr,
quæ scientiarum omnium parens, Raymvndvs
Lvllvs, tam in scientiarum arbore, quam arte
generali tradit ... Avgvstæ Vindelicorum: M.
Manger, 1589.
    4 *l*., 179 p.

4162. VALLEMONT, Pierre le Lorrain. La physique occulte, ou Traité de la baguette divinatoire ... Augmenté en cette edition, d'un Traité de la connoissance des causes magnetiques des cures sympathiques ... Paris: J. Boudot, 1696.
8 *l.*, 422, 34 p., 4 *l.* illus.

VALLENSIS, Robertus. De veritate & antiquitate artis chemicae. *In* De arte chemica ... 1602.

4163. VALLERIOLA, Francesco. Enarrationvm medicinalivm libri sex. Item, Responsionvm liber vnvs ... Lvgdvni: S. Gryphivs, 1544.
8 *l.*, 466 p., 25 *l.*

4164. ——. Obseruationum medicinalium lib. vj. Denuo editi, & emendatiores ... Lugdun.: A. Candidus, 1588.
12 *l.*, 523 p., 18 *l.*
Preliminary leaves 9-12 misbound at end.

4165. VALLERIUS, Nicolaus. Tentamina physico-chymica circa aqvas thermales Aqvisgranenses. Qvibus adjecta ex Anglico ab eo versa R.B. Specimina historiæ naturalis & experimentalis aqvarum mineralium. Atqve Joh. Floyeri Inqvisitio in usum & abusum calidorum, frigidorum & temperatorum balneorum. Lugduni Batavorum: C. Boutesteyn, 1699.
8 *l.*, 282 p., 11 *l.*

4166. VALLES, Francisco. In Hippocratis libros de morbis popularibus commētaria ... Editio tertia ... Neapoli: ex typographia L. Scorigii, sumptibus P.A. Reae, 1621.
3 *l.*, 449 p., 14 *l.*

4167. VALLISNIERI, Antonio. Considerazioni, ed esperienze intorno alla generazione de' vermi ordinarj del corpo umano ... Padoa: stamperia del Seminario, appresso G. Manfrè, 1710.
6 *l.*, 160 p.

4168. ——. De corpi marini, che su' Monti si trovano ... Seconda edizione con nuove giunte, annotazioni, e raccolta d'osservazioni spettanti all'istoria medica, e naturale ... Venezia: D. Lovisa, 1728.
8 *l.*, 272 p., 8 *l.*; 6 *l.*, 176 p., 4 *l.* illus.

4169. ——. Esperienze, ed osservazioni intorno all' origine, sviluppi, e costumi di varj insetti, con altre spettanti alla naturale, e medica storia ... Padoa: stamperia de Seminario, appresso G. Manfrè, 1713.

6 *l.*, 232 p. illus.

4170. ——. Opere diverse ... [Venezia & Padova: 1710-1726.]
3 v. illus.

4171. ——. Opere fisico-mediche stampate e manoscritte ... Raccolte da Antonio Suo Figliuolo ... Venezia: S. Coleti, 1733.
3 v. illus.

4172. VALSALVA, Antonio Maria. De aure humana tractatus, in quo integra auris fabrica ... Lugduni Batavorum: G. Langerak & J. Hasebroek, 1735.
7 *l.*, 143 p., 6 *l.* illus.

4173. VALVERDE, Juan de. Anatomia del corpo humano ... con molte figure di rame, et eruditi discorsi in luce mandata. Roma: A. Salamanca & A. Lafreri, 1560.
18 *l.*, 154 numb. *l.* illus.

4174. ——. Anatome corporis humani ... nunc primùm à Michaele Colúbo latine reddita ... Venetiis: Ivnta, 1589.
18 *l.*, 340 p. illus., port.

4175. VANDELLI, Domenico. Dissertationes tres. De Aponi thermis: de nonnullis insectis terrestribus, & zoophytis marinis, & de vermium terræ reproductione, atque tænia canis. Patavii: J.B. Conzatti, 1758.
vi p., 1 *l.*, 167 p., 6 *l.* illus.

4176. ——. Epistola de holothurio, et testudine coriacea ad celeberrimum Carolum Linæeum ... Patavii: Conzatti, 1761.
12 p. illus.
With his Tractatus de thermis agri Patavini ... 1761.

4177. ——. Epistola de sensibilitate pericranii, periostii, medullæ, duræ meningis, cornæ, & tendinum. [n.p.] 1756.
lxxii p., 2 *l.* illus.
With his Dissertationes tres ... 1758.

4178. ——. Epistola secunda, et tertia de sensitivitate Halleriana. Patavii: J.B. Conzatti, 1758.
lxxx p.
With his Dissertationes tres ... 1758.

4179. ——. Tractatus de thermis agri Patavini. Accessit Bibliotheca hydrographica, & Apologia contra Cel. Hallerum. Patavii: Conzatti, 1761.
4 *l.*, 53, 234 p., 1 *l.*; 44 p. illus.

4180. VANDERBEEG, I.C. von. Manvdvctio hermetico-philosophica, oder Richtige Handleitung zu der wahren philosophischen Medicin ... Nebst einem Anhange: Die flecketen Diamanten rein, und aus kleinen grössere Jubelen und Perlen zu machen ... Andere Auflage. Vermehrt mit dem Tractätlein: Sol sine veste. Hof: G.J. Püttner [n.d.].
4 *l*., 312 p., 3 *l*., 24 p.   illus.

4181. VANINI, Lucilio, *afterwards* Giulio Cesare. De admirandis naturæ reginæ deæque mortalium arcanis. Libri qvatvor. Lvtetiæ: A. Perier, 1616.
8 *l*., 495 p.

4182. VANNOTIUS, Franciscus Maria. De aqva minerali quæ in Piceno propè Asculum scaturit ... Romæ: Mascardus, 1642.
14 *l*., 120 p.

VASTEL, Guillelmus. Quaestio medico-chymia. *See* Ducquerie, J.F. de la *praeses*.

4183. VAUGHAN, Thomas. Anima magica abscondita; or A discourse of the universall spirit of nature ... By Eugenius Philalethes ... London: T.W. for H.B., 1650.
7 *l*., 56 p.
With his Magia Adamica ... 1650.

4184. ——. Anima magica abscondita; oder Eine Rede von dem allgemeinen Geiste der Natur ... Eugenius Philalethes ... Aus dem Englischen ins Deutsche übersetzet. [n.p.] 1704.
83 p.
With his Magia Adamica ... 1704.

4185. ——. Anthroposophia theomagica; or A discourse of the nature of man and his state after death ... By Eugenius Philalethes ... London: T.W. for H. Blunden, 1650.
8 *l*., 70 p.   illus.
With his Magia Adamica ... 1650.

4186. ——. Antroposophia theomagica, das ist, Eine Rede von der Natur des Menschen ... von Eugenius Philaletha ... *A*us dem Englischen ins Teutsche übersetzt. [n.p.] 1704.
75 p.
With his Magia Adamica ... 1704.

4187. ——. Evphrates, or The waters of the east ... By Eugenius Philalethes ... London: for H. Moseley, 1655.
7 *l*., 124 p.   illus.

4188. ——. A hermeticall banqvet drest by a spagiricall cook: for the better preservation of the microcosme. London: for A. Crooke, 1652.
18 *l*., 161 p.

4189. ——. Lumen de lumine: or A new magicall light ... By Eugenius Philalethes ... London: for H. Blunden, 1651.
8 *l*., 101 p.
With his Magia Adamica ... 1650.

——. Aula lucis, oder: Das Hauss dess Liechts. *In* Belin, J.A., Wunderliche Begebenheiten.... 1690.

4190. ——. Magia Adamica: or The antiquitie of magic, and the descent thereof from Adam downwards, proved ... By Eugenius Philalethes ... London: T.W. for H.B., 1650.
17 *l*., 140 p.

4191. ——. Magia Adamica oder Das Alterthum der Magie als dererselben von Adam an herabwärts geleitete Erweisung ... Eugenius Philaletha. Anitzo aus dem Englischen ins Teutsche übersetzet. Amsterdam: 1704.
160 p.

4192. ——. The man-mouse taken in a trap, and tortur'd to death for gnawing the margins of Eugenius Philalethes ... London: [for H. Blunden] 1650.
2 *l*., 116 p.
With his Magia Adamica ... 1650.

4193. ——. The second wash; or the Moore scour'd once more, being a charitable cure for the distractions of Alazonomastix. By Eugenius Philalethes ... London: T.W., 1651.
8 *l*., 188 p., 1 *l*.
Lacking the title page.
With his Magia Adamica ... 1650.

4194. VECOLI, Bernardino. Della preparatione della pietra lazzoli per la confettione alchermes ... Lvcca: O. Guidoboni, 1617.
2 *l*., 36 p.

4195. VÈGE, Pierre de. Tractatus duo. I. Pestis præcauendæ & curandæ methodus certissima. II. Pax dogmaticorum cum spagyricis. Genevæ: J. de Tournes, 1628.
72 p.
With Sendivogius, M., Novvm lvmen chymicvm ... 1628.

4196. VEGNI, Leonardo de. Descrizione del Casale, e bagni di S. Filippo in Toscana

... [Bologna: 1761.]
27 p. illus.

VELSCH, Georg Hieronymus. *See* Welsch, Georg Hieronymus.

VENEROSIUS, Hieronymus. Consvltatio responsiva. *In* Puteo, Z., Clavis medica ... 1612.

4197. VENEL, Gabriel François. Q.F.F.F.Q.S. Quæstiones chemicæ duodecim ... Monspelii: A.-F. Rochard, 1759.
4 *l.*, 35 p. illus.

4198. VENNER, Tobias. Via recta ad vitam longam ... Whereunto is annexed a necessary and compendious treatise of the famous baths of Bathe ... London: F. Kyngston for R. Moore, 1628.
6 *l.*, 226 p.; 2 *l.*, 24 p.

4199. ——. ——. Much more enlarged than the former impressions ... With a censure of the medicinall faculties of the water of St. Vincents-Rocks neer the city of Bristoll. As also an accurate treatise concerning tobacco ... London: J. Flesher for H. Hood, 1650.
6 *l.*, 417 p.

VENTENAT, Etienne Pierre, *jt. auth.* Herbier de la France. *See* Bulliard, Pierre.

4200. VENTURA, Lorenzo. De ratione conficiendi lapidis philosophici, liber vnus ... Huic accesserunt eiusdem Argumenti Ioan-Garlandij Angli liber vnus. Et ex Speculo magno Vincentij libri duo. Basileæ: P. Perna, 1571.
8 *l.*, 203 p., 9 *l.*; 121 p., 3 *l.*; 173 p.

4201. VENTURA PASTOR, José. Preceptos generales sobre las operaciones de los partos ... Madrid: J. Herrera, 1789-1790.
2 v. illus., port.

4202. VENTURINI, Alessandro. Le medicine che da tutti gl'animali si può cauare à beneficio dell'huomo ... Hora accresciuto d'importanti secreti da Francesco Pignocatti ... Settima impressione. Venetia: Curti, 1680.
12 *l.*, 154 p.

4203. VERHEYEN, Philip. Animadversiones in anatomiam Blancardianam, et obiter in quasdam alias. Accessit eju'sdem Epistola ad ... Redericum Ruyschium. [n.p.: n.d.]
24 p.
With his Corporis humani anatomia ... 1693.

4204. ——. Corporis humani anatomia, in qua omnia tam veterum, quam recentiorum anatomicorum inventa, methodo novâ & intellectu facillima describuntur, ac tabulis aenis repraesentantur. Lovanii: A. Denique, 1693.
7 *l.*, 300 p., 7 *l.* illus., port.

4205. ——. ——. Editio secunda ... Bruxellis: F. t'Serstevens, 1710.
2 v. illus.

4206. ——. ——. Editio nova ab avtore novis observationibvs ... Lipsiae: T. Fritsch, 1718.
14 *l.*, 680 p., 6 *l.* illus., port.

4207. VERSUCH diejenigen welche den Stein der Weisheit zu erfinden trachten durch aussprüche hermetischer Schriftsteller von Irrwegen abzuleiten. Franckfurt und Leipzig: 1759.
2 pts. in 1 v.

4208. VESALIUS, Andreas. De humani corporis fabrica libri septem. Basileæ [I. Oporinus, 1543].
6 *l.*, 659 [i.e. 663] p., 18 *l.* illus., port., folio.

4209. ——. ——. Basileæ: I. Oporinus [1555].
6 *l.*, 824 p., 24 *l.* illus., port., folio.

4210. ——. ——. Venetiis: F. Franciscius & I. Criegher, 1568.
6 *l.*, 510 p., 23 *l.*

4211. ——. Anatomia: addita nunc postremo etiam Antiquorum anatome. Venetiis: I. Antonius & I. de Franciscis [1604].
4 *l.*, 510 p., 33 *l.* illus.

4212. ——. De hvmani corporis fabrica, epitome: cum annotationibus Nicolai Fontani. Amstelodami: I. Ianssonius, 1642.
7 *l.*, 112 p. illus.

4213. ——. Anatomia Deudsch, ein kurzer Auszug der Beschreibung aller Glider menschlichs Leybs ... Nürnberg: J.P. Fabricius, 1551.
2 *l.*, 78 numb. *l.* illus.

4214. ——. Heinrich Palmaz Leveling Anatomische Erklärung der original-Figuren von Andreas Vesal, samt einer Anwendung der Winslowischen Zergliederungslehre in sieben Büchern. Ingolstadt: A. Attenhouer, 1783.
9 *l.*, 328 p., 5 *l.* illus., port., folio.

4215. ——. Opera omnia anatomica &
chirurgica cura Hermanni Boerhaave & Bernhardi Siegfried Albini. Lugduni Batavorum:
J. du Vivie, et J. & H. Verbeek, 1725.
    2 v.   illus., folio.

    VESLING, Johann.   De pullitie Aegyp-
tiorum. *In* Bartholin, T., De insolitis partus
humani ... 1740.

4216. ——. Syntagma anatomicum, commentario atque appendice ex veterum, recentiorum, propriisque, observationibus,
illustratum & auctum a Gerardo Leon. Blasio.
Editio secunda ... Amstelodami: J. Jans-
sonios à Waesberge & E. Weyerstraet, 1666.
    13 *l.*, 558 p., 8 *l.*   illus., port.

4217. VICARY, Thomas.   The English mans
treasure: with the true anatomie of mans bodie
... Whereunto are annexed many secrets ap-
pertaining to chirurgerie ... also the rare
treasure of the English bathes, written by
William Turner ... Gathered and set forth ...
by William Bremer ... London: T. Creede, 1599.
    5 *l.*, 110 p.

4218. ——. ——. And now sixtly augmented and enlarged ... By G.E. ... London:
T. Creede, 1613.
    4 *l.*, 224 p., 4 *l.*

4219. ——. ——. And now ninthly much
augmented, corrected and enlarged ... by W.
B. ... London: B. Alsop & T. Fawcet, 1641.
    6 *l.*, 292 p., 7 *l.*   illus.

4220. VIER chymische Tractätlein: I. Lucens
lux in tenebris ... II. De vitriolo & ejus oleo
secretissim ... III. De animali rationali ...
IV. Aurum vitæ ... Von alten und wahren
philosophis beschrieben ... Budissin: druckts
A. Richter, Verlegts B. Kretzschmar, 1677.
    66 p.

4221. VIERO, Francisco.   Descrizione d'un
apparecchio di macchine per cavare e maneg-
giare le arie generalmente dette fisse.
Bologna: Instituto delle Scienze, 1788.
    48 p.   illus.

4222. VIEUSSENS, Raymond.   Nevrographia
universalis. Hoc est, Omnium corporis humani nervorum, simul & cerebri, medullaeque
spinalis descriptio anatomica ... Editio
novissima. Lugduni: J. Certe, 1716.
    8 *l.*, 252 p., 1 *l.*   illus.

4223. ——. Novum vasorum corporis humani systema. Amstelodami: P. Marret, 1705.
    24 *l.*, 260 p.   illus.

4224. VIGANI, Giovanni Francesco.   Medulla
chymiæ, variis experimentis aucta, multisque
... Londini: H. Faithorne & J. Kersey, 1683.
    8 *l.*, 69 p.   illus.

4225. ——. ——. Notis experientia nixis
illustrata observationibusque practicis aucta
a Davide Stam. Lugduni Batavorum: F. Lopez,
1693.
    12 *l.*, 96 p., 4 *l.*   illus.

    VIGELIUS, Ericus.   Diaeta acidularis.
See Linné, C. von, *praeses.* Entry 2427.

4226. VIGENERE, Blaise de.   Traicté dv fev
et dv sel, excellent et rare ... Paris: C. Cra-
moisy, 1622.
    2 *l.*, 267 p.

4227. ——. A discovrse of fire and salt,
discovering many secret mysteries ... London: R. Cotes for A. Crooke, 1649.
    2 *l.*, 162 p.

4228. VIGILANTIUS DE MONTE CUBITI,
pseud., ed.   Dreyfaches Hermetisches Klee-
blat, in welchem begriffen dreyer vornhemen
Philosophorum herrliche Tractätlein ... Nürnberg: M. & J.F. Endter, 1667.
    12 *l.*, 448 p., 16 *l.*   illus.

4229. VIGILLIS VON CREUTZENFELD, Stephanus Hieronymus de.   Bibliotheca chirurgica in qua res omnes ad chirurgiam pertinentes ordine alphabetico, ipsi vero scriptores, quotquot ad annum usque MDCCLXXIX
innotuerunt, ad singulas materias ordine
chronologico exhibentur ... Vindobonæ: J.T.
Nobilis de Trattner, 1781.
    2 v.   port.

4230. VIGO, Giovanni.   The most excellent
workes of chirurgerye ... translated into English. Whereunto is added an exposition of
straunge termes and unknowen symples, belong-
yng to the arte. [London] E. Whytchurch, 1543.
    6 *l.*, 270 numb. *l.*, 15 *l.*

4231. ——. ——. [London] E. Whytchurch,
1550.
    6 *l.*, 270 numb. *l.*, 15 *l.*

4232. ——. ——. [London: T. East & H.
Middleton, 1571?]
    6 *l.*, 270 numb. *l.*, 15 *l.*
    Lacking the title-page and dedicatory
epistle.

4233. VILLAIN, Etienne François.   Histoire
critique de Nicolas Flamel et de Pernelle
sa femme ... On y a joint le testament de

Pernelle & plusieurs autres pieces intéres-
santes. Paris: G. Desprez, 1761.
1 *l*., xii, 403 p., 2 *l*. illus., port.

4234. VILLANI, Giovanni. Chroniche de
la inclyta cita di Napoli, e trattato utilissimo
de li bagni Napolitani e de Puzzolo e Ischia,
nouamente ristampate. [Napoli: M. Euange-
lista, 1526.]
lxxxv numb. *l*., 6 *l*.
The title page is partially mutilated.

4235. VINCENTI, Domenico. Raccolta di
opuscoli inediti riguardanti l'acque minerali
dello stato della serenissma Repubblica di
Venezia ... Venezia: P. Savioni, 1760.
8 *l*., 84 p.

VINCENTIUS BELLOVACENSIS. De
alchimia et rebus metallicis ex Speculo
Vincentii. *In* Ventura, L., De ratione conficiendi lapidis philosophici ... 1571.

4236. VIOTTO, Bartolommeo. De balneorvm
natvralivm viribvs libri qvatvor ... Lugduni:
M. Bonhomme, 1552.
6 *l*., 168 p., 1 *l*.
With Polybus, Opuscule ... 1544.

4237. VIRDUNG, Johann. Nova medicinae
methodvs, nunc primū & condita & aedita,
ex mathematica ratione morbos curandi ...
Item, Summarium atque laudem huius libelli
per Iohannem Sinapium proxima reperties
pagella ... Ettelingae: [V. Kobian] 1532.
4 *l*., 98 numb. *l*., 3 *l*. illus.

4238. VITALIS DE FURNO. Pro conservanda
sanitate, tvendaqve prospera valetvdine ...
Mogvntiae: [I. Schoeffer] 1531.
10 *l*., 271 p.

4239. VITET, Louis. Pharmacopée de Lyon,
ou Exposition méthodique des médicaments
simples et composés ... Lyon: F. Perisse,
1778.
4 *l*., lx, 552, 144 p.

4240. VITRIARIO, Giovanni. Centvria seconda de' secreti materiali, medicinali, e
cvriosi ... Viterbo: appresso i discepoli, 1618.
8 *l*.

4241. VOGEL, Ewald. De lapidis physici
conditionibvs liber. Quo duorum abditis-
simorum auctorum Gebri & Raimvndi Lvllii
methodica continetur explicatio ... Coloniae
Agrippinae: H. Falckenburg, 1595.
18 *l*., 252 p.

4242. VOGEL, Heinrich. Offenbarung der
Geheymussen der Alchimy ... Strassburg: A.
Bertram, 1605.
4 *l*., 192 p.

4243. VOGEL, Rudolph August. Historia
materiae medicae ad novissima tempora
prodvcta ... Editio nova correctior ac emendatior. Francofvrti: T. Goebhard, 1764.
4 *l*., 404 p., 18 *l*.

4244. ——. Institvtiones chemiae ad lectiones academicas accommodatae. Editio
altera polita et locvpletata. Lugduni Batav.:
E. Lvzac, 1757.
6 *l*., 396 p., 4 *l*.

4245. VOGLER, Johann Philipp. Pharmaca
selecta, observationibus clinicis comprobata; tertio edita et additamentis aucta.
Wetzlariæ: P.J. Winkler, 1792.
159 p., 2 *l*.

4246. VOGTER, Bartholomeus. Wie man
alle gebresten vnd kranckheiten des menschlichen leibs ... ärtzneyen vnd vertreyben
soll ... [Augspurg: H. Steyner] 1533.
8 *l*., lxxiii numb. *l*. illus.

4247. ——. ——. [Augspurg: H. Stayner]
1541.
8 *l*., lxxiii numb. *l*. illus.

4248. VOLCKAMER, Johann Georg. Opobal-
sami orientalis in theriaces confectionem
Romæ revocati examen ... Norimbergæ: W.
Ender, 1644.
4 *l*., 224 p., 4 *l*.

4249. VOLTA, Alessandro Giuseppe Antonio
Anastasio. Lettere ... sull' aria infiammabile
nativa delle paludi. Milano: G. Marelli, 1777.
147 p. illus.

4250. VORBERG, Lucas. Zwey opuscula
chymica. I. Deren das erste elucidarius purus
philosophicus de universali arcano ... II. Das
ander ... Balsami et florvm svlphuris ... [Brieg:
J. Eyring und J. Perferts Erben, 1627.]
36 *l*.

VRANCKHEIM, Marcellus. Ἐπίκρισις
στοχαστικὴ. *In* Burggrav, J.E., Achilles
Πανοπλος redivivus ... 1612.

4251. VREESWYK, Goossen van. De goude
leeuw, of Den asijn der wysen ... Amsterdam:
P. Arentsz, 1671.
8 *l*., 246 p., 6 *l*. illus.

W

4252. W***, le chevalier de. Encyclo-pédie pratique, ou Établissement de grand nombre de manufactures. Liege: J.F. Bas-sompierre, 1772.
  2 v. illus.

W., E. Spadacrene Dunelmensis. See Wilson, Edward.

W., G. A rich storehouse. See T., A.

W., T. The optick glasse of humors. See Walkington, Thomas.

WADSTRÖM, Johan Adolf. Meta-morphosin humanam. See Linné, C. von, praeses. Entry 2463.

4253. WAGNITZ, Melchior Ernst. Medi-tatio medica cursoria de mercurio dulci pulverato ... Qvedlinburgi: impensis T.P. Calvisii, literis Sievertinis, 1703.
  46 p.

WÄHLIN, Anders Magnus. De pulsu intermittente. See Linné, C. von, praeses. Entry 2455.

——. Dissertatio medica odores medicamentorum exhibens. See Linné, C. von, praeses. Entry 2462.

4254. WAHRSAGER, Ernst. Höchst nöthige Anmerkungen über des Herrn Joh. Frider. Rübeli ... Observationes vom Friesel und dessen Cur. Freyburg: 1742.
  4 l., 63 p.

4255. WAITZ, Jacob. Analogica veritas cum progressu ad Philalethæ & aliorum adeptorum intimiorem philosophiam, oder Warheit und Grund der besondern und ge-heimen Philalethanischen Philosophiæ ... [n.p.: ca. 1708.]
  39 p.

4256. WALKER, Joshua. An essay on the waters of Harrogate and Thorp-Arch in York-shire ... London: for J. Johnson ..., 1784.
  viii, 208 p.

4257. WALKINGTON, Thomas. The optick glasse of hvmors, or, The touchstone of a golden temperature, or, The philosophers stone to make a golden temper ... Oxford: W.T. for M.S. [1631?].
  13 l., 168 p. illus.

4258. WALL, John. Experiments, and ob-servations on the Malvern waters. The sec-ond edition, with an appendix ... London and Worcester: W. Sandby ... [ca. 1757].
  1 l., 77 p.

4259. WALL, Martin. Dissertations on select subjects in chemistry and medicine ... Oxford: for D. Prince and J. Cooke ..., 1783.
  xvii, 166 p., 1 l. illus.

4260. ——. A syllabus of a course of lectures in chemistry, read at the Museum, Oxford. Oxford: for D. Prince and J. Cooke, 1782.
  2 l., 63 p.
  With his Dissertations on select sub-jects ... 1783.

4261. WALLERIUS, Johan Gottskalk. De l'origine du monde, et de la terre en parti-culier ... Traduit par M.J.B.D. Varsovie: J.F. Bastien, 1780.
  c, 360 p. illus.

4262. ——. Hydrologia, eller Watturiket, indelt och beskrisvit, jamte anledning til vattuprofvers anställande. Stockholm: L. Salvius, 1748.
  9 l., 134 p. illus.

4263. ——. Der physischen Chemie ... aus dem schwedischen ins lateinische über-

setzt und vermehrt herausgegeben von Joh.
Gottschalk Wallerius ... und nunmehr in
deutsche übersetzt und mit ... Anmerkungen
versehen von D. Christ. Andr. Mangold.
Gotha: C. Mevius, 1761-1776.
    3 v.
    Volumes 2 and 3 were edited and trans-
lated by Christian Ehrenfried Weigel, and
have the imprint Leipzig, S.L. Crusius, 1776.

4264. WALLICH, Dorothea Juliana. Das
mineralische Gluten, doppelter Schlangen-
Stab, Mercurius Philosophorum, langer und
kurtzer Weg zur Universal-Tinctur ... Leipzig: J. Heinichens Wittwe, 1705.
    118 p.

4265. ――. ――. Franckfurt: G.C. Wint-
zer, 1722.
    88, 150, 224 p.
    This edition contains two other tracts by
the same author, each with a separate title
page: *Der philosophische Perl-Baum* and
*Schlüssel zu dem Cabinet der geheimen
Schatz-Kammer der Natur.*

4266. WALLIS, Edward. Tentamen sophisti-
con, a chemical essay ... London: Nicoll
and Robson [1767].
    viii, 158 p., 1 ℓ.

4267. WALTER, Johann Gottlieb. Observationes anatomicae ... Berolini: G.A. Lange,
1775.
    4 ℓ., lxxxviii, 13 ℓ. illus., folio.

4268. ――. Anatomische Beobachtungen.
Aus dem Lateinischen übersetz von Johann
Gottlob Daniel Michaelis. Berlin: G.A. Lange,
1782.
    viii, 111 p. illus.

4269. ――. Tabulae nervorum thoracis et
abdominis. Berolini: G.J. Decker, 1783.
    3 ℓ., 17 p., 8 ℓ. illus., folio.

    WARDENBURG, Johann Heinrich. De
morbis. *See* Alberti, M., *praeses.*

4270. WASSERBERG, Franz August Xaver von.
Chemische Abhandlung vom Schwefel. Wien:
J.P. Krauss, 1788.
    375 p.

4271. ――. Institutiones chemiae, in usum
eorum qui scientiae huic operam dant ...
Vindobonae: R. Graeffer, 1778-1779.
    2 v. in 3.

4272. WATSON, Richard. Chemical essays.

Cambridge: J. Archdeacon for T. Merrill ...,
1781-1787.
    5 v.
    Lacking volume 5.
    Volume 3 is from the second edition.

4273. ――. ――. To which is added, Sir
Torbern Bergman's admired essay on the
usefulness of chemistry. Third edition. Dublin: for R. Moncrieffe, 1783.
    viii, 480 p. chart.

4274. ――. ――. Fourth edition. London:
for T. Evans, 1787.
    5 v.
    Volume 3 is from the third edition, volume
4 from the second edition.

4275. ――. An essay on the subjects of
chemistry, and their general division. Cambridge: J. Archdeacon, 1771.
    1 ℓ., 43 p.

4276. ――. Institutionum chemicarum in
prælectionibus academicis explicatarum,
pars metallurgica. Cantabrigiæ: J. Archdeacon, 1769.
    4 ℓ., 58 p.

4277. WATT, James. Description of a pneu-
matic apparatus, with directions for procur-
ing the factitious airs ... The second edition.
Birmingham: T. Pearson, 1795.
    viii, 49 p. illus.

    ――. Description of an air apparatus.
In Beddoes, T., Considerations on factitious
airs ... 1794.

4278. WEBER, Jakob Andreas. Anmerkungen
über die Sammlungen von den Nachrichten
und Beobachtungen über die Zeugung des
Salpeters ... Nebst einem Sendschreiben über
dessen theoretische und praktische Abhandlung von dem Salpeterzeugen von Z. Winzler.
Tübingen: J.F. Heerbrandt, 1780.
    120 p.

4279. ――. Beschreibung einiger zum Ge-
brauch der dephlogistisirten Luft bey dem
Blaserohr und Schmelzfeuer eingerichteten
Maschinen ... Tübingen: J.F. Heerbrandt, 1785.
    45 p., 1 ℓ. illus.

4280. ――. Physikalische-chemische
Untersuchung der thierischen Feuchtigkeiten.
Tübingen: J.F. Heerbrandt, 1780.
    140 p.

4281. ――. Vollständige theoretische und

praktische Abhandlung von dem Salpeter,
und der Zeugung desselben, nebst einer
Abhandlung von der Gährung ... Tübingen:
J.F. Heerbrandt, 1779.
  362 p.

4282. WEBER, Joseph. Ueber das Feuer.
Ein Beitrag zu einem Unterrichtsbuche aus
der Naturlehre ... Landshut & Lauingen: in
Verlag A. Weber, gedruckt bei J. Speck, 1788.
  4 *l.*, 216 p., 1 *l.* illus.

4283. ――――. Vorlesungen aus der Naturlehre ... Landshut: A. Weber, 1793-1796.
  9 v. illus.
  Lacking volumes 5 and 6.

4284. WEBSTER, John. Metallographia: or,
An history of metals ... Gathered forth of
the most approved authors that have written
in Greek, Latine, or High-Dutch ... London:
A.C. for W. Kettilby, 1671.
  8 *l.*, 388 p., 1 *l.*

4285. WEBSTER, Noah. A brief history of
epidemic and pestilential diseases; with the
principal phenomena of the physical world,
which precede and accompany them ... Hart-
ford: Hudson & Goodwin, 1799.
  2 v.

4286. WECKER, Johann Jacob. Antidotarivm
speciale ... in qvo compositorvm medicamentorum formulæ ... proponuntur. Basileae: E.
Episcopivs & Nicolai Fr. hæredes, 1581.
  3 *l.*, pp. 315-898, 29 *l.*
  Lacking all before p. 315.

4287. ――――. Antidotarivm geminvm, generale et speciale ... ex opt. authorum ...
scriptis fideliter congestum, & tandem
methodicè, supra priores editiones, vberrimè
auctum, coniunctim editum, & exornatum ...
Basileæ: C. Waldkirch, sumptibus Episco-
pianorvm, 1595.
  8 *l.*, 222 numb. col., 8 *l.*, 1186 numb.
col., 15 *l.* illus.

4288. ――――. Antidotarivm generale et
speciale ... Nunc verò svpra priores editiones omnes multis nouis & optimis formvlis,
maximè verò extractis auctum ... Basileæ:
C. Waldkirch, sumptibus Episcopoianorvm,
1601.
  8 *l.*, 222 numb. col., 8 *l.*, 1210 numb.
col., 14 *l.* illus.

4289. ――――. ――――. Basileæ: I.I. Genathius,
1617.
  8 *l.*, 1210 numb. col., 14 *l.*; 6 *l.*, 222

numb. col., 2 *l.* illus.

4290. ――――. Le grand dispensaire, ov
Thresor general et particvlier des preser-
vaties ... descovvert aux François et enrichi ... par Ian Dv Val. Geneve: E. Gamonet,
1690.
  8 *l.*, 286 numb. col., 8 *l.*, 1336 numb.
col. illus.

4291. ――――. A compendiovs chyrvrgerie:
gathered, & translated ... out of Wecker ...
Published ... by Ihon Banester ... London:
J. Windet for J. Harrison the elder, 1585.
  12 *l.*, 530 p., 5 *l.*

4292. ――――. De secretis libri XVII. Ex
varijs authoribus collecti, methodiceque
digesti. [Basileæ: 1582.]
  24 *l.*, 960 p.
  Title page mutilated.

4293. ――――. ――――. Basileæ: typis C. Wald-
kirchii, sumptibus L. König, 1613.
  8 *l.*, 667 p., 13 *l.* illus.

4294. ――――. ―――― atque tertia hâc editione
non solum ab innumeris mendis obscuritateque
purgati, sed & Theodori Zvingeri ... Basileæ:
impensis J. L. König, typis J.C. à Mechel,
1701.
  6 *l.*, 764 p., 16 *l.* illus.

4295. ――――. Eighteen books of the secrets
of art and nature ... Now much augmented
and inlarged by Dr. R. Read ... London: for
S. Miller, 1660.
  6 *l.*, 346 p., 5 *l.* illus., port.

4296. ――――. Les secrets et merveilles de
natvre. Recueillies de diuers autheurs, &
diuisez en xvii liures. Reueu, corrigé, &
augmenté ... Roven: I. Osmont, 1614.
  8 *l.*, 858 p., 23 *l.* illus.

4297. ――――. Ein nutzliches Büchlein von
mancherley künstlichen wasseren, ölen, vnd
weinen, jetzt neuwlich in Teutsch gebracht.
Basel: P. Perna, 1570.
  8 *l.*, 127 p.

  WEDEL, Georg Wolfgang. Compositionis artificiosae. *In* König, E., Regnum
vegetabile ... 1688-1696.

4298. ――――. Experimentum chimicum novum
de sale volatili plantarum, quo latius expon-
untur, specimine ipso exhibita. Jenæ: sumptibus J. Fritschii, literis S. Krebsii, 1675.
  14 *l.*, 96 p. illus.

With his Specimen experimenti chimici nova ... 1672.

4299. ——. Introdvctio in alchimiam. Ienæ: sumptibus I. Bielkii, litteris C. Krebsii, 1706.
2 *l*., 60 p.

4300. ——. An introduction to the whole practice of physick, shewing the natures and faculties of medicines, the reason and manner of their operations, and to what particular parts they are appropriated ... Being chiefly a translation of the renowned Wedelius ... London: for W. Thackery & T. Yeate, 1685.
3 *l*., 322 p., 3 *l*.

4301. ——. Pharmacia acroamatica. Jenæ: sumptibus J. Bielckii, literis viduæ S. Krebsii, 1686.
8 *l*., 520 p., 7 *l*.

4302. ——. Pharmacia in artis formam redacta, experimentis ... illustrata. Jenæ: 16——.
245 p., 4 *l*.
Lacking the title page.

4303. ——. Propempticon inaugurale de tabvla hermetis smaragdina. Ienæ: Krebs [1704].
2 pts. in 1 v.

4304. ——. Specimen experimenti chimici novi, de sale volatili plantarum, quo demonstratur, posse ex plantis modo peculiari parari sal volatile verum & genuinum. Francofurti: hæred. Shurerianorum & J. Fritzsch, 1672.
12 *l*., 96 p.

4305. ——. Tabulæ synopticæ de compositione medicamentorum extemporanea, ad praxim clinicam & usum hodiernum accommodatæ. Jenæ: sumptibus J. Meyeri, typis S. Krebsii, 1677.
24 *l*.
With Queitsch, A.P., Ιατρομαθηματογραφία ... 1737.

4306. ——, *praeses.* Dissertatio inavgvralis medica de serpentaria virginiana ... submittit Christophrovs Lvdovicvs Göckelivs ... Ienæ: C. Krebs, 1710.
40 p.

4307. ——, *praeses.* Dissertatio inavgvralis medica de tinctvra bezoardica essentificata ... svbmissa Iohanne Davide Ehrhardo

... Jenæ: C. Krebs, 1698.
30 p.

WEDENBERG, Adolph Frederik. De varietate ciborum. *See* Linné, C. von, *praeses.* Entry 2471.

4308. WEGENER, Georg Wilhelm. Adeptus ineptus, oder Entdeckung der falsch berühmten Kunst Alchimie genannt ... Von Tharsandern. Berlin: A. Haude, 1744.
8 *l*., 495 p., 8 *l*.

4309. WEIDENFELD, Johann Seger von. De secretis adeptorum, sive De usu spiritus vini Lulliani libri IV ... Londini: H. Hills, et M. Pardoe, 1684.
20 *l*., 338 p., 1 *l*.

4310. ——. ——. Lipsiae: J.P. Kraus, 1768.
24 *l*., 548 p., 6 *l*.

4311. ——. Four books ... concerning the secrets of the adepts; or, Of the use of Lully's spirit of wine ... London: W. Bonny for T. Howkins, 1685.
26 *l*., 380 p.

4312. WEIDMANN, Johann Peter. De necrosi ossivm. Francofvrti ad Moenvm: Andrea, 1793.
3 *l*., 60 p., 15 *l*. illus., folio.

4313. WEIKARD, Melchior Adam. Entwurf einer einfachern Arzeneykunst oder Erläuterund bestatigung der Brownischen Arzeneylehre. Frankfurt am Main: Andrea, 1795.
xvi, 335 p.

4314. ——. Magazin der verbesserten theoretischen und praktischen Arzeneikunst ... Heilbronn am Neckar: J.D. Class, 1796.
4 pts. in 1 v.

4315. ——. Der philosophische Arzt. Neue durchaus vermehrte und verbesserte Auflage. Frankfurt am Main: Andrea, 1798-1799.
3 v.
Lacking volume 3.

4316. ——. Medizinisches-pracktisches Handbuch auf Brownische Grundsätze und Erfahrung gegründet. Heilbronn am Nectar: J.D. Class, 1796.
xii, 388 p. port.

4317. WEINHART, Ferdinand Karl. Medicvs officiosvs, praxi rationali methodico-aphoristica, cum selectis remediorum formulis

... Norimbergæ: J.F. Rüdigervs, 1715.
   4 *l*., 477 p., 12 *l*. illus.

4318. Der WEISHEIT Morgenröthe, das ist:
Von den dreyen Principiis oder Ursprung und
Anfang aller Dinge im Geheimniss der Weisheit ... Frankfurt: J.F. Fleischer, 1762.
   128 p.

4319. WEISMANN, Immanuel. Fata & imposturæ variolosorum. Oder: Muthmassliche
Gedancken und Ursachen, wie? und warum?
manche Leuthe die sogenannte Urschlechten
oder Kinds-Blattern als ein Göttliches Straff-
Gerichte nicht erkennen ... Ulm: D. Bartho-
lomæ, 1713.
   48 p.
   With S., G.A.P., Acerra medico-chymica
... 1713.

4320. WEITBRETT, Johann Joachim. Redivivus Fr. Basilius Valentinus ... Das ist:
Eine gründliche, wahrhaffte und aussführliche Erklärung des von Basilio Valentino
in seinem Buch über den grossen Stein der
uralten Weisen ... [n.p.] 1723.
   87 p.

4321. WELL, Johann Jacob. Rechtfertigung
der blackischen Lehre von der figirten Luft,
gegen die vom Herrn Wiegleb ... darwider
gemachten Einwürfe ... Wien: Kraus, 1771.
   8 *l*., 164 p.

4322. WELLING, Georg von. יהוה Opus
mago-cabalisticum et theologicum. Vom
Uhrsprung und Erzeugung des Saltzes, dessen Natur und Eigenschafft, wie auch dessen
Nutz und Gebrauch ... Alles auffgesetzt und
zusammen getragen von ... Gregorius Anglus
Sallwigt ... Franckfurth am Mayn: A. Hein-
scheidt, 1719.
   4 *l*., 80 p. illus.

4323. ———. ———. Saltzburg: 1729.
   3 *l*., 161 p., 10 *l*. illus.

4324. ———. ———. Franckfurt und Leipzig:
Fleischer, 1760.
   4 *l*., 582 p., 11 *l*. illus., charts.

4325. ———. ———. Dritte Auflage. Frankfurt
und Leipzig: Fleischer, 1784.
   4 *l*., 582 p., 11 *l*. illus., charts.

4326. WELSCH, Georg Hieronymus. Dissertatio medico-philosophica de aegagropilis.
Avgvstæ Vindelicorvm: typis J. Prætorii, impensis J. Weh, 1660-1668.
   2 pts. in 1 v. illus.

4327. ———. Sylloge curationum et observationum medicinalium centurias VI complectens, c. notis ejusdem et episagmatum
centuria I. Aug. Vindel.: impensis G. Goe-
belii, typis C.B. Kuhny, 1668.
   6 pts. in 1 v. illus.

4328. WELT, Adrianus Dominicus van.
Chimiæ oppressæ & despectæ gemitus, ad
parentes, phoebum & naturam ... Lvgdvni
Batavorvm: C. Boutesteyn, 1701.
   2 *l*., 19 p.

4329. WEPFER, Johann Jakob. Cicvtæ
aqvaticæ historia et noxæ. Commentario
illustrata. Basileae: apud J.R. König, imprimebat J.R. Genathivs, 1679.
   8 *l*., 336 p., 3 *l*. illus., map.

4330. ———. Historia cicutæ aquaticæ ...
Adjectæ sunt ad calcem dissertationes de
thee Helvetico ac cymbalaria curante Theodoro Zuingero. Lugduni Batavorum: G. Potvliet, 1733.
   8 *l*., 481 p., 6 *l*. illus., chart.

4331. ———. Historiae apoplecticorum ...
Una cum epistola Johannis Ott, de scriptis
Holderi de elementis sermonis, & Morlandi
de stentorophonia. Accesserunt huic editioni
aliorum celebrium medicorum observationes
historiaeque variae circa apoplexiam. Ut &
Bernardi Huete curatio maniae certa & saepius
instituta. Amstelaedami: Janssonio-Waesbergios, 1724.
   8 *l*., 690 p., 14 *l*. illus., port.

4332. ———. Observationes anatomicae
ex cadaveribus eorum, quos sustulit apoplexia.
Cum exercitatione de eius loco affecto.
Schaffhusii: J.C. Suterius, 1658.
   8 *l*., 304 p.

4333. ———. Observationes medico-practi-
cae, de affectibvs capitis internis & externis.
Nunc demum publici juris redditae studio &
opera nepotum, Bernhardini Wepferi, et Georgii Mich. Wepferi. Scaphusii: J.A. Ziegler, 1727.
   16 *l*., 984 p., 20 *l*. illus., port.

   WESER, Daniel. De hirudine. *See*
Linné, C. von, *praeses*. Entry 2468.

4334. WESLEY, John. Primitive physics: or
An easy and natural method of curing most
diseases. The twenty-first edition. Philadelphia: Prichard & Hall, 1789.
   196 p.

4335. WESTENDORF, Johann Christoph. Dis-

pvtatio inavgvralis chemico-medica de optima acetvm concentratvm ... Goettingae: I.H. Schvlz, 1772.
    3 *l*., 75 p., 1 *l*.

4336. WESTMACOT, William. Historia vegetabilium sacra: or, A scripture herbal ... London: for J. Salusbury, 1695.
    12 *l*., 232 p., 4 *l*.

    WESTRING, Johan Peter. De ledo palustri. *See* Linné, C. von, *praeses*. Entry 2451.

4337. WHARTON, Thomas. Adenographia: sive Glandvlarvm totius corporis descriptio. Amstelaedami: J. Ravestein, 1659.
    12 *l*., 261 p. illus.

4338. ——. ——. Dusseldorpii: J. vandèr Smissen, 1730.
    12 *l*., 161 [i.e. 261] p. illus.

4339. WHITE, Charles. A treatise on the management of pregnant and lying-in women ... The second edition, revised and enlarged ... London: for E. and C. Dilly, 1777.
    xxiii, 462 p. illus.

4340. WHITE, John. Art's treasury of rareties, and curious inventions. In two parts ... The fourth edition. London: for G. Conyers [c. 1712].
    1 *l*., 152 p. port.

4341. ——. A rich cabinet, with variety of inventions ... The fifth edition, with many additions. London: for W. Whitwood, 1677.
    7 *l*., 190, 41 p. illus.

4342. ——. ——. The sixth edition, with many additions. London: for W. Whitwood, 1689.
    7 *l*., 128 p. illus.

4343. WHITE, Robert. A summary of the pneumato-chemical theory, with a table of its nomenclature, intended as a supplement to the analysis of the New London Pharmacopoeia. [London] for Cadell and Davies [ca. 1798].
    vi, 26 p. chart.

4344. WHYTT, Robert. An essay on the virtues of lime-water and soap in the cure of the stone. The third edition ... Edinburgh: Hamilton, Balfour, and Neill, 1761.
    xii, 220 p. illus.

4345. ——. Observations on the nature, causes, and cure of those disorders which have been commonly called nervous, hypochondriac, or hysteric ... Edinburgh: for T. Becket ..., 1765.
    viii p., 4 *l*., 520 p.

4346. ——. Les vapeurs et maladies nerveuses, hypocondriaques, ou hystériques ... Traduction de l'Anglois ... Ouvrages revus & publiés par M. Lebegue de Presle. Paris: Vincent, 1767.
    2 v. illus.

4347. ——. The works. Published by his son. Edinburgh: for T. Becket and P.A. Dehondt, 1768.
    11 *l*., viii, 762 p., 15 *l*. illus.

    WICKMAN, Daniel. De viola ipecacuanha. *See* Linné, C. von, *praeses*. Entry 2434.

4348. WIDMER, Georg. Chymia corporis animalis cum lithogeognosia et artificio aquas salsas dulcificandi, methodo scientifica pertractata. Argentorati: A. König, 1752.
    4 *l*., 36 p.

4349. WIEGLEB, Johann Christian. Chemische Versuche über die alkalischen Salze. Neue verbesserte und vermehrte Auflage. Berlin: F. Nicolai, 1781.
    264 p.

4350. ——. Geschichte des Wachsthums und der Erfindungen in der Chemie in der ältesten und mittlern Zeit. Aus dem Lateinischen ubersetzt ... Berlin: F. Nicolai, 1792.
    6 *l*., 260 p.
    With his Geschichte des Wachsthums in der neuern Zeit ... 1790-1791.

4351. ——. Geschichte des Wachsthums und der Erfindungen in der Chemie, in der neuern Zeit. Berlin: F. Nicolai, 1790-1791.
    3 pts. in 2 v.

4352. ——. Handbuch der allgemeinen Chemie ... Zwote neuberichtigte Auflage. Berlin: F. Nicolai, 1786.
    2 v.

4353. ——. ——. Dritte neuumgearbeitet Auflage. Berlin: F. Nicolai, 1796.
    2 v.

4354. ——. Historisch-kritische Unter-

suchung der Alchemie ... Weimar: C.L. Hoffmann, 1777.
   11 *l*., 437 p., 1 *l*.

4355. ——. Kleine chymische Abhandlungen von dem grossen Nutzen der Erkennt-
niss des Acidi pinguis ... nebst einer Vorrede, worinnen Herrn Meyers Leben erzählt
und von dessen Verdiensten gehandelt wird
von G.G. Baldinger. Zweyte Auflage. Langensalza: J.C. Martin, 1771.
   182 p.

4356. ——. Onomatologia cvriosa artificiosa et magica. Oder Natürliches Zauber-
Lexicon ... Dritte Auflage ... Nürnberg: Ras-
pisch, 1784.
   4 *l*., 1744 numb. col.   illus.

4357. ——. Vertheidigung der Meyerischen
Lehre vom Acido Pingvi gegen verschiedene
darwider gemachte Einwürfe. Altenburg:
Richter, 1770.
   113 p., 1 *l*.

4358. WIEL, Cornelius Stalpart van der.
Observationum rariorum medic. anatomic.
chirurgicarum ... Lugduni Batavorum: P.
vander Aa, 1687.
   2 v.   illus., port.

4359. WIENNER VON SONNENFELS, Aloys.
אור בגה Splendor lucis, oder Glantz des
Lichts, enthaltend eine kurtze physico-
cabalistische Auslegung des grösten Natur-
Geheimnuss. Aus dem Hebraeischen Grund-
Text, der heil. Schrift gezogen in Hebraeisch-
und Teutscher Sprach gleichlautend heraus
gegeben ... Wienn: J.J. Pentz, 1747.
   1 *l*., 219 p.   chart.

4360. WILLIAMS, Stephen.   An experimental history of road water in Wiltshire ... In
a letter to the Revd. Dr. Derham ... London:
for A. Bettesworth and C. Hitch, 1731.
   2 *l*., 72 p.

4361. WILLICH, Anthony Florian Madinger.
Lectures on diet and regimen: being a systematic inquiry into the most rational means
of preserving health and prolonging life;
together with physiological and chemical
explanations ... The second edition ... London: for T.N. Longman and O. Rees, 1799.
   2 *l*., 708 p., 2 *l*.

4362. WILLIS, John.   An inaugural dissertation on the chymical analysis and operation of vegetable astringents, with observations on the identity of the vegetable

acids ... Philadelphia: A. McKenzie, 1795.
   36 p.

4363. WILLIS, Thomas.   Cerebri anatome:
cui accessit Nervorum descriptio et usus.
Londini: T. Roycroft ..., 1664.
   15 *l*., 240 p.   illus.

4364. ——. ——. Accessit ... De ratione
motus musculorum tractatus singularis.
Amstelodami: G. Schagen, 1666.
   7 *l*., 342 p., 2 *l*., 37 p.   illus.

4365. ——. De anima brutorum quae
hominis vitalis ac sensitiva est, exercitationes duae ... Londini: R. Davis, 1672.
   24 *l*., 400 p., 8 *l*.   illus.

4366. ——. Diatribae duae medico-
philosophicae: quarum prior agit De fermen-
tatione, sive, De motu intestino particularum
in quovis corpore; altera De febribus, sive,
De motu earundem in sanguine animalium.
His accessit Dissertation epistolica de
urinis. Editio postrema prioribus longè
emandatior atque auctior. Amstelodami: G.
Schaghen, 1668.
   15 *l*., 376 p.

4367. ——. Opera omnia ... Genevae: S.
de Tovrnes, 1676.
   var. pag.   illus.

4368. ——. ——. Studio & opera Gerardi
Blasii. Amstelaedami: H. Wetstenius, 1682.
   2 v.   illus., port.

4369. ——. Pharmaceutice rationalis sive
Diatriba de medicamentorum operationibus
in humano corpore ... Editio postrema, prioribus emendatior. Hagae-Comitis: A. Leers,
1675.
   20 *l*., 426 p., 6 *l*.

4370. ——. Pharmaceutice rationalis: or,
An exercitation of the operations of medicines in humane bodies ... London: for T.
Dring ..., 1679.
   2 pts. in 1 v.   illus.

4371. ——. Practice of physick, being the
whole works of that renowned and famous
physician: containing these eleven several
treatises ... The pharmaceutice new translated, and the whole carefully corrected
and amended. London: for T. Dring ..., 1684.
   var. pag.   illus.

4372. ——. The London practice of physick:
or the whole practical part of physick ... Faith-

fully made English ... London: for T. Basset
and W. Crooke, 1685.
6 *l.*, 672 p., 8 *l.* port.

4373. ———. A preservative from the in-
fection of the plague, or any contagious
distemper in city, camp, fleet, etc. ...
Written in the year 1666 ... London: for A.
Bettesworth, 1721.
1 *l.*, iv, 58 p.

4374. WILLIS, Timothy. Propositiones
tentatïonvm: sive Propaedevmata de vitis
et fæcvndiatate compositorum naturalium:
quæ sunt elementa chymica ... Londini: J.
Legatt, 1615.
4 *l.*, 40 p.

4375. WILSON, Alexander. Some observations relative to the influence of climate
on vegetable and animal bodies ... London:
for T. Cadell, 1780.
xxii p., 1 *l.*, 228 p.

4376. ———. Beobachtungen über den Ein-
fluss des Klimas auf Pflanzen und Thiere.
Aus dem Englischen. Leipzig: Weygand,
1781.
180 p., 2 *l.*

4377. WILSON, Edward. Spadacrene
Dunelmensis: or A short treatise of an ancient medicinal fovntain or vitrioline spaw
near the city of Durham ... by E.W. London:
W. Godbid, 1675.
15 *l.*, 88 p.

4378. WILSON, George. A compleat course
of chymistry, containing near three hundred
operations ... London: the author and W.
Kettilby, 1699.
8 *l.*, 358 p., 12 *l.* illus., charts.

4379. ———. ———. The third edition ... To
which are added the author's experiments
upon metals ... London: for J. Bayley, 1709.
16 *l.*, 413 p., 14 *l.* illus., charts.

4380. WINSHEMIUS, Vitus. Oratio habita
in fvnere reverendi et clarissimi viri Philippi Melanthonis ... die xxi Aprilis. Vite-
bergae: P. Seitz [15]60.
15 *l.*

4381. WINSLOW, Jacques Bénigne. Exposition anatomique de la structure du corps
humain. Paris: G. Desprez et J. Desessartz,
1732.
xxx, 740 p., 4 *l.* illus.

4382. ———. An anatomical exposition of
the structure of the human body ... Translated from the French original, by G. Douglas.
The fifth edition, corrected. London: for J.
Knapton ..., 1763.
2 v. in 1. illus.

4383. ———. The uncertainty of the signs
of death, and the danger of precipitate inter-
ments and dissections demonstrated ...
London: for M. Cooper, 1746.
4 *l.*, 219 p. illus.

4384. WINTRINGHAM, *Sir* Clifton. A treatise of endemic diseases wherein the different
nature of airs, situations, soils, waters diet,
&c. are mechanically explain'd and accounted
for. York: G. White for F. Hildyard, 1718.
xi, 123 p.

4385. WIRDIG, Sebastian. Nova medicina
spirituum: curiosa scientia & doctrina ...
medicis tamen & physicis utilissima ...
Hamburgi: G. Schulz, 1673.
21 *l.*, 238, 284 p., 7 *l.* illus.

4386. ———. ———. Accedit Anonymi Philalethæ Tractatus nunquam antehac editus de
liqvore alcahest. Hamburg: vidua G. Schultz,
1688.
20 *l.*, 198, 236 p., 7 *l.*

4387. WIRSUNG, Christoph. Ein new Artzney Buch darinn fast alle euszerliche vnnd
innerliche Glieder desz menschlichen Leibs
... ubersehen ... vnd auff ein newes ... in
Druck vbergeben durch Iacobum Theodorum
Tabernæmontanum ... Newstadt an der Hardt:
M. Harrnisch, 1582.
14 *l.*, 850 p., 116 *l.*

4388. ———. Ein newes Artzney Buch ...
Darneben auch drey newer Tractat, darvon
Herr Christoff Wirsung nicht geschrieben.
I. Von den Schwachheiten ... II. Von der Kunst
die todten Cörper zu balsamiren. III. Von
dem Schorbock und seiner Cur. Alles ...
verteutsche und an Tag geben, durch ...
Petrum Offenbach ... Franckfort am Mayn:
Z. Palthenius, 1605.
6 *l.*, 222, 261 p., 1 *l.* ports.
With Ryff, W.H., Newe Apoteck ... 1602.

4389. ———. Praxis medicinæ vniuersalis;
or A generall practise of physicke ... Compiled and written ... in the Germane tongue,
and now translated into English ... by Iacob
Mosan ... London: E. Bollifant, 1598.
10 *l.*, 790 p., 61 *l.*

4390. ——. ——. Londini: G. Bishop,
1605.
    10 l., 790 p., 61 l.

4391. WIRTZ, Felix. Practica der Wundartzney, was für schädliche Miszbräuch bey
der Wundartzney in gemeinem schwank, vnd
warumb die abzuschaffen seindt ... Basel
[S. Henricpetri, 1596].
    12 l., dcliii p.

4392. WISDOM reputed folly: or, The composition and reality of the philosophers
stone ... London: for the author and W. Bore-
ham [1720?].
    68 p.

4393. WISEMAN, Richard. Eight chirugi-
cal treatises ... The third edition. London:
for B.T. ..., 1698.
    7 l., 563 p., 7 l.

4394. WITHERING, William. A botanical
arrangement of British plants; including the
uses of each species in medicine, diet,
rural oeconomy and the arts ... The second
edition ... Including a new set of references
to figures. By Jonathan Stokes. Birmingham:
M. Swinney ..., 1787-1792.
    3 v. illus.

4395. WITTESTEIN, Karl. Disceptatio
philosophica de quinta chymicorum essentia.
Accessit Alexandri Carerij ... Quæstio an
metalla artis beneficio permutari possint.
Basileae: S. Henricpetri [1583?].
    8 l., 223 p.

4396. WITTICH, Johannes. Bericht von den
wunderbaren Bezoardischen Steinen ... Leipzig: [H. Steinmans Erben] 1589.
    8 l., 146 p., 4 l.

4397. WITTY, Robert. Scarbrough spaw, or
A description of the nature and vertues of
the spaw at Scarbrough in Yorkshire ... London: for C. Tyus and R. Lambert, 1660.
    8 l., 254 p., 1 l.
    With French, J., The York-shire spaw ...
1652.

4398. ——. Fons Scarburgensis: sive,
Tractatus de omnis aquarum generis origine
ac usu. Particulariter de fonte minerali apud
Scarbrough ... Londini: R. Everingham ...,
1678.
    4 l., 235 p., 1 l.

4399. WOHLFAHRT, Johann August. Specimen inavgvrale anatomico-medicvm de bron-

chiis vasisqve bronchialibvs ... Hala Magdebvrgicae: J.C. Hilliger [1748].
    3 l., 34 p. illus.

4400. WOLF, Kaspar. Diodori Evchyontis
de polychymia, libri qvatvor. [n.p.] 1567.
    7 l., 229 p., 5 l. illus.

4401. WOLFF, Heinrich. Herliche medi-
cische Tractat, vor nie in truck kommen.
Von Cur des Podagrams, des ... Arnaldi de
Villa Nova. Item Vom Holz des Lebens. Vom
Goldöl. Antimonij öl und Wein. Von den
Tugenden der Perlen, Corallen und Spiritus
vini ... Strasburg: B. Jobin, 1576.
    124 l.

4402. WOLLEY, Hannah. The accomplished'd
lady's delight in preserving, physick, beautifying, and cookery. Containing, I. The art of
preserving and candying ... II. The physical
cabinet, or, Excellent receipts in physick and
chirurgery ... III. The compleat cook's guide
... London: for B. Harris, 1675.
    2 l., 382 p., 5 l. illus.
    With The English and French cook ... 1674.

4403. WOODVILLE, William. Medical botany,
containing systematic and general descriptions
... of all the medicinal plants, indigenous and
exotic, comprehended in the catalogues of the
materia medica ... London: for the author, by
J. Phillips, 1790-1794.
    3 v. and supplement. illus.

4404. ——. Reports of a series of inocu-
lations for the variolae vaccinae, or cow-pox
... London: J. Phillips and Son, 1799.
    2 l., 156 p.

4405. WOYT, Johann Jacob. Gazophylacium
medico-physicum, oder Schatz-kammer, medi-
cinisch- und natürlicher Dinge ... Die fünffte
Auflage ... Leipzig: F. Lanckischens Erben,
1727.
    3 l., 1035 p., 34 l.

4406. WÜRTTEMBERG. Laws, statutes, etc.
Hochfürstlich Würtenbergische Medicinal-
Ordnung. Stutgart: J.C. Erhard, 1756.
    1 l., 30 p.
    With Pharmacopoea Wirtenbergica ...
1754.

4407. WÜRTZ, Georg Christoph. Conamen
mappæ generalis medicamentorum simplicium
secundum affinitates virium naturalium, nova
methodo geographica dispositorum. Argentorati: Bauer & Treuttel, 1778.
    1 l., 221 p. chart.

X, Y, Z

4408. XAVIER DO MONTE, Joaõ Pedro. O homem medico de si mesmo, ou Sciencia, e arte nova de conservar cada hum a si proprio a saude ... Lisboa: A. Vincente, 1760.
  179 p.

4409. YEATS, Grant David. Observations on the claims of the moderns, to some discoveries in chemistry and physiology ... London: for the author, 1798.
  xxxvi, 403 p., 1 ℓ. illus., port.

4410. YOUNG, George. A treatise on opium founded upon practical observations. London: for A. Millar, 1753.
  xv, 182 p., 1 ℓ.

4411. YOUNGE, James. Sidrophel vapvlans: or, The quack-astrologer toss'd in a blanket ... London: J. Nutt, 1699.
  8 ℓ., 59 p.

4412. YŪHANNĀ IBN SARĀBIYŪN. Practica Jo. Serapionis dicta breuiarium. Liber Serapionis de simplici medicina. Liber de simplici medicina dictus circa instans. Practica Platearij. [Venetys: expensis O. Scoti per B. Locatellū, 1497.]
  211 ℓ.

4413. Y-WORTH, William. The Britannian magazine: or, A new art of making above twenty sorts of English wines ... The third edition. To which is added, The foundation of the art of distillation ... London: for N. Bodington [ca. 1700].
  22 ℓ., 133 p., 5 ℓ.

4414. ——. Chymicvs rationalis: or, The fundamental grounds of the chymical art ... London: for T. Salusbury, 1692.
  8 ℓ., 154 p., 3 ℓ. illus.

4415. ——. Introitus apertus ad artem distillationis; or The whole art of distillation practically stated ... To which is added,

The true and genuin way of preparing powers by three noble menstruums ... London: for J. Taylor, 1692.
  9 ℓ., 189 p., 1 ℓ. illus.

4416. ——. The compleat distiller: or The whole art of distillation practically stated ... To which is added, Pharmacopoeia spagyrica nova: or An Helmontian course ... The second edition, with alterations and additions ... London: for I. Taylor, 1705.
  12 ℓ., 276 p., 1 ℓ. illus.

4417. Z., A. Remarks on Mr. Robert Dossie's Institutes of experimental chemistry, in a letter addressed to the authors of the *Review*, &c. London: for S. Hooper, 1760.
  18 p.
  A contemporary manuscript note on the title-page reads: "By Dr. Lewis." It is ascribed to William Lewis (1714-1781) in the Duveen catalogue.

4417a. ZACAIRE, Denis. Opvscvle tresexcellent, de la vraye philosophie naturelle des metaux ... Plus le traitté de M. Bernard Allemand compte de la Marche Treuisane. Derniere edition ... Lyon: P. Rigaud, 1612.
  280 p., 2 ℓ.

4418. ZACCHIA, Paolo. Quæstionum medico-legalium, tomi tres. Olim aucti et emendati a ... Joh. Daniel. Horstio ... quorum catalogus post præfationem videre est, illustrati, emendati atque adaucti a Georgio Franco ... Francofurti ad Moenum: J.M. Bencard, 1688.
  3 v. in 1.

4419. ZACUTO, Abraham ben Samuel. Operum tomus primus [-secundus] ... Editio postrema, à mendis purgatissima. Lvgdvni: I.A. Hvgvetan & M.A. Ravavd, 1649.
  2 v. port.

4420. ZADITH, *filius Hamuelis*. De chemia Senioris ... libellvs, vt brevis, ita artem dis-

centibus, & exercentibus, utillissimus, & uere aureus, nunc primum in lucem aeditus ... [n.p.: n.d.]
127 p.

———. Tabula chymica. *In* Philosophiae chymicae ... 1605.

4421. ZANNICHELLI, Giovanni Geronimo. De ferro ejusque nivis praeparatione dissertatio physico-chymica, in qua varia de ipso metallo explicantur. Venetiis: A. Poleti, 1713.
8 *l.*, 79 p. illus.

4422. ———. ———. Venetiis: 1719.
3 *l.*, 46 p. illus.

4423. ZAPATA, Giovanni Battista. Li marauigliosi secreti di medicina, e chirurgia, nvovamente ritrovati per guarire ogni sorte d'infirmità ... Carmagnola: M.A. Bellone, 1590.
22 *l.*, 196 p.
With Cortese, I., I secreti ... 1595.

4424. ———. ———. Venetia: I. Imberti, 1629.
24 *l.*, 190 p.

4425. ZECCHI, Giovanni. De aquarum porrectanarum vsu, atque praestantia tractatvs, in septem capita diuisus ... Bononiae: I. Rossius, 1576.
4 *l.*, 72 p., 4 *l.*

4426. ZENEROLI, Lucca. Scelta di storie mediche spettanti alle terme Porrettane 1771. Bologna: 1772.
80 p.

4427. ZERENER, Johann Nicolaus. Kurtze doch hinlängliche Nachricht von nützlichen Gebrauch und kräftiger Würckung verschiedener bewährt gefundener Medicamenten ... [n.p.] 1749.
151 p., 12 *l.*

ZETZELL, Per. Consectaria electricomedica. *See* Linné, C. von, *praeses*. Entry 2424.

ZIERVOGEL, Samuel. Rhabarbarum. *See* Linné, C. von, *praeses*. Entry 2466.

4428. ZIMARA, Marco Antonio. Antrvm magico medicvm ... Accessit Motus perpetui mechanici ... Francofvrti: I.F. Weisil, 1625.
7 *l.*, 525 p.

———. Problemata. *In* Aristotles,

Problemata ... 1569.

4429. ———. Tabula dilucidationum in dictis Aristotelis & Auerrois ... Venetiis: I. Gryphius, 1552.
162 numb. *l.*
Lacking all after leaf 162.
With his Theoremata ... 1553.

4430. ———. Theoremata ... seu Memorabilium propositionum limitationes ... Nunc post omnes alias editiones expurgationesque accuratissime suis meritis restituta ... Venetiis: I. Gryphius, 1553.
4 *l.*, 91 numb. *l.*
Lacking leaf 92.

4431. ZIMMERMANN, Johann Georg. Das Leben des Herrn von Haller. Zürich: Heidegger, 1755.
19 *l.*, 430 p., 1 *l.*

4432. ———. Traité de la dyssenterie. Traduit de l'Allemand, par M. Le Febvre de Villebrune. Paris: Vincent, 1775.
xlviii, 406 p.

4433. ———. Von der Erfahrung in der Arzneykunst. Zürich: Heidegger, 1763-1764.
2 v.
Lacking volume 2.

4434. ———. A treatise on experience in physic. London: for J. Wilkie, 1778.
2 v.

4435. ZINCKE, Johann. De crisibvs commentarius. In qvo de natvra, proprietate, differentiis, speciebvs, vtilitate atque necessitate criseon, & dierum criticorvm ... Nunc primum in lucem prolatus ... Francofurti: haeredes N. Bassaei, 1609.
4 *l.*, 151 p.
With Müller, P., Miracula & mysteria ... 1616.

4436. ZINN, Johann Gottfried. Descriptio anatomica ocvli hvmani iconibvs illvstrata, nvnc altera vice edita ... ab Henr. Avg. Wrisberg. Goettingae: vidva A. Vandenhoeck, 1780.
8 *l.*, 248 p. illus.

4437. ZIPFFEL, Jonas. Theoria metallica ist eine kurtze metallische Betrachtung, aus welcher Materia, in, aus, und oder der Erden die Natur und der Chymicus ... Dresden: M. Bergen, 1678.
80 p.

4438. ZOROASTER, *pseud.* Clavis artis
des berühmten Juden und Rabbi Zoroasters,
wie solcher 1996. von Anfange der Welt in
Arabischer Sprache aufgesetzt, 1236. nach
Christi Geburth ins Teutsche übersetzt von
J.V.S.F.R.O. ... nunmehro ... in Druck befördert durch einen Liebhaber der spagyr-
ischen Raritaeten. Jena: C.F. Gollner,
1738.
    8 *l.*, 147 p., 6 *l.*
    With Faust, J.M., Philaletha illustratus
... 1706.

        ZOROASTER'S cave. *In* Thor, G.,
Cheiragogia Heiliana ... 1659, etc.

4439. ZWELFER, Joannes. Pharmacopoeia
regia, seu Dispensatorium novum locu-
pletatum et absolutum, annexâ etiam Mantissa spagyrica ... Noribergæ: B.J. Endter,
1693.
    16 *l.*, 582 p., 17 *l.*

———. *See also* Pharmacopoea Augustana.

4440. ZWEY schöne chymische Tractetlein:
I. De mercurio alchimistarum. II. De lumine
naturæ ... Jenæ: Weidner, 1612.
    14 *l.*

4441. ZWEY vortreffliche und noch nie im
Druck gewesene chymische Bücher. I. ...
Antonii de Abbatia Bericht von Verwandelung
der Metallen. II. Aufrichtig-teutscher Wegweiser zum Licht der Natur oder Ad tincturam
physicam Paracelsi, und lapidem philosophorum ... [n.p.] 1759.
    62 p.

4442. ZWINGER, Johann. Die Gestalt eines
fürsichtigen Freundes in der Noth. Das ist:
Der mitleidige, dienstfertige und gewissen-
haffte Apothecker ... Nürnberg: W.M. Endter, 1721
    8 *l.*, 508 p., 15 *l.*   illus.